TOTAL WORKPLACE PERFORMANCE

RETHINKING THE OFFICE ENVIRONMENT

Stan Aronoff
Audrey Kaplan

To our parents

Cover design: Artext Electronic Publishing
Interior design: Stan Aronoff and Audrey G. Kaplan

Canadian Cataloguing in Publication Data

Aronoff, Stanley
Total workplace performance : rethinking the office environment.

Includes bibliographical references and index.
ISBN 0-921804-95-4

1. Work environment. 2. Facility management. 3. Human engineering.
I. Kaplan, Audrey G. II. Title.

HF5547.A76 1995 658.2′3 C95-900552-8

Published in 1995 by
WDL Publications
P.O. Box 8457, Station T
Ottawa, Ontario, Canada K1G 3H8

Printed and bound in Canada.

PREFACE

This is a book about office workplaces — what they are, how they operate, and how they affect the people who use them. It offers a perspective on office issues oriented toward senior managers responsible for scrutinizing facility policies and expenditures. We believe that to improve the way in which offices are designed, built, and managed, those who allocate the funds and resources for facilities must appreciate the broader impact of those decisions on the organization's overall performance.

The selection, design, and management of office facilities is inherently an exercise in choosing among competing objectives — seeking to allocate resources in a way that will be commensurate with their contribution to the organization's goals. Unfortunately, attention is often focused on the most obvious trade-offs, though they may not make the most significant impacts.

In recent years, the office environment has been the subject of keen media interest. Sick building syndrome, repetitive strain injuries, and a host of other health issues have sensitized the public and raised concerns about increased regulations and liability risk. However, it is the less dramatic day-to-day choices in the design and management of offices that are the more costly and affect nearly every worker. These costs are borne both by organizations that receive less value from their facilities and their workforce than they could, and by occupants to whom the office presents more obstacles to their work efforts than it should.

Accommodation expenses are typically the second largest operating cost for office-based enterprises (salaries being the largest). Moreover, the physical office setting has a far more pervasive influence on organizations than is commonly appreciated. The time and cost to initiate new projects, introduce new technology, or downsize office-based organizations are intimately tied to the characteristics of a facility. Since the office setting also affects human performance, its design and management impact the return realized from both salary and accommodation expenditures. In an era of global competition, every factor that influences workforce performance is a potential source of competitive advantage. An organization can ill afford to judge facility expenditures without an appreciation of the broad consequences of those decisions.

Although there are many books that address the ultimate "office of the future," few office workers actually experience such settings. Rather than emphasize revolutionary developments in building construction, our book presents what we consider to be the more important issues of today's office workplace. We focus on the types of offices that predominate in Canada and the United States and the changes to those settings that will affect most occupants.

We have sought to provide a balanced perspective on a comprehensive range of issues relevant to the design and management of the office workplace. Many of the topics we discuss are highly controversial. Often, the facts have been obscured by unsubstantiated assertions and strongly held beliefs. For this reason, we analyze as well as critique topics and include references within the body of the text. By clearly presenting our sources, we invite the reader to consider the evidence on which our views are based.

We have presented information in a form accessible to the nonexpert from fields as diverse as engineering, architecture, medicine, psychology, and sociology. This well-referenced discussion of the office workplace complete with the relevant background information, should be of value to senior managers and facility professionals as well as to others concerned about the quality of the office environment.

The myriad of facility issues included in this book are presented in the context of how office buildings and occupants perform as a functional unit — a perspective we call *total workplace performance*. This perspective sheds light on the integration of what might otherwise appear to be separate, and sometimes mundane aspects of facility management.

In developing the material for this book we greatly appreciated the comments and suggestions of the friends and colleagues who reviewed portions of the manuscript. We would like to thank: Leiba Aronoff, Peter Bean, Gail Brager, Greg Clunis, Paul Cornell, Tom DeMarco, Vijay Dube, Alan Hedge, Art Horton, Stephen Kroll-Smith, Adrian Leaman, David LeGrande, Hal Levin, Michael Peterson, Stephen Roach, Steven Sauter, Roger Stevens, Dan Stokols, Forrest Wilson, Jim Woods, Barry Yach, and Cynthia Zawadski for their time and effort, support and encouragement. Our thanks as well to the many people who helped us to obtain illustrations and the permission to use them. The book layout, cover design, and image scanning were done at Artext Electronic Publishing, Ottawa, by Robert Lalonde and Nathalie Czerniakowycz. In addition to producing quality work, they and all the Artext staff were a pleasure to work with. Our thanks as well to our meticulous copy editor, Susan Cohan.

Stan Aronoff
Audrey Kaplan
April 1995

CONTENTS

COVER AND TITLE PAGE CREDITS

Cover	Office building. Photograph by Stan Aronoff.
xii	Office building. Photograph by Harry Turner, National Research Council Canada, Ottawa.
20	Chase Manhattan Plaza, New York.
50	London in the industrial revolution. Etching from the 1860s by Gustave Doré.
78	Building under construction. Photograph by Harry Turner, National Research Council Canada, Ottawa.
152	Research and administration building, Ottawa. Photograph courtesy of Bell-Northern Research (BNR).
220	Computers in the workplace. Design by Artext Electronic Publishing. Inset photographs by Harry Turner, National Research Council Canada, Ottawa.
266	Johnson Wax Company administration building in Racine, Wisconsin designed by Frank Lloyd Wright, constructed 1936-39. Photograph courtesy of S.C. Johnson and Son. Racine, Wisc.
306	Office interior. Design by Stan Aronoff, Audrey Kaplan, and Artext Electronic Publishing. Foreground image courtesy of Steelcase, Grand Rapids, Mich.
358	Office design in context. Design by Stan Aronoff. Floorplan courtesy of Fifth Dimension, Ottawa; work setting photograph courtesy of Rosemount Office Systems, Lakeville, Minn.
394	Office building. Photograph by Stan Aronoff.

Chapter 1

THE CASE FOR OFFICE QUALITY

The worst error we can make in times of change is our own complacency.

— J. Davidson and W. Rees-Moog
The Great Reckoning

In recent years, the office workforce has been downsized, restructured, and reengineered: office workers have been the focus of total quality management and the search for excellence; they have been automated and empowered — all with the objective of giving them the capability, the motivation, and the support to be more productive and more effective.

The quality of the physical work environment directly affects the success of all these initiatives. There is perhaps no more concrete demonstration of corporate commitment to these programs than to improve people's physical surroundings. The office environment is an immediate and ever-present expression of corporate culture that employees see, feel, hear, and live with every working day. The more it supports them in their work activities, the less quickly they will become fatigued, the fewer sick days they will have, and the more energy they will have available for the work at hand.

The better the quality of the physical work setting, the less aware people are of its contribution. At its best, the office environment is a seamless background that the occupants hardly notice. At its worst, it is a major obstacle to productive effort — a place where no real work can be done. People can be found hiding out in cafeterias, empty conference rooms, and at home to escape office facilities that are too disruptive, too uncomfortable, or that make them feel too unwell to do their mind's best work.

Any program to increase the productivity and effectiveness of office-based work should employ the design, management, and quality of the work environment to maximum advantage. The physical office setting should present an image of corporate culture consistent with the organization's policies and principles — an alignment of stated goals and concrete action. Why this is so and how it can be accomplished are the subject of this book.

This introductory chapter presents key issues and trends that are forcing organizations to rethink their approach to the cost and effectiveness of their office accommodations. The rapid pace of office work, made possible by automation, is no longer an option but a necessity to survive in an increasingly competitive marketplace. Global competition, demographics, a greater awareness of the health risks in offices, and more stringent health and safety regulations have made it costly to ignore the impact of the workplace environment on individual performance and organizational effectiveness.

The second chapter looks at the development of the office. The origins of the office lie in the distant past. But the office as we know it today is a recent phenomenon that evolved from the increased administrative needs of the industrial revolution. Over the past hundred years, office work has grown steadily in importance from a relatively minor and peripheral role to one that encompasses a broad range of services without which organizations could not function. The physical design of the office has changed dramatically during this period, in response both to new functional demands and to the availability of new construction materials and architectural innovation.

The management of the office facility has also changed. As these facilities became larger to support a growing workforce, and more complex with the advent of such services as central heating and cooling, facility management decisions have had a greater impact on capital and operating costs. More recently, the ergonomics of the workplace and the operation and maintenance of building systems have become the focus of public scrutiny as the effects of the work environment on occupant health and productivity have come to be better understood.

Chapter 3 examines the issue of office productivity and its measurement. Productivity has been called upon to justify any number of corporate decisions. But methods designed to quantify industrial productivity are not easily adapted to the measurement of office work. The performance of office workers involves quantitative as well as qualitative factors that have proved difficult to define and measure rigorously. Although many ways have been found to measure the productivity of white-collar workers (generally considered to include managerial, professional, technical, sales, and clerical jobs), it is not clear whether those measures have truly captured the contribution of office work to organizational goals or simply quantified what was most amenable to measurement.

Chapter 4 examines the systems that comprise an office building. It is the combined effects of the site, the building enclosure and structure, the building services (e.g., electrical, lighting, and ventilation), and the interior furnishings that together create the work setting that occupants experience. The success with which these components are integrated in a particular building design determines the environmental characteristics of the interior spaces. Efforts to alter those characteristics must be designed in the context of the overall building system in order to avoid making changes that improve one feature while degrading others.

Chapter 5 addresses the health-related concerns of office occupants. The publicity surrounding such issues as sick building syndrome, indoor air quality, temperature shifts, and noise disruption is commonly so focused on specific illness symptoms and on gaining prompt, visible action that, often, insufficient time or resources are devoted to developing a comprehensive assessment and remedy. Yet for sick building complaints to be addressed effectively, the possible contributions of all components of the building system need to be considered.

The quality of indoor air, for example, is not determined solely by the amount of outside air brought into the work space. It is also affected by the rate at which chemical contaminants are emitted from sources within the building such as construction materials, cleaning solvents used during routine maintenance, emissions from office equipment such as photocopiers, and chemicals emitted from personal items like hair spray, cologne, and recently dry-cleaned garments. Other factors that affect indoor air quality include the operating and maintenance procedures for the ventilation system and the scheduling of activities that introduce contaminants, such as renovations. As a result, rectifying one factor, such as increasing the rate of outside air intake, may produce no improvement in the indoor air quality if other factors are the predominant source of a problem. Unless health issues are addressed in a comprehensive manner, expensive studies and renovations can be wasted efforts rather than lasting solutions.

Chapter 6 discusses key health issues associated with the intensive use of computers in offices. The impact of computers on the office environment has been sudden and dramatic. In the space of a decade, office computing has migrated from the climate-controlled enclaves of computer specialists to the desks of office workers throughout the organization. Today, it is common for every employee in an office to have a computer workstation. The office has been revolutionized by this introduction of computers into general office space. But as with most rapid adoptions of technology, there have been unexpected problems that need to be resolved.

Computer work places heavier physical as well as psychological demands on the user. As a result, a number of illnesses and injuries previously rare among office workers have suddenly become commonplace. Cumulative trauma disorder (also known as repetitive strain injury) has become a serious and widespread illness costing billions of dollars in medical compensation, lost productivity, and litigation. It includes a number of musculoskeletal disorders that cause pain and numbness in the hands, wrists, arms, shoulders, and neck. Cumulative trauma disorders associated with intensive computer use have risen dramatically in recent years, coincident with the rapid appearance of computers on the office desktop. Vision difficulties and concerns about radiation exposure have also become important issues.

Recent research has substantially improved our understanding of these issues. It has also led to more effective preventive measures, such as ergonomically superior furniture designs and spatial layouts for computer-based work. The risk of injury can be substantially reduced by decreasing the length and intensity of computer work sessions. Job designs can be changed to include more noncomputer tasks, work schedules can be adjusted to intersperse computer-based work with other activities, and periodic rest breaks can be taken to reduce the strain of long computer work sessions.

Some motions are more likely to cause illness than others. With training, keyboard technique can be improved to reduce the physical strain of computer operation. When such injuries are addressed early, there is less risk of long-term injury and treatment is more effective. For this reason a supportive management environment is important to allay fears of job loss or other retribution so that people will be encouraged to seek prompt medical attention.

Chapter 7 examines aspects of the physical office setting that have important social and psychological effects on the people who use them. The layout of the office space and where people are located affect whom they are more likely to meet and how well they will interact. People whose work activities constantly conflict are less likely to develop a positive and cooperative working relationship. Noise disruptions from adjacent work activities are one of the most common sources of annoyance and disputes. The availability of meeting spaces, informal locales that foster spontaneous discussions, and even the size, light levels, and furnishings of corridors affect the way people interact and, ultimately, their contribution to the organization.

The issue of control and its influence on individual performance is also examined.

The degree of control that individuals can exercise over their work environment figures prominently in their attitude and commitment to the organization as well as their physical comfort.

Health concerns in the office setting have often escalated rapidly to become highly polarized and emotional disputes. The trauma of the dispute and the resulting spiral of distrust can be more destructive than the concerns at issue, seriously damaging the morale of an organization. It is a pattern of behavior commonly seen in chronic technological disaster events (such as exposure to pollution and radiation). The field of disaster research provides valuable insight into the social processes that precipitate a destructive spiral of distrust and the positive steps that can be taken to prevent and resolve such disputes.

Chapter 8 introduces the fundamental concepts of building diagnostics as applied to the office workplace, when diagnostic services should be considered, and how they can most effectively be used. Building diagnostics is a systematic procedure for evaluating the performance of the built environment, identifying deficiencies, and prescribing solutions to optimize the facility for the organization. Based on building science, it draws upon a wide range of disciplines from architecture and engineering to such fields as human behavior and physiology.

Chapter 9 examines how the management of an office facility affects its overall benefit to and support of the organization. More than is commonly recognized, facility management has a pervasive influence on the ways in which work can be structured and how quickly people and their equipment can be reorganized and redeployed to meet changing corporate needs. The choices made regarding the quality and responsiveness of facility management services directly affect the return realized on the sizable expenditures devoted to office accommodations. Senior management's decisions, involvement in, and support of facility management largely determine the quality of the occupants' work environment. This chapter also considers the scope of the facility management process, the tailoring of services to the needs of the organization, and alternative methods of service delivery.

Chapter 10, the concluding chapter, summarizes how offices came to be accommodated in the facilities we know today. Then, looking to the future, the issues that must be addressed and possible changes to how we think of an office — be it a physical or virtual entity — are presented.

This book presents a foundation of information for senior managers and others interested in the quality of the office environment. It also tries to answer the difficult "So what?" questions by which information becomes the basis for action. Its form and content seek to illustrate a practical approach — a systematic way to address the quality of the office environment in a comprehensive manner without being swamped with information and paralyzed into inaction.

THE OFFICE ENVIRONMENT IN CONTEXT

In Canada and the United States, more people work in offices than in any other work setting. About 42% of the U.S. workforce are office workers. Their occupations are extremely diverse. Of these, roughly 26% are clerical workers, who perform tasks that are more or less procedural in nature. The remaining 74% are commonly categorized as knowledge workers, which includes managerial and professional workers (Panko 1992).

Estimates of the proportion of clerical and knowledge workers vary depending on the way different researchers choose to categorize occupations. But contrary to popular belief, offices generally do not consist of large numbers of clerical workers supervised by a small group of managers.

Office jobs encompass a broad range of activities, from routine administration to creative problem solving and high-level decision making. Clerical jobs range from data-processing clerks to executive secretaries. The professional categories include such occupations as engineers, health workers, and lawyers — specialties that are fundamentally very different and require different equipment and facilities.

The activities of managers are also diverse. Managers may be responsible for a relatively small number of workers or an entire multinational enterprise. They may spend most of their time in the head office or on the road. There simply is no typical office worker.

Office workplaces can be large and devoted to clerical work such as insurance claim processing. They may serve small organizations dominated by professionals such as a law office. Organizations may be highly automated, with a computer terminal, electronic mail, and integrated information access at every desk, or they may be primarily paper-based. Offices not only differ in the type of work that is done and the procedures used; they also differ in key social dimensions such as the number of employees, the physical grouping of workers, work organization, supervisory policies, and morale.

Despite this diversity, people have a common understanding of the term *office*. The office is a physical place that accommodates certain work activities of an organization. Typical office activities include filing, planning, designing, supervising, analyzing, deciding, and communicating — all of which are predominantly information processing activities.

Offices developed from the need for organizations to coordinate, plan, and administer their activities. The mass production and distribution of goods required efficient methods of record keeping to track large numbers of transactions and coordinate ever more diverse endeavors (Figure 1.1). The office facility that we know today came into existence as a place from which an enterprise could effectively be controlled.

Clerical work at first was done wherever space conveniently permitted. In manu-

Figure 1.1 Office facilities developed, in part, from the need to store large volumes of records. (*Source*: Chris Lund, National Archives of Canada, PA144872.)

Figure 1.2 Office work arose from the need to efficiently maintain large numbers of records. This 1878 engraving of order fulfillment processing at Montgomery Ward & Company shows clerical work being done in the same warehouse area where orders were assembled and packaged. As a mail order retailer, this company had to develop an efficient system to receive and process large numbers of small orders and ship them to destinations throughout the United States.

facturing and merchandising, clerical activities might be done in the same area that products were fabricated or packaged for shipment (Figure 1.2). Later, this work was done in physically separate rooms — offices.

The office gathered together in one place the key decision makers and the staff who supported them. It was a place to accommodate three principal functions: people's interaction with each other, with the information they needed, and with the equipment they used. Accommodating in one location the people who needed to communicate with each other enabled them to meet more quickly and more frequently. The information they needed could be accessed more easily by having it stored and catalogued in a single location. The specialized equipment for handling that information could be concentrated at the place where it was needed — the office.

Most offices today look, feel, and sound different from their pre–World War II precursors. The high-ceilinged rooms with incandescent lights, heavy desks, and fixed, solid walls have been replaced by rooms with overhead florescent lights, systems furniture, and movable partitions (Figure 1.3). Offices in the United States and Canada usually have centrally controlled air-handling systems that provide consistent environmental comfort year-round. While some office buildings have been the target of occupant complaints, the overall quality, safety, and comfort level of most offices have improved over the past century. As the quality of office working conditions has risen, so, too, have the occupants' expectations.

Historically, the direction, coordination, and execution of office activities have been supported by the technological devices of the day. In the 1800s, pens, ink, and suitable paper were the office equipment. By the turn of the century, the letterpress and early typewriters expedited clerical tasks. Between the two world

Figure 1.3 Florescent ceiling lights, systems furniture, and movable partitions are common features of today's offices. (*Source*: Industry, Science and Technology Canada, Ottawa.)

wars, telephones became commonplace in American offices, and punched-card tabulating equipment became a mainstay of the accounting profession. Since World War II, office technologies changed from manual typewriters, carbon paper, ball-point pens, and check-writing machines to photocopiers, fax machines, and computer-based word processors (Whalen 1983).

All the while, office equipment has become smaller and more powerful. In the 1960s business depended on armies of keypunch operators to produce the computer punch cards needed to enter data and programs into large mainframe computers (Figure 1.4). Today, data can be input directly into computer systems or can be generated in computer-readable digital form in the first place — eliminating manual data entry.

The twentieth century has seen the rise of mammoth organizations — insurance companies, banks, engineering design firms, and government bureaucracies — with proportionately extensive office support. Some organizations use an entire floor of an office building as one vast room, sectioned into smaller work spaces by partitions and systems furniture. Hundreds of staff can be accommodated in such open plan areas while enclosed offices are reserved for senior managers.

Accommodating the office workforce demands that the unique activities, physical attributes, and individual work styles of the occupants be addressed. Operating a computer-aided design (CAD) system often requires large work surfaces to lay out oversize drawings (Figure 1.5). The standard-issue office furniture may not fit everyone. If chairs or work surfaces cannot be adjusted properly for very short or very tall people, then alternatives are needed.

Individuals differ in their visual acuity. People who don't normally require eyeglasses may need prescription lenses when they work at a computer monitor for several hours a day. (Subsequent chapters examine how work-setting characteristics affect individual performance and the way facilities can best be designed and managed to support the office worker.)

Figure 1.4 This 1961 photo shows keypunch operators at work. (*Source*: Dominion-Wide, National Archives of Canada, PA144831.)

Initially, the rapid automation of offices tended to severely compromise environmental quality and ergonomics. Existing buildings simply had not been designed to accommodate the automated office. Computer equipment adds significantly to the quantity and quality of building services required. Without additional cooling and ventilation the heat generated by the new equipment made offices hot and stuffy. The quality of many building services had to be upgraded as well. For example, not only is more power needed in automated offices, the power must be of higher quality as well. Voltage dips and surges can play havoc with sensitive computer circuitry.

Automation of the office also affected the physical characteristics of the work done and the worksettings that were used. Lighting, cooling, acoustic separation, table heights, quality of seating, and other facility characteristics were often so unsuited to computer-based work that they caused physical injury and illness. Media attention attracted by such workplace issues as sick building syndrome and repetitive strain injury has sensitized office workers and the general public to the health risks of the office workplace.

The amount of space, access to a view outside, degree of privacy, office furnishings, and decor are perceived as indicators of power and stature within an organization. As a result, a difficult trade-off must often be made between giving the best office settings to those who can make the most productive use of them or matching the quality of the work setting to the occupants' rank in the organization, even though they may rarely use their office.

FORCES DRIVING THE RETHINKING OF THE OFFICE

Organizations are reevaluating the way they look at the office facility — whom it should serve, how its value should be assessed, and how its performance should be measured. Aware of the high cost of office accommodation and pushed by competitive pressure to enhance the productivity of their employees, organizations want maximum value from their facility investment.

The concept of the office itself is being reexamined. The growing demand for improvements in the office environment has met considerable resistance. But as is often the case, such changes are being driven by powerful external forces, which are examined in the following subsections. Alternatives that would have been anathema only a few years ago are now being readily accepted.

Costs

Perhaps the most compelling force in rethinking the office facility is its cost. Traditionally, office accommodation was viewed primarily as an overhead expense — a money-losing cost center to be controlled. Since senior managers generally rise from product-generating areas of an organization, their view of the facility as a cost center is not surprising. Facility costs were treated as an issue separate from the salaries and benefits of the office occupants who used them. As a result, facility decisions were often focused on cost cutting without fully accounting for their

Figure 1.5 Work areas must accommodate the individual's or group's activities, physical attributes, and work style. For example, this CAD workstation requires a large work surface to lay out oversize material and considerable floor area for coworkers to gather around. (*Source*: Bell-Northern Research (BNR).)

broader consequences. Facility management was judged to be successful if annual expenditures could be held steady or reduced.

It is estimated that 20% to 30% of commercial buildings in the United States have some form of sick building syndrome, which costs billions of dollars annually in lost productivity from illness, absenteeism, and reduced worker effectiveness. In most cases, sick buildings are the result of deficiencies in building design, maintenance, and/or operating procedures. Although some of these deficiencies occur inadvertently, they commonly are a direct result of conscious efforts to reduce the cost of the building design, construction, and operation costs (Woods 1989). However, when these apparent cost savings are compared with the value of lost time or productivity at risk, they are seldom appealing.

The annualized labor costs of office workers in America are so much greater than those related to the buildings they occupy that annual savings of even 25% on energy, utilities, maintenance, or operations are readily negated if the rate of absenteeism due to illness increases by 1 to 3 days per year per employee or a loss of about 2 to 6 minutes a day of productive concentration per person (Woods 1989).

For example, insufficient outside air is a major contributor to indoor air quality problems. The annual energy cost per employee to condition sufficient outside air is about $270 in temperate zones of the United States (Stewart 1992). In decreasing the outside air fraction to reduce energy costs, there is a risk of reducing the indoor air quality and increasing illness symptoms and absenteeism. Since the average salary of an American office employee is about $30,000, even if the entire energy cost for conditioning air could be saved, the $270 per employee that was recouped would be more than offset by the productivity lost if that employee was just 1% less productive over the year (1% of $30,000 is $300). In other words, if sick building symptoms caused the employee to be absent an additional 1 or 2 days per year or to lose 5 or 6 minutes a day of productive concentration, there would be no true cost saving.

When the additional risk of expenses for medical treatment, litigation settlements, and increased insurance rates is also considered, a narrow focus on cost cutting as a facility management approach becomes difficult to justify. Cost avoidance is more likely to be achieved by investing enough in office accommodations to minimize illness and optimize individual performance. What's more, as regulatory guidelines and legislation set more stringent office quality standards, offices with poor environmental quality are more likely to be seen as evidence of professional negligence.

Accountability

Organizations have long been held legally accountable for health and safety in the workplace. Occupational health and safety regulations define minimum standards, and government regulatory agencies carry out inspections and accident investigations to verify compliance. Although these standards apply to all workplaces, they were originally developed for the industrial work setting. As a result, they focus on minimizing dangers not usually encountered in the office environment, such as acute exposures to toxic chemicals and life-threatening injury from heavy equipment or dangerous working conditions. It is rare that an office fails to meet these standards, even if it has been shown to be the source of sick building symptoms.

The office is not an overtly dangerous place. Occupants do not work with heavy equipment, in risky settings such as underground mines, or with materials that cause injury on contact (Figure 1.6). In the office, the risks to occupant health and safety are from chronic exposures to chemicals and working conditions that do not usually produce symptoms from

Figure 1.6 Office work is not overtly dangerous in the same way that certain manufacturing jobs can be. The man shown in this 1945 photo is operating a 500-ton ram used for punching holes in metal angles. (*Source*: A. W. Gifford, National Archives of Canada, PA164006.)

short-term exposures. Even among those most sensitive to sick building conditions, it is exceedingly rare that a few hours in a sick building would have any long-term health consequences. (For some people, such as those who are severely asthmatic, even short-term exposure to an unhealthy office setting could be serious. But they would be sensitive to other indoor settings as well, not just offices.)

Health and safety risks in the office setting arise from chronic exposures. Constant exposure to chemical irritants in the indoor air, awkward work postures, and other insults to the body can result in illness symptoms that make it difficult or physically impossible to perform work tasks. Allergic reactions to chemical pollutants and cumulative trauma disorders related to computer use are among many medically verifiable health conditions commonly associated with deficient office environments.

Not surprisingly, workers' compensation awards have risen steadily as more has been learned about the health consequences of the office setting. Union grievances are often filed along with compensation claims for injury, creating additional costs and frustration for employers. Litigation has also risen. Employers and suppliers of office furniture and equipment have become frequent targets of lawsuits arising from work-related injury to office employees.

Nor is accountability limited to the corporate entity. The ergonomic safety and environmental quality of the office are being seen as a legal responsibility of management. Building owners, senior managers, and even facility management personnel have been held personally responsible for environmental illnesses and injuries suffered by office occupants.

In a recent California court case, the plaintiffs' experts specifically cited the building owner, the contractor, the architect, and the facility manager personally as being responsible for the illness of employees exposed to poor air quality during office renovations (*Call et al.* v. *Prudential Insurance Company of America*). While facility renovations were under way, employees' complaints of poor air quality were not addressed to their satisfaction. When employees became ill, they filed a liability suit. Based on the facts presented at the hearing and expert testimony, it was concluded that the owner, designers, builders, and operators all bore some responsibility. Although numerous factors in the development and operation of the building had been addressed, the effects of the renovations on the occupants had been given little attention. The occupants' expectation of a reasonably safe indoor environment had been largely ignored. The dispute was eventually settled out of court for a sum rumored to be in the hundreds of thousands of dollars (Levin 1990, 1994).

Overzealous efforts to reduce accommodation costs can easily compromise the quality of the office workplace to a level where employees or their unions take legal action. Senior managers are finding themselves held more directly accountable in legal proceedings related to the health and safety of the office environment. Ignorance of the issues or controversy over appropriate remediation is no longer an acceptable defense for disregarding occupant complaints. It is expected that occupant health complaints will receive a sympathetic hearing and be addressed in a responsible manner. In order to protect themselves from liability, managers need to be sufficiently well informed about office environment issues so as to demonstrate reasonable diligence in making facility-related decisions.

Real Estate Asset Management

The quality of the office environment has become a valuable amenity in the commercial real estate market. Tenants are willing to pay a premium for offices with superior indoor environmental quality. Buildings that offer such premium space can command higher rents and maintain a higher occupancy rate even in tough economic times (Figure 1.7).

The way that real estate is valued often leads to underinvestment in facilities. Traditional accounting practices assess real estate according to its original purchase price (termed the **book value**) regardless of how long it has been held. But over time, the value of a building or the land it occupies tends to appreciate. When book values are substantially lower than market values, the facility expenditures needed to maintain a high-quality office environment may appear to be excessive relative to the asset valuation. However, it is more realistic to compare current facility expenditures to current valuations (i.e., the **market value**).

For owners who occupy their offices, recognizing the market value of their real estate can change the level of spending that appears reasonable for its maintenance and enhancement. Crediting the market value of real estate assets may also improve the firm's financial liquidity. A larger asset base can secure more attractive lending rates.

Flexibility

Many organizations find that their office work processes change continually. On average, organizations move about one-third of their office employees each year (Brill 1987) and reorganize each department about every 18 months (Bellas 1992). Decisions to downsize, expand, or simply change staff allocation require relocating people; moving furniture, files, and equipment; and reassigning telephones and other servicing.

The choice of building design, office furnishings, cabling, and other characteristics affects the time and cost of such a redeployment. If the organization is one that

Figure 1.7 A high quality office building not only enhances the occupants' corporate image it also adds to the value of the real estate asset. (*Source*: Bell-Northern Research (BNR).)

must adapt to frequent changes, then more flexible facility designs and management practices can minimize disruption and downtime as well as permitting the arrangement of workstations to be optimized for project needs. Matching facility flexibility to the organization's activities is another means of enhancing the productivity of the office workforce.

Knowledge Work

A recent television ad for a computer company shows a young man preparing to leave the office at the end of the business day. He is evidently the last person there. As he puts on his coat and turns off the lights, the telephone rings. After a moments hesitation the young man decides to answer. The unseen caller apparently asks about prices, and after a few keystrokes at a computer console, the man explains that a price will remain in effect until a certain date. Before he has a chance to leave, the phone rings again. Another few keystrokes, and changing his voice to sound like a second person, he answers a question about shipping dates. In response to a third call, he becomes the research department and, in a stuffy accent, answers another question. Finally, he dons his hat and coat and leaves after a grateful salute to the machine.

The ad is promoting a particular brand of computer. The tasks the computer performed are not unique to that machine: many systems could be programmed to operate in that manner. What is more interesting is that this knowledge worker is using the power of the company's technology to perform, in a confident and competent manner, a myriad of jobs. The critical question for organizations is where they can find people with the skills and motivation to perform this way, and once they find those people, how they can attract and keep them.

It is predicted that by the year 2000, 80% of all jobs in America will predominantly involve cerebral skills rather than manual skills, a reversal of the situation some 50 years ago. Moreover, half the cerebral jobs will require higher education or professional qualifications (McKinsey & Company 1986).

Office work has increasingly become **knowledge work** (i.e., tasks that require information to be created, analyzed, evaluated, or acted upon). Jobs that require little thought and understanding are increasingly relegated to computers. The people who remain fill roles that are progressively unique and ever more valuable. As a result, measures that can improve the productivity of this workforce, decrease absenteeism, or simply make the workplace setting more conducive to good work habits directly contribute to the success of the organization.

The growing importance of knowledge workers has increased their power and influence. So, too, has their uniqueness. As Toffler (1990) has aptly described it, knowledge workers have become less interchangeable. In the industrial revolution, not only parts but people were designed to be easily replaced. Industrial work was broken down into relatively simple rote tasks that could be learned quickly and required little skill. If a replacement was needed, the unemployed provided a ready supply of labor. However, as the knowledge content of work increases, the job becomes more individualized. Each person tends to use tools a little differently than the next and will approach a problem in his or her own way according to the unique skills and experience that person brings to the task.

When a knowledge worker leaves the organization, finding another person with comparable skills can be difficult and costly. The more sophisticated the skills, the greater the challenge to replace them. Training someone to provide the lost capabilities is expensive. Merck and Company found that the administrative cost and disruption involved in replacing employees was about 1.5 times their annual salary. Other studies have found that new employees take about a year to reach their

Figure 1.8 To benefit from heavy investments in office automation, an organization's procedures and individual's work methods must be modified to take advantage of the new technology. It is not uncommon to have two computers at a workstation. The knowledge worker in this photo needed two computer systems to access different networks and operating systems.

maximum efficiency (Phillips 1990; Schlesinger and Heskett 1991). When all these factors are taken into account, it becomes clear that a high turnover of knowledge workers is a major drain on an organization's resources. As the cost of replacing knowledge workers rises, so, too, does their bargaining power. To attract and retain talented people, the organization must be prepared to address their interests and concerns.

Productivity of Office Workers

In the 1980s, corporate America invested billions of dollars in office automation without seeing any appreciable increase in white-collar productivity. The reasons for this *productivity paradox*, as it has come to be known, have been widely debated and are examined in Chapter 3.

In manufacturing, production can be rapidly increased by automation. A machine can immediately assist workers to perform tasks more quickly or do work they would not have the strength or precision to do themselves, or it may even replace human workers altogether. But office computers in themselves do not generate such immediate benefits. The technology can only increase productivity to the extent that users integrate it into their way of working (Figure 1.8).

In the 1990s, people are seen as the key to thriving in an increasingly competitive global marketplace. As organizations have downsized to control costs, they have had to accomplish more with fewer people. Office technology alone was not enough to boost productivity. People have had to work smarter, and organizations have had to find new ways to motivate and retain their talented producers. Providing an environment where people can produce their mind's best work should be part of this effort. A disruptive, uncomfortable work environment is not merely a less desirable place to work; it also exacts a performance cost, no matter how talented the individual.

Changing Demographics

Since 1980, there has been a major downward trend in the size of the 18- to 24-year-old age group in the United States, Canada, and much of Europe. From the early 1980s until about 1995, the numbers of this age group are expected to fall by one-quarter to one-third (OECD 1992). In both Canada and the United States, 50% of the workforce was under 34 years of age in 1985. In the year 2000, only 39% will be in this age group (Johnston 1991).

Despite the reduced numbers, there has been an increase in college and university enrollment among this age group. This has largely been due to the stronger presence of women in higher education, as well as the increased numbers of mature students, part-time students, and immigrants. As the number of female students approaches fifty percent of total enrollment this increase appears to be levelling off.

Industrialized nations will face shortages of skilled workers during the economic cycles of the 1990s. The combined effects of slow workforce growth, earlier retirements, and shrinking high school and college enrollments will force employers to look beyond national boundaries for the people they need. As a result, a growing number of occupations will become internationalized. For example, by the end of the 1980s, a shortage of nurses led New York hospitals to seek qualified personnel in Dublin and Manila. Similarly, the shortage of engineers has led rapidly growing systems development companies to turn to foreign universities in such countries as England and India to fill some of their U.S. job openings.

It is expected that demographics and changing career choices will result in shortages of scientists and engineers by the mid-1990s, with these shortages being more severe for more highly qualified individuals. In Canada and the United States, student enrollment in science and engineering has fallen steadily in recent years. Canadian enrollment peaked at 32,000 in 1984–85 falling to 25,000 in 1988–89. In the United States, enrollments reached a maximum of 406,000 in 1983, then dropped to 346,000 in 1988 (OECD 1992). Not only is the quantity of science and engineering graduates of concern; the quality is also at risk. As enrollment drops off, the entrance requirements for science studies may also come down. In standardized international tests of high school students conducted during the 1980s, U.S. students' scores in mathematics and science ranked well behind those of students from many other nations. When the scores of students from 13 nations were compared, U.S. students ranked thirteenth in biology, twelfth in chemistry, and tenth in physics (Johnston 1991).

The developing world is producing a rapidly increasing share of the world's skilled workers. In 1970, the United States and Canada had 35% of the world's college enrollment; by 1986, their share had fallen to 23%. By the year 2000, 60% of the world's college students will be from developing countries. Global competition is not limited to goods and services; it will increasingly include labor as well. The worldwide standard of education is steadily improving, and a growing share of the world's high school and college graduates will be produced by developing countries (Johnston 1991).

With a smaller population of qualified youth entering the workforce, employers will have to work harder to attract skilled employees. To compete successfully for the limited supply of talent, they will have to offer more of what this group wants. The quality of the work environment is an amenity that can give an organization a competitive edge in attracting and retaining hard-to-find talent.

Alternative Accommodation

The need to do more with less has prompted organizations to seek alternatives to expensive office accommodations. Telecommunications have enabled organizations to move much of their office space to less expensive suburban locations while maintaining a smaller "front office" presence in the more expensive downtown core. Between the downtown and the suburbs, costs can differ by 50% to 100% in the same metropolitan area (Apgar 1993).

Modems, fax machines, computer networks, and mobile phones have enabled the work process to be decoupled from the locations where individual tasks are performed. Functions that previously had to be done in one location to ensure a smooth work flow can now be dispersed to multiple sites across town or across the globe without compromising the work process or the final product.

Not only can office work be made independent of place; it can also be made independent of time. The **virtual office** concept employs computer and telecommunications technology to connect office workers to the information and services they require, wherever and whenever they may need them. **Telecommuting**, working from an off-site location electronically connected to the organization, can be structured to reduce the amount of office space an organization needs. However, to do so requires that the office concept itself be rethought so that when telecommuters must spend time in-house, they are provided with facilities appropriate for the way they work.

It is increasingly common for employees to use the office as a home base rather than as their sole place of work. The growing trend is for office work to be done wherever it is done best, which may often be outside the formal office setting. In 1993, 6.1% of the adult U.S. workforce (7.6 million American workers) were **telecommuters** (i.e., they were company employees who worked from home part- or full-time during normal business hours). This represented a rise of 15% from the previous year (Link 1993).

The Greening of the Office

Environmental conservation exerts a growing influence on the way public as well as private organizations operate their facilities. Publications like *Fortune* magazine, committed to free enterprise and a stalwart supporter of big business, now run articles in praise of corporations that have become more active in addressing environmental issues. The reduction of toxic emissions and solid wastes, the adoption of comprehensive environmental policies, and the introduction of employee incentives to achieve environmental goals have entered mainstream corporate culture.

The **greening** of the office, as this shift in attitude has been termed, commonly rewards organizations with unexpected financial benefits in return for their altruistic expression of environmental responsibility. Efforts to reduce, reuse, and recycle are not only environmentally friendly; they enhance an organization's public image, can save money by improving operating efficiency, and win contracts by earning preferential supplier status.

Focusing creative talent on issues such as reducing paper consumption, once considered too mundane to warrant serious attention, has produced significant financial as well as public relations benefits. For example, AT&T embarked on a program to reduce paper usage. By eliminating cover pages and making greater use of electronic rather than printed media, the internal information management unit reduced paper consumption by 22% within a year. The long-distance division revised the formatting of customer bills so that more information was printed on each page. As a result, it printed 3 million fewer sheets of paper per year and reduced postage expenses, to reap annual savings of $4 million (Rice 1993).

Public sector organizations encounter increasingly strict environmental policies that mandate recycling, reuse of capital equipment and materials, and the modification of procedures that unnecessarily waste paper and other consumables. As well, it is now common for preference to be given to suppliers with active recycling programs. A firm's environmental record can be instrumental in winning lucrative contracts. Some large private sector firms have instituted preferential purchasing programs as well. For example, S. C. Johnson Corporation and Apple Computers have made the environmental record of their suppliers a selection criterion.

It is also becoming more costly to dispose of office waste. Municipalities, straining under the burden of spiraling costs and public pressure to adopt environmentally responsible policies, have raised the price they charge for garbage trucks to empty their load in landfill sites (known as the **tipping fee**). Most sites won't accept recyclable materials such as fine paper, corrugated cardboard, recyclable wood waste, and scrap metal.

The rising cost of disposal has made the implementation of recycling programs financially more attractive. For example, at First Canadian Place, a major office complex in Toronto, the daily waste production was reduced from 40 metric tons (41 short tons) per day to 7 metric tons (7.7 short tons) a day, for annual savings of CDN$1.3 million (approximately US$1 million) (Wood 1991). The overall cost of a recycling program and the benefits in employee involvement and community recognition depend upon the ingenuity of its design and its suitability to the specific organization and facility.

The compatibility of furniture system components over time and between model lines has become a more important criterion in the selection of office furnishings. An organization can realize far greater value from its expenditures on office furnishings if components with standard fittings and sizes are chosen. Furniture can then be readily disassembled and reconfigured as the organization's needs change. New components can be added without having to abandon serviceable tabletops, storage units, and other components simply because they are incompatible with newer designs.

Finding and maintaining an organization's office furnishings can be a monumental task. For many large companies, the process of finding furniture available for reuse was more costly than simply ordering new pieces. Now, computerized inventory systems coupled with bar-code identification tags on each item enable facility managers to track the location and condition of every component. Using handheld scanners, staff can efficiently maintain an up-to-date record of the furnishings in use and those in storage. They can go to any facility, rapidly collect the

Figure 1.9 Old screens from open plan offices which would otherwise be bound for landfill sites, can be refurbished and resold. (*Source*: Advanced Business Interiors, Ottawa.)

location and condition information for each item, and then transfer the data to their inventory database. Requests for additional furniture can be compared with the existing inventory and new purchases limited to those components that are truly needed. Furniture in storage can be readily retrieved and redeployed.

In response to customer demands, furniture manufacturers have developed designs with interchangeable components for greater flexibility. Most major furniture manufacturers have also implemented buyback programs wherein components can be sold back to the manufacturer, to be refurbished and then resold (Figure 1.9).

These initiatives, taken together, enable a professional and effective work environment to be assembled in an environmentally responsible way (Figure 1.10). Carpet can be manufactured from disposable soda bottles or used nylon carpet, ceiling tiles can contain as much as 70% recycled material, and drywall can be reused or can be completely manufactured from recycled materials. The useful life of office furnishings can be extended by reupholstering chairs and refinishing table tops, filing cabinets, and other furniture.

Less visible, though equally important, is the judicious selection of environmentally-appropriate products to construct

Figure 1.10 The appearance of this well-appointed executive office belies its origins from remanufactured components. All the furniture was previously used and has been refinished. The ceiling tiles, carpet, and drywall are manufactured with some recycled materials. The energy efficient flourescent lighting system consumes less power than conventional systems and the ballasts do not contain PCBs. An infrared motion detector automatically switches off the lights when the space is unoccupied. (*Source*: Environment Canada, Ottawa.)

and finish the space. Paints are available that do not contain toxic heavy metals such as mercury, lead, cadmium, or chromium and its oxides. Carpets should be installed using water based adhesives that offgas little or no volatile organic compounds. Living plants can be used to help trap airborne contaminants and give indoor spaces a natural appearance.

Organizations are being enticed, cajoled, and legislated into adopting environmentally responsible management practices in their office facilities. Despite the obstinacy with which this shift was initially greeted, the greening of the office has become a well-established trend that has delivered diverse tangible and intangible rewards.

CONCLUSION

The physical setting is being recognized as critical to an organization's long-term success. It affects the organization's cost of labor and accommodation, the productivity of its workforce, and the quality of worker it can attract. These compelling forces have led organizations to invest more in their people. The physical office environment is one component of that investment. Instead of being viewed as a luxury, workplace enhancements are being accepted as part of the ongoing process of improving organizational effectiveness.

LITERATURE CITED

Apgar, M. 1993. Uncovering your hidden occupancy costs. *Harvard Business Review* (May–June): 124–136.

Bellas, J. 1992. President, Interior Space International. Comments quoted by Linda Monroe. What do facility managers need? *Buildings* (October):38–45.

Brill, M. 1987. When politics is the name of the FM game. *Facilities Design & Management* (July–August):58–61.

Davidson, J., and W. Rees-Moog. 1991. *The great reckoning.* New York: Summit Books, Simon & Schuster Books.

Handy, C. 1990. *The age of unreason.* Boston: Harvard Business School Press.

Johnston, W. B. 1991. Global workforce 2000: The new world labor market. *Harvard Business Review* (March–April):115–127.

Levin, H. 1990. Multimillion-dollar SBS lawsuit settled. *Indoor Air Quality* Update 3(11):1–5. Arlington, MA: Cutter Information Corp.

Levin, H. 1994. Personal communication. Santa Cruz, Calif.: Hal Levin & Associates.

Link. 1993. *Telecommuting fact sheet.* New York: Link Resources Corporation.

McKinsey & Company. 1986. A study by the Amsterdam office, discussed in *The age of unreason*, C. Handy, pp34.

OECD. 1992. *Technology and the economy: The key relationships.* Paris: Organization for Economic Cooperation and Development.

Panko, R. R. 1992. The office workforce: A structural analysis. *Office Systems Research Journal* (spring):3–20.

Phillips, D. L. 1990. The price tag on turnover. *Personnel Journal* (December):58–61.

Rice, F. 1993. Who scores best on the environment? *Fortune* July 26, 114–122.

Schlesinger, L. A., and J. L. Heskett. 1991. The service-driven service company. *Harvard Business Review* (December):71–81.

Stewart, S. M. 1992. Reaching agreements on indoor air quality. *ASHRAE Journal* (August):28–32.

Toffler, A. 1990. *Powershift.* New York: Bantam Books.

Whalen, T. 1983. Office technology and socioeconomic change: 1870–1955. *IEEE Technology and Society Magazine* 2(2):12–18.

Wood, V. 1991. Going for the green. *Office Systems & Technology* 37(6):16-18.

Woods, J. E. 1989. Cost avoidance and productivity in owning and operating buildings. *Occupational Medicine: State of the Art Reviews* 4(4):753–770.

Chapter 2

THE OFFICE FACILITY

From time immemorial, people have met to exchange information, make decisions, develop plans, and to buy and sell goods or services. They have conducted these activities while seated on a carpet, amid the bustle of a coffeehouse, in the consulting room of professionals, and in the study of the aristocracy (Figure 2.1).

The choice of location has always entailed trade-offs in the physical setting. The privacy of a secluded spot might be more important than the convenience and comfort of the home or shop. The security of a crowded coffeehouse where one could be anonymous and a conversation would be difficult to overhear might take precedence over a quieter setting. For businesses today, the office has become the setting of choice for the generation, coordination, and communication of information. It is a facility in which people can interact with each other, with their information, and with their information-processing tools.

Our current concept of an office as a facility built especially for that purpose emerged in Europe in the mid-1800s. Office buildings of that time were comprised of rooms that were rented to a single company or to several small firms for transacting clerical or executive business. Since the emergence of the single-purpose office building, the office workplace has evolved with advances in construction technology, improvements in office equipment, and developments in organization theory.

In the 1970s, the introduction of electronic office equipment to the workplace brought about a series of dramatic changes both to the way business was done and to the setting in which business was transacted. Today, the rapid pace of change is an ever present force driving building owners, business managers, and office workers to rethink how workplaces are designed, managed, and used.

Our concept of the office is undergoing a remarkable change. Portable computers,

Figure 2.1 This 1830 engraving of life in Palestine shows merchants conducting business in the open air.

fax machines, electronic mail, and cellular telephones enable more and more office functions to be freed from the location and time constraints of the traditional workplace. The recent increase in telecommuting and home-based businesses is bringing the office facility full circle to its origins in the home-centered cottage industries and home offices of the past. Today, in Canada and the United States, a home-based office to support part-time or full-time work activities is becoming commonplace, as it was at the turn of the century (Figure 2.2).

In the competitive business environment of the 1990s, organizations have become increasingly receptive to innovative ways of enhancing worker productivity. The past decade has seen a host of new management approaches designed to motivate and empower office workers with the goal of increasing productivity. The design and operation of the physical office setting also contribute in important ways to the performance of the employees who use it. An awareness of this contribution offers the opportunity to tailor the office setting in a way that better serves the needs of the organization and its workforce.

THE EMERGENCE OF LARGE CORPORATIONS

Today's large corporations of the industrialized world are the culmination of a long process of organizational development that began with the small shops and cottage industries of the preindustrial age. The latter half of the eighteenth century saw the industrial revolution begin to transform European societies from their traditional agricultural base to a manufacturing one. People left their work on the farm and moved to the city for jobs in factories and offices. The new commercial and manufacturing enterprises operated on a larger scale than before, with more employees involved in a greater range of activities. Coordinating and controlling these larger enterprises demanded information that was more accurate, more timely, and more comprehensive. Improved record keeping was needed to produce this information, and closer communication was required to disseminate it. A clerical workforce was rapidly developed to deliver these administrative ser-

Figure 2.2 This Wooton desk is an example of the type of personal office furniture that professionals and business people would have in their homes, circa 1876-1882. (*Source*: R and E Dubrow Antiques, Whitestone, N. Y.)

vices, and with it came the appearance of the career office worker.

The phenomenon of large corporations emerged in the United States after the American Civil War and the economic growth that followed. Business empires such as Standard Oil and Woolworth were established at that time (circa 1880). Extensive record keeping was needed, and a large proportion of staff was dedicated to paper-based office work. Pen and paper were the principal office equipment of the day. Subtle differences in the style and performance of pens attracted user interest just as the pros and cons of different computer keyboard and mouse designs do today (Figure 2.3).

The rapid increase in the volume of clerical work during the latter half of the 19th century was made possible by new technologies appearing at that time. In 1867, Christopher Sholes produced a workable typewriter (using techniques developed to manufacture high-precision guns and pistols with interchangeable parts). Trained personnel could type up to 100 words per minute, which represented a substantial

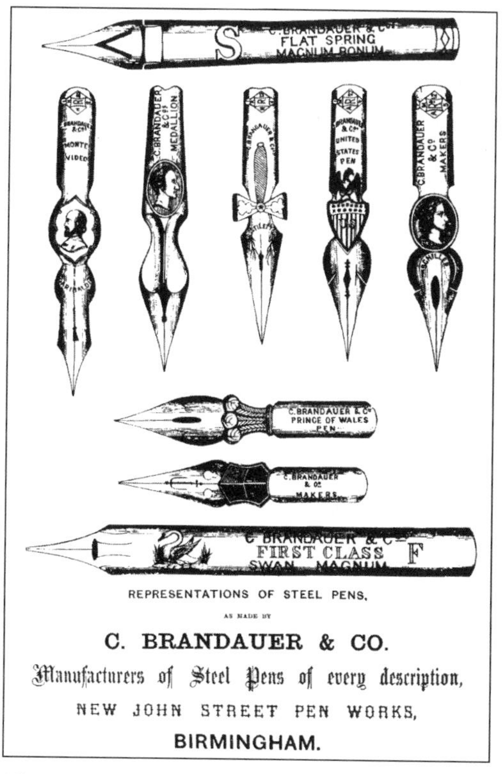

Figure 2.3 Decorative steel pen nibs, as shown in this 1862 advertisement, were much sought after when record keeping was done by hand with pen and ink.

Figure 2.4 Office work emerged as a career when large numbers of trained clerical staff were needed to handle the increased administrative needs of business and to operate office equipment such as typewriters. Office interior of Molson's Brewery, Montreal, circa 1900. (*Source*: National Archives of Canada, PA119420.)

Figure 2.5 Telephones began to appear on office desks at the turn of the century. Typical of the introduction of new technology, there was no standard way to connect the telephone line to the handset. Here the telephone line was simply hung from the ceiling light and wrapped around the desk. 1902. (*Source*: W. J. Topley, National Archives of Canada, PA008980.)

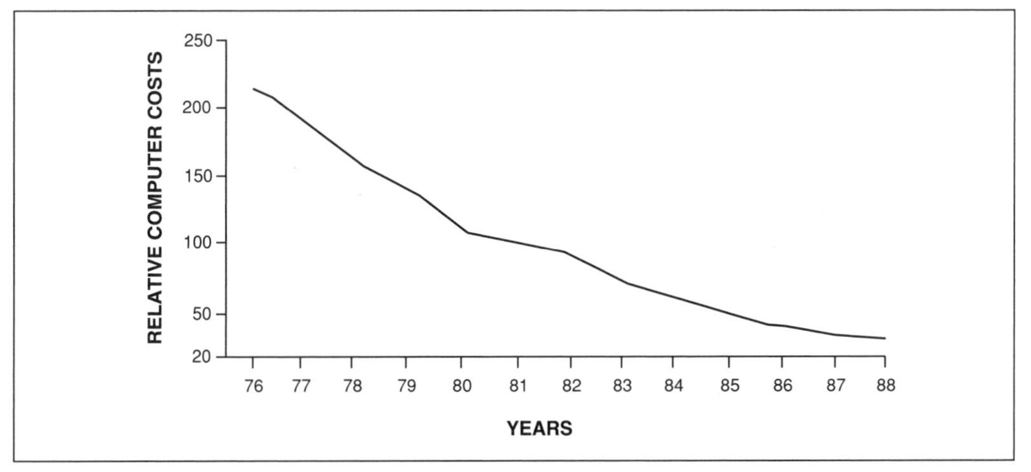

Figure 2.6 The decreasing cost of computer hardware in the United States adjusted for inflation and changes in product quality. The 1981 cost is set at a cost index of 100. (*Source*: OECD, 1992.)

increase in productivity over writing the material by hand as well as an improvement in legibility and consistency. The telephone and the mechanical calculator began to appear in offices between 1880 and 1900 (Figures 2.4 and 2.5)(Armstrong 1972).

The industrial age dominated Western society's sense of values and progress for two centuries. Then, in the 1950s, there was a shift toward a service-based economy and the rapid development of information-intensive enterprises. The first commercial electronic computers were very costly, difficult to program, and demanded constant maintenance. They were so large that they filled a good-sized room, yet their computing power was a fraction of today's desktop personal computer. Despite their limitations, they represented a dramatic advance in computational capability. Today, the computer has revolutionized the way office work is done.

The steady decrease in the price of computers, coupled with their ever increasing capabilities have led to their pervasive use (Figure 2.6). Buyers of personal computers have come to expect that the high-end machine purchased today will be available at half the cost in 18 to 24 months. The cost of mainframe and minicomputer power has been falling steadily as well, though at a somewhat slower pace.

So integral has computer-based information processing become in industrialized countries that the success of their economies has become dependent on the effectiveness with which organizations can access and use information. Society itself has rapidly become knowledge-based and more information dependent than ever before. From automated banking machines to the administration of government programs, individuals depend on ever more integrated electronic information networks for the services they receive and the work they do. In this information-intensive environment, workers have rapid access to large quantities of data that are analyzed to support faster and more complex decision making in an increasingly competitive global market. The rapidly evolving electronic information infrastructure has changed the way we work and in so doing has dramatically changed the types of office settings needed to support the new tasks and equipment.

DEVELOPMENTS IN CONSTRUCTION TECHNOLOGY

By the 1800s, the shift of population from the farm to city-based jobs precipitated a growing demand for offices located in central business districts. The economies

Figure 2.7 Tall commercial and office buildings constructed at the turn of the century. Photograph of downtown Toronto taken in 1924. (*Source*: National Archives of Canada, PA187930.)

Figure 2.8 Office towers along Wall Street in the financial district of New York City.

of land prices that encouraged the division of property into ever smaller lot sizes, cramming buildings together at increasingly high densities, promoted the construction of multistory buildings. However, the masonry wall construction techniques of that era limited the height of a building to 10 storys. To support that height, the wall at the ground level had to be 1.2 meters (4 feet) thick, greatly reducing the usable interior area. For this reason, office buildings were generally of moderate size and comprised of small individual rooms, making the office spaces relatively private. They were designed with fewer and simpler building systems than today's office structures. There were no centralized heating and cooling systems, for example. As a result, the skills needed to operate and maintain these offices were straightforward and required no specialized training (Pile 1984).

The introduction of iron girders and pillars in the 1860s, followed by structural steel in the 1880s, marked the beginning of the skyscraper design (Figure 2.7). During the same period, Otis Elevator Company invented safety brakes for passenger elevators (1870). With a safe method for vertical transportation and stronger structural support systems, buildings of 30 to 50 storys were constructed. In New York City, structures such as the 30-story Park Row Building, built in 1899, the 50-story Metropolitan Life Building, completed in 1909, and the 58-story Woolworth Building, constructed in 1913, were landmark architectural and engineering achievements of their day (Figure 2.8).

Until the 1930s, building designs relied on windows to provide daylight as the primary source of illumination and natural ventilation for outside air. The wider the building, the more limited the penetration of light and outside air to the central core. So office buildings had a maximum practical width of about 15 – 20 meters (40 – 60 feet). The creative design of floor plans in such shapes as L, T, I, U, and O enabled the overall size of the building to be increased while remaining within these width limitations (Figure 2.9).

As technological advances brought electric lighting and mechanized ventilating

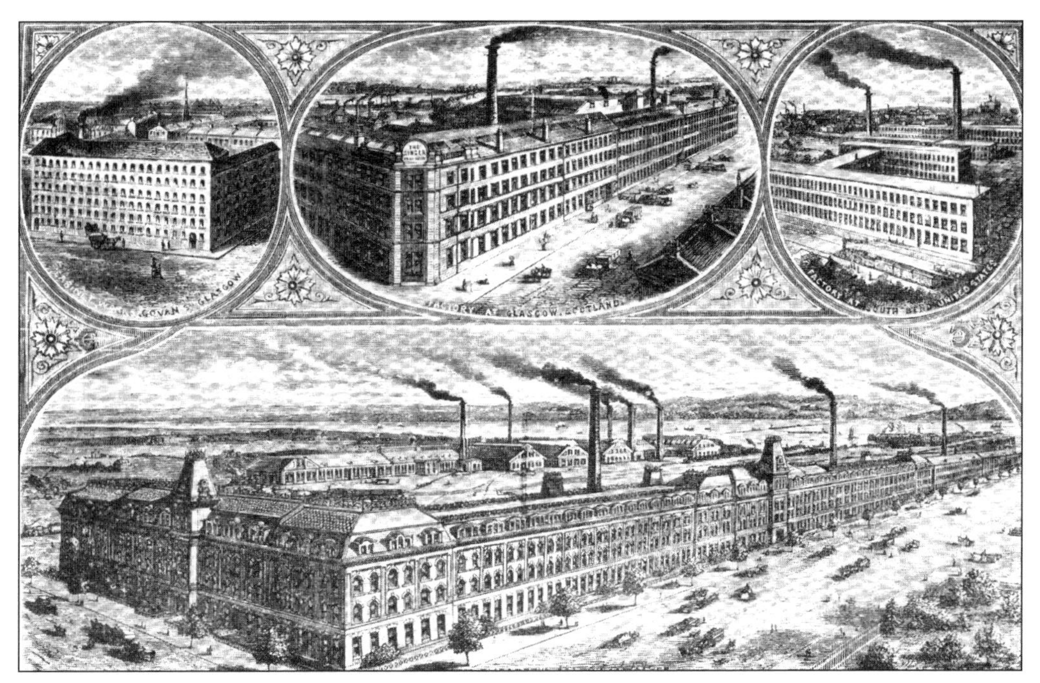

Figure 2.9 This 1868 engraving of four factories owned by the Singer Sewing Machine Company illustrates the way large buildings were constructed of narrow sections so that windows could provide sufficient daylight and outside air to the interior.

systems into common use, restrictions on the width of office buildings were relaxed. The introduction of acoustic ceiling tiles that reduced sound propagation made it possible to lower the noise in a large office space to an acceptable level. With the support of these environment-modifying systems, office building widths were rapidly increased and large interior spaces were created. Today, office towers with floor plates (the area of a single floor) of 3,000 square meters (30,000 square feet) and more are common.

The interior environment of early offices was similar to that of residential housing. Window coverings such as blinds or drapes controlled interior light levels, and a small stove or fireplace in the room provided heat. Gas light became available in major cities in the late 1800s (Figure 2.10). Environmental controls for light, heat, and ventilation were necessarily operated from within the individual office areas. With the introduction of artificial sources of light, heat, and later cooling, office servicing and environmental controls became more centralized. A single furnace could supply heat for an entire building. Banks of light fixtures could be controlled by a single switch. One thermostat could regulate the heat for an entire floor or building.

The early centrally controlled building systems had their limitations. A large building does not lose heat evenly and is

Figure 2.10 A London office setting of 1871. Early office interiors were similar to those of residential housing. Windows supplied natural light and ventilation; a small stove or fireplace supplied heat. In major cities gas lamps, such as that shown here, could provide sufficient light for work activities.

difficult to ventilate uniformly. As a result, certain areas might be drafty while others were too stuffy, some rooms too cold and others too hot. To provide better environmental control throughout the building, more sophisticated forced-air systems were developed, with heating, cooling, humidification, and dehumidification integrated into a single system, termed the **HVAC** (heating, ventilating, and air-conditioning) system.

Integrated HVAC systems are now standard in office buildings. Not only do they provide improved control of temperature, humidity, and air movement; they are designed to service ever smaller areas of the interior space. The building is divided into areas, termed **zones**, each of which is separately controlled. For example, a forced-air central HVAC provides conditioned supply air for the entire building. Each zone then has a mixing chamber to further modify the supply air. In this way, the heating or cooling provided to each zone can differ, compensating for the varying conditions that exist within a large building.

The current trend in building control systems is to monitor and regulate an ever wider range of environmental conditions more precisely, more frequently, and over smaller units of space (i.e., larger numbers of smaller zones). Building control systems are also becoming increasingly automated. A large office tower can now be regulated from a single control room within the building or even from a remote location. A network of sensors detects temperature, static pressure, light levels, smoke, carbon dioxide, security access, and other conditions in the facility and transmits these data to a central computer system. A computer monitors the status of the various sensors and electronically controls the building services equipment.

Automated building control systems have been of great value in regulating indoor environmental conditions within a narrow tolerance. Stringent climate control is needed for such facilities as laboratories, critical health care units, and semiconductor plants. Where a wider range of environmental conditions is acceptable, automated building control systems can reduce operating and maintenance costs by taking advantage of the greater tolerance range. For example, at night and on weekends, when a building is unoccupied, the temperature can be allowed to vary more widely than during the day. This saves heating and cooling costs when the building is vacant while maintaining conditions within a narrower comfort range when the building is in active use. The same strategy can be applied to zones of a building. If some areas are used in the evening, full servicing can be maintained while the servicing to unoccupied areas is reduced. However, to provide this level of flexibility, the HVAC system must be properly adjusted or **balanced** to operate under these different operating conditions. Not all system designs can support such complex operating procedures.

Automated building control systems can increase safety, security, and individual comfort in the workplace. They also provide flexibility, making it easier to optimize the overall performance of the building while delivering different interior environments tailored to specific activities and individual needs. However, these systems are more costly than conventional building control systems as well as more complex to operate and maintain. Inadequate maintenance and operating procedures have been a major cause of sick building syndrome and building-related illness in mechanically ventilated offices (see the subsection "Automated Control of Building Services" in Chapter 4).

CHANGING STYLES OF OFFICE ACCOMMODATION

Office designs from the middle of the nineteenth century to today have primarily served the burgeoning clerical and administrative components of business. As organizations became larger, their

Figure 2.11 Large clerical workforces were initially accommodated in open spaces such as this. General Office of Canadian Aeroplanes, Toronto, 1918. (*Source*: National Archives of Canada, PA25186.)

growing clerical and administrative workforce, which had previously been housed in private and shared quarters, was accommodated in ever larger general-purpose office spaces (Figure 2.11). The placement of enclosed offices on the perimeter created sizable interior spaces that became known as **bullpens**. It was common to have dozens and even hundreds of clerical work settings in these expansive interior spaces.

Bullpen layouts consisted of a rigid arrangement of desks, usually in rows (Figure 2.12). They provided individual workers with no visual or acoustic privacy and were typically noisy, poorly lit, and uncomfortable places to work. Ergonomics was not considered an issue in the office. Unlike factory work, for the office there was little concern that furnishings be selected to suit the task or the individual.

In the late 1950s, a new office design called the *burolandschaft* (translated from German as "office landscape") was developed in Germany. It was heavily promoted by two brothers, Ebehard and Wolfgang Schnelle, who were leaders of the Quickborner team of management consultants (named for the town of Quickborner, a suburb of Hamburg where they were based). The office landscape design sought to provide flexible, interesting interiors that could easily be adapted to individual tastes and group needs. Layouts were spacious and used high-quality furnishings. Arrangements of live plants, artwork, and other unconventional devices were employed to divide the space into individual work areas. The concept underlying this design was for the physical layout to reflect a democratic and egalitarian style of management as well as to provide high-quality interiors tailored to the occupants' needs. It was a philosophy that fit well with the architectural design ideas that came into vogue in the United States and Canada during the 1960s.

The office landscape was used extensively in Germany and then in other European countries. It was introduced on a wide scale to the United States and Canada in the 1960s. At about that time, Robert

Figure 2.12 A bullpen layout of work settings allowed large numbers of office workers to be accommodated in one expansive space. 1958. (*Source*: National Archives of Canada, PA144840.)

Propst, a U.S. inventor-researcher, was developing an unconventional approach to furnishing offices. His idea, called the "action office," was to replace such traditional office furniture as desks and credenzas with furniture components and panels that could be assembled into a wide range of work settings (Figure 2.13). Work surfaces, storage units, and other elements were hung on freestanding panels, which could be arranged as needed to form a complete office work setting (Propst 1968). It was the beginning of what today is called systems furniture. Hundreds of office furniture designs are now based on this concept. Today, over 30% of all businesses use **systems furniture** in open plan work spaces (Herman Miller 1994).

Systems furniture was well suited to furnishing open areas of office space. Office layouts could easily be designed using the standardized elements of a furniture system. This new North American type of office design was termed the open plan concept (Figure 2.14). It was welcomed as being versatile and flexible. The concept sought to capitalize on the success of the open plan in manufacturing, where sequential operations converted raw materials to finished goods. There the open plan facilitated the flow of materials and finished goods. Over the last 30 years the **open plan** office has been widely adopted throughout Canada and the United States.

The use of systems furniture to set up open plan areas was a divergence from the strict rules of the office landscape design as they were applied in Europe. The office landscape employed high-quality furnishings and provided spacious work settings. By contrast, the open plan/systems furniture design was used to increase the number of workers who could be housed in a given floor area.

Compared with the bullpen arrangement, an open plan layout offered more privacy, greater noise control, and more convenient storage of papers and files. But most occupants preferred the private or shared enclosed offices of the time. Proponents of the open plan arrangement emphasized more open communication among office workers as a major benefit — although communication was not seen as a significant problem. Early on, occupants complained of a lack of privacy, noise distraction, and insufficient space in the open plan office (see, for example, Brookes 1972).

However, it was the higher density of work settings that made the open plan office most attractive to cost-conscious organizations. The same number of people could be housed in significantly less space, directly reducing accommodation costs. Reducing the number of walls and doorways made initial construction less costly. Moreover, it was easier and less expensive to install centrally controlled systems for lighting, heating, and ventilation. While the dollar savings were readily apparent, it was difficult to assess whether occupant complaints represented any real cost to the organization. Assertions that employee performance was reduced were difficult and expensive to quantify and still are largely unproven.

There has been little incentive to determine the hidden productivity costs of controversial designs such as the open plan office. Research is expensive, and evaluating the productivity of office workers, especially that of knowledge workers, is a particularly difficult and controversial subject. Furniture manufacturers have conducted worthwhile research into office work. However, this research, though often broad in scope, must at some point promote the benefits of the sponsoring organization's products. Private corporations actively seek ways to improve employee productivity but are reluctant to invest substantial funds in research that may not, in the end, improve productivity. Also of concern is that the information collected could provide the basis for liability suits from workers. Once the deficiencies in an accommodation have been identified, the organization cannot claim to be unaware of them.

Given the choice, most office occupants invariably prefer an enclosed office to an open plan work space. (See, for example, Hedge 1982; Marans and Spreckelmeyer 1982; and Zalesny and Farace 1987.) Many studies of the open plan office have found a high incidence of problems that affect

Figure 2.13 The "action office" developed by Robert Propst in the 1960s was an early example of furniture comprised of interchangeable components, a design now commonly known as systems furniture. Unusual for its time, the filing cabinet had wheels so it could be easily moved. (*Source*: Herman Miller, Inc., Zeeland, Mich.)

Figure 2.14 Example of a landscaped office, typical of designs popular in North America during the 1970s and 1980s that used systems furniture. The layout is less formal than the rigid alignment of desks typical of bullpen arrangements. Individual workstations were clustered, sometimes placed at different angles and separated by curved screens, as shown here. Shared facilities — such as conference rooms, closets, and centralized storage — were at either end of the floor. 1981. (*Source*: Steelcase, Grand Rapids, Mich.)

employee's performance as well as their health and well-being. The most common occupant complaints involve high levels of distraction, insufficient privacy, and the inability to control lighting, temperature, and other environmental conditions that directly affect individual comfort.

Studies such as that by Hedge (1982) found no evidence to support the claim that open plan offices improved productivity. If anything, the data suggested a decrease. What's more, although open plan designs offer the potential for extremely flexible accommodation, they are seldom used that way. In practice, open plan office layouts tend to remain virtually static for several years. Reconfiguring a work setting usually requires special tools and know-how. It is a job that normally calls for at least two people who are strong enough to move relatively heavy or awkward loads. It is not a task users can or are permitted to do themselves. This led to facility management approaches that moved people, not their furniture. Work settings were standardized, so that when employees had to be relocated, they could be reassigned to any new work space. Every work setting had the same furnishings and servicing, often termed a **universal footprint**, so relocation simply involved moving the individual's belongings.

The open plan has a useful role to play, but it is not well suited to every office task. It can be the design of choice for activities that demand frequent interaction among work group members. People working at tasks of low complexity often prefer to be with others doing similar work even though the task doesn't require them to consult coworkers. The more social setting can make mundane clerical tasks less boring and actually improve performance (Block and Stokes 1989).

Recent workstation designs for the open plan office incorporate features allowing them to be more closely matched to the needs of the occupant. For example, the use of panels with improved sound absorption qualities reduces noise distraction. Panels are available in a range of heights, with and without windows and adjustable window coverings to provide privacy and individual control of visual distractions. Improved lighting designs, larger work surfaces, and greater adjustability have made workstations better suited to computer-based work and more easily tailored to the individual needs of occupants (see Chapters 5, 6, and 7).

Many office environment problems — such as privacy, noise, and visual distraction — can be mitigated by separating incompatible activities. Occupants themselves can significantly improve their work environment by being more aware of the impact of their behavior on others. For example, noise distraction can be reduced if occupants choose to have their casual conversations outside the work area.

Employees' satisfaction with their work space is heavily influenced by factors other than its physical qualities, such as satisfaction with the overall job, social support from coworkers, positive management relations, and the status within the corporate culture of an open plan work setting. While most office occupants will never prefer an open plan space to an enclosed office, there are ways to design and manage such work settings so as to minimize their limitations.

Another concept in office accommodation is to provide shared work settings that people can reserve for activities that are not well accommodated at their own workstation. For example, small conference rooms can be made available for a few hours or a few days at a time, either as a group work area or for individual use. The concept of having a private "home base" work setting supplemented by access to quiet spaces, rooms housing shared equipment, and other public spaces can be a particularly effective approach to accommodate office workers who perform a wide variety of tasks. It is also a cost-effective way to mitigate the limitations of an individual's assigned work setting. (See, for example, Stone and Luchetti 1985.)

A variation on this concept is an arrangement whereby workers also reserve their "home-base" work space. It can be a successful means of accommodating workers who need to be in the office infrequently or who spend a few consecutive days in the office and then several days elsewhere. With this arrangement, known as "hoteling" or the "free-address" work space, an organization provides a number of flexible or permanent offices for the use of a specific group of workers. Each space is equipped to suit the workers' common needs (e.g., hookups for voice and data, environmental comfort, adjustable furniture). Individuals may have private, lockable, and movable storage units that can be rolled into whichever location they were using for a particular office stay.

A natural extension of this multiple work setting concept is for some of the activity settings to be entirely outside the physical office facility. **Telecommuting** — working at an off-site location while maintaining contact with the office by means of fax, computer modem, and telephone — is being rapidly adopted by large and small organizations as a way to enhance productivity and improve customer service. The impact of telecommuting on the design and operation of office facilities is discussed in subsections "Telecommuting" and "The Virtual Office" later in this chapter.

OFFICE AUTOMATION

Until recently, offices supported a relatively limited range of activities — paper-based reading and writing, face-to-face meetings, telephone discussions, and the maintenance of paper records being the principal ones. The equipment needed was fairly simple: paper and pens, telephones, typewriters, calculating machines, and storage cabinets. The 1980s saw the widespread adoption of computer-based office equipment and advanced telecommunications technology. With the availability of inexpensive computing technology, computer screens proliferated throughout the office. In 1980, there were 10 computer keyboards for every 100 office workers in the United States. By 1989, there were 107, more than 1 for every desk worker (Panko 1992). Office environment studies conducted by Louis Harris and Associates found that the proportion of U.S. office workers using computers rose from 66% in 1986 to 85% in 1991. In Canada, computer use rose from 64% to 88% over the same period (Harris 1991).

In 1990, the service sector accounted for 75% of all jobs in the American private economy. Of these, about two-thirds could be considered "white-collar" positions (managers, executives, professionals, clerks, sales staff, and administrators). In 1982, the service sector invested $6,000 in information technology for each white-collar worker. By 1990, this annual investment had doubled, and U.S. service companies were spending more than $100 billion annually on new office technologies. The service sector owned more than 85% of the installed base of information technology in the United States (Roach 1991).

The computerization of the office has done more than change the tools of the trade; it has changed what office work there is to do and how it is done. Automation has eliminated many routine, repetitive tasks. Instead of having a person retype an entire document to incorporate a few changes, with word-processing software human input is needed only for the corrections. The computer takes care of retyping the document. Even the task of filing is gradually being automated. Paper documents can now be scanned in a matter of seconds to produce electronic images that can be stored in a computer database. These images can then be directly accessed by whoever needs to use them whenever they are needed. The same electronic document can be accessed by multiple users simultaneously and never needs to be refiled.

The impact of computer-based office technology has been highlighted by the way organizations have downsized and restructured during difficult economic times. Levels of middle management whose principal task was the collecting, checking, and repackaging of information have been eliminated by changing the way information flows within the organization and by the judicious use of computer technology. For example, in the early 1980s, Ford Motor Company examined a number of its departments in an effort to cut costs. Accounts payable was one of the departments scrutinized. Whereas Mazda's accounts payable organization consisted of 5 people, Ford's had almost 400. Even after adjusting for Mazda's smaller size, Ford considered its accounts payable organization to be about five times larger than it should have been.

In the existing system, the purchasing department sent a copy of each purchase order to accounts payable. When the goods were later received, copies of the receiving documents were sent to accounts payable, where they would be matched with the purchase order and the supplier's invoice. If all the documents matched, payment would be sent. In the event of a mismatch, an accounts payable clerk then had to investigate and reconcile the documents. Most of the department's time was spent on mismatches.

By reengineering the work process and using information technology, the procedure was dramatically streamlined. The purchasing department now enters orders into an on-line computer database. No copies are forwarded to anyone. Instead, when the order is received, it is checked against the outstanding purchase orders; if the order matches, the receiving clerk enters the transaction on the computer and accepts the order. Payment for the order is generated by computer, and no supplier invoices are needed. As a result, the accounts payable staff was reduced by 75% (Hammer 1990).

Automation of the office had a tremendous impact on facility performance. As microcomputers became widely used in existing general-purpose office space, a host of unexpected problems arose. Overhead lighting designed for paper-based tasks was too bright and produced glare on computer monitors. The quantity and quality of electric power needed for the new equipment was far greater than existing offices were designed to provide. The additional heat generated by the proliferation of computers, printers, and other new office equipment overtaxed the cooling systems of existing facilities.

There was also an increase in the number and variety of physical ailments reported by workers. Some of these ailments were related to ergonomically unsuitable chair and table arrangements. Computer-based work demands a different seated posture and different motions than paper-based tasks, so furniture and work procedures tailored to these physical demands had to be developed (see the section "VDT Work Settings" in Chapter 6).

With automation, management of the office facility suddenly demanded expertise in a number of subject areas foreign to facility management such as power quality, ergonomics, specialized lighting designs, and communication cabling. The automated office requires not only more power but a better quality of power. Voltage fluctuations that have no effect on basic building services can crash an entire computer network. Communication needs have expanded from the basic telephone to include high-speed digital data lines as well. The management of cables for telephone and electronic data transfer has become a specialty of its own. Cable layouts must take into account such issues as the number of users to be serviced, where service access is needed, and must allow for future growth. The continuing trend to automate the office with ever more sophisticated electronic equipment has made the job of managing the office facility an increasingly complex task.

BUILDING PERFORMANCE

The design life of modern office buildings is 20 to 50 years, depending on the objectives of the builder. As in any engineering endeavor, building design requires that innumerable trade-offs be made. It is not only costs that are involved. Buildings are designed to meet a prioritized set of objectives. If flexible space is a high priority, then movable partitions and raised floors may be the preferred solution. But movable partitions cannot be soundproofed to the same degree as fixed walls. A raised floor allows cables to be routed beneath the floor and easily modified. But to accommodate a raised floor, the height of each story must be increased, thereby increasing construction costs and perhaps reducing the total number of floors in the structure. So in choosing a design that makes the interior space easy to reconfigure, choices are also being made about acoustics, construction costs, and many other factors.

Design is a process that seeks to optimize a chosen set of objectives, all the while trading off competing objectives according to some more or less rational system of priorities. Once the building is complete, it is impractical and costly to change the trade-offs. It is far less costly to modify a building during the design process than to correct deficiencies after it is constructed.

For example, it is now well documented that in mechanically ventilated office buildings, there is a substantial increase in illness symptoms among occupants when the rate of outside air intake becomes low. Before this was understood, the heating systems of some buildings were designed with the expectation that on very cold days, the outside air fraction could be reduced to as low as 5%. In this way, the energy needed to heat the building would be reduced, and a smaller-capacity heating unit could be specified. Once the ill effects of delivering so little outside air were recognized, the operating procedures for these buildings could be modified to use a higher outside air fraction most of the time. But on very cold days, these buildings did not have the heating capacity to condition the larger volume of air, they had to be operated with the lower air fraction for which they were originally designed unless additional heating capacity was added.

Building performance is a measure of the overall effectiveness of an indoor environment in meeting the needs of the occupants. It is, in effect, an evaluation of a facility's utility to those who use it. The quality of the physical environment that can be provided in an office is limited by the performance characteristics of the building systems. A building's design, the characteristics of its service systems (e.g., heating and ventilation), and the way it is operated and maintained determine the air quality, thermal comfort, illumination, background noise levels, power quality, and other factors that together comprise the indoor environment.

It is the overall building performance that determines the quality of the office environment. Each building system may be adequate when judged on its individual merits, but the office occupant experiences all the building systems working together. Often, the performance of individual systems is compromised to some extent by the simultaneous operation of the others. For example, an overhead lighting system might be well suited for use with computer monitors. If the overhead lighting is properly designed, the glare on computer screens can be eliminated. But if the window coverings are not sufficiently opaque, the glare from the window areas on a bright day could make the computer screens all but unreadable. Though the office lighting design might be first-rate, the overall building performance for that space would be inadequate to support the work activities.

Building performance has received greater attention as more has been learned about the health effects of the office environment. The design objectives behind many of the general-purpose office buildings constructed in North America since the 1970s were to provide a comfortable indoor climate throughout the year while optimizing energy efficiency and minimizing cost. Initially, mechanically ventilated office buildings with sealed windows that could not be opened were more expensive to build and operate than conventional offices. Their appeal lay in the fact that they provided a more comfortable indoor climate through the heat of summer and the cold of winter. By designing buildings to minimize the uncontrolled infiltration of outside air through walls, joints, and other openings in the building envelope, uncomfortable drafts could be eliminated and the interior climate could be maintained within the desired comfort range (Figure 2.15).

It was only when energy costs rose precipitously in the mid-1970s that these climate-controlled buildings became cost-effective because they could be operated using less energy. Centralized servicing made it easier to control and reduce energy consumption. Heat loss was reduced by fitting building materials more tightly to minimize air leakage through the building envelope and insulation was increased. Although significant reductions in energy consumption were achieved, other unexpected and unwanted effects arose.

In designing a building so that the interior environment could be ever more tightly regulated, the impact on people became more significant. So long as buildings had a substantial mixing of outside and inside air through the opening and closing of

Figure 2.15 Office towers introduced in the 1960s and 1970s, like that shown on the right, were designed to minimize air movement across the building envelope and relied on mechanical ventilation to maintain a comfortable indoor environment year-round. By contrast, the conditions inside office buildings of earlier construction, like that on the left, tended to be drafty and difficult to regulate. (*Source:* Hayward Studios, National Archives of Canada, PA078338.)

doors and windows and the leakage of air through walls and joints, the concentration of chemical contaminants indoors remained no worse than the outdoor levels. This uncontrolled air exchange tended to dilute any introduced chemical contaminants or flush them out of the building.

As buildings became more tightly sealed, the indoor environment could be more precisely controlled. The proportion of outside air to recirculated indoor air could be selected. In an effort to reduce energy costs, less outside air was mixed with recycled air when the outdoor temperature was hotter or cooler than the desired indoor temperature. As a result, the chemical contaminants released into the air (termed **offgassing**) by furniture, carpets, and other materials, along with cigarette smoke and photocopier vapors, became more concentrated over time because the dilution with outside air was so greatly reduced.

Other troublesome features of mechanically ventilated office buildings also came to light. For example, standing water in the central humidification system proved to be an excellent breeding site for bacteria and fungi. If these units were not regularly cleaned and maintained, high concentrations of infectious microorganisms could develop and be distributed through the air ducts. Many people are allergic to molds and other biological materials that can be introduced into the air supply in this way. Perhaps the most widely publicized example of this type of building-related health problem was an outbreak of Legionnaires' disease in 1976. The infection was caused by bacteria harbored in the air-cooling system of the hotel in which an American Legion convention was being held. Over 200 people contracted the disease, and 34 eventually died. (This issue and other health effects of offices are discussed in Chapter 5.)

A great deal more has been learned about the health effects of the office environment since climate-controlled buildings were first introduced in North America. As well, society's priorities have changed. The quality of the indoor environment is now given greater emphasis. But many existing office buildings were designed before these environmental quality considerations were such a pressing issue. Modifying these buildings to reflect these new values can be difficult and costly, and may not be entirely successful.

Today's office facilities are expected to offer higher levels of performance than were previously demanded from buildings. They are expected to provide a comfortable indoor climate, safe equipment with which to work, and healthy air quality. At the same time, office facilities must accommodate ever more diverse electronic equipment, from computers to photocopiers, which require power, generate heat, and emit chemical contaminants.

Offices must also support a wide range of activities that may change often and unpredictably. Many organizations require that facilities be more flexible so that people and equipment can be redeployed more quickly in response to a rapidly changing business environment. Office occupants have come to expect that their office facility will accommodate their activities and equipment without any degradation of the quality of the indoor environment. To do so requires that offices be designed, operated, and maintained to deliver higher levels of building performance than ever before.

HUMAN PERFORMANCE AND THE OFFICE WORK SETTING

A person's work environment directly affects the quality and quantity of work they are able to produce. Management practice has long recognized the importance of job satisfaction, motivation, and team building in maximizing employee performance. Yet limitations of the physical work setting that compromise worker performance are often given little attention.

Individuals place great importance on the quality of their work setting. This is clearly reflected in the use of higher-quality work settings as a reward for superior performance and as a symbol of elevated status. It is not just sumptuous decor that is sought. Comfort, environmental control, space, and views to the outside are key amenities. While these features are often treated as luxuries, they all have a direct impact on human performance.

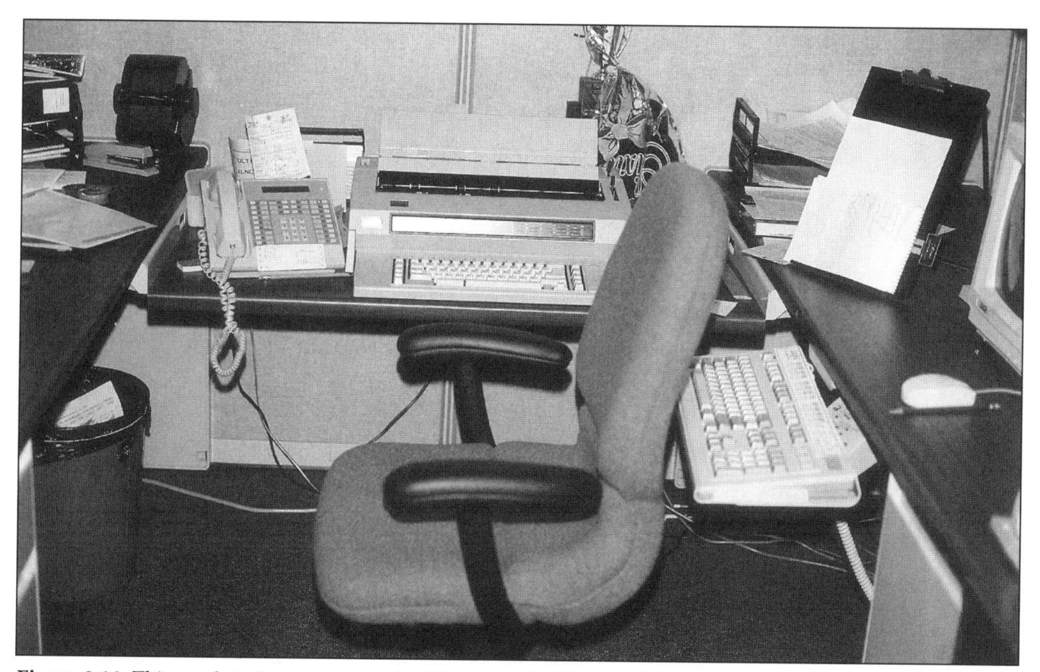

Figure 2.16 This workstation is crammed with new and old technology — a computer, enhanced telephone, and a typewriter amidst a clutter of paperwork — making tasks more difficult to perform and equipment awkward to use.

The quality of the physical work setting affects how long people can work at a task, the degree of concentration they can devote to it, how easily they can collaborate with coworkers and how effectively they can use equipment such as computers. It also affects their physical health — how they will feel after a day's work and how often they will become ill.

The quality of work produced is directly affected by the suitability of the surroundings to the task. It requires a great deal of effort to apply focused attention to a task amid the bustling cacophony of a busy office. Similarly, a collaborative team effort can be substantially more effective if group members can meet and work together as needed.

The work setting will affect how quickly people will fatigue. A chair that offers good support will be comfortable for a longer period of time than one poorly suited to individuals and their tasks. People become drowsy when the temperature is too high or the carbon dioxide level is elevated. When using a computer screen, being able to look at a distant view relaxes the eyes and retards the onset of visual fatigue symptoms such as sore eyes and headaches.

Insufficient work space makes tasks more difficult to perform and can make equipment awkward to use (Figure 2.16). The frequency of interactions among supervisors and coworkers is influenced by where they are located in the office space. Even the nature of those contacts is affected. It is more difficult to maintain a positive working relationship with someone whose activities are a constant source of distraction.

No matter how well motivated and committed individuals may be, they cannot deliver their best effort if they are unwell. A great deal of publicity has surrounded the effect of the office environment on health, with air quality and ergonomic issues attracting most of the attention. (These and other health-related issues are addressed in Chapters 5 and 6.)

It is now well documented that some buildings cause illness among an inordinately large proportion of their occupants. As a consequence, they are often termed **sick buildings**, and the ailments are collectively known as **sick building syn-**

drome. Irritation of the eyes, nose, throat, and lower airways; skin reactions; non-specific hypersensitivity; mental fatigue; lethargy; headache; nausea; and dizziness are common symptoms. There is no single cause of sick building syndrome. The causes are usually multiple and cumulative. Chemical contaminants, biological agents, the physical work setting, and psychosocial factors have been shown to be contributing factors (see, for example, Hedge et al. 1989; Potter 1988).

People can sustain physical injuries from using chairs and desks that force them to work in uncomfortable postures or repeatedly perform awkward motions. Some of these injuries are minor and are quickly resolved by improving the work setting. Others, such as cumulative trauma disorders (also known as repetitive strain injuries), can leave people so debilitated that they are unable to type or write and require months of treatment.

Optimizing the physical setting is as much a factor in improving human performance as management style and performance incentives. Over the past decade, innovative management styles have focused on downward delegation of decision making with greater flexibility and a more motivational approach. But the message of a more caring and flexible organization rings hollow if changes in organizational policy to optimize the management environment are not accompanied by changes in office accommodations to optimize the physical work environment as well.

ISSUES OF TODAY'S OFFICES

The office must serve the needs of both the workforce to be accommodated and the equipment they use. But as the nature of the work, the technology, and the personal values of the office workforce have changed, so, too, have the standards expected of the office workplace.

The priorities and attitudes of office workers and the impact of global competition are major forces shaping the way workplaces are designed and the way work is structured. Attracting and keeping talented personnel demands more than a competitive salary, interesting work, and an opportunity for advancement. The quality of work life and the quality of life outside work are highly valued by employees and figure prominently in their employment decisions.

High labor costs make employee turnover increasingly costly. In addition to incurring the expense of training replacement workers, the organization loses valuable knowledge and expertise when experienced employees leave. Attracting and keeping talented staff is critical to the success of organizations facing increased competition in global markets. Workers with skills in high demand can be selective in their employment choice and can easily accept a better offer from a competitor. The more dissatisfied they are, the more likely they will leave. A high-quality office workplace is one of the factors that may influence their choice.

The physical office environment directly affects the occupants' life, both at work and outside the office. For example, air quality problems increase the incidence of respiratory illnesses (see the subsection "Microorganisms" in Chapter 5). Ergonomically deficient work settings increase the risk of musculoskeletal disorders, such as repetitive strain injuries, that can become crippling disabilities (see the section "Cumulative Trauma Disorder" in Chapter 6). These and other problems persist after people have left their workplace.

Physical characteristics of the office can significantly increase the stress load of work. Just as poor management can destroy initiative and precipitate physical and psychological fatigue, so, too, can an uncomfortable and disruptive work setting. Workplaces that are not conducive to people's physiological comfort have been linked to emotional stress and lower satisfaction among office workers (Klitzman and Stellman 1989). Although people can work under extremely adverse conditions — noise distractions, uncomfortable seating, headaches, and frequent interruptions — they must expend considerable effort to do so, and the quality and quantity of their work tends to suffer. For example, they fatigue more quickly and tend to use simpler problem-solving techniques (see the section "Acoustics" in Chapter 5). The energy spent on tolerating difficult working conditions could be more gainfully applied to productive work.

Health Concerns

During the 1980s, workers became more concerned about the health effects of the physical office environment. In some cases, occupants were sufficiently concerned about their health and frustrated by inadequate management response that they walked off the job. One early example occurred in 1979, when the recently completed multistory office complex Les Terrasses de la Chaudière (translated from old French, the name means "terraces overlooking the bubbling water") opened in Hull, Quebec. Linking their sudden onset of sickness to polluted air inside the building, its new occupants promptly dubbed the development Les Terrasses de la *Shoddy Air*.

Numerous studies were done to probe the interior environmental quality of that building. Some studies concluded that the conditions were within statutory health and safety standards and were therefore acceptable. Others acknowledged finding design and construction errors such as rotting food and other debris left in air ducts during construction, washroom vents that had not been connected to roof vents, and migration of air from the exhaust vents to the building's air intake. None of the investigations found a pattern to the problems or identified specific conditions that would account for the intense occupant complaints. Officially, the problems identified in that office complex were declared to have been corrected, yet worker complaints and incidents of sick building syndrome persist.

This building is not unique. Studies suggest that some 20% to 30% of office buildings have problems that cause illness symptoms among occupants. However, it is not always the same buildings. A once-healthy building can be sick temporarily due to a change in its operation or a renovation. Similarly, sick buildings can be cured after a problematic source of air contaminants has outgassed. In most cases, inadequate building maintenance, unsuitable operating procedures, and deficiencies in the design of the building systems are among the physical causes of sick buildings (Woods 1989).

Today's modern offices are characterized by mechanically controlled air supplies and sealed windows that occupants cannot open, locked thermostats that occupants cannot adjust, and open plan layouts that offer little privacy or control over interruptions. Poor air quality, inappropriate lighting, and noise distractions are common sources of physical ailments among office workers. These conditions have been the target of increasingly serious criticism from disgruntled workers who blame their office environments for a host of maladies ranging from headaches, backaches and sore eyes to nausea, chronic colds, and miscarriages.

Individuals differ in their physiological tolerance of environmental conditions. They also have definite preferences for their work setting. It is therefore difficult to prescribe the office conditions that will be comfortable for every occupant. As well, the environmental conditions of the office fluctuate with changes in season, rearrangement of work spaces, and shifts in work activities.

A comfortable workplace is one in which the environmental conditions match the physical needs of the workers and also meet their expectations of what the setting should be. Workers are more likely to complain about the physical working conditions when they consider those conditions to be worse than necessary. The nature of the work in a coal mine is that the shafts are dark, cool, wet, and potentially dangerous. Miners expect and accept these conditions. Office work however, is expected to be done in bright, comfortable, and safe settings. Although the conditions in an office may be considerably better than those in a manufacturing plant, a mine, and many other work settings, if the office environment is worse than expected or there are unpleasant features that could be avoided, workers will consider the level of accommodation to be substandard and resent it (see, for example, Brown 1954).

Accommodation Policies

Office automation has challenged many traditional accommodation practices. New office setting design ideas have been proposed to facilitate collaborative work and enhance productivity. But many of these alternative designs conflict with established space allocation policies.

The location and size of an office are important indicators of status within the organization. Tradition still demands that advancement be recognized by the granting of additional work-setting amenities as well as increased salary and benefits. It is expected that the higher the status, the more private the work setting, the larger the space, the more sumptuous the furnishings, and the more pleasing the views to the outside. Some organizations are modifying this strict allocation of space according to rank with function-based standards that more closely reflect the type of work setting individuals need in order to do their job effectively. This means that junior people with bulky computer equipment at their work area may be allocated more floor space than a manager who is frequently off-site and has more compact equipment. However, space allocation is a politically sensitive issue and change has been slow. In North America, there is little evidence that function-based space standards are being widely applied.

Women in the Workforce and Changes in Child-Care Responsibilities

The rapid increase in clerical jobs in the late 19th and early 20th centuries offered women attractive employment opportunities. Office jobs were less strenuous, less dangerous, and soon became much more plentiful than factory work. With a shortage of male workers during World War I, the ranks of women in the office workforce increased dramatically. Despite the large influx of veterans seeking employment after the war, many women chose to keep their jobs (Morgan 1988). During World War II there was a similar shift of women into the office workforce.

Over the past three decades in Canada and the United States, there has been a steady increase in the proportion of women in the workforce. This increase has had a dramatic effect on lifestyles. The U.S. labor force now includes more than 70% of all women with children between the ages of 6 and 17. Among office workers today, in the majority of families, both parents work; hence, employees and their spouses must both juggle career and family responsibilities. It is no longer the norm for employees with families to have a full-time caregiver at home, thereby enabling them to work extra hours or travel on short notice. As dedicated as an employee might be, the pressure of outside responsibilities commonly makes putting out extra effort for the organization unfeasible.

The demands of family life restrict the amount of time that employees can devote to their jobs and constrain the work schedule they can accommodate. Studies in the United States indicate that as many as 35% of working men and women with young children have told their bosses that they would not accept jobs involving shift work, relocation, extensive travel, intense

Figure 2.17 Daycare facilities at the workplace are one of the family-responsive benefits some organizations now offer their employees.

pressure, or frequent overtime. The trade-off between career and family life has not been the same for men and women. Two-thirds of American women under 40 who have reached the upper echelons in large companies and organizations are childless, while virtually all men in leadership positions are fathers. However, the trend is for men to be more affected by family matters than before. In two studies at Du Pont, reports by men of family-related problems doubled between 1985 and 1987 (Rodgers and Rodgers 1989).

Realizing that employees are able to work more effectively when their obligations are met, organizations have begun to offer more family-responsive benefits (Figure 2.17). Child-care facilities and support programs; expanded medical, dental, and retirement benefits; and more flexible work hours are being introduced. As well, the entire concept of where office functions can and should be done is being reconsidered. For example, work arrangements that reduce the time spent commuting to and from the office each week, such as working at home some days, save workers valuable hours they can devote to family responsibilities.

Flexibility of Location

The location where office functions take place no longer need be limited to the traditional office tower. Many business and management activities lend themselves to alternate locations. Legal, architectural, and small specialty offices can often be found in converted buildings, ranging from former railroad depots and canneries, to warehouses, supermarkets, or Victorian homes. (See, for example, Fracchia (1979) for a description of a number of such innovative approaches to office accommodation.)

An organization's office computers can be networked among multiple buildings thereby making it feasible to divide the physical location of workers among several locations yet maintain operation almost the same as being in a single building. Many companies that need a presence in high-rent locations, such as a downtown business district, have cut accommodation costs by reducing the staff at that locale to those directly providing the client services. The bulk of the office staff is then accommodated in suburban locations that in most metropolitan areas are less than half the cost of a downtown address (Apgar 1993). For some organizations, proximity to the workforce may also be an important benefit of electronically linking multiple office sites. To many employees, a shorter commute time is a valuable benefit that can outweigh minor differences in the salary and benefits offered by competing firms.

The capability to be highly mobile, to have the technology to work wherever and whenever a situation demands, while at the same time remaining closely connected to one's organization has long been an attractive idea (Figure 2.18). But it has been only recently that telecommunications and computer technology have made

Figure 2.18 The portable office is not a new idea. This 1905 advertisement extolling the benefits of a portable typewriter presents the concept — though the implementation might not have been very practical.

the necessary mobile equipment sufficiently affordable and powerful to be widely adopted. Cellular telephones, portable fax machines, and modem-equipped laptop computers have become standard tools of mobile office workers, be they technicians or senior executives. Wireless modems are now available that enable a laptop computer to communicate with an organization's computer system without even being physically connected to a telephone line. Using this variety of technology, employees can receive assignments, write and send correspondence, arrange appointments, collaborate on projects, and submit completed work — all without setting foot in the organization's physical premises (Figure 2.19).

The option of having people do certain types of office work at home is being given serious corporate-level consideration. Not only does this move have a major impact on the corporate culture and management environment; the introduction of work-at-home arrangements directly affects office space requirements and facility management practices.

Telecommuting

In 1993, some 7.6 million company employees were **telecommuters**, working from home part- or full-time during normal business hours. Now representing 6.1% of the adult American workforce, the number of telecommuters is growing at an average annual rate of 15% (Link 1993). A survey of Fortune 500 companies conducted in 1991 found that 21% had telecommuting programs (Jones 1991).

Telecommuting has been common for sales staff who spend most of their time on the road. But this work arrangement can be adapted to a broad range of office activities for which employees need not be physically present in order to do their job and their performance can be adequately monitored. Inspectors, tax assessors, consultants, and purchasing agents are among the many types of workers whose jobs lend themselves well to telecommuting.

Telecommuting offers compelling opportunities. The benefits most often cited for telecommuting include greater productivity, reduced office space requirements, more flexible staffing, an expanded employee market, and lower employee turnover.

With fewer employees in the office, less space is needed, and accommodation costs can be reduced without sacrificing quality. However, telecommuters generally require some form of temporary office space for the times they have to work in the office. Innovative facility design and management are needed to provide the special office services these workers require. Shared, reservable office settings (i.e., settings that can quickly be tailored to a new user each day) can provide a fully equipped and functional work setting for the days when a person must be in the office without tying up expensive office space on the days when they are away (see subsection "The FUNDI Design" in Chapter 7). As well, office support staff are needed to provide continuity of basic services for telecommuters when they are off-site, such as receiving mail, forwarding messages, and sending out correspondence.

To capture the benefits of telecommuting, employee management practices

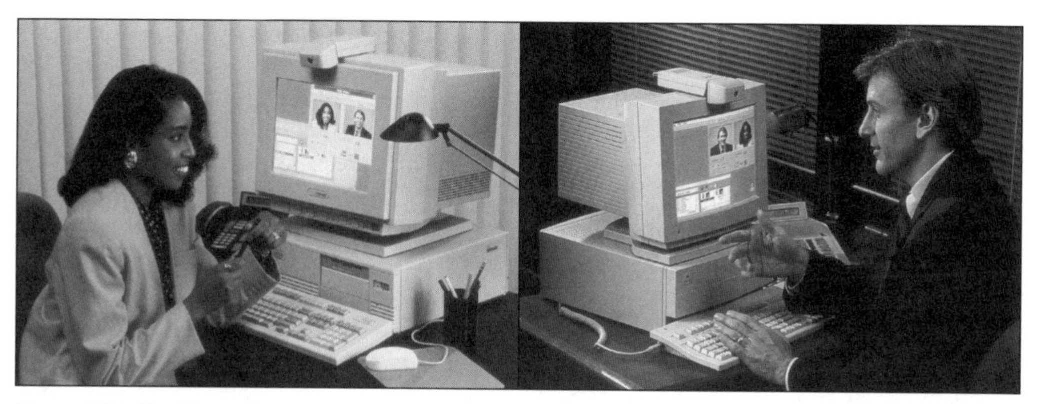

Figure 2.19 Combining the two most common tools that businesses rely on — the telephone and personal computer — this communications system helps people work together from separate locations. The small camera mounted on top of each computer monitor allows the users to see as well as hear each other while they together review text, graphics, and images on the screen. (*Source*: Northern Telecom, Brampton, Ont.)

must also be modified to support this style of work. For example, the methods of employee supervision and evaluation commonly need to be changed. Many managers find it difficult to supervise or evaluate employees unless they can physically see them working every day.

Once an organization has the policies and procedures in place to manage outside workers, the difference between an in-house employee and an employee working across town or across the country becomes less significant. With innovative work arrangements, organizations can expand their available labor pool, so they are no longer limited to hiring people within commuting distance of their office.

Thus a telecommuting work option can attract and retain talented employees whose skills might otherwise be lost because they cannot or don't want to come to an office every day. For example, account executives in financial services companies have been able to continue servicing their clients while on maternity leave by working from home. Linked to the office computer system by modem and with "call-forwarding" functions that transfer their phone calls to their home, account executives can provide the same level of service as if they were at the office.

The Travelers Corporation is one of many financial services firms that offer telecommuting. Based in Hartford, Connecticut,, the company has had a telecommuting program since 1987. Seen as a means to attract and retain employees, the program has reduced retraining costs and, by offering another work option, has proved to be a valuable recruitment tool.

Organizations such as AT&T and Andersen Consulting have capitalized on the opportunity for those who work primarily outside the office to remain off-site most of the time. AT&T's service personnel can spend more time helping customers if they don't have to keep "checking in" at the office. Similarly, consultants can spend more billable time at the client's site if they don't have to put in an appearance at the office.

Two new acts of U.S. federal legislation are making it necessary for employers to develop work-at-home arrangements for their employees. Amendments to the 1990 Clean Air Act, which took effect in November 1992, required that employers in certain high-pollution metropolitan areas develop plans to reduce the number of commuters. Several states, such as California, have introduced their own legislation to reduce commuter traffic. Telecommuting is one of the most cost-effective ways to satisfy this requirement. The Family and Medical Leave Act, signed in the summer of 1993, entitles employees to 12 weeks of unpaid, job-protected leave each year for specified family and medical reasons. Under the act, companies are permitted to develop telecommuting plans that let employees perform some work activities at home.

Telecommuting raises numerous liability issues that have yet to be resolved. For example, it is not clear to what extent the employer remains responsible for the health and safety of telecommuters when they are working at home. Is it the employer's responsibility to provide office furnishings such as a desk and chair? Some employers supply ergonomically appropriate chairs and desks to ensure that telecommuters receive the same standard of furnishings as in-house employees. But many homes don't have the space to accommodate standard office furniture. If an employee develops repetitive strain injuries or backaches while working at home, is the employer responsible for medical and rehabilitation costs? Since the employer has no control over the furnishing of a private home, what should be the limit of its liability for injuries to a telecommuter that occur in his or her home?

To date, these liability issues remain largely unaddressed. Telecommuting is generally viewed as a privilege granted to motivated employees with good work habits. There tends to be an implicit assumption that employees are responsible for themselves when they work at an alternative location of their choice — such as their home.

In a 1991 poll of managers conducted by the University of San Francisco, 32% reported that the productivity of telecommuters was higher than that of their in-office peers (Jones 1991). Employees report greater independence and productivity as key benefits. Working at home can offer a work setting with fewer interruptions, freedom from direct supervision, reduction in stressful office politics, and virtual elimination of commute time. However, working at home is not a panacea. Some people find that, as telecommuters, they lose touch with the office and feel isolated. They miss the camaraderie, ready access to the support of coworkers, and the motivation and dynamism of a successful office setting. It may also be difficult to separate home life from work. But the growing popularity of working at home suggests that, for many, the advantages outweigh the drawbacks.

The fact that a rapidly growing number of people want to work from their home may reflect the failure of contemporary offices to meet the needs of the occupants as much as it reflects changes in societal values regarding home and family. No matter which is the dominant cause, there is a strong trend for more of the work now done in offices to be done at alternate locations that the individual considers to be a better work setting — be it a library, meeting room, or home office.

Working at home or at other off-site locations is becoming more common for many office-based jobs. As more experience has been gained with telecommuting, it has come to be seen as an arrangement well suited to certain types of workers doing certain kinds of jobs. When the work is appropriately structured and managed, telecommuting can offer benefits to both the employee and the organization.

The Virtual Office

Telecommuting is but one aspect of a broader trend. Work is becoming increasingly independent of place and time. It is tied to the individual who can perform it, not to a place where it must be done. In fact, there is a productivity premium for doing work wherever it is done best. The greater the value that an organization places on an individual's time, the greater the incentive not only to permit but to encourage these individuals to work whenever and wherever they are most productive.

With today's technology, a team can work at different physical locations yet be able to interact as if they were located in the same building. They speak by phone, send memos by fax or electronic mail, and submit reports by modem. From a remote location, they can have the same access to the organization's information and communication systems and be almost as accessible to their coworkers as they would be in a conventional office accommodation. Their phone calls can be automatically rerouted to their remote site, and their electronic mail and fax transmissions can be handled by logging their remote computer on to the organization's computer network. They are supervised without being observed. Their work is evaluated on its quality and timely delivery. When and where the work is done becomes irrelevant. They need be physically present only when a face-to-face discussion is essential.

It is developments such as these that highlight a fundamental change taking place in our understanding of the working office. It is becoming more a concept than a physical entity. It represents a set of functions and services, and a place to meet for the purpose of promoting and carrying out the business of an organization. Among the functions of an office is the building of rapport among the organization's members. Face-to-face encounters are important, but so too are other forms of communication such as electronic mail, which may actually enable people to interact more frequently and more quickly than arranging a meeting or getting them on the phone. Far more time can be wasted trying to get hold of a busy person than actually communicating with them once they've been reached.

Technology enables the fundamental functions of an office to be performed at different locales yet still be provided as an integrated and comprehensive set of functions and services. In that sense, an office can be virtual. The **virtual office** provides the package of functions and services we expect of an office. It allows people to interact with its personnel as if they were present in the same locale, even though the people and services may be located at multiple locations.

AT&T was an early proponent and implementer of the virtual office concept. Traditionally, the company had assigned full-time office space to its sales personnel. Recognizing that members of the sales staff spend most of their time on the road visiting customers, it instituted a temporary office policy. Using portable equipment, phones, and laptop computers equipped with fax/modems, a vast array of information and processing capabilities can be accessed remotely at any time. Employees can schedule temporary office space and support services when and where they need them. A network of regional offices offers facilities for meetings, report production, customer contact, and administration. The employee in effect is no longer tied to any one of an organization's physical offices, they use all of them.

For such innovative approaches to office accommodation to be successful, new systems of information flow, supervision, and working relationships have to be developed. The corporate culture has to be modified as well as the procedures. But in doing so, the office facility can be made more flexible, more effective, and less costly.

In fact, as more individuals have left organizations to become independent consultants, it has become common for them to collaborate on projects using the virtual office model. Working from separate locations, they meet by phone and exchange documents by courier, fax, or modem. The "office" where they meet for this collaborative work is not a physical place; rather it consists of their combined information, communication, and organizational resources. Perhaps the ultimate expression of the separation of the integrated business entity from the people and physical components of which it is comprised is the virtual corporation.

The **virtual corporation** is a new term for a technologically sophisticated implementation of a commonly used business practice. It is not unusual for a group of individuals or companies to combine their individual skills and resources in order to undertake projects they could not do alone. If the project is large enough, it may even be worthwhile to form a new company as a separate legal entity, even though the personnel may all remain employees of the participating organizations. The idea of the virtual corporation extends this concept to create businesses that are comprised of independent individuals and/or businesses that provide the physical resources of the corporation. Though operating from separate locations, they function together as an integrated business entity. Judicious use of telecommunications and computer technology can enable such a collaborative business arrangement to function as if it were a conventional corporate entity, even though there is really no one physical corporate headquarters from which the enterprise is run.

Virtual corporations and virtual offices are interesting concepts, useful as a source of ideas rather than as a specific organizational model to be followed. Every organization is different and will find different aspects of these concepts to be of value. Their importance lies in the stimulating framework they offer to explore and develop new ways of working using the myriad technologies evolving around us, and hopefully, to discover the truly useful ways they can be applied.

CONCLUSION

Offices are in a state of transition. For them to be effective at this time when work is rapidly being restructured, they must be flexible. Yet to support the work activities they accommodate, offices must be tailored to the needs of their users. Balancing these often competing objectives at a cost the organization is prepared to pay is key to optimizing the overall return realized from an office facility (i.e., the combined benefits obtained from the accommodation, the equipment, and most importantly the office workforce).

Media attention has sensitized the public to sick buildings and unhealthy office environments. It is well documented that office space that is poorly designed, maintained, and operated can represent a substantial hidden cost to the organization, compromising employee health and workplace morale as well as the quality and quantity of work that is produced.

Surveys conducted over the past 20 years indicate that office workers are becoming increasingly negative toward their workplace (Klien 1983; Harris 1991). But despite the publicity given to some exceptionally poor office buildings, most can provide an indoor environment of adequate quality. Improving the way a building is operated and maintained can minimize or entirely prevent many office environment problems. For example, changing air filters and cleaning the air-handling system more frequently can significantly reduce the levels of bacteria and fungi. Ensuring that adequate outdoor air is supplied and distributed throughout the interior can correct many indoor air quality problems. (However, not every indoor air quality problem results from insufficient outside air — in which case, increasing the outside air fraction will not resolve the problem.) Changing the facility management practices can be surprisingly effective in improving the indoor environmental quality.

The growing awareness of the effect of the office environment on workers has gained the attention of management as well as labor. Labor has focused on the health and safety issues. Management has been forced to make changes in response to new health and safety regulations set forth in collective agreements and recent legislation.

The quality of the office environment has become a more serious issue as a result of recent legislation. But there is also a growing body of research to show that the office setting can significantly contribute to worker productivity, particularly the productivity of knowledge workers (see the subsection "Knowledge Workers and the Productivity Paradox" in Chapter 3). Drucker (1991) and other influential management experts have stressed that the competitive performance of organizations has become increasingly dependent on the productivity of their office workforce. As a result, new approaches to office accommodation that can boost productivity are attracting the genuine interest of corporate leaders. By recognizing and actively managing the diverse and interrelated factors that influence human performance in the work environment, organizations can secure better value from their office workforce.

LITERATURE CITED

Apgar, M. 1993. Uncovering your hidden occupancy costs. *Harvard Business Review* (May–June):124–136.

Armstrong, R. 1972. *The office industry: Patterns of growth and location*. Cambridge, Mass.: MIT Press.

Block, L. K., and G. S. Stokes. 1989. Performance and satisfaction in private versus nonprivate work settings. *Environment and Behavior* 21(3):277–297.

Brookes, M. J. 1972. Office landscape: Does it work? *Applied Ergonomics* (December):224-236.

Brown, J. 1954. *The Social Psychology of Industry*. Baltimore, Md.: Penguin Books.

Drucker, P. 1991. The new productivity challenge. *Harvard Business Review* (December):69–79.

Fracchia, C. A. 1979. *So this is where you work! A guide to unconventional working environments*. New York: Viking Press.

Hammer, M. 1990. Reengineering work: Don't automate, obliterate. *Harvard Business Review* (July–August):104–112.

Harris. 1991. *The office environment index — 1991*. New York: Louis Harris and Associates.

Hedge, A. 1982. The open-plan office: A systematic investigation of employee reactions to their work environment. *Environment and Behavior* 14(5):519–542.

Hedge, A., T. D. Sterling, E. M. Sterling, C. W. Collett, D. A. Sterling, and V. Nie. 1989. Indoor air quality and health in two office buildings with two different ventilation systems. *Environment International* 15(1–6): 115–129.

Herman Miller. 1994. News release. Zeeland, Mich.: Herman Miller, Inc. March 23.

Jones, C. L. 1991. There's no place like home. Telecommuting: A growing trend. *Facility Management Journal* (September–October):12–19.

Klien, J. 1983. *The Office Book*. New York: Quarto Marketing.

Klitzman, S., and J. Stellman. 1989. The impact of the physical environment on the psychological well-being of office workers. *Social Science Medicine* (29)6:733–742.

Link. 1993. *Telecommuting fact sheet*. New York: Link Resources Corporation.

Marans, R. W., and K. F. Spreckelmeyer. 1982. Evaluating open and conventional office design. *Environment and Behavior* 14(3):333–351.

Morgan, N. 1988. *The equality game*. Ottawa: Canadian Advisory Council on the Status of Women. Report #88-S-147.

OECD. 1992. *Technology and the economy: The key relationships*. Paris: Organization for Economic Cooperation and Development.

Panko, R. R. 1992. The office workforce: A structural analysis. *Office Systems Research Journal* (spring):3–20.

Pile, J. 1984. *Open office space*. New York: Quarto Marketing.

Potter, I. N. 1988. *The sick building syndrome: Symptoms, risk factors, and practical design guidance*. Technical note 4/88. Bracknell, Berkshire, United Kingdom: Building Services Research and Information Association.

Propst, R. 1968. Action Office. Zeeland, Mich.: Herman Miller, Inc.

Roach, S. 1991. Services under siege — The restructuring imperative. *Harvard Business Review* (September):82–91.

Rodgers, F. S., and C. Rodgers. 1989. Business and the facts of family life. *Harvard Business Review* (December):121–129.

Stone, P. J., and R. Luchetti. 1985. Your office is where you are. *Harvard Business Review* (March–April):102–117.

Woods, J. E. 1989. Cost avoidance and productivity in owning and operating buildings. *Occupational Medicine: State of the Art Reviews* 4(4):753–770.

Zalesny, M. D., and R. V. Farace. 1987. Traditional versus open offices: A comparison of sociotechnical, social relations, and symbolic meaning perspectives. *Academy of Management Journal* 30(2):240–259.

PARTINGTON & Co
SALE OVER HALF A MILLION
LLOYDS NEWS
DAILY NEWS
STANDARD

Chapter 3

PRODUCTIVITY, KNOWLEDGE WORK, AND THE OFFICE FACILITY

A nation's quality of life depends on the productivity of its people. In the **production sector** (which includes manufacturing, farming, mining, construction, and transportation), U.S. productivity has risen at an annual rate of 3% to 4% for the past 120 years — a 45-fold expansion overall. This increase in worker productivity has led to gains in disposable income and purchasing power, the provision of such services as education and health care, and the availability of leisure time. In 1914, the average worker labored 3,000 hours per year. Today, on average, Americans work 1,800 hours, West Germans work 1,650 hours, and the Japanese work no more than about 2,000 hours (Drucker 1991).

In the 20 years from 1947 to 1967, productivity growth in the United States was 3.3% per year. However, in the 1980–1990 period, productivity growth declined to an annual rate of only 1.2% and actually fell in 1990. By comparison, productivity grew 3.1% in Japan, 1.9% in France, and 2.8% in the United Kingdom during the same period (Thurow 1992).

Productivity growth has not been equal among the different sectors of the U.S. economy. Contrary to popular belief, during the 1980s, productivity in the production industries continued to increase at about the same rate as before. For example, manufacturing productivity increased at about 3.9% a year, and agricultural productivity increased 4% to 5% annually. But this productivity increase was primarily in the making and moving of things, not in knowledge-intensive activities focused on creating, manipulating, and interpreting information (Drucker 1991). The reduction in American productivity growth during the 1980s was due largely to the lower output of the white-collar workforce.

Today, more than half of the North American workforce is employed in

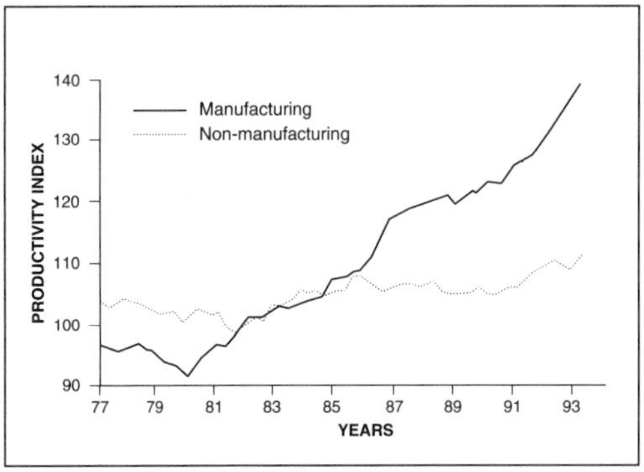

Figure 3.1 Comparison of productivity in the manufacturing and non-manufacturing (i.e., service) sectors from 1977-1993. (*Source:* Morgan Stanley estimates based on U.S. Department of Commerce and Bureau of Labor Statistics data.)

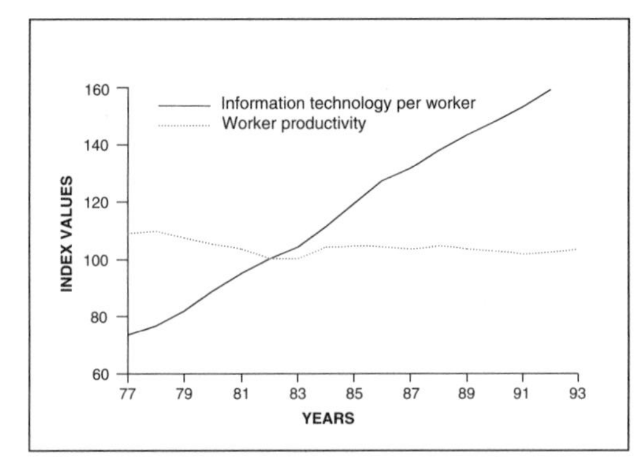

Figure 3.2 American service sector investment in information technology appears to have outpaced productivity growth between 1977 and 1993. (*Source:* Morgan Stanley estimates based on U.S. Department of Commerce and Bureau of Labor Statistics data.)

white-collar occupations (managers, executives, professionals, sales staff, administrative and technical support personnel). In 1991 about 57% of the employed population in the United States and Canada held white-collar jobs. Most of these white-collar jobs (80% in the United States) were in the **service sector** (which includes public utilities, transportation, government administration, retail and wholesale trade, and services — financial, health, and professional services). The remaining white-collar jobs were in the goods producing sector — mining, construction, and manufacturing (U.S. Bureau of Labor Statistics, Statistics Canada)

In the 1970s, the service sector accounted for 55% of all jobs in the private economy. By 1990, its share had grown to 75%. About two-thirds were white-collar jobs, of which 43% were knowledge workers (executives, managers, and professionals) and the remaining 57% were administrative and support personnel (technicians, sales and administrative staff) (Roach 1991). Unfortunately, while service sector employment increased dramatically during the 1980s, the productivity of this group did not (Figure 3.1).

In the 1980s, the United States lost 2 million manufacturing jobs but created nearly 20 million new jobs in the service sector. This was largely the result of increased global competition and the growing importance of information-based industries. During this expansion of the service sector, organizations invested heavily in computer technologies to automate the office, expressly to increase white-collar productivity.

In 1982, the American service sector invested $6,000 in information technology for each white-collar worker. Since then, this level of investment has doubled (Figure 3.2). By 1991, the service sector was spending in excess of $100 billion to equip its white-collar workforce with the latest technologies, and the service sector owned more than 85% of America's installed base of information technology (Roach 1991). Yet there was no evidence that this capital investment had delivered any appreciable increase in productivity. It appeared that the industrialized nations had failed to translate their unequaled scientific and technological advances into measurable productivity gains — a situation now commonly termed the **productivity paradox**.

Today, too few people are employed in the manufacturing, agriculture, and extractive industries for improvements in their productivity to drive the level of national productivity. Whereas 30 years ago they were the majority of the U.S. workforce, these sectors now comprise only about a fifth (Drucker 1991) (Figure 3.3). The service sector is now the dominant force in national productivity. Maintaining or raising the standard of liv-

Figure 3.3 Up until thirty years ago, the majority of the Canadian and U.S. workforce was employed in manufacturing, agriculture, and extractive industries. Radios being assembled in the 1940s. (*Source:* Canadian Marconi, Montreal.)

ing therefore depends on increasing the productivity of this sector, particularly its large white-collar component.

With economic success now so heavily dependent on white-collar productivity, especially in the service sector, improving the performance of these workers has become a fundamental key to the success, if not the survival, of many organizations.

THE OFFICE WORKFORCE

In 1990, white-collar jobs accounted for 57% of American employment, of which a sizable proportion (42%) were office jobs (Panko 1992). Office work is commonly divided into clerical and knowledge-intensive jobs. **Clerical work** is considered to be more or less procedural, such as routine administrative tasks. The word *clerical* is in fact derived from *cleric* — in reference to the monks or clerics of the Middle Ages who spent their lives laboriously copying religious texts (Figure 3.4). **Knowledge work** involves the creation, analysis, and production of information.

Researchers commonly classify jobs as involving either clerical or knowledge work. Managers, executives, and professionals are typically included in the knowledge worker category. Depending on the particular definitions chosen, the proportion of the American workforce that performs knowledge work ranges from 20% to 45% (Van Dyke Parunak 1992). However these workers are defined, a disproportionately large number of them work in offices. By some counts, knowledge workers comprise as much as 74% of the office workforce. Labor statistics for the United States and Canada do not identify office workers as a separate category. Panko (1992) estimated the number of office workers by analyzing the detailed job classification data from the U.S. Department of Labor. Data from Statistics Canada suggest that a similar analysis would give about the same percentage value. The proportion of knowledge workers varies considerably between industries. The financial and professional service industries, for example, have a much larger proportion of knowledge workers than the retail and construction sectors.

Figure 3.4 The word *clerical* is derived from *cleric* — in reference to the monks or clerics of the Middle Ages who spent their lives laboriously copying religious texts. (*Source:* Herman Miller Inc., Zeeland, Mich.)

In the service sector, knowledge workers generally perform the core activities of the business. A lawyer provides legal services, a consultant delivers management advice, and a physician provides medical diagnoses. They are the segment of the workforce responsible for product creation. Their activities are inherently labor-intensive and not amenable to automation — though efficiency enhancements such as information technology can facilitate important aspects of their work.

Knowledge worker–intensive industries make up some 50% of the service sector, including a broad range of business, personal, and professional services, ranging from health and educational institutions to engineers and management consultants. For these industries, knowledge workers comprise 52% to 77% of the white-collar workforce (Roach 1992).

Knowledge Work

Office work is often viewed as being organized in two ways. One way involves reducing work to a set of procedures — an attractive approach because the job can be made highly efficient. Close supervision can ensure that established procedures are followed, and if the task can be automated, even greater efficiencies can be realized.

But some work cannot be reduced to procedures because it is unique. Instead, it is assigned to someone qualified to judge the specific circumstances and develop a solution. For this type of task, procedures are rare and, if they exist, are only peripheral to accomplishing the task. Proposal preparation cannot be proceduralized, but it can be supported by a variety of procedures (e.g., by providing standardized text for commonly repeated items). This type of work can only be supervised broadly. The responsibility for completing the task is assigned, but a great deal of discretion must be given to the individual to choose how it is to be done. People can't be held responsible for this nonprocedural type of work if their supervisor is constantly interfering to tell them how to do it.

Traditionally, office workers whose jobs were seen as primarily procedural have been categorized as clerical or support staff. Those whose work primarily involves nonprocedural tasks have been classified as knowledge workers. However, the distinction between clerical and knowledge workers is not as clear as it once was. All office work is becoming more *knowledge-full*, demanding the comprehension, evaluation, and creation of information as well as the skills and initiative to act on it.

Studies by the Xerox Palo Alto Research Center found that neither formal procedures nor the explicit structure of an organizational chart defined what employees in so-called highly routine clerical jobs actually did. The workers' description of what they did was consistent with the formal procedures they were supposed to perform. However, direct observation of their work activities showed they did not really follow those procedures. Instead, they relied on a rich variety of informal practices without which the job could not be done. These clerical workers were constantly improvising, inventing new ways to deal with unexpected difficulties as they arose — a characteristic ascribed to *knowledge* work, not *clerical* tasks. They were, in fact, far more creative and innovative than their own description of their "routine" jobs would indicate (Brown 1991).

What's more, the overall complexity of office work has tended to increase as advanced technology has become an integral part of all job functions. Administrative staff who previously typed letters, filed documents, and answered telephones are now being asked to use computer-based word processors, spreadsheets, and databases. For many, it's a matter of learning a new set of standard procedures. But for those who develop the skill and understanding, the job can expand to become an information-processing task in which the power of standard business software is used to create original information. The intelligent use of a database and spreadsheet can turn basic customer-accounting records into valuable marketing information.

For example, Ault Foods, an Ontario-based dairy products firm, found that some of its secretaries were particularly adept at developing novel computer applications. The firm not only promoted these employees to positions that better utilized their skills; it instituted a voluntary program for secretaries who wanted to become computer application specialists. The program was a conscious management effort to capture and develop the learning and problem-solving skills of the secretarial pool — to develop the knowledge skills of individuals who have traditionally been regarded as clerical workers (Walmsley 1993).

Xerox Corporation sought to capitalize on the creativity of its clerical workers by developing a software tool called "Buttons." Using Buttons, secretaries, clerks, technicians, and others could create bits of computer code to automate functions they found useful for their everyday work. They could also send these miniapplications over the electronic mail network to others in the organization who could, in turn, use and modify them to suit their needs. It was a way for the organization to capture and share this valuable informal knowledge (Brown 1991).

The nature of office work is shifting to be predominantly knowledge based. More and more jobs that require little thought and understanding are relegated to computers. Those that remain are done by people who fill roles that are increasingly unique and valuable. As a result, measures that can improve the productivity of this workforce, decrease absenteeism, or simply make the workplace setting more conducive to good work habits directly contribute to the organization's success.

Knowledge Workers and the Productivity Paradox

Industry made large investments in information technology to support knowledge work, apparently without receiving the expected productivity benefits — the productivity paradox. Why should investments in the work environment be any more successful?

The productivity paradox has been the subject of considerable research and controversy. The issues tend to be of two kinds: (1) problems that inhibit the performance of office work and (2) limitations on the measurement of office productivity. There is agreement, though, on a number of factors that bear directly on how offices should be designed.

INTEGRATION

Improving white-collar productivity involves more than supplying advanced information technology. Simply providing access to greater volumes of information at higher speed does not necessarily improve a person's ability to comprehend, think, and make decisions. For a tool to be effective, it must be integrated with the work process and matched to the needs of the user.

Exchanging a secretary's typewriter for a computer-based word processor may or may not increase the amount of work done. But putting word-processing technology in the hands of knowledge workers so that they can create their own documents directly reduces the amount of typing the secretary has to do in the first place. The way the organization is restructured to take advantage of the technology and to optimize the contribution of those who use it is a key factor in realizing productivity gains.

THE NEED FOR WORK SETTINGS CONDUCIVE TO KNOWLEDGE WORK

Knowledge workers require periods of private concentration to develop a creative understanding of information and solutions to complex problems. At other times, they need to work in collaborative groups. Knowledge workers who work together to accomplish some common goal tend to function as a **community of practice**. They build a rapport that enhances their individual capabilities. Critical to their success is for all members of the group to be able to communicate and collaborate as needed. Neither the bustle of an open plan work setting nor the isolation of small private offices *alone* is ideally suited to these activities. There are benefits to be gained by providing different work environments so that both these modes of effort can be supported.

RESISTANCE TO THE POWER SHIFT

As the complexity of the work world continues to increase, the knowledge load and the decision load are being redistributed and delegated downward throughout the organization. One of the consequences is a shift of power, which managers may resist by seeking excessive control of information or work methods to the detriment of the workers' productivity.

When organizations were small, the head of the organization was able to know virtually all the information needed to run the business. As organizations grew and became more complex, a single individual could not carry the entire knowledge load. Managers and specialists were added to the organization, forming the now familiar hierarchical structure of conventional bureaucracies. The knowledge load was then distributed throughout these managerial ranks. The decision load also came to reside at the managerial level as a result of its having the necessary information.

New technologies and changing market conditions are once more forcing a redistribution of knowledge to lower levels in the organization. Both knowledge and clerical workers now demand more access to corporate information because they can't do their jobs effectively without it. Having gained entry to the company's information system, these workers are suddenly privy to news and data once reserved for managers two or three organizational rungs higher. With greater command of tools to interpret these data, the working level is often better able to make decisions than the managers to whom they report. Organizations need the ideas of this empowered group in order to be competitive and their increasing influence represents a power shift that many managers find difficult to accept (Toffler 1990).

Management insecurity can be a troublesome inhibitor of productivity enhancements. Management's power and authority are based largely on access to restricted information that is used to coordinate other workers. If this information is more widely available and worker interaction is increased, the traditional base of management authority may be weakened or destroyed. As a result, managers wishing to maintain their traditional level of control may choose to thwart productivity enhancements that infringe on symbols of their authority, be they information technology enhancements or work-setting enhancements.

TIME LAG BEFORE PRODUCTIVITY GAINS APPEAR

In manufacturing, state-of-the-art factory equipment makes workers more efficient immediately. Soon after the new technology is in operation, individuals produce more and the unit labor costs go down. But information technology is different. Installation of the equipment does not generate immediate benefits. The number of employees tends to remain the same, at least initially, and so labor costs stay the same.

When information technology is first introduced into an organization, it is commonly used to perform tasks that previously were done another way. There may be improvements in performance and quality, but fundamentally, the new equipment is used to perform the old tasks. As the organization becomes more familiar with the technology, novel and useful applications will be identified and implemented. But the greatest gains are realized when the technology is understood well enough for work flows to be restructured in ways made possible only by its use.

There is some evidence that this has indeed begun to occur. Michael Hammer (1990) used the term **reengineering** to describe the process of rethinking an organization's work processes around required outcomes and then redefining the tasks and functions needed to achieve those outcomes. In 1993, business activity increased and corporate profits rose, but unlike the previous economic recovery, there was no dramatic increase in hiring. In the process of downsizing and restructuring, companies developed new ways of working, many of which were made possible only by the use of relatively inexpensive computer technologies. In so doing, such reengineered organizations were able to increase output without increasing labor to the same extent as before. It may be that the productivity payoff from office automation will only become apparent as economic conditions change and these organizations begin to demonstrate the benefits of rapidly increasing their output with minimal hiring.

David (1991) draws a striking analogy between current concerns about the productivity payoff from information technology and the same fears expressed about the electric motor at the turn of the nineteenth century. Both situations involved the introduction of general-purpose engines — the computer being an information engine and the motor a mechanical one. In both cases, the full potential of these technologies could not be realized until the work to which they were applied was restructured to take full advantage of the unique capabilities they offered.

Around 1900, leading industrial nations were in the early phase of their transition from the use of steam to the use of electricity for industrial power. In the United States as well as in Great Britain, the decades surrounding this time were marked by substantially slower rates of industrial productivity growth. The initial applications of electricity to lighting and urban transportation involved substantial qualitative improvements that the conventional productivity measures of that era (1890–1914) did not reflect. To make use of steam power, factories were designed so that energy from a single drive shaft could be mechanically distributed to several machines (Figure 3.5). Initially, the electric motor was simply substituted for steam, but the complex array of belts and drive shafts was retained. This retrofitting of existing machinery was cheaper than outfitting each machine with its own motor because many components were already in place.

Figure 3.5 This mid-nineteenth century rope factory was designed so that energy from a single drive shaft (mounted overhead) could be distributed to several machines.

It was only some 25 years later, with the widespread electrification of American manufacturing, that factory designs and internal layouts were changed to take full advantage of the flexibility made possible by the electric motor. Once each machine was driven by its own electric motor (the "unit drive" approach), the machines could be positioned independently to optimize work flow and materials handling instead of being clustered in groups around a common power source (the "group drive" approach). Because the old, complex belt-drive apparatus was no longer needed, maintenance and labor costs were reduced. More important, improvements in machine control led to increases in the quantity and quality of output.

As well, the adoption of the unit-drive electric motor provided a number of important indirect benefits by enabling the factory structure itself to be redesigned. Bracing to support the heavy shafting and belt housings (generally mounted overhead) could be eliminated, allowing for lighter and less costly factory construction. The greater flexibility of unit-drive-powered machinery also reduced downtime dramatically, since maintenance and repair of one machine did not require others to be shut down as it did when one source powered a group of machines.

In sum, the introduction of the new technology of the electric motor spanned a period of some 40 to 50 years from when it was first invented to when its productivity benefits were clearly recognized. In a similar manner, disappointment over the meager benefits of information technology (at least as evidenced by our conventional productivity measures) may be due to an unrealistic impatience with the process of adopting a revolutionary technology.

Though organizations may lament the apparent absence of a productivity payback from the invasion of information technology into the office, they can no longer survive without that technology. Today, an organization that lacks appropriate computer resources is unable to keep pace with administrative tasks, let alone accomplish work objectives. That observation alone suggests that information technology has become indispensable to maintaining our material standard of living even though we may not yet have developed adequate measures of its importance.

DIFFICULTIES IN RELIABLY MEASURING OFFICE PRODUCTIVITY

It is hard to measure the productivity of office workers, particularly that of knowledge workers. This issue is addressed below in some detail. While such measures may be eagerly sought to guide corporate planning, their use must be tempered by an understanding of their reliability. There simply may be no way to measure whether separate changes in equipment, tools, management style, or physical office setting have improved the productivity of an individual or a work group. However, difficulties in objectively quantifying change are not proof of its absence. Organizations support training and education programs, counseling services, substance abuse rehabilitation programs, and other employee benefits with the expectation that worker performance will be enhanced even though such gains are not readily quantified.

THE PURSUIT OF PRODUCTIVITY

Efforts to improve productivity by changing the work setting and work method are not new. At the turn of the century, Frederick Taylor developed his concepts of the scientific management of work as a rational way to raise the productivity of the individual worker. Introduced at a time when assembly lines and mass production were fueling an explosive growth in American industry, his approach was based on the idea that expensive machines could be used best if workers were trained to handle them in the most efficient way. He believed that specialists in the analysis of work could design a more efficient method to do the job than the operators themselves.

Taylor reasoned that all the tasks involved in making and moving things could be broken down into a series of unskilled operations. If a job that demanded a high level of skill were systematically analyzed, it could be reduced to a series of simpler tasks that could quickly be learned by less skilled workers. The most efficient way to perform each task was prescribed in detail, and each worker was expected to follow the specified procedures precisely. In this way, all discretionary activity and all worker control over how work was done could be systematically eliminated. This also made jobs more specialized, in that each worker performed fewer steps of the overall production process.

A natural extension of Taylor's ideas was to try to optimize the work setting and the tools used in performing a task. L. M. Gilbreth, a contemporary of Taylor, conducted detailed time-and-motion studies of work. By carefully analyzing all aspects of a job, he could often reduce the number of motions, the amount of time, and the level of exertion. For example, he found ways to eliminate motions needed to lay a brick, reducing the number from 18 to 5. When the consistency of the mortar was adjusted, fewer motions were needed to tap the brick into position at the correct height.

In the 1930s, Elton Mayo sought to discredit Taylor's scientific management and replace it with his own focus on human relations as the driving force in improving productivity. His now famous studies of worker productivity at Western Electric's Hawthorne Works illustrated the effect of motivation on worker productivity. A major finding of these studies came to be known as the **Hawthorne effect**.

Mayo selected a group of workers who wired telephone equipment. These study subjects were taken out of their normal work setting and placed in a separate room for the experiment. The lighting and other physical attributes of the environment were varied to study how changes in the physical setting would affect productivity. To the surprise of the researchers, productivity increased in response to virtually any change in the work setting. For example, productivity increased when the level of illumination was raised or lowered. Even when the level of illumination was so low that it was difficult to see the components being assembled, the productivity of workers in the experimental setting was still higher than in the factory work space.

The reason for the unexpected productivity increase was that the study participants found the experimental setting a much more pleasant environment in which to work. Unlike their normal work setting, they were allowed to talk to each other, sit next to whomever they chose, and take more frequent rest breaks. The study strongly supported the case for a less rigid and more caring style of management in motivating employees and raising productivity. Management styles have changed dramatically since that time and have become less authoritarian. It is now accepted in management theory, and there is growing acceptance in management practice, that individual workers and work groups should be given more responsibility for defining how work can best be done and even what work should be done.

Unfortunately, the results of Mayo's study were treated by many as proof that changes to the physical setting did not reliably improve productivity. It was a conclusion that has severely hampered research in this area ever since. The physical environment did make a difference. But as many researchers have since noted, it was not a simple cause-and-effect relationship (see, for example, Sommer 1968, 1969; Becker 1981). Moving the study participants to a separate area, paying special attention to their work needs, and listening to their comments provided tangible evidence from both the physical work setting and the less authoritarian supervisory style that someone was concerned about the employees' well-being and was willing to change the environment to better suit their needs. The researchers attributed their findings to the operation of social forces. Yet it was the physical setting they created — the special room and the physical arrangement of workers — that facilitated interaction, allowing these social forces to develop and raise productivity.

The physical setting is only one aspect of a person's work environment. Although it can improve the work environment in important ways, individuals experience the office as a whole — the physical, psychosocial, and management setting together. Each of these three aspects invariably affects the others. Changes need to be in alignment so that they reinforce the desired message instead of contradicting it. For example, improving the physical setting while ignoring major supervisory problems sends conflicting messages that can negate the benefits of any enhancements. It is this interaction of effects that makes it so difficult to demonstrate direct cause-and-effect relationships between the physical setting and individual productivity. Yet the difficulty of isolating and measuring the relationship doesn't mean that the physical setting is unimportant.

People can tolerate minor nuisances and distractions and even major disruptions in their work setting if they believe their sacrifice is for a good cause. Consider, for example, a small start-up company with a handful of employees developing some novel device, such as a revolutionary computer. They toil away in a rabbit warren of mismatched and ill-suited tables and chairs, buried in circuit boards and test equipment — hardly what an ergonomist would regard as a "productive work environment." Yet there they work day after day generating valuable innovations at a prodigious rate. If asked about their work environment, they describe the importance of their work, the excitement of being at the leading edge, or their commitment to succeed. The physical work setting is low on their list of concerns unless it specifically interferes with something they want to accomplish.

Considered in isolation, the physical work setting would appear to be of little importance to their productivity. But

Figure 3.6 Once a company is established and accommodates managers in richly appointed offices, all employees expect their work settings to be above average in quality and comfort. (*Source:* Photo by Tony Fouhse, Ottawa.)

when viewed in its historical and social context, the high worker productivity in this type of setting is more understandable. What appears to be, and probably is, a poor physical work environment has a number of compensating factors that lead the occupants to be satisfied enough not only to tolerate their surroundings but to seek out such a work environment, at least for a short time. It may be that they could be more productive in an improved physical setting. But productivity is not a function of the physical setting alone. Motivation, camaraderie, respect, and the satisfaction of other personal goals and needs all affect the quality and quantity of work that an individual will produce. Other motivators might be the youthful excitement of participating in a groundbreaking project, the expectation that this type of environment is where the *real* leading-edge work is done, and perhaps the hope that the company might one day be catapulted to success and employees' shares might be worth a fortune. Apple Computer and Microsoft are but two of the many high-technology success stories that developed from the humble beginnings of a few young and idealistic innovators.

But that same work setting could take on an entirely different meaning if, instead of being a cash-starved start-up company, the firm was an established organization and its managers were comfortably accommodated in richly appointed offices (Figure 3.6). The cramped work setting of the development team could then become a symbol of management's lack of interest and concern for those creating the new products upon which the organization depends. Everyone in the organization might have been willing to accept difficult working conditions in the past, but when one group is favored with upgraded work space, the social and historical context makes the physical setting a source of resentment. The same cramped work setting the developers once enjoyed would no longer convey the message it did when the company was young and struggling, and so its users would be less willing and less motivated to accept its limitations.

Ideally, the physical environment should be so unobtrusive that occupants are not consciously aware of it. However, when people are oblivious to their environment, they are largely unaware of the reasons why the physical setting does not intrude upon them and fades into the background. The factors that act as inhibitors of productive work when they are present aren't necessarily recognized as facilitators when they are absent. For example, Crouch and Nimran (1989) found in their study of managers that when noise distraction was a problem, people rated it as a serious impediment to their productivity. But people did not report the absence of noise as an important benefit of their work space. Instead, more active features — such as comfortable furniture, pleasing decor, or a supportive social environment — were perceived to be the factors responsible for making their work environment "good."

Studies like this one show, and experience in assessing working offices corroborates, that occupants have a biased perception of the factors in their work setting that contribute to productivity. People tend to forget the physical work environment when it is not a problem but complain vociferously when it is an irritant. Consequently, the physical work setting, when it is reported at all, tends to be rated negatively. When it is neutral or positive, it usually is not mentioned. As a result, the positive contribution of the physical setting to productivity and satisfaction tends to be ignored or masked by other factors. Masking factors include those unique to the individual (such as tolerance and physical strength) or controlled by the individual (such as level of nutrition, exercise, and rest), social cues (such as status within the organization and relationships with coworkers), and other external factors (such as work or family pressures).

Conversely, environmental factors related to social interaction, aesthetics, and display of status (such as location of parking spot or office decor and size) tend not to be subject to this bias; they are perceived as important whether positive or negative. For this reason, unraveling the features that make a work setting "good" as perceived by the occupants is not simply a straightforward matter of asking them. Features of which they are unaware contribute significantly to the workplace attributes they value.

Measuring the Productivity of Office Workers

Productivity improvement is commonly the justification for enhancements to the office work environment. It would seem reasonable to assess the benefits of such expenditures by measuring changes in the productivity of the office workers affected. Does the benefit justify the cost? But productivity is only one of several measures of organizational performance, and it is not necessarily the most important one.

PERFORMANCE MEASURES

Sink (1985) defines seven distinct measures of organizational performance: effectiveness, efficiency, quality, profitability, productivity, quality of work life, and innovation. Though not mutually exclusive, these measures are useful in examining the range of standards that organizations employ to monitor, evaluate, control, and manage their activities.

Effectiveness is the degree to which defined objectives have been accomplished. Its assessment employs at least three criteria: (1) Quality: Were the "right" things done (i.e., did the output satisfy the predetermined specifications?)? (2) Quantity: Was enough produced? (3) Timeliness: Was the output produced on time?

Efficiency is a measure of the expected use of resources (e.g., materials, labor, capital, information) to accomplish some objective or activity relative to the actual use. It is usually expressed as a ratio:

$$\frac{\text{Expected resource use}}{\text{Actual resource use}}$$

The expected resource use is commonly based on past performance. An efficiency of 1.00 indicates that resource use was as expected, whereas a value greater than 1.00 would indicate an increase in efficiency.

Quality is the degree to which results conform to requirements or expectations. What distinguishes it from the effectiveness measure is that it is a measurement of specific quality attributes of the product or service that can be subjectively or objectively assessed.

Profitability is the ratio of total revenues (or in some cases, total budget) to total costs. A wide range of profitability ratios are used to assess a firm's financial health. For example:

$$\text{Profit margin on sales} = \frac{\text{Net income (after taxes)}}{\text{Sales}}$$

$$\text{Return on total assets} = \frac{\text{Net income}}{\text{Total assets}}$$

$$\text{Return on net worth} = \frac{\text{Net income}}{\text{Total worth}}$$

Productivity is the relationship between the outputs produced during a given period of time and the inputs consumed to create them — for example, the value of the goods and services produced compared with the value of the resources (e.g., labor, capital, energy, and materials) used. By inference, the concept of "output" employed in productivity measures assumes a minimum acceptable level of quality for inclusion. The measure is calculated as a ratio:

$$\frac{\text{Quantity of outputs}}{\text{Quantity of inputs}}$$

Productivity measures are used extensively in business to monitor production costs, assess market opportunities, predict future performance, and guide strategic planning.

Quality of work life involves the individual's psychological and social response to the organization. It is well documented that human performance is affected by the social as well as the physical surroundings. As such, improvements in the quality of work life can contribute to an organization's performance. (Psychosocial aspects of the work environment are addressed in Chapter 7.)

Innovation is the process of developing new products and services or new ways of working. It is applied creativity. Innovation is critical to competitive success, and as markets have become more global in scope, this aspect of performance has been given greater attention. Recent office designs, particularly those for knowledge workers, have sought to provide a range of work settings that facilitate collaborative as well as individual work activities.

Although the physical work environment can have a positive effect on all these aspects of performance, it is unlikely that any given change in the physical setting would produce measurable effects in all of them. In part, this is because so many factors contribute to performance that it is often difficult to show a definitive cause-and-effect relationship. As well, the effect of change on some aspects of performance can be recognized subjectively long before there is enough quantitative evidence to prove the existence of that effect. For example, the effect of improvements in the quality of work life may become readily apparent through more positive and cooperative employee attitudes long before a change in the pattern of staff turnover will be discerned.

Taken in this context, productivity measures may not be sufficiently sensitive or specific to evaluate the benefits of enhancements to the physical workplace. Still, there is considerable pressure to justify investments in the office environment in this way. For this reason, the following discussion is presented both to show the difficulties in measuring the productivity of office workers and to illustrate the types of measures that are commonly suggested.

ASSESSING THE PRODUCTIVITY OF OFFICE WORK

In applying productivity assessment techniques to office work, a number of difficulties in measurement and interpretation arise. Two that are particularly relevant to the evaluation of individual productivity are the range of factors measured and the evaluation of quality.

If the range of input and output factors used in the measurement of productivity is too narrowly defined, the resulting information tends to be unreliable and misleading. For example, in a manufacturing setting, labor productivity is commonly assessed as the ratio of the value of goods produced to the cost of labor. If a new piece of equipment were added to an assembly line, the change in productivity could be assessed by comparing the labor productivity with and without the new equipment. But focusing on the cost of labor could be seriously misleading if there were other significant expenses. For example, the new equipment might require different maintenance, or the failure rate might change. If these factors add significantly to the cost of production but are not included in the calculation, the productivity measure may indicate an increase in productivity when in fact there was a decrease.

Similarly in the office setting, eliminating support staff and having everyone answer their own telephone, assemble their own reports, and make their own photocopies may immediately lower salary expenses by reducing the number of support staff. But for a realistic assessment of the productivity impacts, the factors measured should be broad enough to capture the impact of the increased load of "busywork" on the productivity of all those who lose support services. What's more, the effect may ripple through the organization, indirectly affecting other groups and slowing the organization's overall ability to function and respond to change.

As noted previously, productivity measures assume that quality is taken into account in the quantification of outputs. Economists commonly assume that prices reflect the relative values of products as judged by consumers and that the prices of labor, materials, and other factors of production reflect product quality with reasonable accuracy. The rationale is that if market prices did not reflect these relative values, consumers would buy less of the overpriced commodities and producers would want to sell more, thus driving prices lower. Similarly, for labor, the quality of a person-hour is measured by the wages and benefits paid. The amounts assigned for the capital and operating cost of equipment would assume that outputs are of acceptable quality.

There is a growing recognition within the management community of the limitations in measuring an organization's productivity using traditional cost-accounting data (see, for example, Drucker 1990; Eccles 1991; and Kaplan 1984). Even at the aggregated level of national economies, there are difficulties in assuming that quality is accounted for in the valuation of outputs. For example, an OECD (Organization for Economic Cooperation and Development) report on technology and productivity found that in comparing the productivity growth rates among major industrial nations, there were serious problems in the measurement of productivity, particularly in the service sector. It was concluded that conventional price index measurements of productivity failed to capture changes in quality (Bozdogan 1991).

There are many office jobs in which the quality of what is produced can reasonably be assumed to be constant. In those instances, a measurement of the quantity of output may fairly represent productivity. For example, in filing records, an item is defined as "filed" (i.e., the task is completed) when it has been correctly stored. How the task is done does not affect the utility of the completed work. So in this case, the productivity of someone doing filing work can be measured by the quantity of files handled per unit of time. The quality is defined primarily by external criteria rather than being an attribute of the way the work is done.

The processing of insurance claims is often treated in this way as well. The items measured are the number of completed claims per unit of time. The quality of the completion process is assumed to be included in this measure. By implication, clerks who take longer to process claims because they provide more customer service would be "less productive" according to this measurement.

Where output can be defined by quantity alone, conventional industrial-engineering methods can be used to improve productivity. Standards can be defined and engineered into the work process by analyzing the work, dividing the work into a series of efficient operations, and combining the operations into a complete job.

Comparing the productivity of people using different work settings is relatively straightforward if the measure of productivity can be restricted to quantity. For this reason, efforts to relate enhancements in the physical setting to productivity gains have focused on activities that can be defined in this way — activities that tend to be procedural.

But knowledge work is less easily assessed in this way. Although it is possible to find items of output to count (e.g., the number of legal cases completed, the number of research papers written), it is questionable whether measurements derived in this way truly capture what makes one person's performance more valuable to the organization than another's. The productivity of physicians depends on the quality of their diagnoses as well as the number of patients they service. For the majority of knowledge and service work, performance is defined by quality and quantity *together.*

Consider, for example, research scientists developing new drugs. The quality of their discoveries is far more important than the quantity of new drugs they develop. Developing one new drug that dominates the market for a decade and generates annual sales of $500 million is more valuable than developing dozens of drugs similar to those already on the market with annual sales of $30 million (Drucker 1991). It is also difficult to assign an appropriate time frame to the productivity assessment. The quality of knowledge work may not be recognized for months or years, and numerous contributors may have substantially improved the original work. Such is the case with knowledge-based activities like strategic planning, policy formulation, and design for which the fundamental measure of success is *how well the result works.*

Productivity Measurement Methods

Efforts to study the relationship of the physical office environment to the productivity of the workers have employed a variety of measurement methods. They can be broadly divided into four categories: absence measures, activity logs, attitude and opinion surveys, direct measurements.

In general, the greater the knowledge component of the work, the more difficult it is to develop reliable measures of productivity that are strictly objective. Discrete activities such as completing forms, phoning people, contacting customers, and processing purchase orders can be defined clearly and counted objectively. As it becomes more important to include quality in the assessment, more subjective measures must generally be used.

ABSENCE MEASURES

One undisputed fact is that people do not contribute to the productivity of an organization when they are physically absent *and not working*. Records of people's absence are coarse but relatively objective measures of lost productivity. **Absenteeism** (the number of days an employee is not working), **turnover** (the rate at which employees leave an organization and must be replaced), and **lateness** are three such measures. Health care expenses, health insurance premiums, and occupational injuries are also indicators of the cost of absenteeism to the organization.

It is important to recognize that measures such as absenteeism and turnover do not directly assess productivity. They assess conditions under which productivity is considered to be zero (such as workdays lost). Situations in which productivity is merely reduced are not represented.

In the past, data on absenteeism and lateness were objective measures that could readily be obtained from existing records and were relatively accurate. Today, however, work is considerably more portable, and a great deal of productive effort takes place away from the formal office setting and outside of normal business hours. The accuracy and objectivity of these data are no longer as dependable.

Another limitation on the use of absence data is distinguishing productivity losses attributable to the work setting from losses due to other causes. Absenteeism will increase in seasons when ailments such as allergies, colds, and flu are more prevalent. Office-related absenteeism may be the result of factors other than the physical setting, such as management problems or individual psychosocial difficulties. For this reason, the statistical validity of these data needs to be evaluated before conclusions can be drawn.

Staff turnover represents a costly disruption to an organization's work flow. Hidden expenses, estimated to account for 80% or more of turnover costs, are rarely measured. They include inefficiencies of the incoming employee, emotional upset to colleagues who worked with the outgoing employee, and the declining productivity of the employee prior to departure. There are also costs associated with having a position vacant, possible relocation expenses for the new employee, and the administrative burden to update salary, benefit, and other records.

Merck & Company found that the cost of disruptions in work relationships and the transactional costs of getting employees on and off the payroll were equivalent to about 1.5 times the annual salary of the position being replaced. Other studies found that it took about a year for a new employee or for executives relocated within an organization to reach their maximum efficiency (Phillips 1990; Schlesinger and Heskett 1991).

These detailed studies indicate that the hidden costs of employee turnover can be significant. However, as in the case of absenteeism, turnover can be motivated by many factors unrelated to the work setting. Although turnover is readily quantified, it is difficult to assess the influence of the work environment on individual decisions to leave a job.

ACTIVITY LOGS

Activity logs seek to assess productivity by measuring the time spent on each task during the workday. Daily logs usually must be produced by the individual being evaluated. The activities are then classified as productive work time, overhead tasks, and other categories. Ratios of time use can then be employed as productivity indicators (e.g., the ratio of productive time to total time). It is an indirect measure that is actually assessing the *time available for work* rather than an individual's productivity when he or she is working. Also, if the data are self-reported, a high level of cooperation and commitment is needed from those being evaluated or the data can be heavily biased. So the validity of the activity log itself depends on the individual's perception of how the information will be used.

DeMarco and Lister (1985) used activity logs to calculate the proportion of time that programmers were free of distractions and able to concentrate on their programming work (Table 3.1). The quality of work and the speed of task completion were positively correlated with the proportion of work time that was uninterrupted. Thus the proportion of uninterrupted work time

Table 3.1 Segment of a time log from the Coding War Games showing the frequency of interruptions to the work. (*Source:* DeMarco and Lister 1987.)

Time of work period (From – To)	Type of work	What interruption caused the end of this work period?
2:13 — 2:17	Coding	Phone call
2:20 — 2:23	Coding	Boss stopped in to chat
2:26 — 2:29	Coding	Question from colleague
2:31 — 2:39	Coding	Phone call
2:41 — 2:44	Coding	Phone call

was a useful indirect measure of productivity for that type of activity.

ATTITUDE AND OPINION SURVEYS

Attitude and opinion assessments of employees who work in a particular building are commonly termed **occupant surveys**. This measurement method can employ questionnaires, interviews, or group meetings to assess employee attitudes, opinions, morale, and self-reports of productivity. Provisions to ensure confidentiality are usually required. If people feel that their responses might be used against them, the data will likely be inaccurate.

Occupant surveys generally measure individuals' perception of their physical, psychosocial, and management work environment as well as their rating of its performance. Attitude measures such as job satisfaction are commonly included and are often interpreted as indirect productivity measures. Information that characterizes the respondents — such as age, sex, education, general health, and length of time in the current job — can be used to divide them into similar groups for statistical analysis. This procedure, termed "stratification," can improve the reliability of the analysis and uncover trends that would otherwise be hidden in the data. Respondents may also be asked to estimate the amount of time lost due to specific nonproductive activities such as waiting for services, finding information, doing unnecessary administrative tasks, and suffering from eyestrain, headaches, or other ailments.

A survey is relatively easy to administer. To obtain valid information, though, the survey needs to be designed by an expert and tailored to the situation. Evaluating occupant survey data, assessing validity and reliability, and interpreting results are a specialty in themselves. (Diagnostic methods are discussed in Chapter 8.) Surveys that are appropriately designed, administered, and analyzed provide valuable information on the effects of the office setting on individuals. However, they do not directly measure productivity. A self-report of productivity is an individual's opinion about his or her own productivity, not an independent measure. That opinion can easily be biased by a variety of factors, including a desire to influence the outcome of the survey. Yet a person's truthful report of the features that most reduce his or her productivity is probably the least expensive and most reliable way to obtain this information.

Figure 3.7 illustrates the results from an occupant survey of symptoms associated with sick building syndrome and self-reports of productivity. The summarized data shown in the graph indicate that self-reported productivity tended to decline as the number of illness symptoms increased. This was, in fact, a major con-

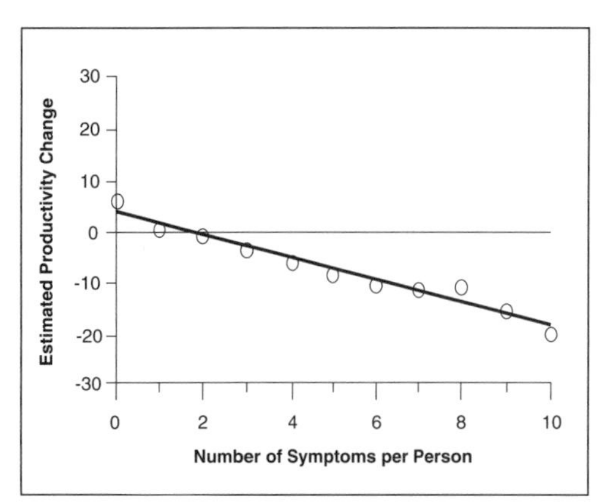

Figure 3.7 Relationship between self-reports of productivity and the incidence of sick building symptoms. The data, from 4,700 occupants in 47 offices, were grouped by number of reported symptoms. The plotted points are the average productivity change reported by each group. (*Source:* Building Use Studies, London.)

clusion of the researchers (see Raw, Leaman, and Roys 1989). Although the productivity measures were self-reports and subject to individual bias, the strong trend and large sample size (4,700 office workers in 47 offices) combined to give a statistically significant result. What also lends support to this interpretation of the data is that the notion that people are less productive when they feel ill is consistent with most people's own experience.

Other indirect measures of employee attitude and morale are the number of worker strikes, grievances, and the incidence of sabotage or noncooperation. Such activities obviously obstruct work and would reduce productivity. Although there have been a few cases in which office workers walked out of buildings to protest the poor interior environment, so many factors are involved that, in general, such activities are rarely useful in relating the physical office environment to worker productivity.

DIRECT MEASUREMENTS

Direct measurement of productivity is most reliable and valid where the quality of the task is inherently consistent and measurable so that a count of quantity is a valid gauge of productivity. Examples are highly repetitive or predictable tasks (such as handling purchase requisitions or verifying bank transactions) for which the number of transactions is a reliable unit of measure for both the quality and quantity of work output. The validity of the data is further increased if they can be collected without changing the work process or otherwise alerting those being measured.

Dressel and Francis (1987) used the number of purchase requisitions handled by individual procurement officers to compare the productivity of different workstation designs. Although each requisition was somewhat unique, the large volume of work items averaged out most of these variations so that each officer's workload could be considered equal. Adjustments to the productivity measure were made for the few exceptional tasks that were inherently more time-consuming than the norm. In general, the researchers found that the number of items handled represented well the value of the work to the organization.

As previously noted, the more important the variations in quality, and the fewer and more unique the individual tasks, the more difficult it is to develop direct productivity measures that capture the value of the work to the organization. Knowledge work that requires a large component of analysis and judgment falls into this hard-to-measure category. It then becomes necessary to use subjective measures of performance or to devise artificial measures, such as a standardized test.

The performance of an individual knowledge worker tends to be highly dependent on his or her interaction with coworkers. While the measurement of individual performance may be desirable for certain types of research, such as the effects of the work setting on the individual, in terms of the organization's objectives, it is generally more useful and valid to measure the productivity of groups of knowledge workers rather than the productivity of individuals.

In general, the less repetitive and routine the work, the more difficult it is to develop an objective measure of productivity. In addition, the more specialized and knowledge-based the work, the more difficult it is to evaluate performance without the individual's full cooperation. As such, evaluation techniques based on partnership, trust, and confidentiality are more likely to provide meaningful results than the traditional approaches of measuring the quantity of work done or analyzing the way an individual chooses to do the work. Often, the people best able to judge an individual's productivity are his or her peers. Though peer assessments are subjective and therefore subject to bias, the information can be more accurate than an objective evaluation because the full scope of the job, as only a practitioner could know it, can be taken into account.

One of the more unusual efforts to examine the effect of the physical work setting on individual productivity for jobs with a high knowledge component was a series of trials conducted by Tom DeMarco and Timothy Lister called the "Coding War Games" (DeMarco and Lister 1985, 1987). Designed to compare the productivity of computer programmers, the Coding War Games were conceived as an opportunity for individuals to find out how well they performed relative to their peers. The data were also analyzed to identify factors associated with individual levels of performance, including characteristics of the work setting.

Coding War Games: Research Design

Initially conducted in 1984 with 166 participants from 35 companies, the Coding War Games were repeated (with different participants) over several years as one component of a software development consulting practice. From 1984 to 1986, over 600 participants from 92 companies were involved.

Participation was entirely voluntary. The incentive for organizations to participate was to find out how well their software developers compared with others in the industry. Individual results remained confidential to protect the participants. Participating organizations only received aggregated scores showing the performance of their software developers as a group relative to the scores from the entire study. However, the individual participants received their own scores as well as the group averages.

Every participant was given identical work: designing, coding, and testing the same medium-size program to a fixed set of specifications at his or her own place of work. There was a minimum of two participants from each organization. Participants competed individually, and there was little incentive for them to work together since the results were confidential. Over the years that the games were conducted, there was no evidence that developers helped each other.

Participants worked in their own offices, during normal business hours, using the same languages, tools, terminals, and computers that they used for their own projects. This was done to eliminate any bias due to unfamiliarity with the work environment. During the exercise, each participant completed a time log and a questionnaire. After submissions were received from all participants, the programs were assessed using standard software acceptance procedures.

In designing the experiment this way, DeMarco and Lister overcame a number of obstacles commonly encountered in measuring the productivity of knowledge workers. Their consulting work involved the evaluation of software development and improvement of procedures for a wide range of clients. As skilled practitioners, they had in-depth expertise both in performing the coding task and in evaluating the work. As a result, it was much easier for them than for researchers unfamiliar with the craft of the professional programmer to identify which factors were likely to be important to the productivity of this group. Their experience with software acceptance tests gave them confidence in the validity of their evaluation method. They also structured their investigation broadly to include work experience, education, the programming languages and tools used, and features of the physical work environment. Perhaps most important, they were viewed as an outside third party, and participants trusted their assurance of confidentiality.

Coding War Games: Key Findings

The Coding War Games results regarding the programmer's performance and his or her physical work environment are summarized below.

Performance. As expected, there was wide variation in individual productivity. It is common in software development for the best people in a group of programmers to outperform the worst by about 10:1, with the best performer being about 2.5 times better than the median performer. In general, for any group of programmers, the better-performing half will outperform the other half by more than 2:1. The results from the 1984 Coding War Games were consistent with these rules of thumb.

Factors that had little or no correlation with performance were the computer language used, years of experience, number of defects, and salary. The better-performing half of the sample performed nearly twice as well on average as the worse-performing half, but their average salary (though higher) was within 10 percent of the other half. Though perhaps counterintuitive, these observations are corroborated by other studies (see, for example, Lawrence and Jeffery 1983). At any given salary level, the performance spread was nearly as wide as for the entire sample. Those who used older languages such as COBOL and FORTRAN did as well as those who used newer languages such as Pascal and C. There was no correlation between experience and performance except that those with less than six months of experience with the language they used in the exercise did not do as well as the rest of the participants. (This result can be misleading. The small and detailed nature of the task, sometimes called *programming in the small,* was such that greater experience did not improve performance. For larger development projects, *programming in the large,* more experience does improve performance significantly (DeMarco 1992).) Nearly a third of the participants produced programs with zero defects. As a group, it did not take them more time to do more precise work. In fact, zero-defect work was done in slightly less time than the average.

Despite the wide range of performance within the group, the performance scores of pairs from the same organization differed, on average, by only 21%. The fastest and second fastest performers were from the same organization, and the overall slowest and second slowest performers were also from the same organization. In fact, one of the best predictors of individual performance was the score of the other participant from the same organization (most organizations had only two participants).

This result was surprising since pair members did not work together. What they did have in common was the organization in which they worked. They experienced the same physical environment and the same corporate culture. Despite the wide spread in individual performance across the sample, two people from the same organization tended to perform alike. Whether the workplace attracts people who perform alike or creates people who perform alike, the data showed a strong clustering of good performers in some organizations and poor performers in others.

Environment. Programming requires long periods of uninterrupted concentration. Noise, privacy, and the frequency of interruptions were found to significantly affect productivity. To provide information about the work environment, each participant completed a questionnaire. Table 3.2 compares some of the responses of the total sample to the highest-performing quarter and the lowest-performing

Table 3.2 Comparison of environmental factors for the highest-performing quarter, lowest-performing quarter, and total sample in the Coding War Games. (*Source:* DeMarco and Lister 1985.)

Environmental Factor	Highest-performing quarter (Top 25%)	Lowest-performing quarter (Bottom 25%)	All Performers
Average dedicated floor space	78 square feet	46 square feet	63 square feet
Acceptably quiet work space	57% yes	29% yes	42% yes
Acceptably private work space	62% yes	19% yes	39% yes
Can you silence your phone?	52% yes	10% yes	29% yes
Can you divert your calls?	76% yes	19% yes	57% yes
Do people often interrupt you needlessly?	38% yes	76% yes	62% yes
Does your work space make your feel appreciated?	57% yes	29% yes	45% yes

quarter. The highest quarter performed on average 2.6 times better than the lowest quarter. The top performers had more space and perceived their work space to be quieter, relatively private, and better shielded from interruptions. In contrast, the bottom quarter had as little as 3.7 square meters (40 square feet) of dedicated space with little protection from interruptions.

This doesn't mean that changing the physical work setting of the lowest quarter would necessarily improve their productivity by 2.6 times. The inferior working conditions were considered to be associated with an overall poorer attitude toward these programmers that would be expressed in the style of management, social interactions, overall view of quality, and other aspects of the corporate culture. Under such circumstances, changing one aspect of a poor work setting would be unlikely to produce measurable gains.

To test whether better performers had been rewarded with better work space, the researchers investigated three organizations that had each entered 18 or more programmers in the trials. Comparing their reported floor space and noise level, there was no significant difference between the best performers and the worst performers *within the same organization*. That is, organizations did not appear to be rewarding better performers with better work spaces. Work space conditions tended to be the same for programmers within an organization. However, when performance and work settings were compared *between* organizations, there was a clear association of better workstations with better performance.

DeMarco and Lister concluded that whether a better workplace improves individual performance or more productive workers gravitate to organizations with better work environments, there are measurable productivity benefits to be gained by improving the physical workplace environment. The study did not provide conclusive proof that improvements to the physical work setting alone would produce significant productivity gains. However, it presented a strong case that good work environments and workers with high productivity tended to occur together, whatever the cause may be.

Though this study was specific to one type of knowledge worker, software developers, the association of better work environments with better performance is consistent with the needs expressed by other knowledge workers.

IS THERE A PRODUCTIVITY PAYOFF?

Assessing the benefits of infrastructure to an organization is like assessing the benefits of water to a living being. By conventional measures of food value, the benefit of water is zero — no calories, no protein, no fat, no vitamins. Yet without water, the organism could not survive. Infrastructure is essential, yet the tools we use to measure it assess its benefit to be zero. But we know that organizations do not survive without infrastructure. The assessment is a limitation of the tool we use — it is an artifact of the measuring system. To follow the results of the analysis blindly would be folly.

So it is with the work environment — an integral component of an organization's infrastructure. As long as the benefits of improvements to the work environment are sought only in increased profits, they are unlikely to be found. The major benefits are hidden as avoided costs, but they are nonetheless real. Illness absenteeism that did not occur because air quality was improved, injuries that did not happen because ergonomically appropriate furnishings were chosen, or ideas and initiative that were not lost because the work setting facilitated collaboration are all important benefits that are virtually invisible to financial-accounting measures.

There is justified reluctance to increase expenditures when the returns are difficult to monitor. For office-based organizations, accommodation costs are generally the second largest operating expense after salaries. Understandably, there is considerable resistance to initiating changes in the office setting that would increase that expense. However, the cost of labor is about 15 times greater than the cost of the facilities they occupy (Brill et al. 1983). That is, for every $15 an organization spends on employee salaries, it spends only $1 on accommodation. Therefore, efforts to save dollars on accommodation can easily become a net loss for the company if they somehow lead to reduced worker productivity. The problem here is that the costs are much easier to assess than the benefits.

For example, it is easy to compare the cost to lease work space and purchase furniture for different office layouts. There is a direct financial incentive to accommodate more people in less space. But the consequences of a higher-density layout on the productivity of the people who use it are virtually impossible to predict. As seating density increases, the noise level and occurrence of disruptions would be expected to increase, making it more difficult for people to concentrate. But there is no way to quantify how such a reduction in environmental quality would affect productivity.

A valuable approach to judging the relative merits of uncertain benefits is to compare projected savings to the risk of incurring additional costs that would negate them. Whereas the productivity of office workers is relatively difficult to measure, the cost of work time is readily evaluated and can provide a valuable comparative context for judging the merits of facility costs.

Consider, for example, a proposal to save $150,000 by selecting a lower-performance HVAC (heating, ventilating, and air-conditioning) system for a 10,000-square-meter (100,000-square-foot) office building. The initial cost of HVACs averages about $100 per square meter serviced ($10 per square foot) (Rosenfeld 1989) and the annual operating costs are about $30 per square meter ($3 per square foot) (Haines 1988). So the HVAC for a 10,000-square-meter (100,000-square-foot) office would cost about $1 million, and its operation would be about $300,000 per year.

A commonly used rule of thumb for American offices is that an organization requires about 11 square meters (120 square feet) per person. This average figure allows for different sizes of work spaces as well as corridors and storage areas that do not accommodate workstations. So a 10,000-square-meter (100,000-square-foot) office space would accommo-

Table 3.3 Comparison of HVAC cost savings and labor cost.

Assumptions:

HVAC initial cost	= $10/ft²
HVAC operating cost	= $3/ft²/year
Worker space	= 120 ft²/employee
Average annual salary	= $30,000/employee
Standard work year	= 220 days

Cost calculation for a 100,000-ft² building:

HVAC initial cost ($10/ft² x 100,000 ft²)	= $1 million
15% savings on the initial cost of an HVAC (.15 x $1 million)	= $150,000
Approximate number of employees (100,000 ft² ÷ 120 ft²/employee)	= 830 people
Savings/employee ($150,000 ÷ 830 employees)	= $180/employee
Time equivalent of $180/employee ($30,000 ÷ 220 days = $136/day) ($180 ÷ $136/day = 1 1/3 days)	= 1 1/3 days

date about 830 people, and the cost of the upgrade would be about $180 per employee. At an average annual salary of $30,000 per employee for a 220-day work year, the average daily salary is about $136.

So the HVAC savings are equivalent to about 1 1/3 days per employee (Table 3.3). If the lower-performance HVAC increased the rate of illness absenteeism by a little more than a day per employee over the life of the investment, the savings would be lost. A sick building can easily generate that level of lost time in a single year. For example, Leaman and Borden (1991) found that in a single month, 41% of the 486 office workers in a sick building left for home early because they were suffering illness symptoms. Savings on facility costs are quickly negated by a small loss in work time because the cost of a worker's time is so high relative to the facility costs per worker. Furthermore, the effect on worker morale of a poor-quality work setting remains long after the short-term benefit of the initial cost avoidance.

The development of an organization's workforce is an important investment in its future. At the organization's expense, employees attend conferences and management courses, hold memberships in professional associations, and participate in programs designed to develop individual skills; worker assistance programs help employees control alcohol abuse, stop smoking, lose weight, exercise regularly, and improve their literacy; corporate sponsorships support community projects and charities, contributing products and services to worthy causes — all without a detailed accounting of the benefits.

Many important and costly decisions regarding workforce development are made on the basis of expected but unproven benefits. Yet decisions to invest in these programs are not based on a quantitative assessment of the productivity gains they will produce for the organization. Cost-benefit analyses may support the decision to fund these programs, but they are not the determining factor. It is recognized that while the costs in lost labor hours are easily quantified, many of the benefits — such as improved health, higher morale, and better-qualified employees with more diverse skills — are intangible. Though it is difficult to prove that these benefits are actually obtained, the programs continue to be supported because senior management believes they are beneficial. Motorola invests $60 million annually to train and educate its employees and, in effect, invests an additional $60 million in the work time lost when people are being trained. Though the benefits are difficult to measure, education is seen not as a cost but rather as an indispensable investment critical to the organization's success (Wiggenhorn 1990).

Further contributing to the difficulty of judging which improvements to the physical setting enhance productivity is the bias of personal experience. There is a tendency for everyone to consider themselves qualified to judge the office environment. People who have worked in an office tend to view it as a more or less generic setting and have definite opinions on which elements of the physical setting are important and which are extravagant amenities.

Office occupants generally play only a minor role in the design and furnishing of their work space, if they are consulted at all. Managers are usually called upon to make decisions about the work settings of administrators, secretaries, researchers, and other office occupants for whom they are responsible. Their decisions are commonly based on their personal opinion of how they would feel doing certain jobs in a given work setting. Yet without the experience of actually working at those jobs, their judgments are more conjecture than reality.

The tasks performed in an office are, at first glance, deceptively similar. Working at a desk with printed material or a computer, speaking on the telephone, and attending meetings are activities that every working person has experienced. Yet the person who performs certain tasks at a specific work setting, day in and day out, has a very different appreciation of which environmental factors contribute most to his or her performance and which detract. For example, the salesperson welcomes the ring of her phone as an opportunity to receive another order, whereas the computer programmer debugging complex code is frustrated at having his flow of thought interrupted by the telephone. Most phone calls (67%) are less important than the work they interrupt (McMillen 1992). Yet it's difficult for someone to understand how disruptive answering a phone can be if it is not a problem he or she experiences. In the same way, it can be difficult for supervisors who do not themselves suffer illness symptoms caused by the office environment to believe that one member of their staff is more sensitive and becomes ill while others are unaffected.

The assumption that someone can judge what would be a productive work environment for someone else is a major stumbling block to optimizing the work setting for occupants. Designers and managers alike need to understand which aspects of the physical setting promote human performance and productivity. They need to be willing to listen to those who must work in the environments chosen for them by others and to act on the experiences and perceptions these occupants report. Without effective and ongoing feedback from the users to the decision makers, efforts to optimize the office environment to suit the people who use it are unlikely to succeed.

There are no reliable methods for measuring the business value of improving the workplace environment. Senior executives are caught in a dilemma. Economically, companies are being driven by competitive necessity to reduce costs. Efforts to upgrade workplace quality are actively discouraged by concerns that accommodation costs may increase, by the risk of raising worker awareness of deficiencies in the work setting and perhaps their sensitivity to those deficiencies, and by the uncertainty of the benefits.

However, improvements to the work

Figure 3.8 Steelcase Corporation sought to convey its corporate values in the physical design of its new Corporate Development Center as well as in the management structure of the organization. The pyramid-shaped building was designed to recognize the value of individuals, respond to the changing dynamics of people and their work, and encourage the evolution of effective work processes rather than simply imposing one design team's concept of an efficient office layout. (*Source:* Steelcase, Grand Rapids, Mich.)

Figure 3.9 Informal group meeting area in the Steelcase Corporate Development Center. (*Source:* Steelcase, Grand Rapids, Mich.)

environment must be viewed as longer-term investments in the future. There is no reliable yardstick for deciding how much to spend on workplace quality. Moreover, it is unclear how to act on comparisons of a facility's cost to an average for the industry (see the subsection "Benchmarking" in Chapter 9). If a company is spending more than the average, is it a breakaway company ahead of the others, or is it spending stupidly? Is it funding infrastructures that others are neglecting, or is it catching up after years of underspending?

The costs of upgrading the work environment will always be more visible and easily measured than the benefits. The benefits of enhancements to office quality would be better captured by focusing on the process of managing improvements (i.e., resolving facility characteristics that inhibit work activities) rather than on trying to measure the productivity gains from separate workplace alterations.

No measurement has yet been devised to calculate the productivity benefits of a high-quality office environment. Yet many organizations are sufficiently convinced of the importance of the work setting that they have invested heavily in it. For example, Steelcase Corporation, Chrysler Corporation, and Digital Equipment have all built multimillion-dollar facilities designed around the concept of providing work settings tailored to the tasks of the occupants (Figures 3.8 and 3.9). Ultimately, decisions on the quality of the office workplace demand informed judgment. Although there are no studies that can reliably predict the returns on such facility investments, the evidence that a better work environment promotes better performance is compelling.

LITERATURE CITED

Becker, F. 1981. *Work space.* New York: Praeger Publishers.

Bozdogan, K. 1991. Overview, key findings, and conclusions of the OECD report on technology and productivity. In *Technology and productivity: The challenge for economic policy.* Proceedings of a conference held in June 1989. Paris: Organization for Economic Cooperation and Development.

Brill, M., S. T. Margulis, E. Konar, and BOSTI (Buffalo Organization for Social and Technological Innovation). 1983. *Using office design to increase productivity.* Buffalo, N.Y.: Workplace Design and Productivity.

Brown, J. S. 1991. Research that reinvents the corporation. *Harvard Business Review* (January–February):102–111.

Crouch, A., and U. Nimran. 1989. Perceived facilitators and inhibitors of work performance in an office. *Environment and Behavior* 21(2):206–226.

David, P. A. 1991. Computer and dynamo: The modern productivity paradox in a not-too-distant mirror. In *Technology and productivity: The challenge for economic policy.* Proceedings of a conference held in June 1989. Paris: Organization for Economic Cooperation and Development.

DeMarco, T., and T. Lister. 1985. Programmer performance and the effects of the workplace. In *Proceedings of the 8th International Conference on Software Engineering,* 268–272. New York: Institute of Electrical and Electronics Engineers.

DeMarco, T., and T. Lister. 1987. *Peopleware: Productive projects and teams.* New York: Dorset House Publishing Company.

DeMarco, T. 1992. Personal communications.

Dressel, D. L., and J. Francis. 1987. Office productivity: Contributions of the workstation. *Behaviour and Information Technology* 6(3):279–284.

Drucker, P. 1990. The emerging theory of manufacturing. *Harvard Business Review* (May–June):94–102.

Drucker, P. 1991. The new productivity challenge. *Harvard Business Review* (November–December):69–79.

Eccles, R. G. 1991. The performance measurement manifesto. *Harvard Business Review* (January–February):131–137.

Haines, R. 1988. Comfort: Forgotten factor in economic analyses. *Heating/Piping/Air Conditioning* (September):37–38.

Hammer, M. 1990. Reengineering work: Don't automate, obliterate. *Harvard Business Review* (July–August):104–112.

Kaplan, R. S. 1984. Yesterday's accounting undermines production. *Harvard Business Review* (July–August):95–101.

Lawrence, M. J., and D. R. Jeffery. 1983. Commercial programming productivity — An empirical look at intuition. *The Australian Computer Journal* 15(1):28–32.

Leaman, A., and I. Borden. 1991. The responsible workplace: User expectations. In *The Responsible Workplace,* 13–29. London: DEGW Limited and Building Research Establishment.

McMillen, P. 1992. Computers, phones converge. *Computing Canada* 18(11):30.

Panko, R. R. 1992. The office workforce: A structural analysis. *Office Systems Research Journal* (spring):3–20.

Phillips, D. L. 1990. The price tag on turnover. *Personnel Journal* (December):58–61.

Raw, G., A. Leaman, and M. C. Roys. 1989. *Further findings from the office environment survey, Part 1: Symptoms.* Report. London: Building Research Establishment.

Roach, S. 1991. Services under siege — The restructuring imperative. *Harvard Business Review* (September–October):82–91.

Roach, S. 1992. *White-collar shock: Services face the 1990s.* New York: Morgan Stanley.

Rosenfeld, S. 1989. Worker productivity: Hidden HVAC cost. *Heating/Piping/Air Conditioning* (September):69–70.

Schlesinger, L. A., and J. L. Heskett. 1991. The service-driven service company. *Harvard Business Review* (December):71–81.

Sink, D. S. 1985. *Productivity management: Planning, measurement and evaluation, control and improvement.* New York: John Wiley & Sons.

Sommer, R. 1968. Hawthorne dogma. *Psychological Bulletin* 70:592–598.

Sommer, R. 1969. *Personal space.* Englewood Cliffs, N.J.: Prentice Hall.

Thurow, L. 1992. *Head to head: The coming economic battle among Japan, Europe, and America.* New York: William Morrow and Company.

Toffler, A. 1990. *Powershift.* New York: Bantam Books.

Van Dyke Parunak, H. 1992. Knowledge infrastructure engineering: A synthesis of PIKIO '92. In *Productivity in knowledge-intensive organizations: Integrating the physical, social, and informational environments.* Ann Arbor, Mich.: Industrial Technology Institute.

Walmsley, A. 1993. The brain game. *Toronto Globe and Mail,* Report on Business — April Edition. Toronto, Ontario.

Wiggenhorn, W. 1990. Motorola U: When training becomes an education. *Harvard Business Review* (July–August):71–83.

Chapter 4

BUILDING SYSTEMS

The principal objective of an office building design is to provide accommodation, at an acceptable cost, where people can work productively. To achieve this objective, office buildings are designed to provide a controlled interior environment protected from the outside. The cost and quality of the occupied space depends on the many choices made in the design, construction, and operation of the building (see the subsection "Why buildings fail" in Chapter 8).

A building acts as a buffer between the indoor and outdoor conditions. It is easier to design a building and less expensive to maintain a comfortable environment inside it, when the outside climate is moderate year-round than when it reaches extremes. A moderate climate is more forgiving of deficiencies in the basic design. But in extreme climates with subzero winter temperatures and summer temperatures of 30°C (86°F) or higher, the building design and choice of materials is a more direct and significant determinant of the building's overall performance. Flaws in the insulation, for example, can make a building considerably more expensive to heat in winter and to cool in summer. Materials poorly suited to the climate will deteriorate more quickly, thereby increasing maintenance expenses and lowering the overall building performance.

To casual observers, the features that most influence their perception of the quality of an office space are the features they can most readily observe — such as the furnishings, color, illumination, window views, odors, and noise level. But the characteristics of an office are largely determined by equipment and services that are hidden from view and of which observers tend to be unaware. This chapter provides an overview of building systems, the components that together make possible functional office spaces.

The diverse factors that affect a building's overall performance can usefully be grouped into four categories: the site, the building envelope and structure, the building services, and the occupied space.

Site refers to the physical surroundings in which a building is located. The outside environment affects the amount of heating and cooling needed. The orientation of the building on the site will determine which areas are exposed to greater heat gains and losses. An organization's image is influenced by the reputation and ambience of its office location. For a bank, locating in the central business district may be essential to project an image of permanence, stability, leadership, and financial strength. For a design firm, locating in a trendy area may be an important statement of its leadership in change and openness to new ideas.

The **building envelope and structure** consist of the walls, floors, roof, windows and other openings, and the supporting structure. The envelope serves to buffer the indoor space from the outdoor climate. The design of the envelope and choice of materials affect the degree of protection that is provided from such environmental factors as moisture, air movement, and heat gain or loss. The trade-offs made in the design of the structure and envelope affect the initial construction costs, ongoing operating expenses, and the performance characteristics of the completed building. Durability is not solely dependent on the nature of a given material, component, or assembly. Rather, it depends on the overall performance of the materials as they behave in the specific functions for which they were chosen and in the particular environments to which they are exposed.

The **building services** provide the interior climate and utilities to meet the occupants' work-related needs. They include systems to supply lighting, heating, ventilation, air-conditioning, electric power, hot and cold water, and communication. Communication services have become so extensive and complex that the management of cables (for voice, data, and video) has become a specialty as well. Secondary services such as safety, emergency response, elevators, parking, food preparation, and eating areas are tailored to the unique characteristics of a building and the needs of the organizations using the space.

More so than with other building systems, building services can be designed to give individuals considerable control over the environment in their own work space. Occupants believe, and numerous surveys corroborate, that for office workers, the ability to control their physical environment is a valued amenity and improves their perceived comfort as well as their performance. With the automated building control systems now available, it is technically possible and economically feasible to provide individuals with control of lighting, temperature, air movement, and acoustics at their own work space.

The **occupied space** of an office building comprises the furniture; nonstructural walls, partitions, and screens (acoustic or visual dividers); floor, ceiling, and window coverings; artwork, plants, and diverse work aids and personal items introduced by the occupants. The arrangement or layout of these elements is as important to the overall success of an office facility as the characteristics and quality of each item. The same components can provide entirely different work settings depending on the design of the layout and how it relates to the building services. For example, in an open plan office, the same furniture can provide many private work spaces or a few larger group work areas, depending on the arrangement of partitions. In addition, ergonomics and aesthetics influence people's comfort and perception of the occupied space.

Occupants perceive the quality of their work space as an integrated whole. It is the characteristics of the site, the building envelope and structure, the building services, the furnishings, and the way they interact that together create the impressions of the interior environment that occupants actually perceive. For example, people judge the lighting in their work area by such factors as whether they experience discomfort (e.g., do their eyes become sore), the degree to which they can adjust the illumination level for the work they're doing, and whether the light fixtures produce glare on their computer screens or generate an annoying hum. In a windowed work area, the view outside and natural light are usually a welcome and valued amenity. However, direct sunlight can make an area overly bright and warm. Adjustable window coverings, such as curtains or blinds, may be needed to control the light level or certain kinds of work must be moved to areas that don't receive direct sun. A lighting system of excellent design and manufacture may deliver inadequate illumination because it is not suited to the visual tasks done in the work space or its operation conflicts with other building systems.

To the occupants as well as to the organization, it is the overall performance of the building systems as they function together that determines the quality of the work setting. The term **total workplace performance** refers to this user-oriented perspective. It is an approach introduced in this chapter and carried through the remainder of the book. Though site, building envelope and structure, building systems, and furnishings are discussed in separate sections for clarity, the success of any office facility depends on the way these components operate together — that is, the total workplace performance.

SITE

The land on which a building is located and the immediate surroundings are termed the **site**. This discussion focuses on site issues relevant to existing buildings. For new construction, site selection and design are part of the building design and delivery process, which must deal with a wider range of issues than are presented here.

The characteristics of the site affect people's first impression of a building and the organizations accommodated there. A building may occupy most of the lot leaving little open area, or it may have extensive landscaped grounds. It may be in a downtown location or in a suburban area. The surrounding buildings may be tall structures or low-rise.

The site of an office facility is critical to many organizations. The selection of a location involves multiple trade-offs, such as cost, image, access, and amenities. When there is a surplus of office space, landlords offer many enticements to attract tenants. Commercial rental agreements may offer free renovation of space, several months of free rent, cash, or other incentives to sign a long-term lease. When office space is in short supply, a tenant's bargaining power is more restricted.

In selecting a site, an organization is committing substantial financial and infrastructure resources. It is also making a decision that affects its image and may influence its future success. Not surprisingly, decisions about location are commonly made at the highest levels in the organization. Although the opinions of a range of experts are sought, the final say resides at the senior executive level.

Site as Image Maker

Location makes a strong statement about the kind of image an organization wishes to portray to the outside world. An outsider's initial perception of an organization is powerfully influenced by the site of its offices. For example, financial institutions in major cities find that they must first have an office in the central business district for prospective clients to give them serious consideration. Prestigious law firms find it important to be located near the courthouse, even though their work could be done just as effectively in a less expensive area.

An unusual site is itself a statement. An architectural design and consulting firm chose a refurbished warehouse within an

Figure 4.1 A seafood restaurant was built to look like a ship's bow, a theme that capitalizes on the site's triangular shape and advertises the house speciality.

urban renewal district for its offices. The firm wanted a location that would express its support for rejuvenating the inner city and preserving historically significant structures as working buildings.

Odd-shaped sites can be used to an organization's advantage. A seafood restaurant distinguished itself in a highly competitive market by locating on a triangular lot (Figure 4.1). The building is designed to look like a ship's bow, a theme that capitalizes on the site's shape and advertises the restaurant's specialty.

Access

The choice of site affects the ease with which people can reach and enter a facility. Access to public transit, major traffic arteries, airports, and the availability of parking affect the time and effort that clients and employees spend on transportation.

In the past, accessibility to clients and suppliers was a principal site selection criterion. A location close to the services that were critical to an organization's business activities was commonly the dominant consideration. However, as more services are delivered electronically, physical proximity to service providers is becoming less important. Now, the effect of location on the cost, quality, and availability of labor is often more important. As lifestyle values have changed, employees are giving greater weight to quality-of-life issues such as commute time. In New York, Los Angeles, and other large metropolitan areas, employees can spend three or four hours a day commuting to and from work — time that might otherwise be spent on productive work, recreation, or family activities. Many people are willing to accept a lower salary in exchange for a shorter commute to work. As a result, some organizations — particularly those with highly skilled knowledge workers who are difficult to find and keep — have selected office locations near their workforce (Figure 4.2).

Site selection may also be used as a means of developing a new workforce. A number of car manufacturers have chosen to locate new plants away from traditional automotive manufacturing centers like Detroit, Munich, or Coventry. Pressures of global competition have encouraged a variety of initiatives to improve product quality and worker productivity. These firms want employees to take charge, do each other's work when necessary, and care more about quality.

Instead of trying to change the work attitudes of an existing trained workforce, some companies have chosen to build factories where the workforce has the attitudes they seek and then give the workers the training to do the job. For example, at the same time General Motors cut 80,000 jobs in North America and closed 21 factories, it opened a manufacturing plant in Tennessee to produce its new Saturn product line. Auto manufacturing was a new industry for that region, and that plant operated at full capacity while the production at others was being scaled back (Economist 1992b).

The amenities of an area can be a factor in attracting clientele as well as high-caliber workers. Employees prefer an office where it is easy to get outside for lunch or a short work break, as well as the convenience of services near work where they can take care of personal business. A location close to financial services, retail stores, and restaurants may also be important to them.

Figure 4.2 This leading-edge research and development organization sited its world headquarters on scenic grounds, close to attractive residential areas where many of its employees live. (*Source:* Bell-Northern Research (BNR).)

Safety

The safety and security of a neighborhood change as it develops over time. Indeed, they may vary over the course of the day. Business districts can be safe during the workday but deserted and dangerous after hours. For organizations where people work extended hours, this can cause serious problems (see the subsection "Security" later in this chapter).

In manufacturing and essential services, night-shift work is commonplace. But among office workers, it is not the norm, and siting decisions may overlook current or future needs for a location that is safe outside normal business hours. For example, when a firm develops global markets, extended hours of operation may be needed to service clients or monitor events (such as money markets, politics, and even weather) on the other side of the world.

In recent years, the history of a site has become a potential safety and security issue as well. A number of important legal decisions in the United States and Canada have assigned responsibility for toxic waste to the owner of the site, regardless of whether the owner had any responsibility for or knowledge of the hazard. There is every indication that these decisions will stand and, if anything, expand the site responsibilities of ownership.

Figure 4.3 At certain sun angles the sloped glass wall of this building reflected sunlight into the eyes of drivers on the adjacent highway. The glass wall was later treated to reduce the troublesome glare.

Natural hazards such as the presence of radon gas emitted from the soil, a high water table, unstable soil, or earthquake risk should have been taken into account in the engineering design of the building. Where such hazards have not been adequately addressed, they may pose a safety risk.

An often-overlooked aspect of safety is that a site must provide a hazard-free environment for *all* users, including those only passing by. For example, the design of an office building located beside a highway made driving conditions more difficult and sometimes hazardous. The building's entrance featured a sloped glass wall extending the full height of the structure (Figure 4.3). At times, the glare of the setting sun reflected off the mirrored glass facade could distract or briefly blind drivers on the expressway. The problem was corrected by modifying the glass wall to reduce the reflections and the design of a second "twin" building, being planned for the adjacent lot, was altered to prevent this problem.

Local Climate

Small differences in the local climate affect the way a building performs. For example, a street running east-west that is lined with tall buildings will be in shade most of the day. A neighboring street with the same orientation and low-rise buildings would receive more direct sunshine at street level and tend to be warmer.

In the same way, site characteristics can affect the conditions to which different portions of a building are exposed. As a result, offices within a building may be identical in layout and furnishings yet their location may give them substantially different qualities. Offices that receive direct sunshine can become too warm and bright for comfortable work, while those on a side of the building that is exposed to high winds may be drafty and cool.

A building is not only affected by its local climate; it also influences that climate. Massive buildings, such as large concrete structures, can have a moderating effect on temperature in their immediate vicinity because they gain heat slowly

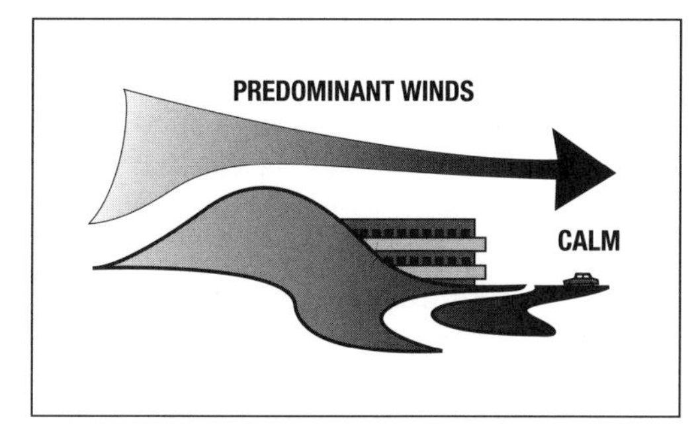

Figure 4.4 The natural topography can provide shelter from prevailing winds.

from direct sunlight and warmer daytime temperatures, and then lose their heat slowly as they cool in the evening.

The size, shape, and proximity of surrounding natural features and buildings can mitigate the effects of wind on a building. For example, locations on the downwind or leeward side of a hill can offer protection from cold winter winds (Figure 4.4). Natural or man-made features can also accentuate wind force. For example, a street lined with tall buildings can create a **wind tunnel** condition, which occurs when a steady wind blowing in the same direction as the street is forced through constricted areas (Figure 4.5). The funneling effect causes the wind speed to increase either in gusts or in steady, strong currents. The resulting powerful turbulence on the surface of a building can force air through exterior walls, pushing air into the building or drawing it out. Exterior doors can be difficult to open against the wind, or may be caught in the airflow and difficult to close.

The shape, size, and orientation of the building itself modify wind effects. For example, a sloped roof provides a larger sheltered region downwind from a building than a flat roof (Figure 4.6). Wind is forced around the sides, over the roof, and through passageways such as ground-level driveways. Wind speeds are higher at the corners of a building because the volume of air striking the surface must squeeze around the edge of the structure. As the wind moves over and around a building, it is forced into the area of reduced wind speed on the lee side, creating complex vortex patterns (Figure 4.7).

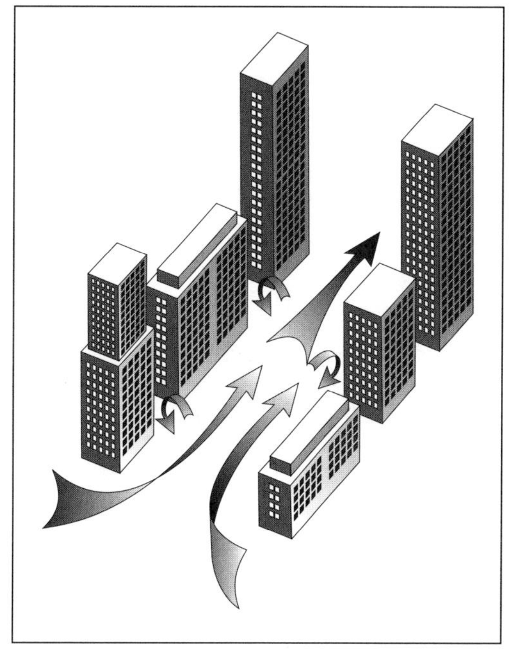

Figure 4.5 When air is forced through a confined space its velocity increases. Streets lined by tall buildings can create the confining conditions to produce an urban wind tunnel effect whereby the wind speed at ground level becomes much higher than that of the prevailing wind.

The difference in wind pressure on different sides of a building tends to force air through the exterior wall. The increased air pressure on the windward side pushes air through the exterior wall into the building, and the reduced air pressure on the leeward side produces a suction effect

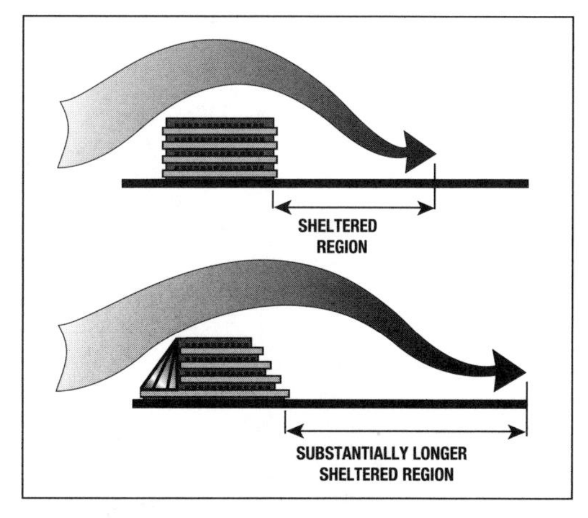

Figure 4.6 Influence of roof design on the wind pattern around a building. The addition of a sloped facade on the windward side increases the sheltered area of reduced wind velocity on the lee side of the building.

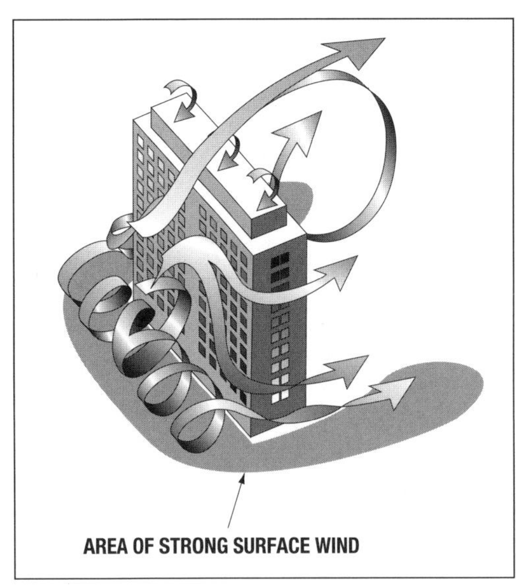

Figure 4.7 Wind blowing against a tall building creates areas of increased wind velocity, speed vortices, and air turbulence.

that draws inside air through the exterior wall to the outside. This air movement through the walls of a building can make the interior drafty and will increase energy consumption as the building systems work longer to maintain the indoor temperature and relative humidity. The uncontrolled flow of outside air into the building may also carry unwanted dust, airborne particles, or chemical contaminants inside.

In climates where there is significant snowfall, the site as well as the shape and orientation of a building affect where and how much snow will accumulate around it. Snow accumulation tends to be heaviest wherever the wind speed is reduced, such as on the lee side of a building (Figure 4.8). By contrast, snow will tend to be blown away from some places. These areas of reduced snow accumulation should be used to advantage for emergency exits, doorways, exterior signs, air intakes, exhausts, or other services that need to remain clear.

The building exterior is exposed to the adverse effects of the local climate. A serious threat to its performance and durability is man-made pollution that causes **acid rain**. The combustion gases released in burning coal and oil as well as those emitted by motor vehicles react with water, sunlight, and other chemical constituents to form corrosive acids which then are deposited in the form of acidic precipitation — rain, snow, fog, or dry particles. These acidic deposits can discolor and dissolve stone (particularly sandstone, lime-

Figure 4.8 The shape and orientation of a building affect the quantity and location of snow deposition. Wind-deposited snow piled against this emergency exit could render it unopenable or impede escape in the event of an emergency.

stone, and marble). Even stainless steel and glass can be etched by the corrosive acids.

Damage from acid rain can be accelerated in older buildings where there are more cracks and fissures in and between materials. Precipitation can seep or be driven by the wind into the building's inner layers, where the acid can eventually penetrate to the steel reinforcement bars embedded in concrete. Rust develops, weakening the structure and causing extensive deterioration.

The orientation of a building can mitigate the damaging effects of rain, wind, sun, and snow on building materials. Furthermore, a number of measures can be taken to significantly slow climate-related building deterioration. Protective coatings can be applied to exposed components as a barrier to corrosive materials such as acid rain or exhaust gases. An effective flashing system should be designed into the exterior wall to direct water runoff away from interior layers and protect less resistant components on the building exterior.

Figure 4.9 It is becoming more common for satellite and microwave communications equipment to be installed on office roofs. Ensuring that new buildings do not block or interfere with the existing communications servicing on surrounding structures has made siting decisions increasingly complex.

Site Characteristics Over Time

A site's effect on an organization's image changes over time. Recognizing a site's trends is as important as assessing its current status. The recent history of an area, zoning regulations, and current development plans are important sources of information for evaluating the future prospects of a locale. The central cores of many North American cities, once the heart of the business district, have been abandoned as they became crime-ridden and run-down. On the other hand, many blighted areas have been renovated and have become trendy high-rent districts.

The characteristics of a site can significantly restrict future uses. For example, tall buildings cast long shadows, which reduce the amount of daylight available to adjacent lots. New construction can compromise the amenities of a site by obstructing a pleasant view, reducing the hours of direct sunshine, or blocking satellite or microwave transmissions (Figure 4.9). Property owners have successfully sued for damages when new buildings significantly increased the shade on adjacent properties. If there is a quantifiable loss, such as higher heating costs because a new structure shades existing solar panels, there is the potential for legal liability.

The addition or removal of buildings or stands of trees alters the local climate and can compromise the indoor environment. For example, at the time it was built, the 6-story downtown office building shown in the left photo of Figure 4.10 was surrounded by smaller buildings. Over time

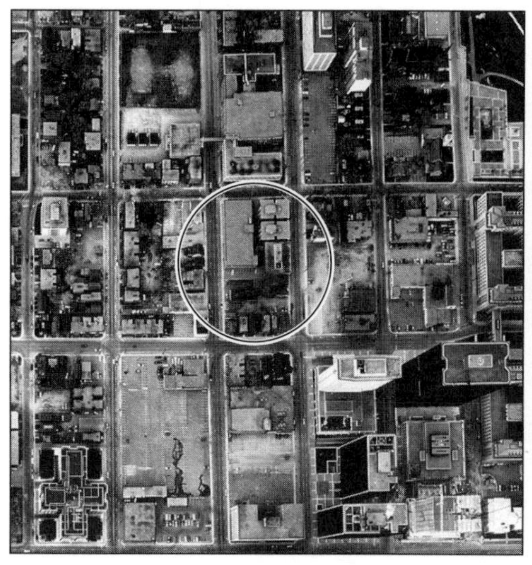

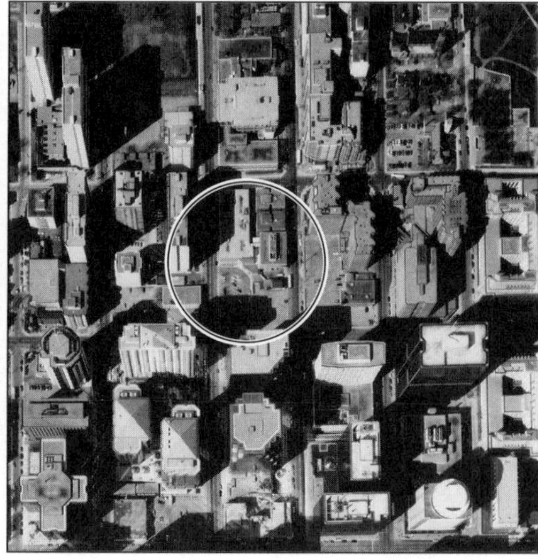

Figure 4.10 These two aerial photographs show the same urban area in 1971 (left) and 1993 (right). Over a 20-year period, the 6-story office building (circled) was gradually dwarfed by new construction. The new structures changed the pattern of air movement around this building in unexpected ways. The prevailing winds produced a pattern of air flow that caused motor vehicle exhaust from the loading dock to be drawn into the building's air intake polluting the indoor air. (*Source:* Reproduced from the collection of the National Air Photo Library with the permission of Energy, Mines, and Resources Canada. Ottawa. Detail from photos A22225-60 ©1971 and A27909-44 ©1993.)

it became dwarfed by 12- to 20-story office towers (right photo). The tall structures changed the wind pattern around the building such that motor exhaust from vehicles in the adjacent alleyway was drawn into the air intake (even though it was located on the roof). Because the problem did not begin suddenly but evolved gradually over time, its cause was difficult to determine. When it was finally diagnosed, repositioning the air intake was too costly a solution. Instead, the situation was addressed by changing the management of the loading dock. Vehicles were no longer permitted to idle while stopped in the alleyway.

Ongoing Maintenance and Monitoring

For most office buildings, a site assessment is conducted annually as part of a maintenance inspection. Such inspections generally focus on identifying needed repairs or replacements. They do not assess the overall impact of the site on the organization. An independent assessment of the site should be conducted periodically to evaluate its suitability to the organization's current and future plans as well as to monitor the impact of developments planned for the surrounding area.

The original decision to choose one site over another is usually a judgment call influenced by so many objective and subjective factors that the criteria upon which the decision was actually based are rarely recorded. Even when detailed documents on site requirements are prepared, the optimum choice may be overridden by unreported factors, such as the personal preference of the company's president. It is therefore difficult to assess when the features of a site have changed to the point that the original benefits are no longer realized. What's more, once a site is chosen, it is generally considered to be a closed decision that cannot be changed. As a result, site issues tend not to be monitored because it is assumed that the site cannot be changed. Yet today, especially with the greater flexibility provided by communications technology, there can be greater latitude in site decisions. For example, when additional office space is needed significant savings can be realized by choosing a less expensive area than the current locale. The judicious use of communication links can provide the level of integration needed for a distant site to function as efficiently as if it were physically adjacent.

Areas of a city that are deteriorating do so progressively, becoming a little more run-down each year. The change is difficult to see on a daily basis. It often takes a shocking event — such as major vandalism, or a robbery, mugging, or murder — for people to become aware of the considerable changes that have occurred. By monitoring the site from the broad perspective of image, access, safety, and cost, an organization can better identify when the site's characteristics no longer suit its needs.

THE BUILDING ENVELOPE AND STRUCTURE

The load-bearing components of a building — such as columns, supporting walls, and floors — comprise its **structure**. The **building envelope** consists of the exterior walls, windows, and roof. Together they enclose and define the interior spaces and act as a buffer and barrier between the outside and interior environments.

The performance of the building envelope and structure has a more significant effect on the usability of the interior space than is commonly recognized. The structural design affects the spacing of columns and placement of load-bearing walls. This, in turn, affects the dimensions of the office areas that can be created and the efficiency with which they can be arranged.

A building envelope that is well insulated and allows little air movement across it will provide more comfortable interior spaces with less energy consumption. The areas next to outside walls will not be drafty or susceptible to uncomfortable shifts in temperature. To some extent, the deficiencies of a building envelope that performs poorly can be minimized by changing the way interior space is used. For example, areas that are drafty can be used for circulation or file storage instead of prime work space for people. However, altering space use to avoid placing work settings in problem areas imposes an additional constraint on the layout of office space. Such a loss of flexibility lowers the value of the space to the occupants and their organization.

More serious deficiencies in the envelope can require expensive renovations that may interfere significantly with office activities. Even if the work is financed by the landlord, the disruption it causes can be costly. In addition to the lost work time, exposing office occupants to construction debris and irritants (such as noise, dust, and fumes) is stressful, unpleasant, and can cause illness symptoms in some people. Repairs to building exteriors can take weeks or months to complete and produce so much noise, vibration, and irritants that tenants are forced to relocate.

The Building Envelope

The exterior walls and roof are multilayered components comprised of an exterior cladding, insulation, air/vapor barrier, and interior finish integrated with the structural support (see the subsection "The Structure" later in this chapter). Working as an envelope system, these components control the movement of air, moisture, heat, light, and sound across the exterior wall. Control of these elements is important not only to provide the desired interior conditions but also to minimize the deterioration of the building materials and maintain the integrity of the structure. As well, the performance of the building envelope affects the facility's operating costs for heating, cooling, and humidity control — costs that continue throughout the service life of the building. It is one component for which short-term savings can be very costly in the longer term.

The exterior cladding prevents precipitation (such as rain and snow) from entering the wall cavity, where it can moisten the materials and cause them to deteriorate. Insulation in the wall retards **heat transfer** — the loss or gain of heat between the building's interior and the outside. The greater the insulating capacity, the less energy will be needed to control the indoor temperature and humidity.

The principal source of moisture that occurs within exterior walls is the seepage of interior air into the wall cavity. Some moisture also diffuses from the exterior through the wall material. The layer that restricts the movement of air within and through the wall is called an air/vapor barrier. A separate layer of plastic sheeting may be used, or the barrier may be incorporated into the insulation. Some types of insulation, such as rigid or extruded foam boards, are impervious to water and air. They can act as an air/vapor barrier as well as function as insulation if properly installed to minimize air and water leakage through gaps where the sheets of insulation join. Excessive air movement can result in significant moisture accumulation within the wall cavity, wetting the surfaces of materials and causing them to perform poorly (by lowering their insulation value) and deteriorate more quickly (thus increasing maintenance costs). Excessive air movement will also increase heat transfer.

Windows are a design element that can enhance the interior and exterior appearance of a building. On exterior walls, windows provide a view to the outdoors. Most occupants prefer to be near a window. A window is not only an aesthetic amenity; it provides relief from the monotony and potentially claustrophobic feel of small rooms and windowless spaces. A view outside can make an office feel more spacious and less isolated. Occupants can be aware of the outside world — for example, as time passes the weather, the quality of the daylight, and other features change. In addition to daylight, windows are also points of entry for sound (glass is generally a better transmitter of sound than the other materials in the exterior wall) and for outside air (if the windows open). In low-rise buildings, windows may also serve as emergency fire escapes.

WALLS

The walls and roof of a building envelope perform similar roles in acting as a barrier to heat transfer and moisture penetration. Walls are more or less vertical, and roofs on commercial buildings are often nearly horizontal. However, certain structures blur these distinctions. Examples are Quonset huts and A-frame buildings, popular for church architecture and alpine or arctic structures, where the walls rise at an angle to meet overhead and form the roof. In effect, the walls and roof are the same structural element.

The wall of an office building can be 150–254 millimeters (6–10 inches) thick (Figure 4.11). The exterior cladding is the outermost surface. Since it is directly exposed to the weather, durable, moisture-resistant materials are used, such as brick, concrete, metal siding, glass, or plastics. Brick or concrete will be about 100 millimeters (4 inches) thick whereas the other materials will be less than 25 millimeters (1 inch). Behind this layer, there is often a narrow space of trapped air (19-100 millimeters, ¾ - 4 inches) that serves both to equalize the pressure across the exterior cladding and to retard heat transfer.

Exterior cladding. An important function of the exterior cladding is to shed water. Moisture accumulation and water hasten the deterioration of many building components and reduce building performance. For example, moisture can cause insulation to break apart, thus reducing its insulating properties. There may be more serious consequences when other components are regularly wetted. Metal supports attaching the exterior cladding to the building will deteriorate and weaken more quickly if they are frequently exposed to moisture. Although a rare

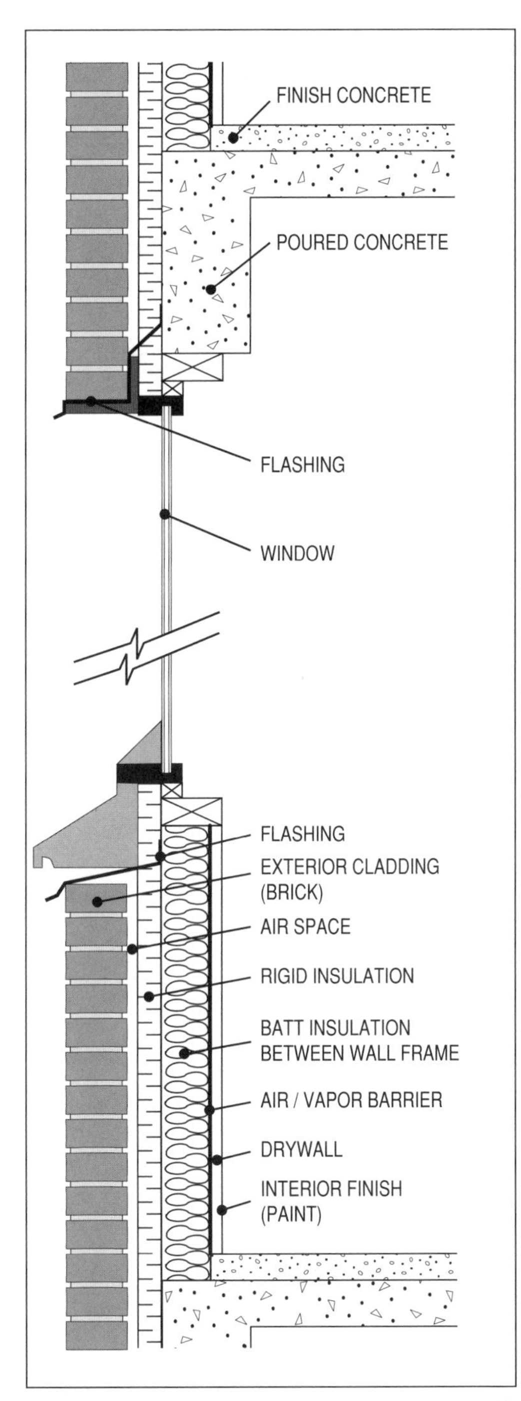

Figure 4.11 Principal components of an exterior wall, typical of office buildings.

event, there have been cases in which support anchors have rusted so severely that they could no longer hold the weight of the exterior cladding. Panels have detached from buildings, falling to the street below, and causing damage and injury.

Insulation. Moving toward the interior, the next layer in a wall section is the insulation. This layer provides most of the thermal resistance across the wall. Depending on the maximum expected temperature difference across the wall (i.e., outside versus inside temperature) and the type of insulation material used, this layer ranges in thickness from 25 millimeters to 130 millimeters (1 inch to 5 inches).

Batt insulation is a soft porous material that is easily cut to size and fitted into wall cavities or stuffed into odd-shaped openings. Rigid insulation, as the name implies, is stiff and must be cut more precisely to size. It provides about twice the insulation value as batts (i.e., a batt must be about twice as thick to provide the same degree of insulation). Rigid insulation can thus provide greater insulating capacity in less space, permitting a thinner wall. However, it is also a more expensive material and is more difficult to install on curved surfaces or small, odd-shaped areas.

To install rigid insulation on the curved exterior wall shown in Figure 4.12, slots had to be cut into the boards so they could be bent into position. The cuts and the difficulty of fitting the sheets onto the wall significantly reduced the insulation's effectiveness. A building's design as well as its construction affect how well materials can be fitted together, and will affect the performance of a given insulation material.

The **R-value** is a unitless measure that represents the insulating ability of a material relative to a standard. It can be thought of as the amount of time it takes a unit of heat to penetrate a standard thickness of a material for each degree of temperature difference between the two sides. The higher the R-value, the longer it takes for heat to travel from the warm side of the material to the cool side, so the greater its insulating value. In the past, most U.S. and Canadian structures were designed for walls and roofs to have R-values of 12 and 20, respectively. Today, to save ener-

Figure 4.12 To achieve acceptable building performance, architecturally interesting or novel features, such as this curved wall, often require superior design detailing and close supervision during construction.

gy much higher values are specified — typically, 40 for walls and 60 for roofs.

The R-value represents the theoretical maximum insulating value a material can provide. But when installed, insulation rarely provides this level of performance. Wherever materials such as insulation (as well as the air/vapor barrier) must be cut to wrap around joints and obstructions, the fit will not be perfect and some performance losses will result. Better workmanship will thus boost insulation performance, as will improvements in the design of construction details.

The way R-values are reported is quite misleading. The insulation performance of a building envelope is usually represented by only two numbers — one for the walls and one for the roof. The quote for the walls is a theoretical value for the best-insulated sections (those areas without windows, frames, or other features that may be poor insulators).

Curtain wall construction, a popular choice for office buildings, typically comprises insulated opaque panels, window units that vary widely in their insulating properties, and metal frames (Figure 4.13). Unless the frames are designed with an adequate **thermal break** (i.e., materials and assembly that retard heat transfer across the frame), they will act as a thermal conductor (i.e., have an effective R-value of zero). For a curtain wall, the windows and frames make up a significant proportion of the total surface area of the envelope. As a result, the effective R-value will be much lower than the rating for the wall would indicate.

Air/vapor barrier. An air/vapor barrier is placed on the warm side of the insulation. This barrier is a sheet of plastic about 6 millimeters (.24 inches) thick that serves to block interior air and moisture from moving across the envelope wall to the exterior. Wind blowing against a building creates a pressure difference across the walls, forcing air through the envelope. Excessive air infiltration causes drafts that make areas next to exterior walls uncomfortable. As well, operating costs are increased as more energy is needed for temperature and humidity control. The better the performance of the air/vapor

Figure 4.13 The sleek exterior of a glass curtain wall has become a standard form in office building architecture. More recent designs, like that of the foreground office tower, employ unusual elements to distinguish them from more conventional buildings, like that in the background.

barrier, the less air leakage will occur and the less energy will be needed to maintain the indoor climate.

Air moving from the interior to the outside can also be troublesome, particularly when the outside temperature is low. If warm, moist interior air contacts cold surfaces in the wall, condensation may occur, and materials within the wall will be wetted by the condensing moisture. Water is one of the principal agents that cause building materials to deteriorate, lowering their performance.

If water accumulates inside a wall, certain materials will rot, and some insulation materials will deteriorate. Where freezing occurs, the expansion of the water as it forms ice will physically break components apart. As the ice melts, water can leak into the interior, damaging surface finishes, furnishings, and office contents. Although damage to the interior space is the most visible consequence of a moisture problem, the unseen damage within the wall can be more serious and more costly to repair.

Interior finish. The innermost layer of the building envelope is the interior finish. Wall finishes are often panels (wood, vinyl-covered) or sheets of drywall that are painted or wallpapered. Interior finishes differ widely in their cost, durability, and ease of repair. Unlike the other components of the wall, the interior finish is frequently changed to suit the tenant and is refurbished every few years. It is the interior wall finish that most attracts the attention of prospective occupants, yet it is the least important factor in the overall performance of the building envelope.

ROOFS

The principles of good wall design apply to roofs as well. Commercial buildings commonly have flat roofs that are nearly horizontal — a design that captures more interior space than a pitched roof, but one that has more stringent demands. A flat roof must tolerate greater exposure to environmental forces, such as strong sunlight and high winds. They must also support greater loads from standing water and accummulations of snow. As well, mechanical services, large ventilation fans, and ever more communication devices (e.g., satellite dishes, microwave antennas) are installed on roofs. The weight of these loads and their related traffic is factored into the structural design of roof systems to the extent that they can be anticipated. However, over time, a building may be used in a manner far different from that originally intended and for purposes it is not well-designed to accommodate.

The many items of mechanical and electronic equipment placed on roofs and the activities necessary to maintain them are a common source of roof failures. Few people appreciate that roofing systems are fragile. Roof materials are vulnerable to compression from being walked over and punctures where equipment is anchored. In one electronics laboratory, the scientists often installed experimental devices on the roof for testing. Since these were only short-term installations, the facilities group was not advised and the punctures were not sealed. By the time the roof was examined during a routine building inspection, substantial deterioration of materials within the roof structure had already occurred.

As with walls, the roof is constructed of multiple layers (Figure 4.14). The outermost layer of a flat roof is a hard-wearing material such as gravel or concrete tiles. In addition to their weather-resistant properties, these materials are heavy enough to resist the lifting effect that can occur when high winds blow across a roof. They also serve to shade the materials underneath from the sun's damaging rays (particularly the ultraviolet wavelengths).

The next layer in the roof is a waterproof membrane. Felt paper embedded with tar or pitch is most commonly used. It is applied in overlapping layers and sealed with heated bitumen (a tar compound that becomes liquid when hot). The layer below the waterproof membrane is the insulation, with an air/vapor barrier

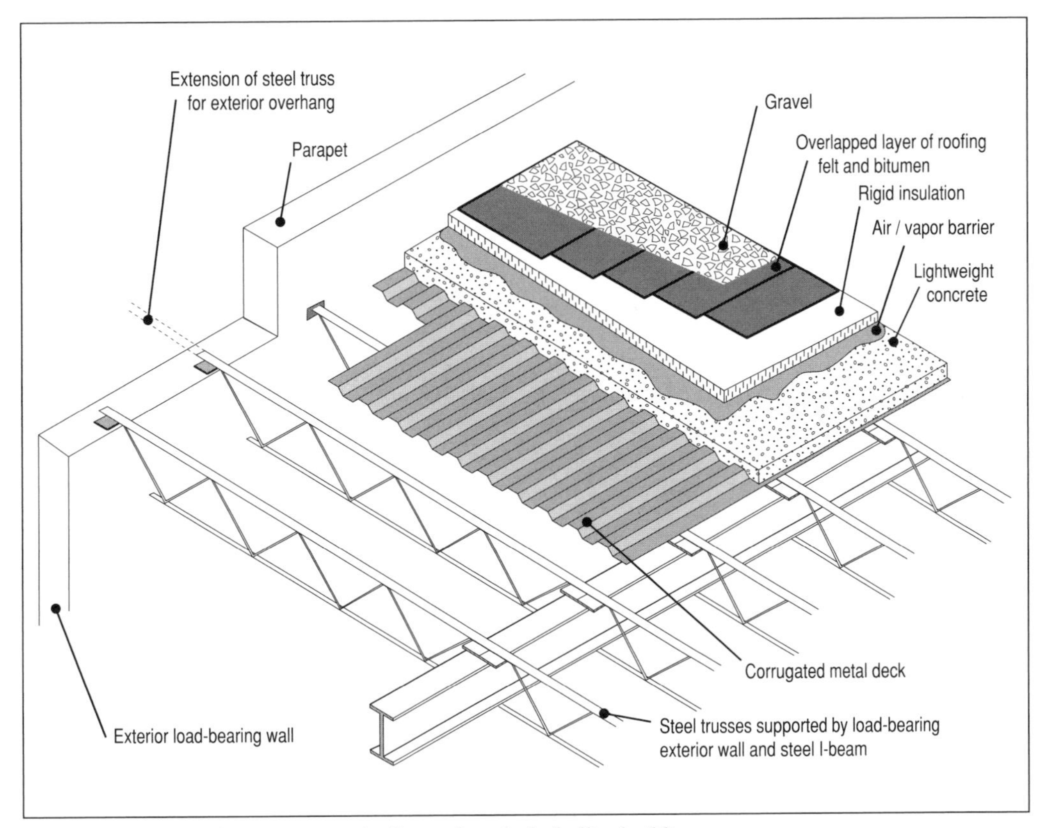

Figure 4.14 Principal components of a flat roof, typical of office buildings.

beneath it (i.e., on the side of the insulation toward the building interior). An alternative roof design, the **protected roof membrane system,** positions the waterproof membrane under the insulation where it is in a thermally-stable environment and is sheltered from environmental forces. In this assembly the waterproof membrane also serves as the air/vapor barrier. This design is often referred to as an **inverted** or **upside-down roof system.**

The final layer is the roof deck, made of a rigid material such as corrugated metal with a layer of lightweight concrete. This multilayered roof structure is supported by the trusses, beams, or walls that are part of the building's structure. If the space beneath the roof deck is occupied, then a ceiling is usually added to cover the underside of the structure. The uppermost level of tall buildings often houses the mechanical systems and is not occupied. In these cases, the roof structure may be left exposed.

As with walls, the continuity of materials is important to the optimum performance of a roof assembly. More so than with walls, roofs have many services that must run through them. Washrooms must be vented to the roof through pipes, termed **soil stacks**. Roof drains that direct water off the roof and pipes or ducts that connect external components of the mechanical system to the interior of the building are other examples. Each puncture of the roof system is a potential source of leakage. For this reason, routine preventive maintenance of roofs is important to avoid water leakage to the interior.

Roof assemblies experience wide temperature swings from day to night and through the seasons. Even in temperate climates, the heat buildup from the sun's rays can raise roof temperatures to the point at which the bitumen in the roof membrane liquefies. Then, at night, it may cool to the ambient air temperature. Over time, such temperature swings make the roof materials brittle and more prone to leakage, and promote other types of deterioration that reduce the roof's performance. The conditions under which a roof is built, the local climate, and the materials of which it is constructed all affect its durability. Even so, flat roofs generally last about 20 years.

WINDOWS, DOORS, AND OTHER OPENINGS

Most openings in building enclosures — such as windows, doors, and skylights — are preassembled units fitted into the walls or roof during construction. Windows in commercial buildings are rarely designed to serve as the prime source of outdoor air, and so the glass is usually fixed in its frame and cannot be opened. The performance of these sealed windows is determined by the quality of materials and factory workmanship.

Because openings in the building envelope are always locations where different materials meet, these openings are where performance failures are likely to occur. A window opening is the junction of the exterior cladding, insulation, air/vapor barrier, interior finish, and window frame. The design and workmanship of the construction details at these junctions are very important in preventing air leakage. Maintaining the continuity of materials and preventing gaps and holes from being made during installation are key to the successful performance of the overall building envelope.

There can generally be tighter quality control of window, door, and skylight units assembled in a factory than for building components assembled at the construction site. For a big office building, the large quantity of units enables custom designs to be produced economically.

Windows differ in the number of glass panes, the gas injected into the space between the panes, and the tinting or films applied to the glass surface. Generally, the more panes of glass the greater the thermal resistance of the window. Today, office buildings are usually constructed using double or triple rather than single pane windows. The space between panes must be sealed to prevent air leakage. The space can be empty (a partial vacuum) or filled with a gas that gives the window specific properties such as a higher R-value (better thermal resistance), a reduction in the transmission of sunlight, or blocking of ultraviolet rays. To conserve energy, surface coatings can be used to reduce light transmission and heat loss or gain. Window coverings such as blinds and drapery as well as coatings on the glass can be used to control the amount and quality of daylight in a space. External shading devices may be attached to or integrated with the exterior wall. In Figure 4.15, the concrete awnings are designed as an integral part of the building's exterior.

The location of openings on the building envelope affects how well even the best of components can perform. From the outside, doors, windows, and other openings on different sides of a building look quite similar. Their size, style, and tinting are designed to be aesthetically pleasing and visually consistent, yet each wall is exposed to different conditions. Doors located on the windward side of a building will be hard to open against a strong wind, and air leakage will be difficult to control. Doorways and canopies on the lee side will tend to collect snow, leaves, or trash blown by the wind.

In the Northern Hemisphere, southern exposures can receive direct sunlight throughout the day, whereas a north-facing wall receives only diffuse light. East and west exposures will have intermediate conditions. The shadows cast by surrounding structures will also affect the hours of direct sunlight received. As a result of this variability, the performance of a particular type of window or door may be adequate on one wall yet deficient on another.

The placement of openings may also be governed by municipal statutes. A developer may wish to provide direct vehicular access from the main street to the building entrance. However, city authorities may

Figure 4.15 In hot climates, external window shading can substantially reduce a building's solar heat gain. The sloped concrete window awnings of this office building in Nairobi, Kenya, are a feature of the exterior panel design. The windows are also angled downward toward the street, further reducing the amount of direct sun reaching the interior.

Figure 4.16 Warm, moist indoor air escaping through inadequately sealed openings around this air grille and light fixture has condensed on the cold exterior surfaces, wetting the wall (the dark areas). This wetting will accelerate the deterioration of the wall materials.

decide that street traffic would become too congested and specify in the building permit that road access be from a side street.

PERFORMANCE OF THE BUILDING ENVELOPE

The performance of the building envelope depends on the design as well as the quality of the workmanship. No matter how thick the insulation or how weather-resistant the exterior cladding, if joints do not fit properly, much of the intended benefits of the design can be lost. For optimum performance, it is important that each layer of the building envelope be continuous. Insulation should be fit snugly, leaving no gaps, especially around odd shapes such as round pipes and electrical conduits. There should be no holes in the air/vapor barrier through which air and moisture can pass, and the exterior cladding should form a continuous layer of protection for the structure.

Maintaining a continuous barrier to protect against air leakage is more difficult where different materials meet and where sections of the same material are joined — for example, where walls meet floors or roofs and at openings for windows and doors. Building services such as plumbing and cabling often must pierce the envelope. Unfortunately, those who install these services are less concerned with the integrity of the envelope than with the correct and convenient installation of the service. As a result, the holes made in the envelope's layers of material commonly are not adequately sealed afterward, creating points of weakness (Figure 4.16). These deficiencies in the building envelope are often associated with the installation of electrical conduit and outlets and the pipes and radiators of perimeter heating systems.

The Structure

Most office buildings have a structure of vertical columns that support horizontal slabs and tie in with the building envelope. Depending on the region where the building is located, there may be special structural requirements to address local conditions such as earthquakes, high winds, or height restrictions. Relatively few office building designs employ unique and innovative structural systems. Those that are, tend to be commissioned works tailored to the needs of a specific organization and designed to look novel and exclusive.

Concrete and steel are the preferred structural materials for commercial buildings. They offer strength, fire resistance,

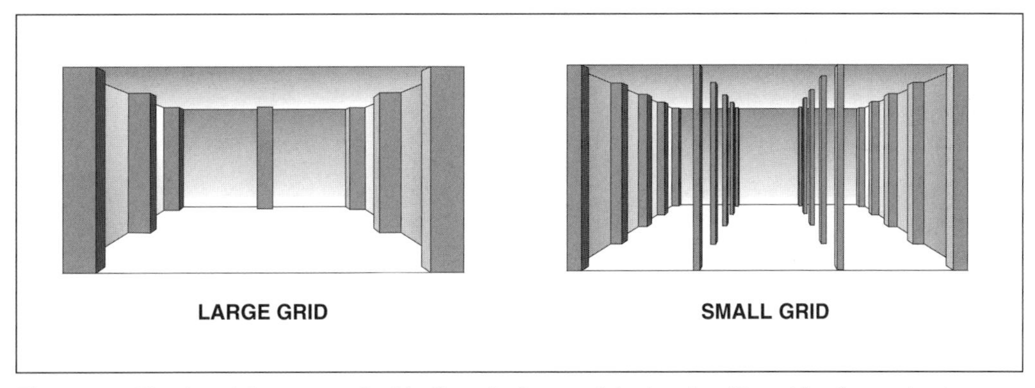

Figure 4.17 The size of the structural grid affects the layout of the interior. The wider the spacing between columns, the greater the load each must carry, and usually the larger each column will be.

and design flexibility at reasonable cost. Most structures use both materials to provide the optimum compressive (load-bearing) and tensile (tension) strength. Plywood made with adhesives resistant to heat and moisture is used extensively for walls and floors as well as in the construction process. Wood frame construction is limited to smaller buildings (one to four stories) and must satisfy strict codes for fire containment.

The proportion of concrete to steel will vary with the number of floors in the building, the weight to be supported (for both the structure itself and the occupant load), and the spacing required between columns. If there is an underground parking garage, then the column spacing may be adjusted to efficiently accommodate the greatest number of cars.

At the design stage, key decisions are made about a building's structure that limit subsequent design options available for the building envelope and services. The choice of structural system affects the number of vertical supports and their spacing, which, in turn, is a constraint on the layout of the interior spaces. The load-bearing walls and columns in a building are designed on a specified pattern, termed the **structural grid**. Although interior partitions can be located anywhere, they normally follow the grid so that structural columns are incorporated into walls as much as possible. In this way, the number of columns within the open spaces is minimized. The larger the grid, the fewer the columns (although they may be bigger) and the greater the span between them (Figure 4.17). A larger grid offers more flexibility in the layout of walls to form offices as well as in the layout of furniture, equipment, and other office furnishings.

The greater the distance between columns, the greater the load that each column must support. The columns in office buildings typically range in size from .18 meter to .37 meter (2 to 4 feet) in diameter. Services such as plumbing and cabling that must run vertically through a building are commonly installed along the structural columns. The additional bulk and boxing in of the pipes and conduits for these services further increase the columns' size.

Large structural grids are generally more expensive to construct. However, this premium can allow greater flexibility in the interior design (Figure 4.18). However, columns can become so large that they become significant obstacles to the design of efficient layouts in the occupied spaces.

If smaller columns are used, such as .3 meter (1 foot) in diameter, more columns will be needed to support the same load, and they will be spaced closer together, perhaps 3 or 6 meters (10 or 20 feet) apart. But smaller columns may be easier to incorporate into interior walls and allow for a more efficient and more aesthetically pleasing layout.

Modern office buildings often have sleek exterior walls consisting of a continuous

Figure 4.18 These columns are spaced 9 meters (30 feet) apart. The large structural grid creates unobstructed, open areas that gives great flexibility for the interior design. (*Source:* Bell-Northern Research (BNR).)

glass surface or precast concrete panels. To achieve this exterior design, the main structural supports are placed on the inside of the building envelope. There are a number of advantages to this design. The structure is in a stable environment protected from the elements, which virtually eliminates deterioration caused by exposure to weather and also reduces stress on the structure caused by expansion and contraction of materials with changes in temperature. A disadvantage for tenants, however, is that there are more columns within their space. Although the area occupied by the columns is not usable, it is considered part of the rented area. Since load-bearing columns can be quite large, the area they occupy can represent a significant rental cost. In addition, the small, odd-shaped areas between the perimeter columns and the exterior wall may be virtually unusable (Figure 4.19).

Structural frames that are incorporated within the building envelope or on the exterior do not occupy the space rented by tenants. However, a drawback to these designs is that the structure is exposed to the elements. It expands and contracts with changes in the outside temperature, accelerating the deterioration of the building envelope and making it more susceptible to leakage through cracks and joints.

Municipal planning regulations specify the maximum usable floor area of a building relative to the lot size (termed the **floor area ratio**). There are also regulations governing a structure's maximum height, but there is usually considerable latitude in the number of floors permitted.

Selecting the floor-to-floor height is both a financial and a structural design decision that affects the building plan and imposes limits on the design of building services. With a smaller floor-to-floor height, a building can have more floors

Figure 4.19 Supporting columns placed on the inside of the building envelope can occupy a sizable amount of rented floor area. In addition, the columns often divide an office into small sections that are difficult to arrange (top photo) or create odd-shaped spaces between the columns and perimeter walls that are effectively unusable (bottom photo).

and therefore more rentable space. However, lower floor-to-floor heights also mean less vertical space in which both servicing and occupants must be accommodated.

The minimum floor-to-ceiling height is 2.5 meters (8 feet). But such a low ceiling does not provide enough space for overhead servicing such as ventilation ducts. A floor-to-floor height of between 3.0 meters and 3.6 meters, (10 feet and 12 feet) is needed to allow enough room above a suspended ceiling (usually, .5–1 meter, 1.5–3 feet) to house mechanical and lighting services.

Computer and communications cabling, electrical services, and ventilation ducts can be run beneath a **raised floor,** which consists of a frame into which removable tiles are fitted to form a raised floor surface (Figure 4.20). Generally, a raised floor is .1–1 meter (.3–3 feet) in height depending on the space required. First used in computer rooms, raised floors are becoming more common for general office areas as well. They offer ease and flexibility in distributing services throughout a work area. Cables, ventilation ducts, or other services can be poked through a floor tile at any location in the room. When the office layout must be changed, the floor tiles with openings are easily rearranged as needed. As well, since the underfloor services are easily accessed by lifting any floor tile, maintenance, repairs, and new installations can be completed more quickly than if the services were less accessible.

However, with these advantages come additional costs. Raised floors have a higher initial cost than other flooring options, and they require expensive fire detection and suppressant systems. They also require a greater floor-to-floor height. Despite these drawbacks, the flexibility they offer for servicing a floor area has made them attractive for general-purpose office space — especially where information and communications technology is used extensively.

Thus, selecting the floor-to-floor height limits the space available for suspended ceilings and raised floors, which, in turn, limits the usability of the space to the occupant and consequently the rent a tenant would be willing to pay.

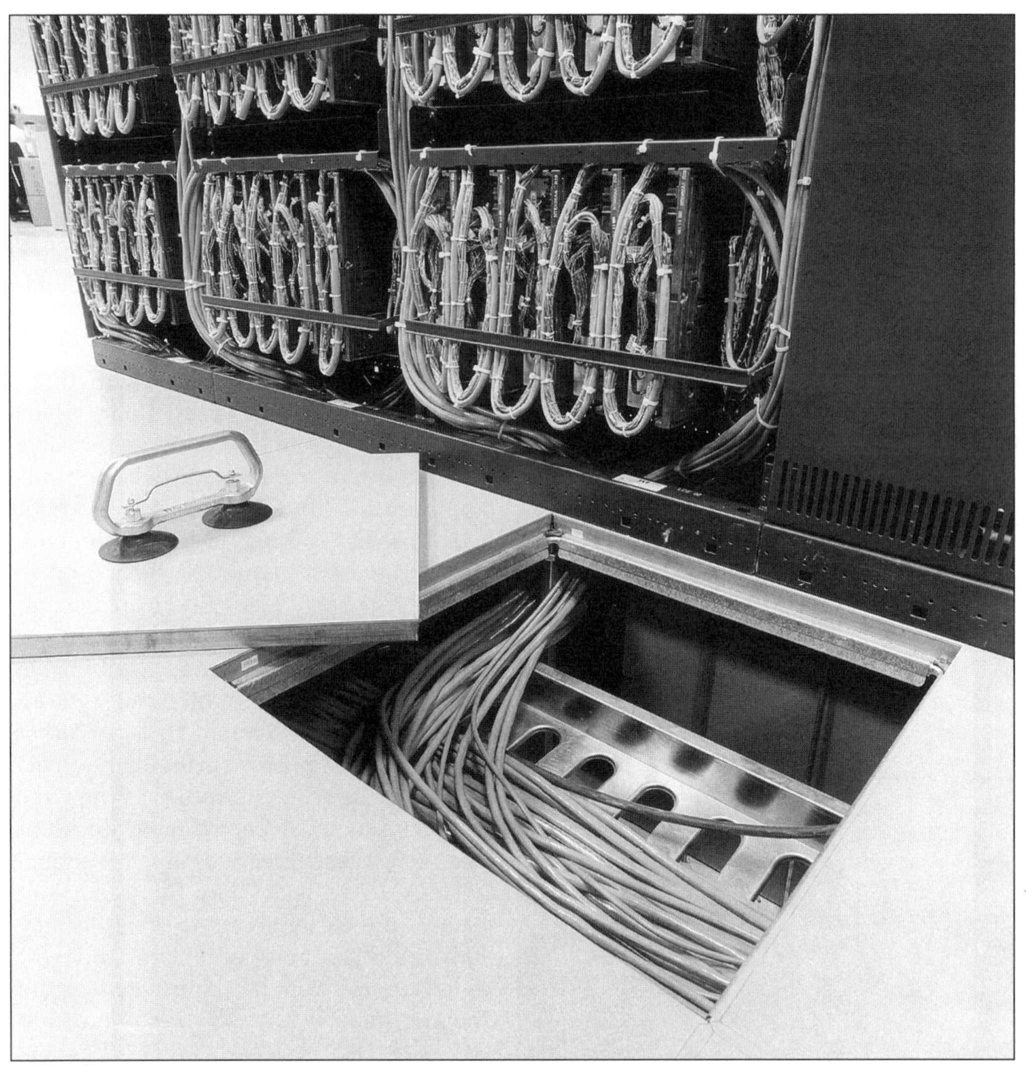

Figure 4.20 A floor tile has been removed to show cables running from a computer into the service area beneath the raised floor system and onto a cable tray. (*Source:* Bell-Northern Research (BNR).)

Structural design decisions are also influenced by important logistical factors such as the time available before construction is to begin, the seasons during which construction will be conducted, and how the project is being financed.

Steel components need to be designed and manufactured off-site at a foundry, well in advance of assembly on-site. However, once they are delivered, construction can proceed rapidly. Concrete needs a shorter lead time and can be poured on-site once the supporting frames (termed **forms**) are built. However, it takes time for the concrete to set and reach sufficient structural strength before the forms can be removed and the next floor prepared. Alternatively, concrete components can be manufactured off-site with steel reinforcements in place, but they must then be ordered in advance (Figure 4.21).

Weather restricts the speed and ease with which certain construction tasks can proceed. Concrete cures more slowly in cold and wet conditions, so lower temperatures and rain slow down the work. There are no engineering limitations to the assembly of steel and precast concrete in cold weather. However, extreme working conditions can be so difficult for the construction crews that the quality of work

Figure 4.21 The selection of a structural system influences how quickly a building can be constructed on site. A steel frame structure (left photo) can be raised rapidly once construction has begun. A poured concrete structure (right photo) rises more slowly because forms must be built and the concrete needs time to cure. (*Sources:* National Archives of Canada, PA187928; Institute for Research in Construction, National Research Council Canada, Ottawa.)

may be compromised. In scheduling a construction project, such weather-related delays are taken into account by referring to historical weather patterns (e.g., the likelihood of cold or wet days). During construction, schedules are adjusted to compensate for actual weather conditions.

The construction of an office building requires that large cash outlays be made at specified milestones in the project. Builders balance the expenses that must be paid up front with those that can be deferred. Custom-manufactured components such as steel and precast beams are paid for early on, whereas payment for concrete poured on-site is due at a later date. The timing of payments in relation to the job schedule and the cash flows expected from the completed building differs depending on the structural design and construction methods used. As a result, the builder's finance requirements may influence the choice of structure.

The structural design also affects the acoustics of the interior spaces. For example, the heavy and dense material of a concrete structure will dampen sound transmission better than a light-weight steel structure with walls of glass panels. Heavier structures are a more effective barrier to outside noise. Glass is a relatively lightweight material with a hard surface through which sound passes more easily. However, sound readily travels through the path of least resistance. Sound in offices is transmitted through holes made in walls and partitions for electrical outlets, air vents, and other servicing; spaces above internal walls or partitions (e.g., the space above suspended ceilings); and gaps between materials such as panels that are not tightly fitted. These

Figure 4.22 Cables being installed in conduit that will become embedded in the floor slab, when the concrete is poured. (*Source:* Walker Systems, Parkersburg, W.V.)

pathways can effectively defeat whatever sound absorption the space would otherwise provide.

Lightweight structures more readily transmit vibrations. Footfalls from people walking can be enough to send vibrations through springy floors. The vibration from footfalls may only be a problem if it interferes with the operation of precision instruments. However, the vibration generated by large equipment such as motors and fans for the ventilation system in buildings can be a problem for the occupants. These low-frequency vibrations can cause people to feel fatigued and in some cases nauseated.

The load that a floor structure is designed to support can restrict how the space is used. Shelves of books in a library or filing cabinets brimming with documents are extremely heavy. Groupings of such loads can exceed the safe carrying capacity of floors designed for normal office use. Excessive loads may have to be located in areas of the building that have greater structural strength or in a basement where the floor rests directly on the foundation. Such restrictions may compromise office layout and work flow design.

Services such as electrical wiring, communication cables, plumbing, and air ducts can be and often are incorporated into the structural system. For example, a network of electrical conduit can be positioned in a regular grid on the floor before the concrete floor slab is poured. The conduits are then embedded in the concrete, and all connections to the cables in the conduit are made through access points that open to the floor surface (Figure 4.22). Access points are located at regular intervals, usually every .6 meter or 1.2 meters (2 or 4 feet).

This **prewiring** (i.e., placement of cables independently of the equipment they are to connect) provides considerable flexibility in the arrangement of work spaces. The availability of connection points throughout the space allows a wide range of layouts to be accommodated with virtually no additional cable installation expense. The initial installation of telephone cable in the conduits will normally be overspecified to provide more wire pairs than will be needed. Then, to add a telephone line, for example, would require only that the outside line be connected to the cable network. The line would then be available from any connection point. Prewiring must comply with stringent load regulations regarding such issues as fire rating and mix of old and new cables.

Should special cabling be required after construction, it can be fished through the conduit if there is space. The conduits in older office buildings frequently become filled, and new wiring must be installed in the ceiling or other locations. With the rapid pace of development in telecommunications, it is difficult to anticipate the new services that will require cabling over the expected life of an office building. Cable management has thus become a technical specialty used by designers to specify the size and location of service conduits for offices.

A limitation of embedding conduits in a floor slab is that making connections to the wiring anywhere other than at the access points is impractical because it requires breaking the concrete. The access points are in fixed positions, so they frequently end up at inconvenient locations such as under desks where people hit them when they stretch their legs. As well, the floor covering (usually carpet) must be cut to access the wiring grid. After several changes in the floor layout, the many cutouts left in the floor covering from previous arrangements can look rather messy. Raised floors (discussed previously) are an alternative solution to cable access that offers greater flexibility; however, this approach is more costly and requires that a greater floor-to-floor height be available.

Some contemporary buildings have architectural features such as curved exterior walls, outdoor terraces, or other nonstandard forms. Although these novelty features add interest and character to a building, they often require deviation from standard construction practices. To maintain the same level of quality, the construction of these features must be more closely supervised.

In addition, unusual design elements may give rise to unexpected problems. For example, an elegant office tower, which appeared to be a conventional rectangular building from the main entrance, was actually a novel design. The back of the building was curved and the main corridor through the office area paralleled the rear wall, so it too was curved. Visitors to the building, seeing what appeared to be a conventional rectangular building from the entrance, expected a straight corridor and were disoriented when they stepped out of the elevator into the curved hallway. Many occupants had difficulty finding their way through the building, even after working in the facility for several months.

BUILDING SERVICES

Heating and cooling, water, power, communication networks, and other office needs are supplied by the building services. They are generally grouped into three categories — mechanical, electrical, and plumbing — corresponding to the organization of construction drawings. The mix of services selected for a specific building largely defines the quality of the interior environment that can be provided. Regular maintenance of the building's services is required to consistently deliver a safe, efficient, and comfortable office environment.

Over a building's service life, occupant requirements may change or components may deteriorate. When the building no longer functions satisfactorily or economically, a decision will be made either to renovate or to demolish. The quality and capability of the building services can be the deciding factor in rendering a facility obsolete. Many buildings became obsolete in the 1980s when electronic office equipment was rapidly introduced. They lacked the cooling capacity to handle the additional heat generated by the new equipment and could not accommodate

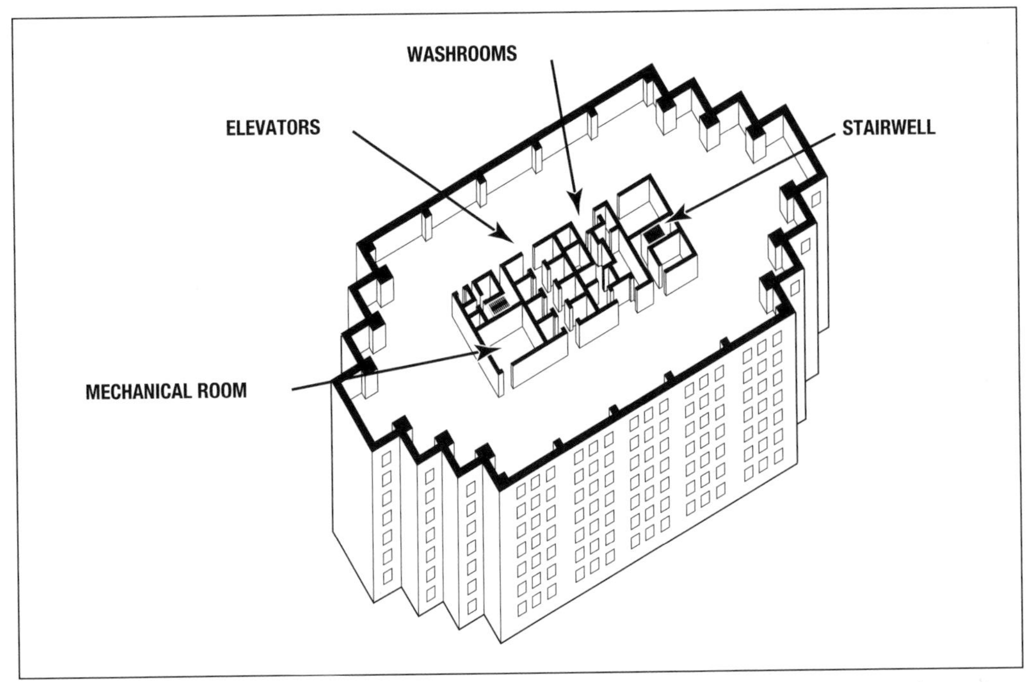

Figure 4.23 A building service core is a continuous vertical zone that houses equipment such as the mechanical system, plumbing, cabling, elevators, and washrooms. Stacking services in this way economizes on floor area and materials.

the bulky vertical and horizontal housings needed to run electric power, computer, and telecommunication cables.

In addition to the functions they are designed to provide, building services also deliver unintended or unwanted side effects. In some cases, the side effects can severely compromise the overall quality of the occupied space. The mechanical services that heat, cool, and humidify the indoor air also generate noise and vibration that can be annoying if they reach the occupants. Electric lights that illuminate work areas also generate heat that must be removed. Aging ballasts in fluorescent fixtures can make a buzzing sound or cause the lights to flicker.

The cooling system is normally designed to handle the heat load from lighting systems as per the original design. However, renovations or even minor tenant alterations can reduce the heat-removing capacity of the air-handling system enough to make the occupied space uncomfortably warm. Adjusting for this type of problem should be part of the regular maintenance and balancing of a mechanical system.

The size and shape of a building affect the way services are integrated. Multistory office buildings require a large number of vertical passageways, or **runs,** for ventilation ducts, cables, and pipes. Services are distributed across the floors through horizontal runs connected to the main vertical supply.

Building services are more easily incorporated into structures designed with a **service core** — a spacious, continuous vertical zone within which building services can be housed and from which they can be distributed (Figure 4.23). Service cores are usually centrally located. They accommodate concealed services such as the mechanical equipment, plumbing, and cabling as well as electrical and telephone closets that house switching and distribution equipment, elevators, and washrooms.

The size, shape, and weight of service equipment affect the design of the service distribution. In general, the smaller the equipment, the greater the number of available installation options. Bulky air-handling ducts need to be placed in deep spaces with relatively straight runs, whereas electrical conduits can be snaked through hollow partition walls, through channels in furniture, or under the floor.

Certain services are incompatible and should not be placed in the same housing. For example, electrical wiring should be separate from water pipes to avoid the risk of leaking water damaging electrical equipment or causing short circuits. To minimize electrical interference, communication cables should be kept away from the ballasts on fluorescent lights and other devices that generate strong electromagnetic fields. Pipes carrying hot liquids should not be placed adjacent to those carrying cold liquids unless there is sufficient insulation to minimize heat transfer between them. There are also special requirements for the placement of pipes carrying hazardous materials such as flammable gases.

Often, the very nature of a service limits where it can be placed in the building. Heavy equipment is usually installed in the basement, where the load can be supported by the ground. In high-rise structures, heavy equipment may be installed on the roof, in a penthouse, or in a service area between floors. The cost of the additional structural strength needed for the upper floor is offset by improved performance and efficiency of the mechanical system, shorter service runs, and easier access to the machinery.

Elevator motors, mechanical fans, pumping equipment, and boilers can be very noisy when in operation. These and other services that generate noise and vibration should be positioned as far away from occupied areas as practical. Sound- and vibration-absorbing materials are used to reduce transmission through the structure. However, mountings are subjected to heavy wear and deteriorate with age. When they no longer provide adequate protection, they need to be repaired or replaced to prevent damage to the structure and discomfort for occupants.

Speculative office buildings are designed to meet *average* or *typical* office needs because the client is not known. There is considerable incentive to provide services as economically as possible. In recent years, organizations renting or purchasing such buildings have become more aware of the pitfalls of inadequate services.

Some buildings offer a higher standard of environmental quality than others. The services may be better designed, use higher-quality equipment, and be more rigorously maintained. Higher-quality servicing can offer a healthier workplace that is more reliable, comfortable, and ultimately more useful and productive. Better-serviced office space may be no more costly. Even at a premium, the additional benefits can make a better quality accommodation less costly in the longer term. Ultimately, the overall quality of commercial office space will improve when clients insist on higher quality, can discern the difference, and, when necessary, are prepared to pay for it.

Most prospective tenants can describe the kind of indoor setting they would like and may consult with experts who translate those needs and preferences into facility specifications. However, by understanding the way a building and its services function, clients are better able to work with these professionals to ensure that their needs are satisfied in a cost-effective manner. The following is a general description of the main building services, what they provide, and generically how they work. Each service is a study unto itself, and each is a specialty in building design. However, the services must ultimately support the occupants in the conduct of their work activities. So it is important that those responsible for choosing office space be aware of the available options and how their choices will affect the comfort and utility of that space for those who must use it every day.

The Mechanical System

The heating, ventilating, and air-conditioning (**HVAC**) services are referred to as the **mechanical system** (Figure 4.24). Its

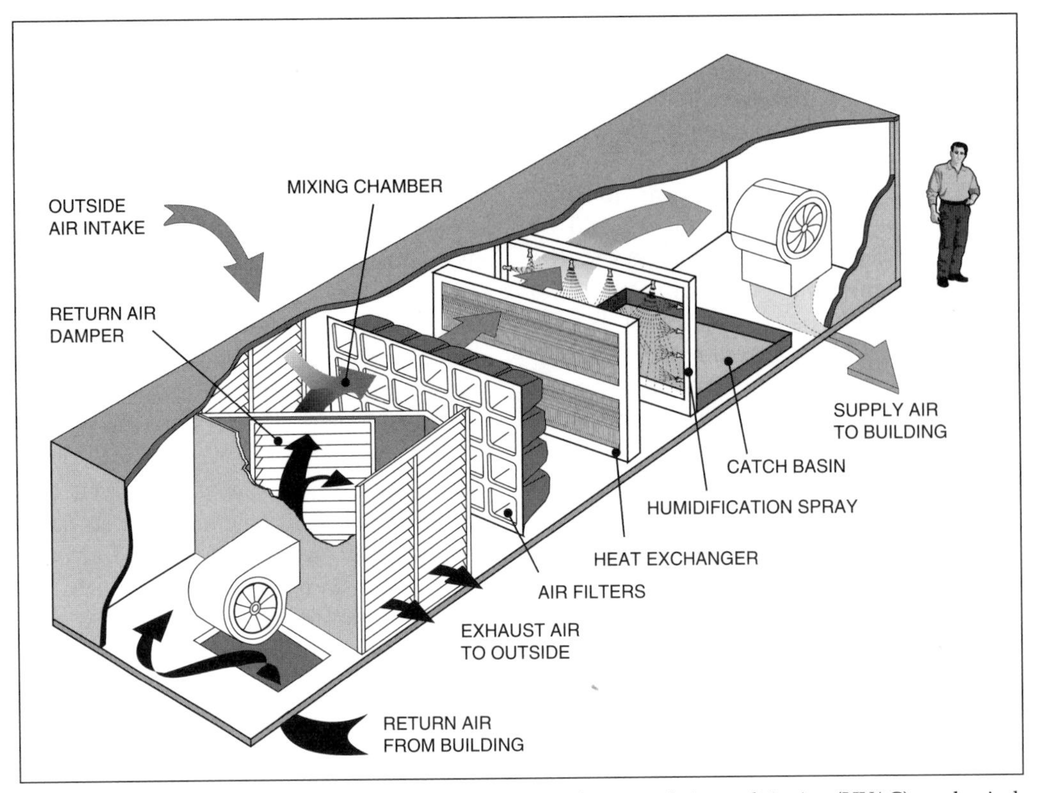

Figure 4.24 Cut-away view of a roof mounted heating, ventilating, and air-conditioning (HVAC) mechanical system, commonly used in office buildings. The person standing next to the unit gives a sense of its size.

main purpose is to control the interior thermal environment and indoor air quality. The common practice in North America is to maintain the air temperature, relative humidity, and airflow rate at levels at which office occupants are comfortable in the style of clothing appropriate to their activities and the corporate culture. Through all seasons, it is expected that people will be comfortable indoors wearing standard office attire such as suits, lined jackets, and even wool slacks, regardless of the outside climate.

Unfortunately, those who dress for warmer outside temperatures, particularly in summer, may need extra clothing to be comfortable in the office. Women in sleeveless summer dresses and sandals or men in short sleeves find mechanically ventilated offices uncomfortably cool for sedentary office work. It is difficult to maintain an office climate that everyone finds comfortable, largely due to the differences between the metabolic rates of men and women as well as the warmth of the different clothing styles they wear (see the section "Thermal Comfort" in Chapter 5).

The HVAC also has an air quality enhancement function of removing dust particles, bacteria, pollen, insects, and other noxious or irritating substances from the air. Air may be filtered through a dry medium (paper, felts, or woven fabric), a wet medium (oil-moistened felts or fabric), or an electrostatic precipitator (a chamber where the particles in the air are given a positive electric charge, causing them to be attracted to a negatively charged plate and be captured).

Whatever method is used, regular replacement or renewal of the filter media and cleaning of the filtration systems are essential to prevent them from becoming clogged and ineffective. A poorly maintained filtration system can itself become a source of indoor air contamination. Once the system's capacity is exceeded, the materials that have been removed from the air may start to be released into the

Figure 4.25 The routine cleaning of this return air grille has been badly neglected. The accumulation of dirt obstructs air flow and is a source of contaminants. As the deposits break away they can fall into the occupied areas or become airborne and circulated throughout the building. (*Source:* Place and Associates, Ottawa.)

building's air supply (Figure 4.25). The HVAC system, designed specifically to circulate air efficiently throughout a building, then becomes an effective distribution system for this accumulated dirt which contains molds, fungi, and other airborne irritants. Not surprisingly, the most common cause of sick building syndrome is a poorly maintained HVAC (Woods 1989). For this reason, an inspection of the HVAC system; cleaning of the central plant, filters, ductwork, and grills; as well as the removal of air contaminant sources are among the first steps taken to improve indoor air quality.

The design of an HVAC system must take into account climate and site factors, the characteristics of the building, and the equipment and activities it will accommodate. The expected range of outdoor temperatures and solar conditions, the characteristics of the site, building orientation, construction materials, sun shading, and internal sources of heat gain and loss are all included in the design evaluation. Differences in any of these factors can significantly affect the heat load and thus the HVAC requirements of different buildings. For example, a video display terminal generates about the same amount of heat as a person. When computers were first introduced into offices, they effectively doubled the occupant heat load for which those buildings were originally designed and overloaded the mechanical systems. Today, buildings are designed with the expectation that offices will be automated.

Heating or cooling can be produced at the point where it is needed or at a central plant, from which it is distributed. Standalone heaters or reheat units in air ducts can provide heating at a single location, and portable air-cooling systems can be used for small areas. But for most commercial office space, heating and cooling are produced at a central plant. The heat-transfer medium can be hot or cold air, hot or cold water, or steam. As the medium circulates through the building, it passes through devices designed to maximize heat transfer (whether heating or cooling) from the medium to the surrounding air.

Various designs of radiators (such as panels or finned coils) are used with water and steam, whereas fans and air supply grilles, termed **diffusers**, distribute heated or cooled air. Air diffusers are usually part of the ceiling and consist of deflecting vanes that promote the mixing of the supply air with the air already in the room. To provide uniform temperature throughout a space, heating or cooling is introduced in the vicinity of the greatest loss or gain, such as at windows, at doorways to the outside, along exterior walls, or near concentrations of equipment.

A pressing issue for facility management is the gradual phaseout of CFCs (chlorofluorocarbons) — an ozone-depleting chemical used extensively as a coolant in air-conditioning equipment. Environmentally friendly alternatives must be implemented as increasingly restrictive regulations limit their use. In the future, CFCs will become more expensive and less available. Those responsible for the HVAC's operation must develop cost-effective CFC programs to prevent and contain leaks, convert to an alternative refrigerant, or replace the equipment. In the United States, the Environmental Protection Agency (EPA) can fine offenders as much as $25,000 per day for violating regulations on the proper handling and disposal of CFCs.

THERMOSTATS

The **thermostat** is the sensing and control device used to regulate heating and cooling of a space. In its simplest form, the temperature-sensing and control functions are combined in a single unit. The desired temperature is selected by turning a dial or entering the value on a keypad. There is commonly a thermometer or digital display to show the current temperature at the thermostat's location. In more sophisticated systems, the temperature sensor and control functions may be in separate units.

Prior to 1980, most thermostats used pneumatic controls (air pressure) to operate valves and dampers that regulated the flow of warm or cool air. Now digital electronic thermostats can provide more accurate adjustment of the HVAC and can be integrated with computer-based energy management systems or automated building controls (both are discussed later, in the "Automated Control of Building Services" subsection).

Thermostats rarely malfunction and need to be calibrated only occasionally. The most common problems with thermostats result from improper placement or inappropriate selection of the temperature setting.

Thermostats control heating and cooling of a space in accordance with the temperature they detect. To provide as uniform a temperature as possible, the temperature sensor for the thermostat should be located where it will give a reading that is representative of the occupied space as a whole. For example, if the flow of room air around the thermostat is obstructed by furniture, wall hangings, or other items, the thermostat will detect temperatures different from those experienced by the occupants and cause the heating or cooling system to make the room too warm or too cool.

Figure 4.26 Thermostats are often locked so occupants cannot change the settings.

Computer monitors, incandescent lamps, laser printers, and photocopiers generate significant amounts of heat. A thermostat located next to these heat sources may be warmed to such an extent that it always calls for cooling. No matter how cool the rest of the room becomes, if the temperature sensor continues to be warmed by the equipment, it will continue to register the room's condition as "too warm."

Thermostat temperature sensors placed in the air supply duct rather than in the occupied space also give poor results. Since the duct temperature is not representative of the air temperature experienced by the occupants, the sensor cannot properly regulate the temperature for them.

Beginning in the mid-1970s, when energy costs soared, thermostats were often locked so the settings could not be changed by office occupants (Figure 4.26). It was reasoned that people should use clothing, such as sweaters, instead of the building system to make minor thermal comfort adjustments. In addition to frustrating people, this unfortunate policy added to the maintenance workload. At that time, few thermostats were centrally controlled, and so periodically, the facility staff had to go to each one and either adjust the setting in response to occupant complaints or make seasonal changes. Many institutional buildings operate with different winter and summer thermostat settings to conserve energy.

Whatever the sophistication of the temperature control system, if thermostat locations and settings are inappropriately selected, the system will not provide a comfortable work environment.

SINGLE- AND MULTIPLE- ZONE TEMPERATURE CONTROL

The heating and cooling of a small building can be regulated by a single thermostat (Figure 4.27). The temperature is monitored in only one room, the one with the thermostat. The system cannot directly compensate for warmer or cooler conditions in other rooms. In the illustration, the room with the thermostat is in the building's interior. So the thermostat cannot compensate for the additional heat load of the sunlight in the room on the perimeter. Other rooms may become uncomfortably warm or cool because they are exposed to different conditions. Single-thermostat control is common in residential buildings but does not provide adequate temperature control for commercial office buildings.

In office buildings, a zone system is used to monitor and control temperature. Each floor is divided into zones of similar exposure (e.g., north, south, east, and west exposures; interior and perimeter spaces), with a separate thermostat controlling the temperature of each zone. In addition, enclosed offices may be treated as individual zones with their own thermostat. If the zones are appropriately chosen, the system provides sufficient monitoring and compensation for the building to be comfortable throughout without directly monitoring each room.

FORCED-AIR HVAC SYSTEMS

113fice space is heated and cooled with forced-air HVAC systems. Although there is a wide range of system designs, they tend to fall into two broad categories: constant-air-volume (**CAV**) and variable-air-volume (**VAV**) systems.

Constant-Air-Volume Systems

CAV systems continuously deliver air to the occupied spaces. The thermostat regulates the temperature of the air used to heat and cool the spaces. In a **terminal-reheat** CAV system, the central HVAC unit supplies air at a low enough temperature to cool the warmest area of the building. Each zone has a separate heating unit, termed the **terminal-reheat unit**, which then warms the supply air to the temperature required in that zone (Figure 4.28).

In a **dual-duct** CAV system, both warm and cool air are supplied to a mixing chamber in each zone. The thermostat for the zone regulates the temperature of the air delivered to the occupied space by adjusting the proportion of warm and cool air combined in the mixing chamber (Figure 4.29).

Variable-Air-Volume Systems

Both the dual-duct and terminal-reheat CAV systems supply air at a constant rate and adjust the degree of heating and cooling by varying the *temperature* of the air. VAV systems employ a different approach. Air is supplied to the zone at a constant temperature. The temperature of an area is raised or lowered by varying the *quantity* of air supplied. The thermostat controls a damper, labeled "VAV valve" in Figure 4.30. Theoretically the airflow could be reduced to zero when no heating or cooling was required. In practice, a minimum airflow is usually maintained to satisfy fresh air requirements.

CAV and VAV Compared

Variable-air-volume systems offer a number of cost advantages. They are less expensive to purchase and install than dual-duct, terminal-reheat, and other commercial CAV systems. They are also less costly to operate. As well, a smaller volume of air needs to be conditioned because areas that change temperature more slowly receive less air. These characteristics make VAV systems more ener-

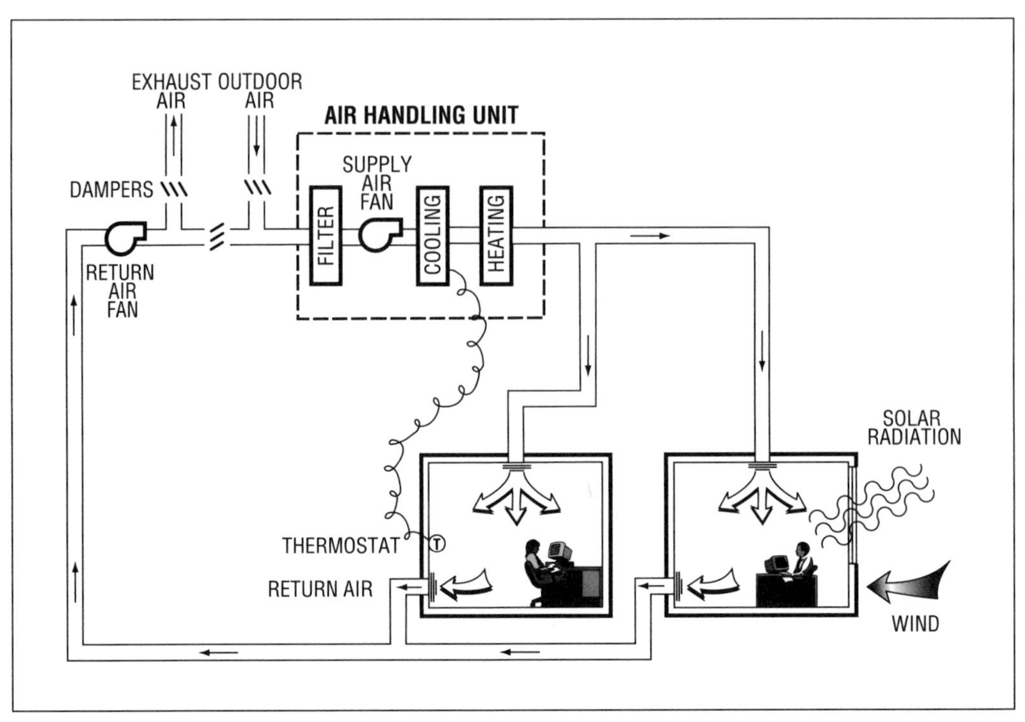

Figure 4.27 Schematic drawing of a single-zone HVAC system. One thermostat controls the air temperature delivered to all spaces along the system's branches. It does not compensate for differential heat gain or loss in different areas.

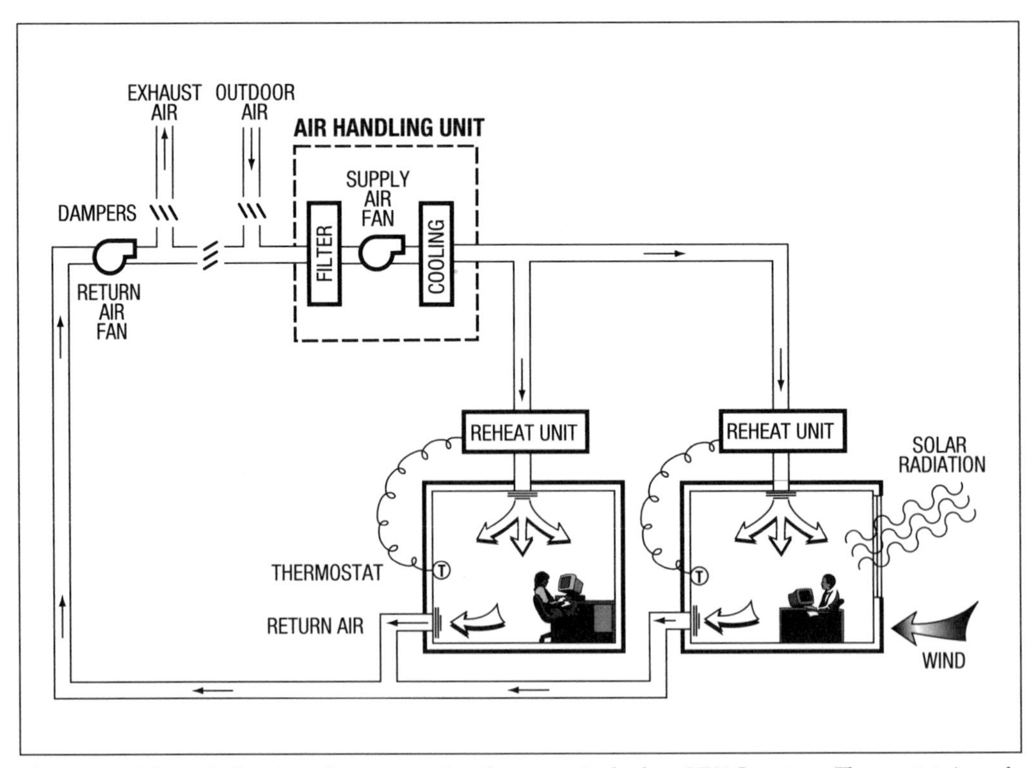

Figure 4.28 Schematic drawing of a constant air volume terminal-reheat HVAC system. Thermostats in each room regulate the supply air's temperature. The reheat unit for each room or zone warms the supply air as needed to maintain the desired temperature.

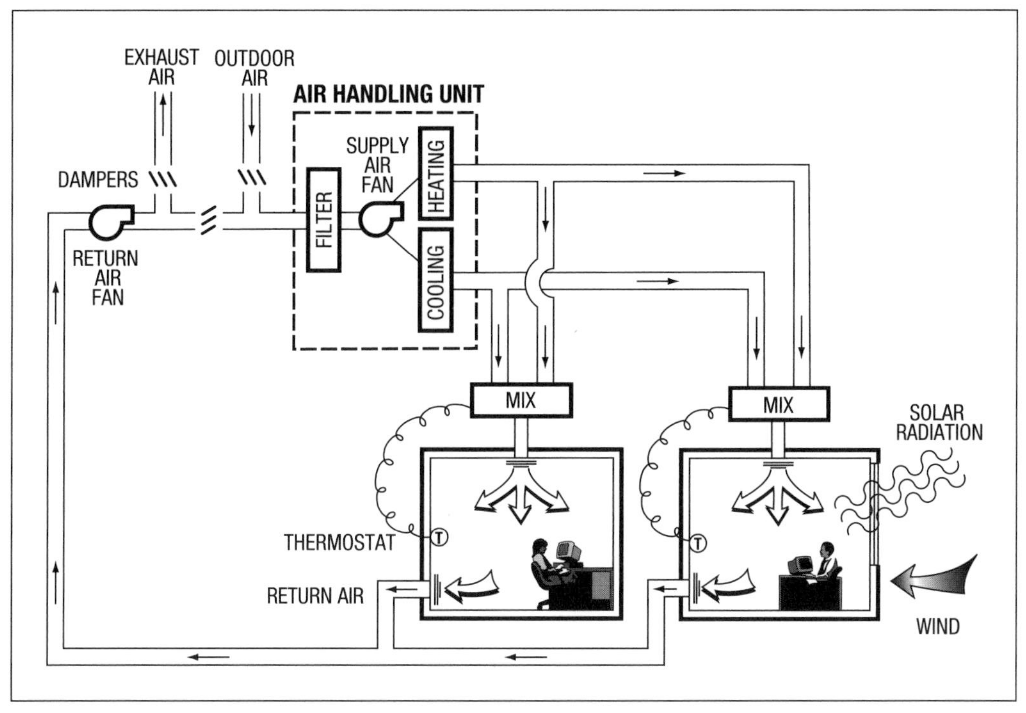

Figure 4.29 Schematic drawing of a constant air volume dual-duct HVAC system. Thermostats regulate the supply air temperature by adjusting the proportion of warm and cool air combined in the mixing chamber and supplied to each room or zone.

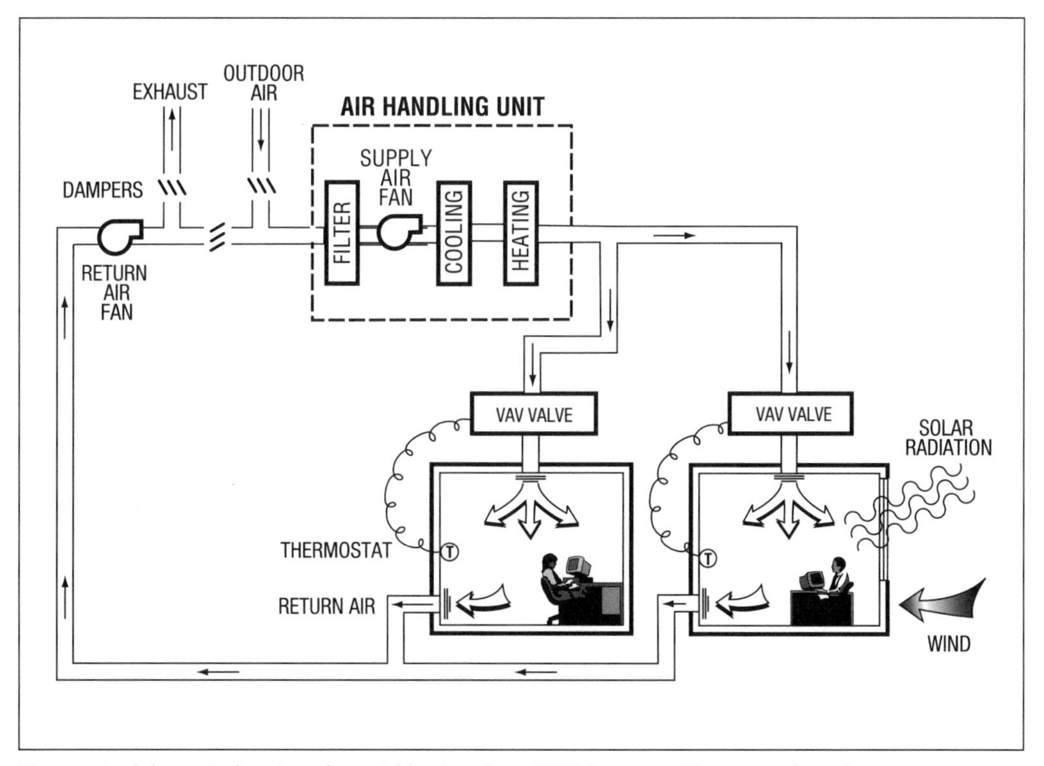

Figure 4.30 Schematic drawing of a variable-air-volume HVAC system. The system furnishes air at a constant temperature. The temperature of the occupied area is controlled by varying the quantity of air supplied. When there is less need for heating or cooling, less air is delivered.

gy-efficient than CAV systems. But the VAV design does not allow as much service flexibility as the CAV design. For example, VAV systems cannot heat selected spaces and cool others at the same time because there is only one air supply and no additional heating or cooling equipment at each zone.

The lower initial cost and lower operating cost of VAV systems have made them attractive, especially for the design of speculative office space (i.e., space not designed for a specific client). Unfortunately, in reducing the volume of air that is conditioned, VAV systems can compromise indoor air quality. A conflict arises because the air supply is used for both ventilation and temperature control. In a VAV system, the ventilation system cycles on and off, supplying warm or cool air as required to maintain the desired room temperature. If the room temperature varies too slowly, the ventilation system may not run long enough to maintain adequate air circulation. Room conditions may then become stuffy, and the concentration of air contaminants may become high enough to make some people feel uncomfortable or ill.

Chemical and biological pollutants are produced inside every building. As long as there is a sufficient flow of outside air into the building, pollutant concentrations can be kept low enough not to trigger sick building symptoms. In controlling temperature by varying the airflow, VAV systems indirectly vary the concentration of these pollutants and, hence, the risk of causing sick building symptoms. For this reason, it is important that a VAV system be set to provide a minimum flow of outside air, sufficient to ensure occupant health. This, in turn, increases the energy cost of operating this type of HVAC.

CAV systems constantly supply both cool and warm air to the building, making them less energy-efficient than VAV systems. The additional equipment and the continuous operation of fans and other machinery make them more expensive to install and maintain. However, the constant air supply provides every space with a continuous flow of air, which helps to ensure that there is sufficient air exchange throughout the building to keep the concentration of air contaminants at an acceptably low level. Also, the uniform sound of the continuous air supply in a CAV system tends to be less annoying to workers than the on-and-off ventilation cycle of a VAV system.

The choice of HVAC involves trade-offs between cost and environmental quality. However, even a high-quality HVAC design will not deliver adequate performance unless it is properly specified and maintained. It is one element of a building that can cause serious health problems if cleaning and maintenance schedules are not rigorously followed. Both the system design and the way it is operated and maintained determine an HVAC system's level of performance.

The Electrical System

Electricity powers a wide range of equipment in office buildings, from basic building services such as elevators, lighting, and ventilation to office equipment and personal appliances. The electrical devices in office buildings differ not only in the quantity of power they use but also in the timing of their power demands and the quality of power they require.

HVAC systems draw large amounts of power. But their demand varies greatly over the day and week as well as with the seasons. During seasons with moderate weather, less heating and cooling are needed. At night or on weekends when a building is unoccupied, the load on the HVAC system is less than during the workday. Not only is there less heat generated by equipment and people so less cooling is needed, but thermal comfort and ventilation requirements can be relaxed to save energy.

Office automation has dramatically increased the power requirements of office buildings. The proliferation of faxes, photocopiers, computers, printers, and similar devices has required a major increase in power supply capacity. Today, it is not unusual for every work setting to have a computer and peripherals.

The voltage and purity of electrical power are not constant throughout the day. They vary with the total power demand and the noise introduced by all the equipment attached to the line. Motors, for example, have a short, high power demand when they start up, which can cause voltage dips. Other devices connected to the same circuit may be disrupted if the voltage drops too low. The sensitive circuitry of computers and communications equipment can easily be damaged by voltage **spikes** (short bursts of elevated voltage levels). Many devices introduce unwanted signals onto the line (termed **line noise**), which can also disrupt the operation of electronic equipment.

Voltage dips and line noise can cause sensitive electronic components such as computer microprocessors to perform erratically. Power disruptions can be catastrophic. When power is cut to computers and communication devices, data can be lost. In addition to the cost of recovering lost data, companies have reported revenue losses of US$5,000–US$78,000 per hour of computer network downtime (Ballou 1992). As organizations increase their dependence on computer systems and data communication networks, they become more vulnerable to costly on-line system failures. Adding specialized conditioning equipment to a building's power supply system can protect electronic devices. Power conditioners are designed to remove line noise, protect against voltage spikes and dips, and even provide short-term emergency power during outages. In addition, a rigorous file-backup system can minimize the data loss and consequent work disruption caused by power-induced computer failures.

Continuous delivery of clean power depends on the quality of power provided by the utility, the design of the power distribution system in the building, and the actions of the users. Occupants can compromise the performance of an electrical system by overloading circuits, causing power failures, or by connecting equipment that introduces line noise. Making occupants aware of these problems and removing troublesome electrical devices (such as toasters, microwave ovens, and space heaters) can go a long way toward preventing power-related equipment failures.

The business sector is the fastest-growing consumer of electric power. It has been difficult for power utilities to satisfy the rapid increase in demand for high quality power in high-density office developments and downtown urban cores. The EPA estimates that computers account for 5% of the United States' commercial electrical consumption and expects that proportion to reach 10% by the year 2000. That consumption could be significantly reduced if computers were turned off when not in use. According to a survey conducted by the National Research Council of Canada, personal computers were idle 90% of the time. Apple Computer estimates that personal computers are idle 60% to 70% of the time. As many as 40% of computers are left running during nights and weekends, adding to the power waste (Economist 1992a).

Some computers must be run continuously because they provide on-line services throughout the day. Turning workstations and personal computers on and off repeatedly during the day can cause excessive wear on moving components such as hard disks. But in most cases, turning computers on when they are needed and off at the end of the workday has no adverse effects and will reduce their annual energy consumption by more than half.

Efforts to conserve energy in offices have become increasingly important. A growing number of computer manufacturers have introduced energy-efficient computers that consume less power and also incorporate features that automatically shut down system components when the machine is idle. Organizations are becoming more interested in adopting environmentally responsible policies. In the case of energy, environmentally sensitive policies not only garner positive recognition by the public and employees; they can also lower energy costs significantly by reducing consumption and the need for utilities to purchase additional generating capacity.

LIGHTING

Electric lighting is the principal source of office illumination. Daylight can provide important aesthetic and psychological benefits but normally is not used as the main source of illumination for work areas. As with most office design decisions, selection of a lighting system involves a number of trade-offs. Compromises are made between energy efficiency, frequency and cost of maintenance, light quality (e.g., color spectrum, variability in light intensity, flicker), aesthetics, and initial cost.

The quality and amount of illumination should be tailored to the tasks occupants perform. Although the human eye is tremendously adaptable, long periods of work under unsuitable lighting conditions cause fatigue, sore eyes, headaches, and other ailments that reduce a person's comfort and effectiveness. The introduction of computers into the office has emphasized the importance of providing illumination suited to the task and grouping work activities with similar lighting requirements.

The illumination level comfortable for computer-based work is somewhat lower than for paper-based tasks. As well, lighting designs should minimize screen glare. Windows should be fitted with shading devices, especially if they receive direct sun. In some cases, lighting systems that are comfortable for unaided vision are uncomfortable for those who wear eyeglasses or contact lenses. This is especially true of lighting that must support both computer-based and paper-based work. It is more difficult to minimize glare effects on eyeglasses and computer screens while simultaneously providing illumination levels suited to both modes of work.

Lighting systems consist of a light source (such as a fluorescent lamp), the fixture in which it is housed, and the electrical wiring that supplies the power (termed the **luminaire**). The light source in most offices is energy-efficient fluorescent tubes that produce relatively little heat. High-efficiency triphosphor lamps are increasingly favored over the general-purpose cool-white or warm-white lamps used in most offices.

The design of a luminaire affects not only the quality of light that is cast but also its characteristics, such as the color spectrum of the light, the proportion of light cast in different directions, and the degree to which the lamps are shielded from view. A luminaire mounted in a high position may be designed to concentrate the light reaching the work area. Alternatively, a low-mounted fixture may be chosen with a luminaire that spreads the light wide to cover a large area. Office fixtures are most often hung from the ceiling and integrated with the ceiling tiles. There are three principal types of light fixtures: direct, indirect, and diffuse. Many fixtures combine features of these basic designs (Figure 4.31).

With direct lighting, most of the light is directed downward to the work surface. It is inherently efficient because there are no intermediate elements between the source and the areas to be illuminated. Direct lighting, being concentrated downward, provides little illumination from the side, and so can produce harsh shadows. A person working at a desk under direct ceiling lighting will cast a shadow down onto the work surface unless side illumination is provided by a task light or other source. The bright, concentrated light sources of direct lighting are strongly reflected in computer screens, causing disturbing glare. Computer screens are available with antiglare coatings, and there are antiglare filters that can be mounted in front of the screen. While these devices are help-

Figure 4.31 Schematic drawings showing the direction and pattern of illumination (indicated as white areas) from different types of fixtures.

ful in reducing glare, they also reduce the sharpness of the image.

With indirect lighting, nearly all the light is directed away from the work surface. It is bounced off the ceiling and walls to illuminate the space. The efficiency of illumination is lower than for direct lighting because before the light reaches the work surface, it is first reflected and partially absorbed by the reflecting surface. For this reason, walls and ceilings need to have a high reflectance. They must also be a neutral color because the color of these reflecting surfaces will affect the color spectrum of the illumination. The design and mounting position of indirect fixtures must be carefully chosen to avoid bright spots on the ceiling and to shield the light sources from view.

Properly designed and installed, indirect lighting provides an even, shadowless illumination. It is well suited to areas for computer-based work because the even ceiling illumination minimizes reflections on computer screens, and virtually no shadows are cast on horizontal work surfaces. However, the illumination can be so even and shadowless that it is aesthetically drab. The brightness variations of direct lighting give a sense of depth and sparkle and make textures stand out. For this reason, indirect lighting is often supplemented with enough direct lighting to make the space appear more interesting without causing disturbing shadows or glare at the work surface.

Diffuse fixtures distribute approximately equal amounts of light upward and downward. A diffusing globe emits light equally in all directions; other types of fixtures may have an open top, luminous sides, and a diffusing bottom. These fixtures produce a bright ceiling and upper wall, thereby providing illumination from above and from the side.

ELEVATORS

Elevators affect a building's overall design and, perhaps more importantly, the quantity of usable space. Judicious placement of elevators can minimize corridor lengths, direct distracting circulation away from work areas, and optimize occupants' vertical travel between floors. The high cost of land in large metropolitan centers such as New York, London, and Tokyo provides a strong economic incentive to build ever taller structures. Buildings of 100 storys are not unusual, and structures of 300–500 storys have been considered. Safe, fast, and efficient vertical travel by elevator makes these tall structures viable. The specification of a building's elevator system has direct financial and technical implications as well as functional and aesthetic ones.

Separate passenger and freight elevators should be provided in office buildings. Safety and convenience are the first considerations in the transportation of people. Passenger elevators generally do not need as great a weight capacity as freight elevators but must provide faster service. In office buildings, the number and size of elevators needed depend on the population of the building, the number of floors, and the acceptable wait time. Ideally, passenger elevators should operate fast enough that people wait only 30–45 seconds for a cab to arrive. Freight elevators are generally larger, with a higher weight capacity to accommodate big, heavy loads, but slower operation can be tolerated.

Elevator service can be scheduled more efficiently if the system knows passengers' destinations before the elevator cab is dispatched to their floor. Sophisticated elevator control systems are being developed that replace the simple Up or Down call buttons with a keypad. Passengers would enter their destination floor to call an elevator. The system would then select which cab to send so as to optimize performance.

Another innovation under development is the use of motion sensors to detect a person walking toward an elevator. In ground-floor lobbies, this would be the signal for a cab to arrive. On other floors, it would prevent the doors from closing when someone is rushing to catch an elevator.

Work scheduling has a major effect on elevator service levels because it is during peak usage that the service is slowest. Staggering activities that generate high use — such as the beginning and end of the workday, lunch and coffee breaks — produces a more even demand, thereby improving the speed of elevator service. Encouraging occupants to use the stairway instead of the elevator to reach the next floor also reduces elevator traffic and provides a little exercise as well.

CABLE MANAGEMENT

Effective electronic communication has become a necessity in today's offices. Cables carry electronic signals for voice, computer data, and video (Figure 4.32). In addition, building services such as alarms, security systems, automated building controls, and mechanical systems all require cabling.

A cable may be a single twisted pair of wires or a bundle of fiber-optic filaments, or it may consist of tens or hundreds of fiber-optic and electrical conductors. Cables differ widely in cost, performance, and complexity of installation. Other selection criteria are the required transmission quality and shielding from interference, as well as the signal power loss that can be tolerated. Characteristics of the building — such as the amount of space available for cabling, circuitousness of the routing, and ease of access — also influence the choice of network and cable technology.

There are two broad approaches to the distribution of cable servicing to individual workstations. With the first approach, cabling is provided on an "as-needed" basis. Cables are installed to connect the specific devices at each workstation (e.g., connection to a telephone system or computer network), and if more devices are added to a workstation, additional wiring is installed.

With the second approach, known as a **structured wiring system,** a standard set of cable connections is provided at every

Figure 4.32 Managing the array of cables in today's automated offices is a speciality unto itself. Unsafe and inaccessible tangles of cable can be avoided by providing ample space and suitable housing to meet current and projected cable needs.

workstation, whether or not all are needed. This arrangement offers greater flexibility than the as-needed approach. People and their equipment can be moved to any workstation, and the connectivity they require will already be in place.

Although initially more expensive to install, structured wiring offers substantial savings of time and money. There is less disruption when people are moved or new equipment is installed, and the need for new cable installation is reduced. For cabling installed on an as-needed basis, each move, add-on, or change cost an average of CDN$750 (or about US$600) in 1991. With a structured wiring system, the cost can be reduced to one-third that amount (PWC 1991).

Cabling demands a significant amount of space in office buildings. Special rooms on each floor, the **telecommunications closets,** house the cables, junction boxes, and other equipment to support communications needs. These closets may be 10 square meters (100 square feet) or more in floor area, depending on the number of workstations and the voice and data communication services provided (Figure 4.33). Although fiber optics are more expensive than conventional wiring, a single conductor carries many more signals with higher transmission quality. It has become a popular choice in high-capacity, high-quality applications and where the space available for cabling is limited.

Cable management is a speciality. The technology, standards, and regulations change rapidly. In planning for their current and future connectivity needs, organizations must take these developments in

Figure 4.33 This telephone distribution and switching equipment for a research organization occupied some 6 meters (20 feet) of continuous wall space.

the technology into account. For this reason, organizations are well advised to review their emerging telecommunications, computer network, and other connectivity needs and incorporate them into their office facility planning.

Plumbing

The supply and distribution of hot and cold water are a basic necessity in buildings. In office facilities, water is needed to supply washrooms, drinking fountains, kitchens and other food service areas, and special occupant requirements (labs, manufacturing, etc.) as well as for emergency fire response. Because water supply and drainage systems are rarely visible to the building user, these services are often taken for granted.

The water for an office building is supplied by the local municipal water board. Because water quality is strictly controlled by health regulations administered by the municipal government, quality is rarely an issue. In regions where water supplies are low, undependable, or contaminated, water conservation considerations may influence the design of the plumbing system and choice of washroom fixtures, drinking fountains, and other plumbing devices.

Cold water for drinking and fire suppression may be piped directly to the locations where it is used. Cold water for other purposes is commonly stored in a cistern near or at the top of the building. Locating the cistern high in the building enables the water to flow down through the distribution system rather than having to be pumped. Often, a hot-water holding tank is supplied from this cistern. In all but the smallest of buildings, hot water is circulated around the building in a pipe loop using natural convection or a pump.

The demand for hot and cold water varies over time. When engineering the plumbing system, assumptions are made to arrive at a suitable pipe size and cistern size to satisfy the demand. Although different design solutions may provide the same service initially, some of those solutions may curtail future expansion or changes. The principal planning constraints for plumbing are to ensure access to the pipes for repairing leaks or blockages, adequate slope on near-horizontal drainage lines, and proper venting of the system.

It is usually difficult to add plumbing services to an existing office building (Figure 4.34). Drain pipes require sufficient slopes to flow, and the piping is often embedded in the structure (e.g., within the concrete floor slab), making it expensive to access and modify. For this reason, it is

Figure 4.34 Unless plumbing services are installed when a building is constructed, it is expensive and often impractical to add facilities that require water. Washrooms, especially for executive areas, are commonly requested during renovations but frequently cannot be added because the building lacks the service runs. (*Source:* Bell-Northern Research (BNR).)

advantageous to overdesign plumbing services in new construction, running pipes to all locations where they might be needed in the future. Overdesign is particularly important for speculative office buildings, where the ability to install additional plumbing may be essential for some tenants.

Security

A key concern in offices is the security of people, contents, and information. Organizations have a strong moral and legal obligation to ensure the safety of their employees, clients, and vendors. The building owner, employer, facility manager, and others responsible for the maintenance and operation of an office can be held legally responsible for the safety and health of all occupants. Employees concerned about sick buildings have brought liability suits against employers and building owners. Particularly in the United States, these court challenges are increasingly successful as the public becomes more aware of building-related health risks.

The theft of office equipment and personal belongings, by either employees or outsiders, makes people feel less secure and disrupts productivity. People working after hours, late into the night, are especially at risk. It may be necessary not only to keep parking areas well lighted but also to supervise them using such devices as closed-circuit television. Organizations in which employees regularly work extended hours may require a full-time security service with parking lot escorts. Building designs and floor layouts can also be optimized for security (Figure 4.35). Effective measures include eliminating long, isolated corridors; screening visitors; and designing the circulation pattern to separate public areas of the building so that strangers cannot easily enter work areas.

Building management and use patterns can also be adjusted to optimize security. Security can be provided more effectively if areas that require greater supervision are grouped together. Offices that are regularly used outside of normal business hours and rooms that house expensive items or sensitive records should be clustered as much as possible.

Maintaining the security of an organization's information used to be a matter of supervising physical access to written documents and other tangible items. Today, so much of an organization's important information is computer-based that the protection of information is a highly technical and sophisticated specialty. The capability to transfer large volumes of data electronically at high speed has meant that even a few minutes of unauthorized access to an organization's computer system can be devastating.

The spread of programs that sabotage computer operations, termed **computer viruses**, which are hidden in applications software and other computer files, has

Figure 4.35 Well-lighted and supervised corridors provide greater security for employees, especially those who need to work in the facility at night or on weekends. (*Source:* Bell-Northern Research (BNR).)

required that organizations adopt stringent procedures for computer use. Authorized users can inadvertently introduce computer viruses simply by using a virus-infected diskette. It has become a challenging pastime for some "hackers" to break through the security system of computer networks to access files and software or sabotage the system. Since these individuals can operate anywhere they have access to a telephone line, their illegal activities are difficult to stop.

By their very nature, security measures restrict or regulate activities and access at the expense of convenience. Security measures necessarily impose a cost, both to administer and by making some activities more time-consuming — whether it's a few more locked doors or the need to get authorizations to access information. Some companies forgo security systems altogether because they find the restrictions too disruptive of communication and creativity. The level of security an organization requires and the scope of implementation must be balanced against these costs.

In some cases, security needs conflict with other safety requirements. For example, doors that allow people to enter a stairwell at any point but only allow them to exit at ground level become a lethal hazard when people fleeing a fire are trapped in a smoke-filled staircase. With some control systems, all doors are automatically unlocked when a fire is detected.

Security needs can be more successfully addressed if organizations evaluate their needs in a comprehensive manner and actively enlist the support of their employees. Safeguards are of little benefit unless people see it in their interest to cooperate: wear their badges, not let strangers slip inside when they enter restricted areas, and report suspicious activities. A piecemeal approach to security management is likely to leave gaps in protection, compromising the overall level of security that is achieved.

EMERGENCY RESPONSE

An office building must be designed and equipped so that occupants can exit promptly and safely in the event of an emergency. Potentially life-threatening situations range from fire and natural disasters (e.g., hurricane, earthquake, tornado) to floods, bomb threats and explosions, armed robbery, and hostage situations.

All buildings must meet the fire safety requirements of the local building code. The municipal fire marshal generally wields greater authority over the use of a building than any other public official. If there is a serious breach of fire safety regulations, a fire marshal can order that a building be vacated immediately and not used until the deficiencies are corrected.

Commercial buildings are usually equipped with water sprinklers, an alarm system, and clearly marked emergency exits. A documented fire response plan and periodic inspections are also generally required by municipal statute. Some office facilities are now equipped with an automated building control system that initiates emergency response actions when a fire is signaled by the smoke detectors. It can simultaneously modify the operation of all the building systems under its control to contain the fire, protect the occupants, and hasten evacuation of the facility.

A typical response program would detect the presence of a fire and determine its location, sound the fire alarm, signal the fire department, and broadcast one or more prerecorded messages throughout the building instructing occupants where to go and what to do. The automated building control system also changes the operation of the mechanical system to optimize occupant safety. Floors above and below the fire location are pressurized to minimize the spread of smoke. Maximum exhaust is provided to the floors containing the fire to remove the smoke as fast as possible. Air recycling is stopped, and 100% outdoor air is used for ventilation so that the air distribution system does not spread the smoke. The operation of the elevators may also be controlled to retard the spread of smoke. In a panic situation, a properly designed automated fire response system can save lives.

However, even the best fire safety system can easily be undermined if occupants store flammable materials improperly, block access to fire equipment, or obstruct emergency exits (Figure 4.36). It falls to the facility manager to ensure that the safety measures designed into a building will be operational should a fire or other emergency ever occur.

An emergency response plan should include a recovery plan that reflects the

Figure 4.36 This room, designed to house ventilation equipment, is also being used for document storage. Not only are the boxes of paper a potential fire hazard, they are blocking access to the fire extinguisher mounted on the wall.

organization's current assets and work needs. The plan should address alternate work sites; insurance coverage; reestablishment of electronic networks, databases, and communication links; and public relations procedures. In this way the optimum response to the immediate effects of a crisis as well as its consequences can be carefully thought out well before it is put into action.

CLEANING

An office needs to be clean enough to comply with local health regulations as well as to provide an aesthetically acceptable setting for a productive workplace. It is difficult to establish and maintain standards for office cleanliness. Supervision of cleaning services is often lax, and the quality of the service can become poor. In addition, office workers tend to leave work-related material spread out for days or weeks at a time, making it hard to clean their area.

Offices are usually cleaned at night, outside of normal working hours. This schedule requires the building to be fully powered (e.g., light as well as heating or cooling) just for the cleaning staff. To conserve energy, many offices now have the cleaning done in the daytime so the building can be operated with minimum servicing at night. However, the noise and disruption can be a major annoyance and time waster to those trying to work. Daytime cleaning can exact a costly productivity loss.

The access that cleaning staff have to the building may also pose a significant security risk. Exit doors left open by the cleaning staff for their convenience offer easy access to intruders. Cleaners can inadvertently flip switches that cut off power to computers, hit sensitive equipment, and spill cleaning fluids onto papers or equipment. In some cases, cleaning staff may themselves be implicated in theft or sabotage.

Problems periodically arise with cleaning services, as with any other building service. But because cleaning is normally done when the building is unoccupied, it tends not to be monitored as closely as other services. As a result, there is a greater opportunity for problems to develop.

Automated Control of Building Services

Systems that control building operation and management are incorporating ever more sophisticated electronic technology. Such systems have become more attractive and cost-effective as the price of environmental sensors, custom-designed computer chips, and the computers themselves continues to fall.

Since the energy crisis of the 1970s, **energy management systems** have been used to optimize the operation of mechanical and electrical building components by turning equipment on or off at preset times — for example, shutting down mechanical systems and lights outside scheduled business hours and starting them up again before people arrive for work.

Energy management systems were the forerunners of today's **automated building control systems,** which employ computer technology to integrate environmental control and facility management functions. Such systems are also called **building automation systems.** Buildings with highly sophisticated automated building control systems are often referred to as **intelligent buildings.** These sophisticated building control systems not only can save energy but can also improve a building's performance and the occupants' comfort.

Automated building control systems were introduced in the early 1980s. Heavy-handed marketing and often-exaggerated claims led many to view them as a vendor strategy for selling high-tech gimmickry. Architects, engineers, and design consultants were reluctant to use them because the technology was largely unproven and the professional liability could be high. Early systems were project-specific and designed on a custom basis because standard equipment was not yet available.

Automated building control systems are now well accepted and widely used. They have been shown to reduce maintenance costs, increase energy efficiency, and enhance occupant satisfaction. By enabling environmental conditions to be tailored to the activities in each space (also called "task/ambient conditioning" or "personalized environmental conditioning"), these systems allow greater flexibility in how a building is used. They not only improve the day-to-day operation of complex facilities but also provide sophisticated emergency response services. (See the description of an automated fire response procedure presented previously in the "Emergency Response" subsection.)

An automated building control system consists of a computer system, its network of sensors located throughout the building, and actuators to operate the building equipment it controls. The sensors detect such environmental factors as temperature, humidity, static pressure, light levels, the presence of smoke, and security access. The system monitors environmental conditions throughout the building and adjusts the indoor climate for each zone according to its preprogrammed optimization procedures. Energy consumption, maintenance schedules, building diagnostics, communications use, fire prevention, and security needs are some of the factors commonly included in the optimization process.

These systems can also support facility management by providing current and historical information about the building's operation. Such data as changes in energy consumption between seasons or during the day, and the duty cycle of the HVAC can be recorded and presented in the form of printed reports, graphs, or on-line computer displays. This information can then be used to assess the loading on different components, establish maintenance programs, anticipate equipment failures, sustain occupants' comfort in the workplace, and generally operate the facility more effectively. A logical extension of delegating the routine and predictable adjustment of environmental control to the automated systems is to have the computer detect the occupants' activities and respond accordingly — an idea that gave rise to the concept of the intelligent building.

INTELLIGENT BUILDINGS

The term **intelligent building** has come to mean many different things. It first came into general use in the American construction industry in the early 1980s. The telephone companies that emerged after the divestiture of AT&T (American Telephone and Telegraph) were looking for a marketing edge to make their products more attractive. Developing applications that employed both computers and telecommunications technology was one strategy to capitalize on the office automation boom.

Suppliers and developers formed alliances to provide what they called "intelligent building services" or "shared tenant services." Equipped with state-of-the-art communications technology, these intelligent buildings not only provided sophisticated voice and data connectivity they also offered advanced automated building services. Common features were self-monitoring energy management systems that responded to the outside temperature, lights that dimmed according to the available daylight or switched off when a room was unoccupied, and highly developed security systems (Bing-Maddick 1988; Duffy 1988).

Today, the term *intelligent building* has come to represent an integration of automated building control technology, advanced telecommunications, and office automation. In combination, these technologies enable the office facility to be operated more efficiently and at the same time be more responsive to occupants' changing needs. There is no specific design or set of features that defines a building as "intelligent." Some of the services that may be provided are energy management, temperature control, lighting, security, emergency response, maintenance scheduling, facilities planning and costing, telecommunications and computer network control, and cable management.

The "free-address" workstation is a good illustration of the intelligent building concept (see the "Telecommuting" and "The Virtual Office" subsections in Chapter 2). This type of workstation recognizes the user by reading an electronically encoded identity card. The workstation is then automatically configured for that individual. The user's electronic mail and telephone calls are routed to that location, and the person's computer files are made available there. In effect, the organization's information system recognizes where that individual is working and takes care of delivering the necessary information and communication services to that location.

In an intelligent building, there would be a degree of integration between the building control system and the organization's information system so that it would also be aware of the number of people working in each area. Sensors could monitor indoor air quality and automatically adjust the quantity of fresh air supplied to each zone. Supplies to densely occupied areas, such as a conference room filled to capacity, could be automatically boosted while supplies to unoccupied areas could be reduced.

As with other sophisticated technologies, the benefits of any of these systems depend largely on the needs of the organization using them. Where the capabilities satisfy existing needs or permit work to be done more effectively, they can be of real benefit. In other cases, these capabilities are well beyond the users' requirements and so appear to them as overpriced.

Probably less than 1% of North American office buildings could be termed intelligent. The intelligent building is perhaps most important as a concept that is changing the way building control systems are viewed, so they can be better designed to support the organization and its activities.

OCCUPIED SPACE

It is the interior furnishings that most directly affect occupants' perception of their office and largely determine a visitor's first impression of the space. Furnishings and the way they are arranged also affect the functionality of the space, the quality of the physical and social environment, individual comfort, and health.

People are strongly influenced by their physical surroundings. An office that looks bright, neat, and comfortable exudes an atmosphere of quality that encourages good work, in contrast to one that is drab and run-down. What's more, a high-quality work environment may help to attract and retain talented workers. The role of office quality as a measure of status is not an arbitrary symbol. It reflects the importance that all employees place on the quality of their work space.

In furnishing an office, difficult trade-offs have to be made among cost, functionality, and aesthetics. There is also the politically sensitive issue of how the budget for furnishings is apportioned among the different levels of the organizational hierarchy. There are no simple solutions to these issues. Each organization presents a unique situation that demands an approach tailored to its particular culture and circumstances.

The topic of furnishings is introduced in this section, and the major types of furnishings used in American and Canadian offices are described. In subsequent chapters, the impact of the office setting on human performance is addressed, and the role of furnishings is further elaborated.

Furniture

Chairs and work surfaces are the most basic furnishings in offices. They are the core of an individual's work setting, around which filing cabinets, side tables, planters, and office equipment are arranged. Surveys consistently show that most office workers are dissatisfied with the quality of their furniture. Chairs that cannot be adjusted to give adequate support and comfort and insufficient work surface area are the most common complaints (Harris 1991).

Though some features may seem like unnecessary luxuries, poor work settings exact a productivity cost. Office workers fatigue more quickly and take more frequent breaks when their work setting is uncomfortable. As well, uncomfortable work postures aggravate or cause back and shoulder injuries, cumulative trauma disorders (also called repetitive strain injuries), and other ailments that result in illness absenteeism.

The design of work settings for office workers who use computers is particularly important. People tend to adjust their body position less frequently when working at a computer than when doing other types of office work. As a result, they are more susceptible to neck, shoulder, and back strain. Ergonomically appropriate furniture designs can significantly reduce the incidence of these problems. Recommendations for the design of computer work settings are presented in Chapter 6.

A wide range of furniture styles and options is available. Furniture should be sufficiently adjustable to properly fit the people who will use it and give them adequate support for the range of work activities they perform. Furniture, especially chairs, differs in its ease of operation as well as its performance once it is correctly adjusted. Users must be shown how to adjust the furniture (not all controls are evident or easy to use) and given guidelines for its proper setup. Investments in expensive ergonomic furnishings are all but lost if they are incorrectly adjusted.

Many of today's offices use systems furniture — furniture designed as a system of component pieces that can be mixed and matched to produce a wide range of work settings. Such systems generally offer work surfaces in different widths and lengths that fit into a variety of upright supports. Work surfaces of various shapes and sizes are easily built up from these individual components (Figure 4.37).

Figure 4.37 With systems furniture, a variety of work settings can be assembled from a standard set of components. Wall panels, desk surfaces, storage compartments, chairs, and other components are available in a wide range of sizes and finishes. (*Source:* Steelcase, Grand Rapids, Mich.)

Overhead storage, lighting, side tables, desk drawers, filing cabinets, acoustic panels, and other furnishings are standard components of most furniture systems. System components are offered with a variety of finishes and colors designed to look pleasing and professional.

Organizations sometimes furnish an entire office facility with brand-new furniture. More often, though, offices are furnished with a combination of old, new, and refurbished pieces that may be more or less compatible. This can present quite a challenge for space planners, especially if components from many furniture systems are used. Not only are components from different suppliers generally incompatible; even components from the same manufacturer may not fit together if they are from different product lines. Clustering furniture into groups of like systems is one approach. A detailed computer-based furniture inventory that includes characteristics such as the manufacturer, color, and dimensions of each component can enable space planners to make better use of existing furnishings.

Some manufacturers offer a buyback or exchange program whereby credits earned from the return of used furniture can be applied to the purchase of new pieces. Such programs may be an important consideration when selecting a supplier.

Walls, Partitions, and Screens

Walls, partitions, and screens divide space into individual work areas, control movement through a space by defining corridors, serve as acoustic and visual barriers, and may conceal cables that connect equipment to its power or communication source.

What most people call "walls" are broadly grouped into two technical categories: walls and partitions. **Walls** run vertically from the floor to the underside of the floor above, an arrangement termed slab-to-slab or floor-to-floor. They may be load-bearing, provide lateral stability to the structure, or contain services such as plumbing, electrical conduits, and communications cabling. For practical purposes, walls can be treated as permanent. If they can be moved at all without risk to the structural integrity of the building, it is invariably an expensive modification. For the same reason, making new openings in walls for doorways or service runs is seldom allowed and, if permissible, is usually costly, especially if existing services have to be rerouted.

Partitions are not load-bearing components of the building structure and contain minimal (if any) servicing, such as telephone lines or shielded power cables. They are usually constructed of a metal frame with front and back panels, and may be hollow or filled with sound-absorbent material. Partitions can be installed and removed fairly easily. They can be any height but usually run either slab-to-slab or from the floor slab to the underside of the suspended ceiling. They provide less acoustic separation if they run only to the suspended ceiling because, even with acoustic ceiling tiles, sound is transmitted through the **ceiling plenum** (the space above the suspended ceiling).

Screens are the modular panels used in open plan offices. They can be freestanding or fit together on interlocking frames, and are available in a dizzying array of styles, shapes, colors, textures, and materials. Their internal construction may incorporate servicing such as electrical and communications cabling; special sound-absorbent materials to reduce noise transmission; magnetic, tackable or erasable surfaces; window panels; and even supplementary ventilation.

Screens are the most flexible way to divide space into individual work areas. Most furniture systems offer screens with windows, doors, and perforated or louvered panels to create as closed or open a space as desired. Screens can be arranged so as to provide as much visual privacy as needed but only limited acoustic privacy.

The choice of materials, internal design, and height will affect the degree of sound absorption that the screen provides. In general, the better the sound absorption, the more costly the screen. The larger the screen, the better it will block sound, but larger screens are more of an impediment to air circulation. Tall screens may also cast troublesome shadows onto work surfaces. For this reason, in making decisions regarding the size and placement of screens, consideration should be given to their effect on all the building services in the space, including illumination, thermal comfort, air quality, acoustics, and aesthetics.

Window Coverings

Window coverings are used to control the direction and intensity of light entering a space and the resulting heat gain. Windows not only allow natural light from outside to enter the office; they give people a view to the outdoors or adjacent spaces such as an atrium. They make an area feel more spacious as well as aesthetically more pleasing.

The design and orientation of a building strongly affect the amount of daylight entering the occupied spaces during the course of a day and in different seasons. The placement of windows, the orientation of the wall, the depth to which windows are recessed, the use of outside shading devices, and the choice of glass coatings can all be used to adjust the quality and quantity of natural light entering a space.

The design and orientation of outside shading devices must take into account the movement of the sun across the sky. Geographic latitude determines the maximum sun elevation and sun position during the day and over the seasons. Local climate must also be considered, especially since its effects may only be evident in certain seasons. The sloped glass awning around a performing arts building was an attractive design element, but in winter, it became a hazard as the snow it collected periodically cascaded onto the walkway and waiting theatergoers below (Figure 4.38). Once a building is constructed, the control of daylight is generally limited to the use of interior window coverings such as curtains, drapes, and blinds.

Figure 4.38 Effects of the local climate may only be evident in certain seasons. The sloped glass awning around this performing arts building (left photo) becomes a hazard in winter when the snow it collects slides onto the walkway and waiting patrons below (right photo). The dark areas on the glass awning are where the snow has slid off.

Where computers are used near windows, the coverings should be capable of completely blocking the incoming daylight as well as be able to allow the desired amount of daylight in. Computer screens, being made of glass, are reflective. Bright light sources appear as distracting glare spots on the screen and make the screen difficult to read. Antiglare computer screens or antiglare devices mounted on the screens can reduce glare problems, but even these measures cannot compensate for a very bright light source such as direct sunshine.

Adjustable vertical louvered blinds are a good choice of window covering for rooms where computers are used. The blinds can be adjusted to direct light away from the screen, while permitting some daylight to enter and not completely obstructing the view to the outside. When necessary, they can be adjusted to completely block incoming daylight (Figure 4.39).

Although it is less expensive to install blinds as one long unit with a single control, this approach generally leads to problems. No one angle or position of the blinds will be suitable for everyone seated along the length of the unit. For this reason, it is better to have separate, individually controlled blinds next to each work space.

Window coverings also help to control unwanted sound reflection. Glass, being a hard surface, is a strong sound reflector. To reduce background noise in rooms with large window areas, window coverings can be chosen that have good sound-absorbing characteristics. Drapes made of heavy fabric with a very full design absorb sound well. However, they tend to trap and hold dirt, they are expensive to clean, and their removal and rehanging are somewhat disruptive. Also, they may not suit the sleek, neat lines of current office designs. Sheer drapes are made of a light fabric. They diffuse light but offer virtually no acoustic absorption. They are often used on the glass walls of interior meeting rooms, particularly small ones, to give visual privacy without making the space feel closed in.

Floor Coverings

The choice of floor coverings is not solely a matter of aesthetics. As with other elements of the office, their selection involves a number of trade-offs. Office floor coverings are selected for their durability, cost, ease of maintenance and renovation, aesthetic appeal, and such performance criteria as flame, stain, and rot resistance. They not only affect the look of an office; they also affect the acoustics and air quality.

Figure 4.39 Although no computer is used at this workstation, the blinds must be kept shut to suit the needs of neighboring VDT operators. Those not using VDTs must work without the benefit of natural light or a view of the outdoors that their prized window location offers.

Where equipment must be moved frequently, durability and rolling resistance are important. High-traffic areas such as entrances and corridors need rugged floor coverings or the areas will soon look shabby and run-down. Office areas that are frequently subjected to rough use, such as rearranging furniture or moving equipment across the floor, also require extremely durable floor coverings. Hard floor coverings (such as tiles, wood, marble, or terrazzo) are favored for these heavy-use applications. In some cases, a durable carpet tile may be used. Since they are not normally glued in place, carpet tiles can easily be replaced as they wear out.

Most office areas do not receive such heavy use that durability is the overriding concern, so other considerations dominate the choice of floor coverings. Carpet is the most common type of floor covering in offices. A carpeted floor absorbs sound from people, equipment, and footfalls much better than a hard surface.

Carpets suitable for office use are available in a wide range of colors, patterns, and textures. Natural fibers such as wool and jute are attractive but expensive. They are often used to indicate more exclusive areas and higher status. Synthetic fibers such as nylon and polypropylene cost less and tend to be more durable.

Static charges can play havoc with computers, particularly when the relative humidity is low, as commonly occurs during cold or dry weather. The static charge that can be released when someone touches a computer after walking across a high-static material such as nylon can disrupt or damage computer equipment and cause data to be lost. Among carpet materials, polypropylene creates the fewest problems with static charge. A variety of grounding devices can be used to protect sensitive electronic equipment from static charges. Mats connected to an electrical ground can be placed on the work surface and under the seating area. By touching the grounded mat before handling electronic equipment, the user can safely discharge any static electricity.

Figure 4.40 Suspended, or dropped, ceilings, a popular choice for offices, consist of a lightweight metal frame hung from the underside of the floor above. Tiles that absorb sound and reflect light are fitted into the frame, forming the ceiling surface. The tiles can be easily removed, as shown here, giving access to the equipment housed in the **plenum**, the space between the dropped ceiling and the main structure above.

Serious air quality problems commonly arise during and after the installation of floor coverings. Newly manufactured carpets and the adhesives used to install them release chemicals into the air (termed **offgassing**). These chemicals not only produce unpleasant odors but can also cause severe headaches, nausea, and allergic reactions. Solvents in carpet adhesives tend to be more noxious than the chemicals offgassed from the carpet itself. Over time, the rate at which these chemicals are released into the air slows, and the concentration of contaminants will fall to normal levels if sufficient fresh air is circulated through the space and exhausted to the outside.

A number of measures can be taken to substantially reduce the unwanted side effects of carpet installation. Fundamentally, these preventive and mitigative actions minimize both the time that occupants are exposed to the chemical pollutants and the concentration of noxious chemicals.

Carpet materials that pose less of a health risk can be selected. In the water-based adhesives that are now available, many of the chemicals that cause air quality problems have been eliminated or greatly reduced. Wherever possible, these water-based adhesives should be specified. Carpet manufacturers have developed new products that generate much less airborne chemical contamination. As well, carpets can be unrolled and allowed to offgas in a well-ventilated warehouse before they are installed.

Office occupants' exposure to noxious chemicals can be greatly reduced by judicious scheduling of renovations. Since air quality problems will be most severe during installation, carpet should be installed when the office is unoccupied for as long a period as possible, such as during holiday closings. The installation should also be scheduled during a season when weather conditions permit the building to be flushed with outside air for the entire day (i.e., the ventilation system is operated without any air recirculation) in order to dilute and exhaust the chemical contaminants that are introduced. Depending on the air contaminant concentrations that are reached, it may be necessary to flush the building for several days or weeks.

Figure 4.41 Vertical service poles, such as the one shown here, are often used to carry cables from the dropped ceiling space to individual workstations. Frequent moves requiring that the position of the pole be changed, have left this ceiling tile with open holes giving the work area a shabby appearance.

Health complaints related to air quality should be monitored before, during, and after carpet installation. As the offgassing of airborne contaminants subsides, air recycling can gradually be reintroduced. If health complaints rise, the fraction of outside air should again be increased. Eventually, the rate of offgassing will become low enough to return to normal rates of air recycling.

Ceilings

The most widely used office ceiling design is the **suspended ceiling,** also called a **dropped ceiling** (Figure 4.40). It consists of a lightweight metal frame that is hung from the underside of the floor above or from the trusses. Standard-size acoustic tiles are then fitted into the frame. Since the tiles are not attached but simply rest in the frame, they can easily be removed for replacement or to access equipment.

Tiles are available in a variety of colors, textures, and patterns. They also differ in their performance characteristics, such as sound absorption qualities and light reflectance. The most widely used tile is a perforated, flat-surfaced, white or off-white, sound-absorbing tile, often referred to simply as an acoustic tile. It is the least expensive, reflects light well, and has a long history of successful use.

Suspended ceilings offer a convenient way to conceal the many services hung from the ceiling while providing ready access. However, frequent moves can leave openings or break the tiles making the ceiling look shabby (Figure 4.41). Raised flooring is becoming more common and offers an alternate route for cables and air supply ducting. If less equipment is housed above the suspended ceiling, it may be possible to reduce its height or eliminate it altogether. However, ceilings in office areas still need to provide enough sound absorption so the room will not be too noisy and reflect enough light to suit the activities for which the space is used, so some form of ceiling material will be needed.

Safety is a prime consideration for ceilings. Whatever services are placed above a suspended ceiling must not be combustible or promote the spread of fire.

Figure 4.42 People rely on signs and other graphic displays to find their way in buildings. This sign has been mounted too close to the ceiling. Part of the sign is brightly lit and the rest is in shadow, making it difficult to read. The glossy finish of the lettering is highly reflective, further reducing legibility.

Ceiling tiles and their suspension system must be sufficiently fire-resistant to remain in place during a fire without falling for one or more hours, depending on the local regulations. Cables installed above a ceiling must be wrapped in a fire-rated material (such as Teflon) or installed in a conduit. Since these materials are more expensive than unwrapped cable, it may be less costly to find alternate routings.

The qualities of ceiling tiles and related materials that make them useful in damping noise in a workplace — porosity, light weight, and brittleness — also make them prone to shed fibers and dust into the air. Recent studies suggest that there may be an association between the presence of man-made mineral fiber dust (such as that shed by acoustic ceiling tiles) and buildings that exhibit sick building syndrome (see the subsection "Airborne Particles" in Chapter 5). If this is a concern, ceiling tiles can be coated with a thin plastic film, reducing the amount of dust shed with little change to their acoustic performance.

Signage and Wayfinding

To find their way in a building, people intuitively develop a mental model of the interior space and solve a surprising array of spatial problems. Because people differ in their ability to solve this type of problem, they depend on orientation aids, such as signs, to negotiate what to the visitor may seem to be a labyrinth of corridors.

Buildings are replete with directional information — some helpful, some erroneous. The architecture, the spatial configuration, graphics (such as patterns or colors on the walls in different areas of a building), and directions given verbally all affect the ease with which visitors and the occupants themselves can find their way.

A successful wayfinding system helps people move through a building by providing coherent, appropriate, and legible information. People obtain the information on signs and other graphic displays by glancing or scanning, usually while they are in a busy corridor with distractions such as noise, people moving, and lights flashing. To make wayfinding as clear as possible under these distracting conditions, it should be standardized. Signs should have a standard format, uniform presentation (layout, logic and content of information, character sizes, color, and material), and consistent placement so people will know where to look for wayfinding information and how to interpret it (Figure 4.42).

Signage can also be used to discourage unauthorized access. Deliberate omission of wayfinding cues makes it difficult for a stranger to move confidently through a building. For example, corridors can be made to look the same by removing names

Figure 4.43 Outdoor signs must often be read and understood at a glance. The original sign in this parking lot (left photo) did not have commas between the numbers. It was unclear whether the numerals represented a single address or a list of buildings. Visitors would unexpectedly slow or stop their car to read the sign and figure out which way to go. Unfortunately, this hesitation was the cause of numerous rear-end collisions. A new sign (right photo), with commas placed between the numbers, resolved the ambiguity and eliminated the traffic problem.

and room numbers from office doors and not providing wayfinding signs except for emergency exits. Those unfamiliar with the layout quickly become disoriented and lost.

Similar principles apply to outdoor signs. In addition, outdoor signs should promote the organization and convey a positive image. People should be directed safely and without confusion to the correct building. This is especially important where several buildings are clustered (Figure 4.43).

Office Layout

An office layout specifies where individuals will work, the amount of space they will have, and the furnishings and equipment they will use. The layout, together with the aesthetic design, projects a certain corporate image — a physical statement to both occupants and visitors.

The importance of layout design is often underestimated. The office layout has a major effect on the ease with which work activities can be done. It will affect whom people are most likely to meet and influence the way they will interact. The office layout also has an effect on the amount of background noise and other disruptive activities.

Ideally, space planning should be preceded by a comprehensive evaluation of the organization's office needs, a process termed **programming**. Programming is a systematic interior design procedure for gathering quantitative and qualitative information about the tasks, equipment, and people to be accommodated. Recommendations are then developed for the allocation of space and equipment for each category of worker and the location of work groups relative to each other, termed **adjacencies**. The projection of future layout needs — arising from the growth or downsizing of the organization, expected changes in activities, and advances in office equipment, especially computers and telecommunications — should also be addressed in the program.

A comprehensive program can provide reliable quantitative data for the space-planning process. In addition to recommending the proportion of space needed for such categories as work settings, meeting areas, circulation, and shared services, the program normally specifies their design. The specifications are formalized as space and furniture standards that define for each category of job and activity center such details as the minimum floor area allocation, degree of enclosure of the space, number and types of chairs, number and size of work surfaces, and storage space (e.g., filing and supply cabinets, coatracks).

The space plan must conform to such government-mandated standards as emergency egress and access for the physically disabled. Since these regulations change over time, the space plan should be reviewed periodically to assure compliance.

In the past, the philosophy of office space planning tended to follow the assembly line model. Adjacencies were designed to optimize the physical work flow. Groups that passed work to each other were placed closer together and those that did not formally work together were farther apart. It is an approach well suited to highly procedural paper-based work flows. More recently, fundamental changes in the nature of office work have led to a rethinking of space-planning objectives. While office work still demands considerable paper-based documentation, information storage and exchange are increasingly done electronically. This change alone has had a dramatic impact on space planning.

For example, Canadian income tax-processing centers were traditionally designed with wide, oversize corridors so that large trolleys of tax returns could be moved easily between work groups. In turn, work groups were placed so as to minimize the distance paper documents had to be moved as they progressed through each processing step. In effect, the space-planning objective was to create an efficient assembly line for masses of paper documents to flow smoothly through a sequence of operations.

The tax-processing system has since changed and is now computer-based. The data from each tax return are entered into a central computer database, after which, the paper document is stored. All subsequent processing of the tax return is done using the electronic records. As a result, the large oversize corridors are now obsolete and have become a liability — representing a considerable area that must be fully serviced but is not readily converted to usable work space. What's more, positioning work groups according to the tasks they perform within the overall sequence of tax form processing is no longer needed either because virtually all information exchange is via the computer network. It makes little difference whether work groups are located on different floors, in different buildings, or in different cities. In fact, the work is now spread over many more geographic locations than in the past.

For people to work productively, the layout must provide suitable separation of private and shared space. Activities and equipment that generate noise — such as printers, coffee/meeting areas, photocopiers, and areas where people regularly speak on the telephone — should be isolated from areas used for more focused concentration. Occupants consistently report the frequency of distractions, be they noise or a view of people walking by, to be a major environmental inhibitor to their productivity.

With the automation of the office, adjacency planning has become less constrained by physical work flow demands. Instead, emphasis can be given to clustering work activities that require similar background environments, services, and equipment. For example, work areas for concentrated effort can be clustered together in a quiet area, away from the noise of printers, telephones, and office chatter. Whether the users are in marketing, engineering, or production is less important than their need for a place to think. In fact, many organizations have set up small meeting areas, individual work rooms, and other spaces as shared facilities that any member of the organization can reserve for their exclusive use on an "as-needed" basis. Similarly, collaborative work spaces should be situated in areas with compatible activities. In this way, organizations can maximize the productivity of their office workforce by offering a choice of settings. Individuals can then select the setting that best suits whatever task they are doing. It is a recognition that people's assigned work space will not be optimal for all their activities.

Figure 4.44 This individual work space is designed to accommodate people working from a wheelchair. (*Source:* Herman Miller Inc., Zeeland, Mich.)

Today, there is a greater knowledge component in all types of office work — from the administrative assistant who may use word-processing, database, and spreadsheet programs to the marketing manager who will directly access the company's computer system to analyze product sales and profit trends. Organizations are finding that people learn many useful tips, techniques, and fresh ideas informally from coworkers with whom they may not normally work.

To take advantage of this serendipitous cross-fertilization, many organizations are now planning adjacencies in a manner contrary to long-standing conventions. Work groups that have no formal need to work together are intentionally being placed next to each other so they will interact and learn from each other. It is an approach that can encourage a more dynamic and innovative work environment.

Accessibility to the Physically Disabled

Buildings have traditionally been designed for the able-bodied. But there is considerable variation in the physical capabilities of the people who use office buildings. In the United States, some 19 million people are mobility impaired, 13 million are visually impaired, 8 million are wheelchair users, 8 million are hard of hearing, and close to 2 million are blind (Kearney 1992).

Traditional office designs present numerous barriers to the physically impaired. Stairways without alternative access routes (e.g., ramps or elevators), narrow doorways, small washrooms, corridors without handrails, and objects that protrude into circulation paths (e.g., fire extinguishers and water fountains) are common obstacles to those in wheelchairs. Washroom fixtures, drinking fountains, signs, and various controls are often installed too high to be easily reached or seen by very short individuals, the elderly, or those in wheelchairs.

Trying to address these deficiencies after a building is constructed is expensive, and retrofitting a building while it is in use is disruptive. It is considerably less costly and more effective to incorporate the needs of the physically disabled when an office building is being designed instead of after the fact.

Office designs have in fact become more responsive to the needs of people with restricted mobility, impaired vision, or limited hearing (Figure 4.44). As well, legislation such as the 1990 Americans with Disabilities Act has required that "reasonable accommodation" be made for people with physical disabilities. Although "reasonable accommodation" is not precisely defined, it is being broadly interpreted as reducing or eliminating barriers that prevent disabled people from participating fully as workers and consumers. As such, the design and management of office facilities will increasingly require that furnishings, accessibility, and spatial layouts take into account the special needs of the disabled.

Aesthetics

Aesthetics is the branch of philosophy concerned with the theory and description of beauty. The term is used informally to mean the accepted notions of what is beautiful, pleasing to the eye, or "in good taste."

Few discussions of building performance include the subject of aesthetics. The choice of colors and textures; the style of furniture, light fixtures, and other furnishings; and the use of line and form to define space are treated primarily as matters of taste or preference rather than as influential factors that affect workplace performance. Yet virtually all aesthetic choices in office design affect human behavior and job performance. The choices made and the process by which aesthetic elements are selected also affect occupant satisfaction and morale. Aesthetic elements convey the identity and culture of an organization to both visitors and employees. As well, the choice of materials and other aesthetic decisions affect maintenance and operating costs.

Aesthetic elements influence the social behavior of office occupants, their perception of the work setting, how quickly they fatigue, and how tolerant they are of physical stressors. For example, textured materials trap airborne particles and are more difficult to clean than smooth surfaces. Working near textured drapery can cause an allergic reaction in people sensitive to dust and molds. For such individuals, a plastic blind that collects less dust and is more easily cleaned would be a better selection. The choice is more than an aesthetic decision; it has direct health implications.

Fashion trends and personal taste have exerted a strong influence on office design. In the 1970s, earth colors such as brown, yellow, green, and orange were popular choices. In the 1980s, the fashion changed to gray tones with accent colors such as burgundy. Some offices were designed entirely in shades of gray. Gray concrete columns were often left exposed if they blended with the color scheme.

There is a role for current fashion and personal preference in office design, but that role should be subordinate to issues of human performance. Decisions about aesthetics are too important to be treated merely as a matter of popular trend. As with other facility trade-offs, the priorities used in making aesthetic choices must be consistent with their contribution to the success and productivity of the organization.

PHYSIOLOGICAL AND PSYCHOLOGICAL RESPONSE TO AESTHETIC ELEMENTS

People respond physiologically and psychologically to aesthetic elements. We depend on our five senses (sight, hearing, touch, taste, and smell) to detect the physical aspects of our world. The information we receive depends on the characteristics of our senses and the way the brain processes those sensations. There are substantial differences between the physical dimensions of our environment and the way they are perceived by a human

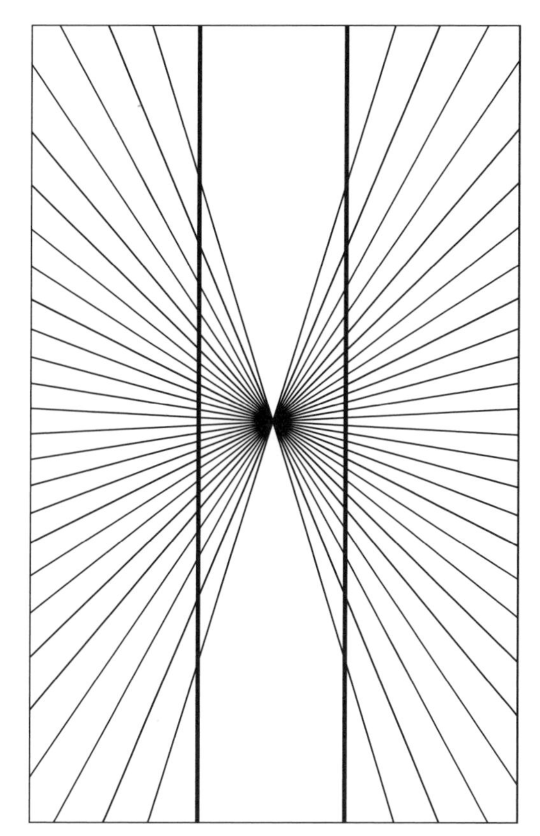

Figure 4.45 Hering's illusion. All the lines in this drawing are straight, but the interaction between them makes the pair of vertical lines appear curved.

observer. In fact, our perception of the physical world is much less accurate than we commonly assume.

Optical illusions, for example, result from inaccuracies in our visual perception. In Figure 4.45, the two vertical lines appear curved, even though they are straight. The background of diagonal lines causes the brain to form a perception that is fundamentally incorrect. Yet even when we are fully aware of the misrepresentation, the straight lines still appear to be curved.

Many of the discrepancies between the physical environment and the way we perceive it result from the highly adaptive nature of human perception. For example, if the human perception of color were solely dependent on the spectrum of light that reached the eye, then objects would appear to be different colors when illuminated by different sources. Compared to the color rendition under daylight, objects appear to have a yellow cast when photographed under incandescent lamps and a green cast when photographed under fluorescent lights. But to the human observer, the colors appear the same under all three illumination conditions. The brain calibrates our color perception by reference to the colors of surrounding objects in our field of view so that they appear to remain the same color under a wide range of lighting conditions — a phenomenon termed **color constancy**.

The first impression people have of an office is visual. As they enter and move through the space, visual indicators guide their way and define functional work areas, public and private spaces, and emergency exits. Since people depend so heavily on visual cues, it is important that the idiosyncrasies of the human visual system be taken into account so that design elements create the intended visual effects.

The eye responds strongly to linear elements in the visual field. Bold lines catch our attention and certain colors appear to clash — that is, most people find it physically uncomfortable to view them together, and the image may even appear to vibrate. Such effects are characteristics of the human visual system, not a matter of personal preference.

Extremes of contrast are visually fatiguing. The eye adapts to differences in light level by opening and closing the pupil. If there are relatively large very bright and very dark objects within the visual field, the eye is continually adjusting the pupil size in an attempt to accommodate the extreme contrast. As a result, viewing is uncomfortable, and the eye quickly fatigues. Similarly, having to look at bright and dark objects repeatedly is also visually fatiguing.

A well-established guideline is that the difference in brightness of the immediate work area should not be greater than three times that of the background (Grandjean 1987). For example, a wall in a person's field of view should not be more than three times brighter than their work surface.

Figure 4.46 In this furniture layout, a runout extended by a rounded work surface can be used for small group meetings. (*Source:* Rosemont Office Systems, Lakeville, Minn.)

The change to light-colored work surfaces from dark-colored wood finishes was largely an effort to improve visual comfort. Placing a light-colored paper document on a dark work surface creates a high-contrast condition that is more difficult to look at for extended periods. Work surfaces with a reflectance of about 30% and soft hues, such as the beige and gray tones favored today, minimize visual fatigue (Birren 1968, 1978).

The brightness of a room also affects its perceived spaciousness. People find that light-colored walls make a room feel more open, whereas dark-colored walls make a room feel more enclosed. Formal restaurants and lounges commonly use darker-colored walls, ceilings, and furnishings, together with muted lighting, to give what most people find to be a welcome feeling of enclosure. But in an office setting, space is usually at a premium, and visual cues that make a space feel larger are generally preferred.

Although the appearance of office furniture has changed to incorporate new design concepts, the new look involves more than evolving aesthetic tastes. Office furniture designs have had to accommodate new technology. The use of computers, for example, has required that work surfaces be wider, have openings for cables and paper feed to printers, and accommodate keyboard supports.

Office furniture has also had to accommodate new styles of work. People commonly have several reference documents spread out around them while working at their computer. The rectangular desktop, once the standard office work surface, has given way to work settings that have two or more work surfaces commonly arranged in an L, or U shaped configuration providing more space to lay out documents and place equipment. Work has become more collaborative, and some designs have altered the rectangular work surface shape to incorporate an enlarged rounded end that can serve as a meeting table for two to five people (Figure 4.46).

A number of modifications to furniture detailing have been introduced to accommodate new work habits. For example, in using a computer, the operator frequently rests his or her arms on the work surface edge. Changing from the conventional

Figure 4.47 A round-edged work surface offers a more comfortable support for wrists and forearms than a conventional squared edge. (*Source:* Herman Miller Inc., Zeeland, Mich.)

sharp, right-angled edges of earlier designs to the now common rounded edges offered an improvement in comfort and performance (Figure 4.47).

Varying the texture of furnishings adds visual interest. It also affects acoustics, illumination, the cost of maintenance, and human health. The softer and more textured a surface, the better it will absorb sound. Heavy drapery placed in front of a window reduces sound reflection, thereby diminishing the background noise level.

Indirect lighting systems depend on light being reflected off walls and ceilings to illuminate an area. These surfaces need to be sufficiently reflective to provide enough light. Smoother surfaces generally reflect more light than textured ones. So the smoother the surface texture of a colored screen, the higher its reflectance and the brighter it will make a space. However, highly reflective surfaces can create bright spots that can distract and visually fatigue workers, particularly computer operators. The choice of surface texture thus affects the quality and quantity of illumination at the work surface.

Heavily textured materials more readily trap dust, dirt, and odors than smoother fabrics or hard-surfaced materials such as plastics, wood, and plaster. In a smoking area, retention of odors by heavy fabrics makes it difficult to clear the tobacco smell from the room. Textured fabrics can be particularly troublesome in high-traffic areas such as public entrances, where dirt is brought in from the outdoors on footwear, clothing, and with drafts of air. Paper products and other office supplies generate dust and odors where they are stored and used. For example, printers and photocopiers continuously generate paper fibers that are carried with the airflow. Especially in these areas, heavily textured surfaces and materials should be avoided.

The spatial arrangement of office furnishings affects the pattern of interaction among office occupants and their level of physical activity. At one time, a principal objective in office layout design was to improve efficiency by reducing physical movement. Storage cabinets were placed within easy reach. Seating was arranged to optimize work flow. Now, office layouts are commonly designed so that people will be less sedentary, especially for those who use computers intensively. Equipment, storage, and seating are positioned so that occupants have to get up and walk around periodically. The activity makes people a little more alert and is healthier than sitting for long periods.

Ventilation efficiency is also influenced by the spatial layout of office furnishings. The size and placement of screens and partitions alter the pattern and speed of air movement through a space, and as a consequence, the frequency of air changes at different locations within a room. If a small area is surrounded by high partitions, it will tend to receive a lower airflow than if the partitions were lower or did not completely surround the space. The degree to which air quality and thermal comfort are affected depends on the unique characteristics of the office space. Screen heights of 1.6 meters (5 feet) generally provide an optimal trade-off. They are low enough for adequate ventilation and overhead illumination, and high enough for visual privacy.

As with other elements of office design, aesthetic issues have multiple effects on human performance. Many of these effects are self-evident and readily accepted once they are pointed out, but others are subtle and not easily foreseen.

COLOR IN THE WORKPLACE

One of the more controversial issues in office design is color. Human response to color is complex. Certain colors have strong culturally defined meanings. For example, in Western cultures yellow is considered to be a cheerful color. Yet in imperial China, yellow was the color of the emperor. The penalty for wearing the emperor's yellow was immediate execution, an association unlikely to inspire joy.

The effort and attention devoted to color selection illustrate the importance that people ascribe to it. Individuals expend considerable time and effort choosing the colors of their living space. Similarly, organizations invest heavily in selecting suitable corporate colors and designing them into every aspect of their operation. A corporate color scheme is expected to communicate a strong image and promote employee identification with the organization. Clearly, in selecting corporate colors, it is important to recognize and avoid colors with negative connotations.

Despite the sweeping generalizations often made about the influence of color on human performance, few physiological effects have been reliably demonstrated. In most cases, any influence that color may have is masked by other factors that have a more direct impact.

For example, it is widely believed that color can influence people's thermal sensation. Warm colors such as red are said to make people feel hot while cool colors such as blue make them feel cool. However, research has repeatedly shown that the color of the walls of a room has no measurable effect on thermal comfort (Fanger, Breum, and Jerking 1977; Rubin and Elder 1980). The dominant factors in thermal comfort are temperature, relative humidity, air movement, the type of clothing worn, and the level of activity.

Some colors have been shown to evoke an immediate physiological response. However, the effect is temporary. For example, it has been demonstrated that the color red can produce an arousal response in humans. The heart rate is elevated, and there is a change in skin conductance. This makes red an appropriate color to use for warnings and to catch people's attention. However, once the viewer has accommodated to the color (which can take as little as 50 seconds), the physiological indicators return to normal levels (Wilson 1966).

In the treatment of emotionally disturbed people, there has been some success in using color to influence behavior or mood. However, it is doubtful that research on disturbed patients can be generalized to workers in offices. As well, subjects in an experiment are exposed to a condition for a short period of time (typically a few minutes to a few hours), whereas workers spend day after day in the office. Few studies of color are done in office settings.

The length of time spent in an environment is an important factor in people's reaction to it. For example, people find bright and bold colors to be pleasing, inviting, and cheery for a short time but tire of them over a longer period. Commercial and retail designs are often based on this human reaction. For example, bold colors are commonly used in fast-food restaurants that want to serve people quickly and have them stay only a short time. Where dining is to be more leisurely, muted color are used. Office workers tend to dislike bold designs and saturated colors in the workplace, perhaps for similar reasons. There is no evidence of a psychological benefit to using bold colors in the office, and research indicates that these designs can be distracting (Birren 1978; Brill et al. 1984).

The colors in an office should provide a balance between consistency and variety. Both overstimulation and monotony are visually tiring. As noted previously, the *brightness* of walls and furnishings is more important than their color. From a physiological perspective, any soft hue with a reflectance of about 30% would do equally well (Birren 1968). This gives designers and occupants a wide range of colors that theoretically would work well in an office. However, in practice, not all colors are equally accepted.

In North American offices, the same few restrained colors tend to be used. Work surfaces, storage units, walls, and ceiling are generally off-white, beige, tan, gray, or certain types of wood paneling. Only a few colors are used for chairs and flooring, and these tend to be patterns and accent colors. This relatively narrow range of colors is what occupants most commonly associate with an office environment. Surveys indicate that the color schemes occupants consider to be most appropriate for an office are those they most frequently see in offices. Though occupants might not choose these colors for their own homes, they are the ones that office workers generally believe should be used in their offices (Brill et al. 1984).

CORPORATE COMMUNICATION

Aesthetic choices convey important corporate messages that should be consistent with an organization's culture. The appearance of an office is judged against expectations of what such an office should look like.

There are informal norms for color selection, style and quality of furniture, the design of light fixtures, and other standard elements of an office setting. Deviation from these norms suggests that the organization is somehow different from its peers. A well-appointed law office is seen as evidence of a successful practice, but clients may regard opulent office furnishings as an indication that they are overpaying for services. In contrast, a law office that looks old and shabby does not inspire client confidence. The appointments of a government employment office are expected to be serviceable but not sumptuous. If it looks like a law office, it would probably be viewed as an example of government waste.

Whether by accident or by design, the look and feel of an office makes a statement about the organization. If that message is consistent with the corporate culture, it will generally be accepted. If it is out of character, it will attract attention. For an organization changing its corporate culture, a radically different avant-garde office design can support the message of change. But the same design can appear frivolous or pretentious if its message is inconsistent with corporate policy and actions.

OCCUPANT SATISFACTION

People value their individuality and strive to express their character in their daily lives, including their workplace. The more uniform the office setting, the more occupants will seek to personalize their space. Many aesthetic choices offer an opportunity for office occupants to make their work area unique without incurring additional expense or compromising the overall appearance. For example, in defining an office design, a range of colors could be specified for chairs, workstation panels, and other furnishings. Then occupants could be allowed to choose from that selection.

Not surprisingly, participation in office design can increase the occupant's satisfaction and acceptance of the final design. Aesthetic choices can offer relatively inexpensive opportunities to enhance occupant satisfaction. However, soliciting employee comments bears with it the expectation that their contributions will be given consideration and somehow make a difference in the result. Regrettably, their input is often ignored because it remains a collection of unstructured comments. Unless comments are organized and addressed in a structured fashion, there is no practical way to include them in the design process.

One popular technique for soliciting occupant input is to provide a suggestion box or bulletin board to receive written comments. These freeform comments need to be systematically analyzed and summarized. Otherwise the onus is on the design team to read, mentally evaluate, and remember the comments so they can be taken into account in developing the design.

It is generally more effective for occupants to comment on specific, well-defined design issues. They can also offer unsolicited suggestions, but defining specific topics ensures that every contributor considers the same set of issues. The occupants' input can then more easily be organized, evaluated, summarized, and used.

Office workers may be well qualified to comment on their perceptions, but they are not trained in office design. For this reason, providing them with background information — such as the trade-offs involved with different design alternatives, expected impacts on human performance, and accepted norms for their type of organization — can help them offer more useful and better-informed opinions and suggestions.

Although people are more willing to live with decisions if they were responsible for them, the organization is better served by aesthetic choices with which it will be comfortable for several years rather than choices it is merely willing to tolerate. Colors, textures, and decorations that deviate widely from the norm may at first be received with enthusiasm but often become tiresome or are later seen to be inappropriate.

It is unrealistic to expect unanimous agreement from occupants about aesthetic choices such as color. But it is not difficult to propose a range of choices that meet human performance and corporate requirements and are not offensive. It is more important that an office space meet the occupants' expectations than that it cater to their personal aesthetic tastes (Brill et al. 1984; Whitfield and Slatter 1978).

MAKING CHOICES ABOUT AESTHETICS

Developing successful designs requires expertise. There is an art to selecting colors that form pleasing combinations. The same color will look different when it covers a small area as opposed to a large one. Its appearance will be influenced by the colors next to it and the way it is illuminated. Considerable experience is needed to be able to visualize the finished office setting from a collection of color chips and fabric samples. Similarly, visualizing the look and feel of different furniture arrangements, illumination, accent elements, and furnishing designs requires a trained and experienced eye.

However, the final say in choosing office furniture, colors, layout, light fixtures, and other furnishings commonly rests with senior managers or top-ranking executives who are not experts in office design or its effects on human performance.

Because nearly everyone involved in office design believes he or she knows about aesthetics and can make such choices on behalf of others, aesthetic choices are commonly decided in isolation, separate from other aspects of office design. There is little recognition that these choices have multiple consequences and profoundly affect occupants' perceptions of many office characteristics.

In the context of a working office, aesthetics, as important as it may be, should not be the driving force in choosing among designs. If the principal objective of an office facility is to support the work activities of the occupants, then aesthetic choices must be made in the context of and subordinate to their impact on human performance. Aesthetic design choices should be coordinated with facility operations and management, interior design, and human performance requirements. Facility management professionals can assess the impacts on the building's operation, maintenance, and furnishings, whereas human performance is the domain of such specialties as industrial design, industrial psychology, ergonomics, and human factors. Drawing from both these groups of specialties, aesthetic design choices can be made that better serve the overall objectives of an organization.

There is a role for corporate and personal preference in the aesthetic choices of office design. But first priority should be given to optimizing human performance and facility operations. The office design should then be refined to communicate corporate identity and image, be in suitable conformance to industry norms (or depart from them if appropriate), and meet fundamental design criteria in the use of color, line, and form. And finally, personal preference should be accommodated as widely as possible within this overall design, allowing individuals to make choices for their own work areas.

OCCUPANT EFFECTS ON THE PERFORMANCE OF BUILDING SYSTEMS

Occupants regularly try to modify facility characteristics they find uncomfortable or inconvenient — much to the chagrin of the facility management staff. Yet these initiatives are often well-intentioned efforts to work under conditions that should be better than they are. As such, occupant modifications frequently highlight problems in the operation or design of the building systems.

Unfortunately, these efforts often have unwanted side effects. One of the most common occupant modification is to partially or completely cover air vents that are causing uncomfortable drafts (Figure 4.48). Blocking air vents not only changes conditions in the immediate vicinity, it increases airflow to other vents along the

Figure 4.48 People bothered by drafts from the ventilation system often block the airflow by partially or completely sealing supply vents. Here occupants used paper and tape to partially close off the troublesome air vent, indicated by the arrow.

Figure 4.49 Boxes of computer diskettes placed over the air vent on this window sill block the room's air supply. Furthermore, the direct sun, temperature shifts, and moisture accumulation next to the window can damage sensitive materials.

same duct which, in turn, affects temperature regulation in these areas making them uncomfortable.

Occupants often use windowsills for storage, blocking air vents in the process (Figure 4.49). In addition to reducing the room's air supply, the stored materials may be damaged by exposure to direct sun, temperature shifts, and moisture accumulation.

Occupants may inadvertently increase the energy demands on a building system by adjusting one component of the system without understanding how the total system functions. For example, in northern winter climates, when a home thermostat is set to a lower temperature energy is saved. By setting a lower room temperature the furnace operates for a shorter time, and so consumes less energy. But commercial office buildings function in a different way, and lowering the thermostat in winter can actually *increase* energy consumption.

Large commercial office buildings commonly need to be cooled most of the year. They house so much heat-generating equipment and have such a low surface area relative to their volume that under most weather conditions, the occupied spaces must be cooled down to a comfortable temperature. In such a building, lowering the thermostat usually causes the building systems to provide additional cooling, which *increases* the energy consumed.

Another energy conservation measure that sometimes had troublesome consequences was **delamping** — reducing illumination levels by removing some of the lamps from ceiling fixtures. This can be a relatively inexpensive and unobtrusive way to save energy. Many office areas may be brighter than necessary, and the heat produced by electric lights accounts for as much as 40% of a building's cooling load. With fewer lamps, less electricity is used and less heat is generated.

Unexpectedly, delamping sometimes reduced air quality. In a variable-air-volume mechanical system (discussed in the subsection "The Mechanical System" earlier in this chapter), the amount of ventilation air supplied to a space depends on the

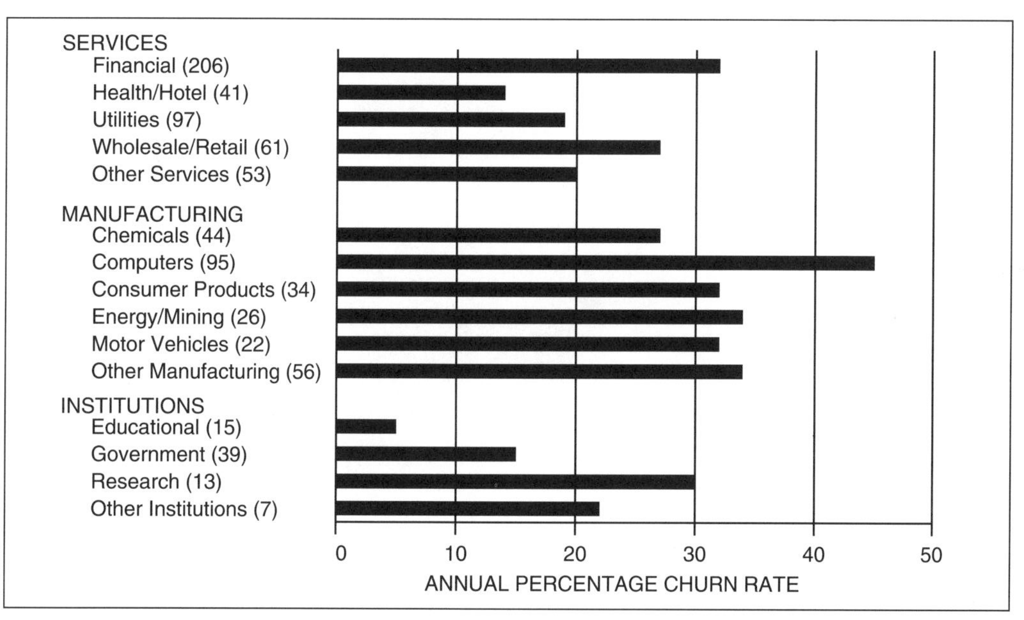

Figure 4.50 The frequency of office relocations in a facility is called the **churn rate**. It is calculated by dividing the total number of employee work space moves made in a year by the total number of office employees and then multiplying that result by 100. This chart shows the average annual churn rate for different types of organizations. The number of organizations in each group is shown in parenthesis. (*Source:* Data from a 1991 survey of 904 organizations by the International Facility Management Association. IFMA 1991.)

room temperature and the temperature setting of the thermostat. Ventilation air will be supplied until the room temperature reaches the thermostat setting. Then the supply of air is stopped or reduced (depending on the VAV system design). When lamps, and thereby some of the heat load, are removed, the space requires less overall cooling, and thus, less air is delivered. This problem can be corrected by adjusting the VAV system's air supply temperature so that it must operate for a longer time.

In one organization, delamping affected the social interaction among office occupants. Corridor illumination is generally brighter than needed to safely navigate the passageway, so corridors were seen as opportune for delamping. Office work areas were also delamped, but they require higher illumination levels and were substantially brighter than the corridors. The difference in illumination made it difficult for people in the work areas to recognize who was in the corridor, so they no longer gave acknowledging gestures to coworkers passing by. Unaware of their new anonymity, those in the corridor felt snubbed. Office morale dropped, and communication became curt and unfriendly. It was only after the problem was recognized and addressed that the escalating social discord was reversed.

On average, service-based organizations move or reconfigure over 30% of their work space each year (Figure 4.50). In addition to the disruption to work, each move increases the wear and tear on the furnishings and finishes, sometimes making the work setting look messy and unsettled (Figure 4.51). Each move leaves its mark on the facility not only physically but also in the way it is operated. The tendency for certain operating procedures to outlive their usefulness is sometimes the cause of troublesome office problems, as the following example illustrates.

Getting to and from a cafeteria on the top floor of a seven–story office building was a constant annoyance and time waster. The building had three elevators — which, for its size, should have been adequate — and the cost of adding another one was prohibitive. Yet it seemed to take an inordinately long time for everyone to get to and from lunch and coffee breaks. Staggering

Figure 4.51 Moving employees and their belongings requires advance planning. These boxes cluttered an entranceway for weeks after a move was completed because insufficient storage space had been set aside for moving.

these break periods was not suited to the organization's activities. Eventually the problem was found to lie not in the capacity of the elevator system but in the way it had been programmed.

Ten years earlier, the tenant on the fifth and sixth floors wanted to reduce disruption caused by people wandering through its space looking for the cafeteria. Since the tenant's floors were equipped with a separate eating facility, the tenant's employees made little use of the seventh-floor cafeteria. The tenant had the elevators reprogrammed so that two of the three elevators went no higher than the sixth floor. People going to the cafeteria were directed to the appropriate elevator, and the unwanted traffic on their floors was reduced. When the tenant moved out and its space was taken over by the organization that rented the rest of the building, no one thought to change the operation of the elevators. So several years passed and there was still only one elevator to the seventh floor. A simple reprogramming of the elevators increased access to the cafeteria and resolved the problem.

Over time, frequent workstation reconfigurations make it difficult to match thermostats and light switches with the areas they control. Sometimes partitions are added to create new offices. Unfortunately, it is more difficult to reconfigure the ventilation system than to add a partition, and it's not uncommon to find an enclosed office with a thermostat that controls a different room! Similarly, the placement of light switches does not always clearly or logically indicate which fixtures they operate — and can become rather annoying. Frustrated occupants in one building made their own labels to resolve such confusion (Figure 4.52).

Sometimes, facility performance can be substantially improved simply by changing the orientation of furnishings. For example, in Figure 4.53, filing shelves were oriented perpendicular to the overhead fluorescent light fixtures. As a result, the aisles were poorly lit for much of their length, and it was difficult to read the file tabs. Had the shelves been

Figure 4.52 Occupants frustrated by having their overhead lights inadvertently turned off solved the problem by labeling the switches.

arranged so that the lights were parallel to and over the aisles, this problem would not have occurred. Unfortunately, once the shelves had been installed and loaded, it was too costly to change their position, and the staff had to live with the poor illumination.

CONCLUSION

The information on building systems presented in this chapter was selected to give managers the background to ask reasonable questions of experts, to determine whether

Figure 4.53 These storage shelves were installed and loaded without regard to the pattern of overhead illumination. The shelves should have been oriented parallel to the ceiling fixtures, with the aisles beneath the lights. Instead, they were placed perpendicularly to the fixtures, making it difficult to read file tabs and labels in the poorly lit aisles.

expert recommendations fit well with the policies and goals of their organization, and to develop some criteria by which to judge the expert advice they receive.

The building industry has a reputation for using bravado to cajole, persuade, and even antagonize reluctant clients. Common to many industries, this style of business can be effective in winning the acquiescence of clients who might otherwise be more critical. However, in the case of buildings, decisions that affect the quality of the workplace have long-term and far-reaching consequences.

The characteristics of an office facility are not benign; they directly affect the way those who use that space will feel, work, and behave. Since accommodation costs are among the largest annual expenses of office-based organizations (commonly second only to labor costs), every effort should be made to secure the greatest performance return — including human performance — from that investment.

Buildings are comprised of diverse systems. The choices made in the design of each one influences a wide range of financial, technological, social, and aesthetic factors. Whether an organization is evaluating building systems for new construction or renovation, or is comparing rental space in different facilities, the issues are complex and broad in scope. Although executives and managers involved in the selection of work space may not be well versed in all the technical aspects of building design, it is important that they appreciate the way specific features of an office facility impact human performance — which is the subject of the following chapters.

LITERATURE CITED

Ballou, M. 1992. Survey pegs computer downtime costs at $4 billion. *ComputerWorld* (August 10):53–56.

Bing-Maddick, C. 1988. The developer's response to the intelligent building. In *Intelligent building guide 1988*, 15–19. London: IBC Technical Services.

Birren, F. 1968. Impact of color on employee morale and productivity. In *New concepts in office design*. Elmhurst, Ill.: Business Press.

Birren, F. 1969. *Light, color and environment*. New York: Van Nostrand Reinhold.

Birren, F. 1978. *Color and human response*. New York: Van Nostrand Reinhold.

Brill, M., S. Margulis, E. Konar, and BOSTI (Buffalo Organization for Social and Technological Innovation). 1984. *Using office design to increase productivity*. Vol.1. Buffalo, N.Y.: Workplace Design and Productivity.

Duffy, F. 1988. The shape of the future. In *Intelligent buildings: Applications of IT and building automation to high technology construction projects*, edited by Brian Atkin, 252–261. New York: John Wiley & Sons.

Economist. 1992a. Energy-efficient computers powered down. *The Economist* (December 5):88–89.

Economist. 1992b. New factories for old. *The Economist* (October 3):16–19.

Fanger, P., N. Breum, and E. Jerking. 1977. Can colour and noise influence man's thermal comfort? *Ergonomics* 20(1):11–18.

Grandjean, E. 1987. *Ergonomics in computerized offices*. London: Taylor & Francis.

Harris, L. 1991. *The office environment index 1991: Summary of worldwide findings*. A study conducted for Steelcase by Louis Harris and Associates, New York.

IFMA. 1991. *Benchmarks I*. Report #7. Houston: International Facility Management Association.

Kearney, D. S. 1992. Meeting the needs of ADA. *Facility Management Journal* (May–June):35–41.

PWC. 1991. *Office design guide handbook*. Draft Internal Document. Ottawa: Public Works Canada.

Rubin, A., and J. Elder. 1980. *Building for people*. Washington, D.C.: U.S. National Bureau of Standards.

Whitfield, T., and P. Slatter. 1978. The evaluation of architectural interior colour as a function of style of furnishings: Categorization effects. *Scandinavian Journal of Psychology* 19(3):251–255.

Wilson, G. 1966. Arousal properties of red versus green. *Perceptual and Motor Skills* 23:947–949.

Woods, J. 1989. Cost avoidance and productivity in owning and operating buildings. *Occupational Medicine: State of the Art Reviews* 4(4):753–770.

REFERENCES

Barton, P. K. 1983. *Building services integration*. London: E. & F. N. Spon.

Bradshaw, V. 1985. *Building control systems*. New York: John Wiley & Sons.

Butler, H. 1977. *Co-ordination of building services — A preliminary study*. Technical note TN 3/77. Berkshire, U.K.: Building Services Research and Information Association.

Markus, T. A., and E. N. Morris. 1980. *Buildings, climate, and energy*. London: Pitman Publishing.

Maver, T. W. 1971. *Building services design*. London: RIBA Publications.

Smith, P. R., and W. G. Julian. 1976. *Building services*. London: Applied Science Publishers.

Szokolay, S. V. 1980. *Environmental science handbook for architects and builders*. New York: John Wiley & Sons.

Chapter 5

THERMAL COMFORT, AIR QUALITY, AND ACOUSTICS

This chapter and the two that follow examine how the office environment affects the occupants — the users for whom the facility is to provide a productive workplace. The office setting influences the quality and quantity of work that occupants produce, their health and well-being, and psychosocial issues such as cooperation and support among coworkers, motivation, stress, and fatigue.

Individuals experience their environment as a whole, so not surprisingly, all these aspects are interrelated. An allergic reaction caused by an airborne chemical contaminant that makes people ill will reduce their productivity, and can make them feel irritable and fatigued. If they are working against a tight deadline, feeling ill can increase their stress level as well. Although the mechanisms by which different environmental factors interact to influence human behavior are not always well understood, the significance of their interaction is not in doubt.

For convenience, our discussion of the office setting and its effects on occupants is divided into three chapters. This chapter examines thermal comfort, indoor air quality, and acoustics. Chapter 6 addresses factors that have been highlighted by the widespread introduction of computers into the office setting. Topics such as ergonomics, illumination, and the health effects of computer monitors are covered. Most of these topics are also important for work that is not computer-based.

A number of issues arise from the interaction of physical, psychological, and social processes that are influenced by the physical office setting, the way organizations are structured, and how people are managed. These issues are discussed in Chapter 7. There is now a trend toward providing individuals with more environmental controls as a means of improving the quality of their office setting. This trend is examined in the context of managing the multiple effects of the office environment on human behavior and well-being.

Our discussion cannot provide a comprehensive review of these topics. A thorough treatment of indoor air quality alone could fill a volume, and several have been written. Rather, this discussion focuses on the major issues and dominant themes in occupants' concerns about their work environment.

The substance of each issue is presented along with relevant research evidence. Although every effort has been made to give a balanced treatment of contentious issues, this is not a literature review. The discussion is necessarily selective and reflects not only the importance of the issues but also the level of misinformation and confusion that surrounds them.

Several of the office environment issues addressed here are controversial. Either the source of the problem is disputed or there is disagreement on effective treatments. For managers dealing with a real and immediate problem, knowing that experts disagree may not be comforting or particularly helpful. Nevertheless, an understanding of what is known and the substance of disputed information at least provides a basis on which to weigh conflicting suggestions and choose a course of action. Ultimately, when office workers have serious concerns about the quality of their work setting, decisions must be made on how to address them and what action should be taken. Choosing not to act is just one of many possible alternatives.

HEALTH CONCERNS OF OFFICE OCCUPANTS

Most occupant complaints about the work environment involve some form of health concern. Because there are health and safety issues associated with every activity, at home as well as at work, many of the concerns expressed by office occupants are reflections of issues they face outside the workplace, too.

In recent years, the public has become acutely aware of environmental health issues. There is concern about contaminants in the food we eat, the water we drink, and the air we breathe. People are afraid of increased cancer risks caused by toxic wastes, the electromagnetic fields near power lines, or emissions from nuclear power plants. Their concerns are based on a mixture of fact, conjecture, publicity, and a fear of the unknown.

Asbestos, urea-formaldehyde insulation, and tobacco smoke were all at one time considered to pose no risk to human health but are now recognized as serious environmental hazards. To some extent, people are more concerned because they are better informed. In addition, many pollutants have become more serious health hazards because they are present in greater abundance or the risk of exposure has changed. The thinning of the earth's ozone layer has increased the danger of sunburn and skin cancer from exposure to sunlight. That sunshine could pose a serious health risk was unknown a generation ago, and because atmospheric ozone used to absorb more of the incoming UV radiation, sunshine was in fact a less serious health threat.

Having learned that today's disputed health risk is often found to be tomorrow's serious hazard, people have become more wary. For many, early reports of potential danger are sufficient justification to avoid possible exposure, just in case a link is eventually found. It can take years to document an environmental health risk and longer to prove that a specific condition is the cause. In the meantime, little or no action is taken to reduce that risk since none has been established. Unfortunately, if an association is eventually proved, many people will already have been exposed and their health placed in jeopardy. No one wants to learn that he or she has developed a medical condition that could have been prevented by being more cautious and avoiding a suspected though unproven hazard. It is against this background of uncertainty and expectation that many indoor environment complaints are played out.

THE NATURE OF HEALTH RISKS IN THE OFFICE SETTING

Individuals differ in their sensitivity to environmental conditions that stress their physical capacity, such as chemical contaminants. Many people suffer from allergies and develop illness symptoms because they react to substances such as pollen, dust, and molds to which others are not sensitive. Corrective lenses are worn to compensate for less than adequate vision. Those who do not themselves experience these conditions recognize that there are others who do. These types of individual differences are accepted without question.

In the same way, people differ in their sensitivity to the physical office environment. Small amounts of a chemical may irritate a few highly sensitive individuals but go unnoticed by most occupants. Although it is often assumed that all occupants would react to any significant problem in the physical office environment, conditions generally must reach extremes before everyone would be affected. A few people suffering illness symptoms may indicate the presence of environmental stressors that could eventually compromise the health and productivity of a much larger proportion of those exposed.

Employee illness is costly. In addition to experiencing a lower quality of work life, people who feel unwell at work tend to be less productive and more irritable, have lower morale, are absent more often, and have a higher rate of job turnover. Employees who are chronically ill or require frequent hospitalization are a costly drain on productivity. As well, organizations with a higher rate of employee illness may face increased medical insurance rates.

Woods (1989) found that the savings that could be achieved by reducing the utility, maintenance, and operating expenses in office buildings were relatively small compared with the labor cost of the office workers. Thus, efforts to reduce facility costs readily became counterproductive if they reduced employee performance or increased absenteeism by even a small amount.

Employees who suffer from unresolved medical problems arising from their workplace are turning to workers' compensation, their unions, and the courts for help. Indoor air quality claims commonly cite chronic respiratory ailments and skin rashes as symptoms. A union grievance is often filed with a workers' compensation claim, adding to the time and effort that employers must spend to address such problems.

The number of indoor air quality–related lawsuits has risen dramatically over the past two decades. A recent California case, *Call* v. *Prudential Insurance,* was settled out of court for an undisclosed amount. Included in the settlement were the plaintiff's legal expenses, alone rumored to be in the millions of dollars. In the United States, powerful provisions in the recently enacted Americans with Disabilities Act may provide additional grounds for employees to seek compensation for ailments linked to their office workplace.

In addition to the somewhat altruistic concern for occupants' well-being, employers have legal obligations to ensure the health and safety of their workforce. The occupational health and safety standards in Canada and the United States were designed to address the physically rigorous working conditions of the blue-collar workforce. Heavy machinery, toxic chemicals, and dangerous working conditions often posed serious health and safety risks (Figure 5.1). Prior to regulation, the quality of the working conditions was left to the employer's discretion. However, the level of occupational injury was considered to be too high. As well,

Figure 5.1 Occupational health and safety standards were initially designed to protect industrial workers from hazardous workplace conditions, such as pouring molten metal at this steel plant in 1960. (*Source:* National Archives of Canada, PA187927.)

employers that chose to implement more stringent health and safety standards found that the increased costs placed them at a competitive disadvantage compared with companies that were more lax. Government-imposed regulations set minimum standards that all employers had to satisfy.

Compared with the physically difficult conditions of the industrial blue-collar workforce, office jobs in the white-collar sector are much safer. The office environment is a relatively secure, clean, and comfortable place to work. There is no heavy equipment to cause injury, no risk of falling trees, mine-shaft collapse, or toxic chemical spills. Protected from the weather, the office setting offers a comfortable indoor climate year-round. Compared with work settings in heavy industry or resource extraction, it is hard to conceive that the office environment could in any way limit people's ability to work, let alone pose a threat to their health and safety.

But office work involves a different set of activities, and employees expect to work in conditions that are suited to their tasks, not just in conditions that are better than those in other industries. Occupational health and safety standards were intended to address industrial workplaces, entirely different from today's office setting. In fact, studies of offices where there are symptoms associated with sick building syndrome almost always find these facilities to be in compliance with health and safety regulations (Lippy and Turner 1991).

The problem does not lie in a failure to comply with regulations; it lies in a lack of knowledge of what those standards should be. In the absence of standards that reliably ensure a healthy office environment, office workers often demand that these standards be exceeded to the point that the office setting produces *no* ill effects.

Most health problems associated with the office environment result from chronic exposure to a low-level stressor rather than sudden exposure to an acute hazard. People are exposed to the office environment for long periods of time. The 40 hours a week spent at an office represent about a quarter of a person's sleeping and waking hours. The concentration of chemical and biological contaminants in the office is almost always far below levels that would cause immediate illness symptoms. Similarly, acute physical injuries such as broken bones, burns, or loss of limb are rare. But long-term exposures can make people feel unwell, make them more susceptible to illness, and in some cases cause serious and debilitating illness or injury (e.g., cumulative trauma disorders, asbestos-related lung diseases, or cancer).

Many health risks in the office developed recently and coincided with changes in construction methods, building design, and facility maintenance that allowed the interior environment to be more tightly controlled. The effort to conserve energy led to the construction of **sealed buildings** in which uncontrolled air exchange between the indoors and outdoors was largely eliminated. Such buildings generally have about 0.2 air changes per hour when the mechanical ventilation system is *not* operating — about the same as an energy-efficient house when air-conditioning and other mechanical ventilating systems are not operating (Levin 1994). However, offices generally have many more sources of contamination than a residence. With low air exchange rates, these contaminants can reach problematic levels. It was not until sealed office buildings were in use that many, now familiar, indoor air quality problems were first recognized.

Only recently has public awareness of the health effects of the office environment generated sufficient research upon which environmental standards for the office workplace can be based. Air quality was one of the first office environment concerns that was highly publicized and for which considerable research was done. Physical ailments, such as repetitive strain injuries, that result from poor furniture arrangements have also received considerable research attention. The seriousness of these injuries has led to the introduction of ergonomic guidelines in many organizations. Several agencies, such as the National Institute of Occupational Safety and Health (NIOSH) in the United States, are actively developing ergonomic standards for the office. Without the knowledge base afforded by rigorous studies, it is virtually impossible to separate fact from conjecture or to propose defensible performance standards.

Implicit in the preparation of any standard is the set of conditions deemed to be acceptable. Every human endeavor involves some risk, and the acceptability of a given risk fundamentally remains a value judgment. The emerging standards for office environments, in part, reflect changing societal values about the level of health and safety that the workplace should provide. The answer is more obvious for some issues than others. Most would agree that people should be able to complete their workday without becoming physically ill from the air they breathe. Exposure to airborne asbestos fibers is no longer tolerated.

But many issues involve progressively greater risks with no obvious point at which to set a limit. Is it acceptable for a few people to develop mild headache symptoms occasionally, and if so, how many people and how often? The quality of ergonomic chairs varies, as does their cost — from a few hundred to several thousand dollars. It is difficult to define at what point higher-quality chairs cease to reduce the risk of injury. What's more, should employers be required to reduce the health and safety risks of the office environment below the level employees provide for themselves outside of work? And if so, how should a level be determined that is fair to both employers and employees?

There has always been some skepticism about employee ailments for which there is no clearly recognized cause. Early reports of sick building syndrome were often received in this way. Complainers were seen as lazy, trying to collect full wages for a partial day's work. Any system is prone to some abuse. Undoubtedly, some employees take sick leave that exceeds the time they are actually ill. On the other side, employers sometimes choose not to disclose occupational health risks fully so their employees will continue working, as was the case with asbestos (Epstein 1978). There will always be a degree of suspicion that employers might be exploitive and that employees might be producing less than they could. The fact that some abuse will occur does not justify dismissing occupant complaints about the work environment, be they rooted in management practices or the physical setting.

As discussed in Chapter 3, issues of the office environment are not simply a matter of comfort. They affect the quality and quantity of work that an individual will produce. As such, the costs associated with the physical office environment involve more than just the cost of office space. Expenditures on office quality need to be viewed in the larger context of the total work output and the total investment in labor, resources, and the facility itself. It is an approach similar to management styles that promote investing in people — giving them more responsibility, greater autonomy, and better career development opportunities. Expenditures on the physical office environment are as much an investment in people as are these management approaches. The two are not only complementary; together they demonstrate a stronger and more consistent commitment than either one alone.

Sick Building Syndrome and Building-Related Illness

Studies suggest that 20% to 30% of commercial buildings may have problems that lead to occupant complaints and illness (Mendell 1993; Woods 1989). Conditions in buildings vary over time. Seasonal changes in climate alter a building's heat loss or gain, and building systems are adjusted to compensate. In some cases, undesirable changes in the indoor environment may result. For example, unusually cold or hot weather may require that a higher proportion of air be recirculated so as not to exceed the building's heating or cooling capacity. Renovation activities may generate contaminants or alter the operation of building systems. Inadequate maintenance of building equipment can also compromise the indoor environment. Thus, a building may produce problem conditions at some times and not at others.

Sick building syndrome (SBS), sometimes called **tight building syndrome,** is a condition in which occupants experience an undue number of illness symptoms when inside a building that diminish when they leave. In SBS, no single environmental factor exceeds the limits of generally accepted thresholds. Current evidence strongly suggests that these illness symptoms result from multiple factors acting together. Chemical, physical, microbiological, and psychological mechanisms are probably all involved (Mendell 1993).

The symptoms of SBS are broadly categorized as eye, nose, throat, and skin irritation; breathing or lower respiratory problems; fatigue and drowsiness; odor and taste complaints; and mild to severe headaches. In a sick building, only a portion of the occupants are generally affected, and they typically experience only some of these symptoms. Different people may exhibit different symptoms from exposure to the same irritants.

Unfortunately, symptoms do not uniquely define SBS. The same symptoms may result from a variety of causes within the office environment or unrelated to it. Indoor air contaminants can cause headaches, but so can viewing a computer monitor with excessive screen flicker, working with inadequate illumination, or illnesses such as the flu or the common cold.

Deficiencies in the physical environment such as air quality, relative humidity, temperature, noise, vibration, and lighting have all been associated with SBS. Studies frequently report air-conditioned buildings to have a higher incidence of SBS than naturally ventilated ones (see, for example, Burge 1992; Burge et al. 1987; Fisk et al. 1993; Mendell 1993; Robertson et al. 1990).

The physical factors most commonly linked with sick buildings are poor indoor air quality and inadequate ventilation. High concentrations of chemical contaminants and allergens (i.e., substances that induce an allergic reaction) often compromise indoor air quality. Sick buildings have generally been found to have outside air ventilation rates less than 10 liters/second/person (20 cubic feet/minute/person) (Hedge et al. 1989; Mendell 1993; Woods 1989).

The widely used guide for ventilation rates in office buildings, ASHRAE Standard 62-1989, specifies a minimum ventilation rate of 8 liters/second/person or 15 cubic feet/minute/person for enclosed offices and 10 liters/second/person or 20 cubic feet/minute/person for open plan office areas. Depending on the number of occupants, the contaminant load, and other variables, the minimum ventilation rate may not be sufficient to prevent SBSs related to poor air quality. Minimum standards serve as useful guidelines but must be adjusted to suit the characteristics of a specific building and the occupant activities it accommodates.

Sick buildings do not always have air quality problems, so increasing the outside air fraction will not always reduce SBS symptoms. For example, improving office cleaning has been shown to decrease SBS symptoms, suggesting that accumulations of dust and dirt contribute to SBS (Mendell 1993; Raw, Roys, and Whitehead 1993). Some individuals are highly sensitive to chemicals that are present in office supplies such as carbonless paper and correction fluids or produced by office equipment such as wet-process photocopiers. Having too many workers in a space, intensive computer use (a factor that tends to increase job stress), and the presence of carpets are all associated with a higher prevalence of symptoms (Mendell 1993).

The incidence and severity of SBS symptoms may also be influenced by factors other than the physical office environment, particularly factors that increase stress at the workplace. Job dissatisfaction, perceptions of environmental conditions, and the level of individual environmental control may also play a role.

Women generally report more physical health symptoms, have higher expenditures for both prescribed and nonprescribed medication, and see a physician more often than men. These observations are consistent across all ages with the exception of people under 15 years of age (Pennebaker 1982). The incidence of SBS symptoms is also consistently found to be higher among women than men (see, for example, Burge et al. 1987; Lenvik 1992; Mendell 1993; Skov, Valbjørn, and DISG 1987). The reasons for this difference are unclear. Although women may be more susceptible to environmental influences on their health and well-being or more aware of changes in their physical health, the overall office environment probably has a major influence.

Women are more likely than men to have less desirable work spaces (e.g., smaller and more congested work areas with no control over temperature). In most North American and European offices, men hold more of the high-status positions than women, and presumably, they receive higher-quality work spaces as well. Women are more likely to have jobs that involve repetitive tasks, require routine computer entry, and offer less personal freedom and control of their work schedule and their environment. These job-related environmental and psychosocial factors would bias gender comparisons of health complaints.

The term sick building syndrome refers to building-associated health problems for which the specific causes are unknown. There are a number of ailments associated with buildings for which the causes are known. These are classified separately.

The term **building-related illness (BRI)** refers to illnesses for which the symptoms are clinically diagnosable and known to be caused by the built environment. Microorganisms that cause Legionnaires' disease, Pontiac fever, and humidifier fever are examples. Radon, a naturally occurring radioactive gas; asbestos; and environmental tobacco smoke are carcinogens and are sometimes treated as sources of BRIs as well.

Illness symptoms known to be caused by high concentrations of airborne contaminants should be referred to as *indoor air pollution symptoms,* not as a sick building syndrome. For example, new carpets and the adhesives used to install them usually release large quantities of contaminants into the air. Many people react to this mixture of chemicals and experience a variety of allergic reactions, headaches, nausea, and asthma. Although the specific substance responsible for the illness symptoms may not have been identified, the cause of the problem is known.

THERMAL COMFORT

Thermal comfort receives the highest number of complaints in most surveys of office occupants. Only about half of North American office workers report the heating and air-conditioning in their work space to be comfortable, yet 80% rate thermal comfort as being very important to them (Harris 1991; Sundstrom et al. 1994). This high level of dissatisfaction may, in part, reflect the fact that the range of conditions that individuals find comfortable changes over the course of a day and with their level of activity.

Feeling uncomfortably hot or cold can be a minor nuisance, but in some cases, it can impair performance and increase the risk of illness. For example, the risk of cumulative trauma disorders of the hands and arms is increased when they are cool. (See the section "Cumulative Trauma Disorders" in Chapter 6.) Overly cool conditions can make people restless, impairing concentration and increasing error rates, particularly for demanding mental tasks. Being too warm can cause weariness, sleepiness, decrements in performance, and a tendency to make mistakes (Grandjean 1980).

Moreover, the discomfort of feeling too hot or too cold is an additional stress that can exacerbate the effects of other environmental stressors. People may become more sensitive to indoor air contaminants, lighting problems, or noise distractions. (The influence of the physical environment on psychosocial factors in the office workplace is discussed in Chapter 7.)

Since thermal comfort is defined by individual perception, some may find a setting comfortable while others experience it as too hot or too cold. People's sense of thermal comfort is affected by the type of clothing they wear, their level of activity, how recently they ate a meal, and their general state of health. Sleep loss, time of day, and gender also affect the perception of thermal comfort (Stephenson and Kolka 1988).

People in temperate climates customarily wear heavier clothing in winter than in summer. More recent assessments of the clothing level worn in offices suggest that people don't vary their clothing that much and they tend to dress toward the lighter level year-round (about .6 clo value). The **clo** is a measure of the insulating value of clothing. Clothing with a higher clo value feels warmer. Sedentary computer-based workers spend a lot of time in upholstered chairs, which provide additional insulation (as much as .2 clo). The office attire of men and women differs and this, too, is

Figure 5.2 This Nepali vendor, warmed only by the small electric heater in front of him, was comfortable in his open air store, even though the outside temperature was not much above freezing.

reflected in the thermal environment they find comfortable. Women wearing skirts and open-toed shoes prefer a warmer temperature than men dressed in jackets, pants, and ties. To provide the same level of thermal comfort, the interior conditions should be adjusted to compensate for these variations in style of dress, office furnishing, and level of activity.

Culture and custom may also influence an individual's thermal comfort. People living in hot climates become physiologically acclimatized and can better tolerate working in warmer conditions than people living in temperate zones. The thermal environment in which they feel comfortable differs from the standards set in countries with temperate climates like Canada, the United States, and northern Europe. (Acclimatization is discussed later in this chapter.) Culture and custom may also affect thermal comfort if they prescribe the style of clothing that is considered acceptable working attire (Figure 5.2).

People differ in the extent to which they are prepared to adjust their clothing or physical setting to make themselves more comfortable. In some cases, their behavior may be strongly influenced by custom. People may willingly close window curtains to block troublesome sunshine, but they may not loosen their ties if it would give them an unacceptably casual appearance.

In general, the lower people's level of activity, the warmer they prefer their environment. For many office jobs, people need to be sedentary at their desks for long periods of time (especially true of intensive computer-based work). An environment comfortable for sedentary workers may be too warm for those who must frequently stand up and walk to retrieve documents and are generally more active. When people in the same work area have jobs that entail very different levels of activity it may not be possible to find a temperature comfortable for both groups.

Office workers report that temperature fluctuations tend to be more irritating than conditions that are consistently too warm or cold (Brill 1984). This may partly be due to the unpredictable nature of temperature shifts. However, there are potential energy savings if temperatures could be allowed to drift slightly and slowly without compromising the occupants' comfort or productivity. In an air-conditioned office building, a 1°C (1.8°F) *increase* in the afternoon temperature would significantly reduce the cooling load and its associated expense.

Indoor temperatures are usually set to meet the requirements of those working in an office rather than for visitors, who spend less time in the building. Main entrances and lobbies are a physical buffer between the outside and indoor conditions. The temperature of these areas can be chosen to make the transition between the outdoor and indoor climate less abrupt. For example, in summer, these areas may be 2°C to 3.5°C (3.6°F to 6.3°F) warmer than the rest of the building. Not only will the transition be less abrupt; there can be an energy saving as well.

In addition to the physiological aspects of thermal comfort, there is the influence of expectations. Satisfaction with the work environment is strongly influenced by perceived discrepancies from expected conditions. People become dissatisfied when the difference between expected and actual conditions seems excessive.

Environmental Factors that Affect Thermal Comfort

Thermal comfort is a state of mind in which a person feels neither too hot nor too cold (ASHRAE 1993). It is a perception of satisfaction with the thermal environment.

Air temperature, relative humidity, air speed, and the temperature of nearby walls, windows, and furnishings all affect an individual's perception of thermal comfort. Temperature largely determines a person's general feeling of hot or cold. The evaporation of sweat at the skin surface is the body's principal means of cooling. A low relative humidity increases evaporative cooling, so a warm temperature with low humidity feels more comfortable than the same temperature with a higher level of relative humidity. Similarly, air movement increases evaporation and for this reason makes people feel cool.

Offices are designed so that air circulates throughout, adding outdoor "fresh" air and removing indoor "stale" air containing the products of respiration, odors, and airborne contaminants. Insufficient air movement is one of the factors that make a room feel stuffy. But excessive air movement can cause uncomfortable drafts. (A **draft** is air movement that is perceived to be excessive and uncomfortable.)

The discomfort of drafts is well illustrated by the battles some occupants wage against the ventilation system. Books, furniture, and any other obstruction may be called into service to stop an irritating flow of cool air (Figure 5.3). Floor heaters and footrests may be used to counter cold air moving along the floor. Some people resort to taping their air vents completely closed.

Figure 5.3 Occupants attached a sheet of plastic below the air supply grille to block an uncomfortable draft.

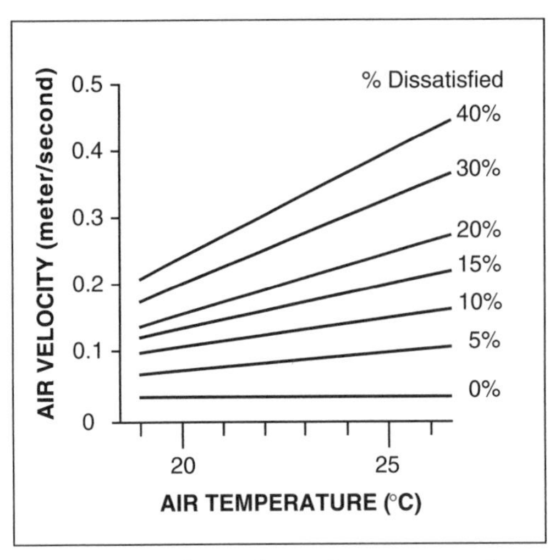

Figure 5.4 This chart indicates the percentage of people expected to be dissatisfied when exposed to air movement at different speeds and temperatures. It was developed from a study of 100 subjects. The results differed from existing standards and suggested that people are more sensitive to drafts than previously thought. (*Source:* Fanger and Christensen 1986.)

As a rule of thumb, air movement less than .25 meter/second (49 feet/minute) goes unnoticed, whereas movement over 1 meter/second (196 feet/minute) is likely to cause discomfort. However, air temperature significantly affects the perceived discomfort of a draft. A lower temperature is generally more uncomfortable (Fanger and Christensen 1986) (Figure 5.4).

Thermal comfort is also affected by radiant heat transfer. Direct sun entering through a window can feel uncomfortably warm even though the air temperature, humidity, and air movement are at comfortable levels. Heat radiating from warm walls, ceiling, furnishings, or nearby equipment will also increase the apparent temperature of a room. Similarly, cold walls and windows act as heat sinks and can make those seated nearby feel uncomfortably cool. People often mistake this type of radiant heat loss for a cold draft.

The combined action of these environmental factors — together with an individual's level of activity, physiological state, and the clothing worn — determine how environmental conditions will affect a person's sensation of thermal comfort. For this reason, it can be difficult to determine the specific cause of thermal comfort complaints.

An office may feel "stuffy" because there is too little air movement, the temperature is overly warm, the relative humidity is too high, or some combination of these conditions. Insufficient outdoor air, overcrowded work spaces, and elevated levels of carbon dioxide or airborne chemical contaminants might also be contributing factors. It is seldom straight forward to change the operation of the building so that occupants perceive a noticeable improvement without creating thermal comfort problems for other people in the same area or in a different area of the building.

THERMAL COMFORT GUIDELINES

There are no legislated requirements for thermal comfort in offices, and most buildings are set to comply with industry standards. In North America, it is recommended that office temperatures range from 20°C to 23.5°C (68°F to 74°F) in winter (the heating season) and 23°C to 26°C (73°F to 79°F) in summer (the cooling season) (ASHRAE 1992). The standard assumes that relative humidity is 50%, air speed is .15 meter/second (29 feet/minute), people are sedentary and wearing typical weight clothing for winter (.9 clo value) and summer (.5 clo).

However, observations under actual office conditions have shown that office workers find the upper extremes of these recommended ranges to be too warm and generally uncomfortable (Schiller 1990). Recent studies suggest that office temperatures in winter should be between 21°C and 23°C in temperate climates. Some researchers recommend providing individual temperature controls that permit an adjustment of about 2°C (4°F) above or below a setting of 22°C (72°F) (Palonen, Seppänen, and Jaakkola 1993).

The recommended range for indoor relative humidity is 40%–60%. Humidities outside this range are easily tolerated, but people begin to feel a dryness in the eyes, nose, and throat when the level falls below 35%. Very low indoor relative humidity has been associated with increased respiratory illness (Green 1985). When humidity is less than 40%, static electricity becomes a problem for sensitive electronic office equipment. At levels above 70%, condensation accumulates on cool surfaces, creating a moist environment conducive to the growth of molds and bacteria that may cause allergic reactions or disease (Potter 1988; Sterling, Arundel, and Sterling 1985). (See the subsection "Microorganisms" and Figure 5.9 later in this chapter.)

Thermal comfort standards are reviewed on a regular basis by organizations such as ASHRAE (American Society of Heating, Refrigerating, and Air-Conditioning Engineers) and ISO (International Standards Organization). Traditionally, their recommendations have been based almost exclusively on laboratory research. More recently, a growing awareness that controlled experimental settings may not be representative of workplace conditions has led to the increased use of data collected in working offices. A number of standards, existing and proposed, have taken this approach and are also addressing the interactions between thermal comfort, acoustics, indoor air quality, and air distribution (Int-Hout 1993).

OFFICE LAYOUT AND SMALL-ZONE CONTROL OF THERMAL CONDITIONS

Work spaces along outside walls are influenced more by daily and seasonal changes than are locations deeper in the building. For example, air leaking across the building enclosure can make areas near the wall feel uncomfortably cool or drafty. Similarly, direct sunshine or a cold night sky will increase the heat gain or loss (respectively) from the building. These effects tend to be accentuated in older buildings, which are more likely to have insufficient insulation, single-pane windows, and excessive air leakage.

The judicious layout of work spaces can avoid or mitigate some thermal comfort problems. For example, instead of placing work settings along a poorly insulated wall, the perimeter area can be used as a corridor so people are removed from the area where thermal conditions are difficult to control. However, such limitations compromise the way an office facility can be used. For example, in choosing a perimeter corridor, a larger floor area must be devoted to circulation than if the corridor were positioned closer to the center. As well, no one has the benefit of a clear view to the outdoors.

A limitation of HVAC (heating, ventilating, and air-conditioning) systems in large buildings is that they cannot compensate for deficiencies in small areas, such as localized air leakage. To deliver conditions more suited to individuals' comfort, systems are now being installed that service smaller areas, on the order of six adjacent work spaces. In this design, termed **small-zone control,** the supply air temperature is adjusted by sensors located in the area that the system serves. (See the subsection "Automated Control of Building Services" in Chapter 4.) This arrangement improves thermal comfort by permitting conditions to be more closely tailored to the needs of the occupants.

Because the thermal conditions that individuals find comfortable are so variable, the ideal solution would be to allow everyone to set the conditions that they find comfortable. Individual environmental controls extend the small-zone control concept by enabling occupants to adjust the thermal environment at their own work settings. Computer-controlled building systems now make it technologically feasible to provide individuals with adjustments for temperature, air speed, light level, and background masking sound. (See the subsection "Individual Control of the Work Environment" in Chapter 7.)

There is a psychological aspect to individual controls as well. Research has shown that people were more satisfied with their thermal environment when they believed it to be under their control, even if they were not in fact actually able to alter the temperature (Schiller et al. 1988).

Human Physiological Response to Climate

In industrialized societies, clothing, shelter, and technology enable a comfortable living and working environment to be constructed virtually anywhere. Space travel and deep ocean exploration have demonstrated an impressive capability to build a comfortable as well as serviceable enclosure. The predominant use of technology to satisfy thermal comfort needs is more significant than the physiological capabilities of the human body to adapt to climatic conditions. Nonetheless, an awareness of these physiological responses can be useful in understanding why individual perceptions of thermal comfort are so varied, especially where a large, diverse workforce is to be accommodated.

The human body adapts continuously to its surroundings. The senses must adjust to the environment in order to function effectively. When people move into a brightly lit space, their eyes must compensate rapidly to enable them to see as well as to prevent injury to the retina. Similarly, exposure to uncomfortable thermal conditions triggers physiological responses such as sweating to cool the body or shivering to warm it. By sweating, humans can lose heat as much as 20 times faster than the body produces it. These are examples of immediate short-term adaptation responses.

Repeated or prolonged exposure to uncomfortably hot or cold conditions causes adaptive physiological changes in the human body that reduce the thermal stress — a phenomenon termed **acclimatization.**

Acclimatization to heat results from repeated exposures that are sufficient to raise the internal body temperature and produce moderate sweating. This can occur during the change from winter to summer. It can also arise from more abrupt changes, such as traveling to a much warmer locale. Heat acclimatization is transient and gradually disappears about a month after the exposure ceases (Wenger 1988).

People show physiological acclimatization to heat within one or two weeks. The process occurs more rapidly and to a greater degree the greater the level of physical activity. Moderate exercise in the heat for an hour a day is usually sufficient to produce an effect within a few days among unacclimatized individuals.

Upon first exposure to heat stress, heart rate and body core temperature become elevated. During the acclimatization process, cardiovascular changes occur that progressively reduce the heart rate toward its previous level. Once acclimatized, individuals exposed to heat stress begin sweating earlier, and sweat more profusely and for a longer period than before they had acclimatized. When drinking water is unrestricted, the rate of sweating can increase as much as two-fold.

Acclimatized individuals show a decreased salt concentration in sweat, which prevents some of the symptoms of salt deficiency from heat exhaustion (e.g., muscular cramps, reduced urine production). Their blood vessels also dilate at a lower core body temperature than before they were heat-acclimatized. As a result, the elevation in core body temperature during heat exposure becomes less pronounced (Garland 1985; Wenger 1988).

There is some evidence that gender and ethnic differences affect the degree of heat acclimatization that an individual will attain. Men tend to sweat more than women, and some indigenous populations of hot countries have been shown to have much lower sweat rates than Caucasians (Garland 1985). Comparative studies of black and white American soldiers have also shown ethnic differences in their physiological response to heat stress (Wenger 1988).

Until modern refrigeration and air-conditioning were developed, inhabitants of hot climates could do relatively little to limit their heat exposure, whereas in cold climates, even primitive societies have developed many behavioral and cultural strategies to reduce their degree of environmental stress by the use of clothing, shelters, and fire (Young 1988). This could be one of the reasons why acclimatization to cold is generally less pronounced than acclimatization to heat.

Most populations that inhabit cold regions have developed suitable clothing and technology to be comfortably warm. Members of polar expeditions show acclimatization to their repeated cold exposure by significant increases in metabolic rate (Garland 1985). However, the adaptive benefits are small compared with increasing body fat or using warmer clothing. People whose occupation requires that they frequently immerse their hands in cold water, such as fishermen of the Gaspé in Quebec, demonstrate a physiological adaptation of increased blood flow to the hands (Young 1988).

PHYSIOLOGICAL DIFFERENCES AMONG ETHNIC GROUPS

Some ethnic groups exhibit remarkable physiological adaptations to their thermal environment. These adaptations are most clearly demonstrated in populations exposed to environmental extremes who do not possess the technological means to compensate and have been relatively isolated from outside influence. For example, the native Alacaluf people of Tierra del Fuego in South America traditionally sleep naked in simple shelters at ambient temperatures of 2°C to 5°C (4°F to 9°F). They do not shiver. They have adapted physiologically by having a basal metabolic rate some 30% to 40% higher than most other human populations (Garland 1985).

Native Inuit (Eskimo) populations of northern Canada and Alaska have been found to have similarly elevated metabolic rates as well. They also differ from Caucasians in the distribution of sweat glands on their bodies. Inuit have a higher density of sweat glands on the face and less on the body — a characteristic that reduces moistening of their clothing, which would destroy its insulating quality (Schaefer et al. 1974). Inuit also have a higher rate of blood circulation to their extremities when exposed to cold. It is a physiological adaptation that helps to prevent cold injury and promotes greater manual dexterity in frigid conditions (Garland 1985).

The Australian Aborigines and the Bushmen of the Kalahari have developed an unusual physiological adaptation to cold night-time temperatures. During a night of moderate cold exposure, their core body temperature can fall 2°C (3.6°F) without an increase in metabolic rate. Europeans exposed to the same conditions showed a rise in metabolic heat production to maintain a higher core body temperature (Garland 1985).

The diving women of Japan (the Ama people) and Korea have harvested shellfish and seaweed for generations. Wearing minimal clothing, they work in water temperatures as low as 10°C (50°F). Their physiological adaptation to the cold is to channel an unusually large proportion of the venous blood returning to the heart through vessels near the skin surface, thereby warming the exterior.

These examples involve extreme conditions, but they clearly demonstrate that physiological differences exist among ethnic groups that directly affect their perception of thermal comfort. Less dramatic physiological differences related to ethnic origin may contribute to the range of thermal comfort preferences observed among office occupants, though they likely are masked by other more dominant factors in the workplace.

ACCLIMATIZATION AND THERMAL COMFORT IN THE OFFICE SETTING

As previously noted, the range of thermal conditions that an individual will find comfortable is influenced by several factors — clothing and activity level, individual physiological characteristics, health and physical condition, and acclimatization. In some cases, ethnic origin might also be a contributing factor. It is not surprising then that people in the same office area may experience quite different levels of thermal comfort.

For air-conditioned offices in hot climates, differences in occupants' degree of acclimatization may make it more difficult to find an optimal indoor climate setting. In regions with hot summer temperatures, such as the southern United States, some office occupants may live entirely in artificially cooled environments. Their homes, cars, and offices are air-conditioned, as are the restaurants where they eat, the malls where they shop, and the facilities where they exercise indoors. These people would not become acclimatized to the hot weather to the same degree as their coworkers who did not live in air-conditioned environments outside of the office.

Those exposed daily to a hot outdoor climate would tend to be comfortable in conditions warmer than the range preferred by those rarely exposed to the heat. Similarly, an indoor temperature that satisfies people who are always in cool air-conditioned conditions may be uncomfortably cold for people more acclimatized to the heat. Since access to air-conditioned living spaces is related to income, it may be that thermal comfort preferences are somewhat correlated with salary levels and consequently with position. Higher level personnel may prefer cooler conditions. However we are not aware of any studies that support or refute this hypothesis.

AIR QUALITY

Indoor air quality (**IAQ**) was one of the first building-related health concerns of office occupants and has been the most highly publicized. The topic attracted so much attention over the past decade that there are now regular conferences devoted entirely to IAQ research. The Indoor Air conference held every three years attracts a large international following. The proceedings typically contain over a thousand pages of research and field studies devoted to this topic. Many large studies have documented symptoms, specific pollutant sources, and the effectiveness of different treatments (see, for example, Jaakkola, Heinonen, and Seppänen 1991; Sundell, Lindvall, and Stenberg 1992).

Before the introduction of the integrated ventilation systems now used in offices, openable windows and uncontrolled air movement through gaps in the walls and roof allowed outside air to readily enter buildings. However, the effectiveness of natural ventilation is reduced as the building becomes deeper. Moreover, areas with a lot of air leakage are drafty and uncomfortable, especially in cool or damp weather. It is also more difficult to heat these spaces evenly.

Systems to heat, ventilate, and cool spaces (known as HVACs), were introduced to improve comfort. Initially, it was more expensive to build and operate buildings with these integrated mechanical systems; however, the indoor temperature and humidity could be better controlled. The addition of cooling as well as heating in the same ventilation system made it possible to maintain a comfortable work environment through summer and winter. What's more, the air could be filtered to remove dirt, pollution, and irritants, thus providing for a healthier indoor environment. Since ventilation did not depend on windows, the building could be whatever depth the designer wanted. (See the section "The Mechanical System" in Chapter 4.)

HVAC systems can better maintain a desired temperature and humidity level when the uncontrolled exchange of air between indoors and outside is minimized. By tightly fitting building components during construction, using caulking compounds, and inspecting the joints regularly, air leakage through the building enclosure could be greatly reduced.

Openable windows made the airflow through a building unpredictable, and it was difficult to adjust or balance the system for optimum performance. Installing windows that could not be opened eliminated this problem. Other benefits of fixed windows were increased security and reduced accumulation of the dirt that would be carried inside with the air. By reducing uncontrolled air exchange between the building interior and the outside the indoor climate could be made more comfortable, building materials deteriorated more slowly under the more stable environmental conditions, there was less heat loss in cold weather and less heat gain in hot weather.

Still, HVAC systems and sealed buildings were an added expense that was difficult to justify for improved occupant comfort alone. It was the energy crisis of the 1970s that provided the additional financial incentive to construct sealed buildings. The energy savings somewhat offset the higher cost of an HVAC system. With the promise of energy savings, together with a more comfortable indoor climate and possibly improvements in productivity, HVAC systems became standard in North American offices by the late 1970s.

Agents of Poor Indoor Air

The principal agents of poor indoor air are chemical contaminants, particles, and microorganisms. Odors are generally more of a nuisance than a health hazard and are presented separately. The following subsections discuss each category, including their common sources in offices, accepted exposure levels, health effects, and methods to avoid or control them. The length of each discussion reflects the level of public concern, controversy, and misinformation surrounding the topic. Undisputed and well-researched contaminants — such as ozone, radon, and sulfur dioxide — can be covered briefly. To present a balanced discussion of more controversial topics, such as negative air ions, more information must be given. The length of the discussion, then, is not an indication of the agent's importance.

CHEMICAL CONTAMINANTS

The indoor environment contains many contaminants in the gaseous state, as vapors, or as airborne liquid droplets. Emissions from building materials and furnishings are typically highest when they are new and generally decrease over time. Other pollutants — such as tobacco smoke, vapors from cleaning solutions, or chemical emissions from photocopiers — are introduced by the occupants themselves and their equipment. Contaminants generated by the occupants and their activities tend to reach a stable concentration, which shifts only when there is a major change in occupancy or building operation.

The combined effect of multiple chemical contaminants may be additive, synergistic, or antagonistic. When the combined effect of multiple factors is the sum of their individual effects, they are said to be **additive.** A **synergistic effect** is one in which multiple factors acting together have a greater impact than the sum of their separate actions. An **antagonistic effect** occurs when multiple factors acting together have a lesser effect than they would individually. Relatively little research has been conducted on synergistic effects of multiple chemical contaminants in the workplace environment. For example, of more than 100,000 references to occupational toxicology found in the TOXLINE database, only 20 referred to synergistic effects (Lippy and Turner 1991).

Synergistic effects can produce illness symptoms that are very difficult to diagnose. The chemicals in indoor office air occur in countless combinations, and the medical effects of variable complex mixtures are poorly understood. Even the development of a research agenda to identify chemical combinations likely to be

Table 5.1 Major indoor chemical contaminants.

CONTAMINANT	ORIGIN OF CONTAMINATION
	Primarily *Outdoor* Sources
Carbon Monoxide	Combustion products (tobacco smoke, vehicle exhaust, appliances, kerosene heaters)
Nitrogen Dioxide	Combustion products (vehicle exhaust, appliances, kerosene heaters, power generating plants)
Ozone	Outdoor air, copy machines, laser printers, ion generators
Radon	Building materials, soil gas
Sulfur Dioxide	Outdoor air, combustion products (coal-fired power generating plants, kerosene heaters)
	Primarily *Indoor* Sources
Carbon Dioxide	Respiration, tobacco smoke, other combustion products
Environmental Tobacco Smoke	Occupants, second-hand tobacco smoke
Formaldehyde	Furnishings, upholstery, consumer products, environmental tobacco smoke, building materials, insulation, plywood, particleboard
Volatile Organic Compounds	Office furnishings, dyes, consumer products, cleaning solutions, building materials, paints, stains, adhesives, caulks. Semi-VOC: pesticides, fire-retardants, insulating fluids for electrical equipment, byproduct of microbes.

health hazards is itself a complex task (Feron et al. 1992).

Some individuals are unusually sensitive to a broad range of chemicals normally present in homes, offices, and certain outdoor environments. This condition has been termed **multiple chemical sensitivity (MCS)**. It is characterized by a wide range of symptoms, including a general feeling of being unwell, joint and muscle aches, skin reactions, food intolerance, and recurring respiratory infections. There can also be behavioral effects, such as memory impairment, that have been verified by standard psychological tests. Those suffering from MCS typically require accommodations with much lower levels of chemical contaminants than can be tolerated by the general population. In extreme cases, these individuals must eat a limited diet, follow a restricted lifestyle, and live in specially constructed buildings to minimize exposure to chemical contaminants.

The major chemical contaminants that have been linked to indoor air quality problems are listed in Table 5.1.

Carbon Dioxide (CO_2)

Though not a contaminant per se, indoor levels of carbon dioxide are a concern in the office setting. Outside air normally has a carbon dioxide concentration of about 300 parts per million, though it can be higher during busy commute times due to vehicle exhaust. The principal indoor sources are human respiration and smoking. The number of people and the rate of outdoor air exchange directly affect the concentration level reached indoors and so, the carbon dioxide level in an office changes over the day (Figure 5.5). Accommodating more people per unit area and reducing the outside air exchange rate tend to raise the level.

The concentrations of carbon dioxide

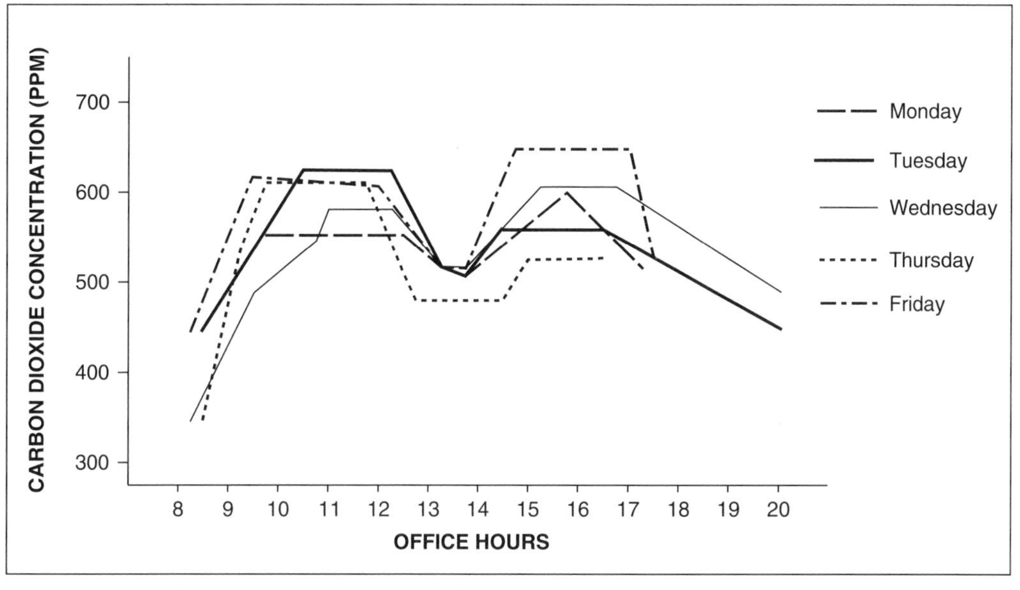

Figure 5.5 Chart of carbon dioxide levels in an office continuously monitored over a one-week period. Based primarily on the number of people on the floor, the pattern of CO_2 levels indicates people's arrival at the start of the workday, their departure for lunch, and then again at the end of the day.

found in offices are generally well below levels that could pose a health hazard, but levels that cause drowsiness often occur. Its effects can, however, be amplified by the presence of other contaminants. Current practice is to design and operate offices for a maximum carbon dioxide concentration of 1,000 parts per million. The concentrations found in office air are generally less than 800 parts per million. A lower level of 500 – 600 parts per million is sometimes recommended (Potter 1988). However, maintaining such low concentrations may require high rates of ventilation that create uncomfortable drafts or are economically impractical.

Carbon dioxide levels are sometimes used as a general indicator of overall indoor air quality. This is inappropriate. Studies have shown that carbon dioxide concentration is *not* a good indicator of adequate ventilation (Putnam, Woods, and Rask 1990), nor is it a good predictor of the concentration of volatile organic compounds, an important class of indoor air contaminants discussed below (Baldwin and Farant 1990). Although a higher outside air fraction will reduce carbon dioxide concentrations, so will reducing the number of people in a space. But having fewer people will not reduce the concentration of other important indoor pollutants, such as volatile organic compounds, that are not directly generated by the occupants and thus tend to be independent of occupant density.

Carbon Monoxide (CO)

Carbon monoxide inhibits the uptake of oxygen by the blood. Concentrations above 400 parts per million cause coma or death by asphyxiation (because the body is deprived of an adequate oxygen supply). Carbon monoxide is particularly dangerous because it is colorless, odorless, and tasteless. Even at toxic levels, those exposed do not detect its presence.

The two principal sources of the carbon monoxide found in offices are engine exhaust and tobacco smoke. Vehicle exhaust most commonly enters the building by leakage from an underground parking structure, or it is drawn into the supply air intake from outside. These sources can largely be eliminated by proper sealing of doorways leading into the building, regular inspection and repair of cracks in the walls or ceiling through which exhausts could infiltrate, and ensuring that vehicles do not idle near the building's air intakes. Banning smoking in offices or providing smoking rooms that exhaust directly to the outside eliminates the introduction of carbon monoxide from tobacco smoke into the general office air.

Government regulations in Canada and the United States generally limit CO levels in offices to 10 – 15 parts per million, but it is uncommon to find concentrations above 2 parts per million unless there is a combustion source. Though these concentrations are well below lethal levels and are assumed to be safe exposures, long-term exposure to these concentrations can cause headaches, nausea, and impaired vision (symptoms that are generally expected to occur only at concentrations above 35 parts per million).

Environmental Tobacco Smoke (ETS)

Smoking tobacco products is an established cause of lung cancer. Tobacco smoke contains tar, benzopyrene, nicotine, nitrosamines, and trace metals, substances known to be carcinogenic. It is estimated that they cause about one-third of all cancer cases as well as contributing to heart disease and other ailments.

Air laden with tobacco smoke, termed **secondhand smoke** or **environmental tobacco smoke** (ETS), is a health risk to nonsmokers as well. The U.S. Environmental Protection Agency (EPA) recently recognized ETS as a carcinogen. The agency reported that nonsmokers whose spouses smoked had an additional risk of 2 in 1,000 of contracting lung cancer and considered ETS to be the cause of 20% of lung cancers due to factors other than smoking. In addition to lung cancer, other reported respiratory effects were acute lower respiratory tract diseases (pneumonia, bronchitis, and broncholitis), acute middle ear infections, reduced lung function, increa-sed incidence of asthma, and acute upper respiratory tract infections — specifically, colds and sore throats (Levin 1993a).

The U.S. surgeon general has also recognized ETS to be a health hazard. This official status will increase the liability risk of employers, businesses, and building operators in the United States who expose anyone involuntarily to tobacco smoke. ETS levels are to be kept below 10 milligrams/cubic meter for nicotine. In offices where smoking is permitted, the minimum air supply rate recommended by ASHRAE is 18 liters/second/person (35 cubic feet/minute/person). For non-smoking office areas it is 8 liters/second/person (15 cubic feet/minute/person).

Tobacco smoke contains a wide range of gaseous air pollutants as well as particles. Many of these constituents are readily absorbed by fabrics, making it difficult to remove the lingering tobacco odor. Furthermore, the particles in tobacco smoke are very small, making them hard to capture. **HEPA** (high-efficiency particle arrestance) filters or electrostatic precipitators must be used to remove them. To be effective, these devices must be regularly maintained, replacing filters and prefilters and cleaning the units as often as every week. It is difficult enough to ensure that centralized air cleaners are properly maintained. Decentralized units, distributed throughout an office, are even less likely to be maintained on a regular basis. In light of the work and expense to cleanse the air of tobacco smoke, the most effective means to control it is to segregate the spaces where smoking is permitted and ensure there is no recirculation of air from those areas. Alternatively, many office buildings have been designated "smoke-free" environments, and smoking is banned.

Formaldehyde

Formaldehyde and other aldehydes are included in the more general category of volatile organic compounds. Because they have attracted considerable public attention, they are discussed separately here.

Formaldehyde along with other aldehydes are a common component of carpets, urea-formaldehyde insulation, finishes for synthetic fabrics, and the adhesives used in plywood and particleboard. Emission rates are highest when the materials are new or are regularly exposed to moisture or heat and generally decrease slowly over time. In some applications, formaldehyde emissions can be substantially reduced by the use of sealants that act as an impermeable surface coating (Godish, Rouch, and Guindon 1989). However, many finish coatings applied to wood materials contain urea-formaldehyde resins, which are themselves significant sources of formaldehyde emissions (Godish and Guindon 1990).

Formaldehyde is a colorless gas that is toxic and can be lethal at high concentrations. It has a pungent odor and can usually be sensed at concentrations of 1 parts per million or lower. A variety of acute and persistent illness symptoms have been associated with low-level exposures to formaldehyde in indoor air (Godish, Zollinger, and Konopinski 1986). Low concentrations (0.1 – 5 parts per million) cause skin rash as well as irritation of the eyes and upper respiratory tract. Higher concentrations produce more severe illness symptoms, including tightening of the chest, vomiting, a feeling of pressure on the head, and heart palpitations. Concentrations above 50 parts per million can cause pulmonary edema, inflammation of the lungs, and death. Formaldehyde has caused cancer in rats but has not been proved to be a human carcinogen. Regulatory bodies have generally set the permissible level of formaldehyde at between 0.05 and 0.1 parts per million for offices.

Indoor air may contain many other aldehyde compounds, some of which have objectionable odors. Their health hazards are generally unknown. Although some are clearly irritants, there are few standards to regulate exposure levels. Formaldehyde and other aldehyde compounds can readily be controlled with charcoal filters.

Nitrogen Dioxide (NO_2)

The principal sources of nitrogen dioxide in the office are tobacco smoke, vehicle exhaust, and combustion gases from such sources as gas stoves and heaters. The adverse effects of nitrogen dioxide range from irritation of the eyes and the mucous membranes of the respiratory tract to destruction of tissues. Nitrogen dioxide is particularly harmful because it does not dissolve readily in water, so once it is inhaled, it can penetrate deeply into the lungs.

Tissue damage and breathing difficulties have been detected at nitrogen dioxide levels as low as 0.5 parts per million. Higher concentrations have caused severe tissue loss and complications such as pulmonary edema. These effects only show up many hours after the exposure has ended. The allowable limit is set at 0.05 parts per million (Godish 1991; OSHA Ambient Air Quality Standards). Nitrogen dioxide can be controlled by the use of charcoal filters.

Ozone (O_3)

Ozone is one of the most toxic pollutants regulated under ambient air quality standards. It causes irritation of the eyes, nose, throat, and upper respiratory tract and has been shown to cause inflammation of the upper airway. Associations between elevated ozone levels and exacerbation of asthma symptoms and hospital admissions for asthma suggest that ozone exposure contributes to asthma-related airway inflammation. Common symptoms at concentrations above 0.12 parts per million (120 parts per billion) include headache, nausea, fatigue, chest pain, and shortness of breath.

The U.S. National Ambient Air Quality standard for ozone specifies a maximum exposure of 0.12 parts per million for any one-hour period. More than half the American population resides in areas that fail to meet this standard. Moreover, studies have reported acute health effects (primarily related to breathing) from exposure to ozone concentrations as low as 0.08 parts per million which are well *below* this level (Spektor et al. 1988). There is evidence that the effects of ozone may be related more to cumulative daily exposures than to the one-hour peak concentration (Aris et al. 1993; Lippman 1989). Thus, this ozone standard does not appear to protect public health adequately (Godish 1991). The U.S. Food and Drug Administration sets a limit of 0.05 parts per million for continuous indoor ozone exposure.

Ozone can be generated by ultraviolet light, by office equipment that uses high voltages (e.g., photocopiers, laser printers), and occasionally by defective electrical equipment or the ballasts in fluorescent light fixtures. Low relative humidity accelerates its formation indoors. However, these sources are minor contributors to the total indoor ozone concentration.

Most ozone in buildings originates outdoors. The dominant factors that determine indoor ozone levels are the outdoor ozone concentration and the building's ventilation rate. Studies have shown that indoor levels are generally 20% to 80% of those outdoors, with higher percentages associated with higher ventilation rates. At ventilation rates of five to eight air changes per hour, indoor ozone concentration will be 70% to 80% of that outdoors. Indoor concentrations rise and fall with outdoor levels, which tend to peak at midday. If the outdoor level is high, the indoor level will be high as well (Weschler and Shields 1989).

Reducing the ventilation rate will lower indoor ozone levels, but it also diminishes the dilution of air contaminants and odors. These may then accumulate and reach undesirable concentrations. Alternatively, activated-charcoal filters fitted to a mechanical ventilation system can remove ozone with an efficiency as high as 95% (Shair 1981). A side benefit is that the high chemical activity of ozone makes it an effective cleanser, so its presence extends filter life.

Radon

Radon is a naturally occurring odorless, colorless, radioactive gas found in certain geologic formations and soils. It can accumulate in buildings, particularly basement areas, and become many times more concentrated than in the surrounding environment from which it has been released. It is recognized as a serious health hazard in residences located within regions of radon-rich soil, and has sometimes been found at dangerous concentrations in offices (see, for example, Turner and Binnie 1990).

The association of radon with lung cancer was first observed among miners exposed to radioactive ores. According to the EPA, second to smoking, radon is the leading cause of lung cancer in America, causing between 7,000 and 30,000 deaths annually. The risk is several times higher for smokers than for nonsmokers. A number of agencies, including the EPA, are currently assessing the health risk of radon in the workplace.

Both radon and its radioactive decay products are carcinogenic. Adverse health effects occur when they are taken into the body and retained inside. Radioactive particles and gases can be removed from the air with filters and other devices. However, the gamma radiation from such materials can penetrate solid walls (Axelson 1991, Morgera 1992).

Activated-charcoal monitors are inexpensive and readily available devices that provide quick and sufficiently accurate readings to detect potentially dangerous radon levels. If these measurements indicate a radioactivity level in excess of 4 picocuries/liter of air a more detailed investigation should be done. Indoor radon levels vary widely over short time intervals. Therefore, a more representative measurement is obtained by sampling over a period of weeks or months using an **integrating detector** — a device that sums the total radon exposure over time. There is no consensus on the most appropriate measurement period. Norwegian guide-

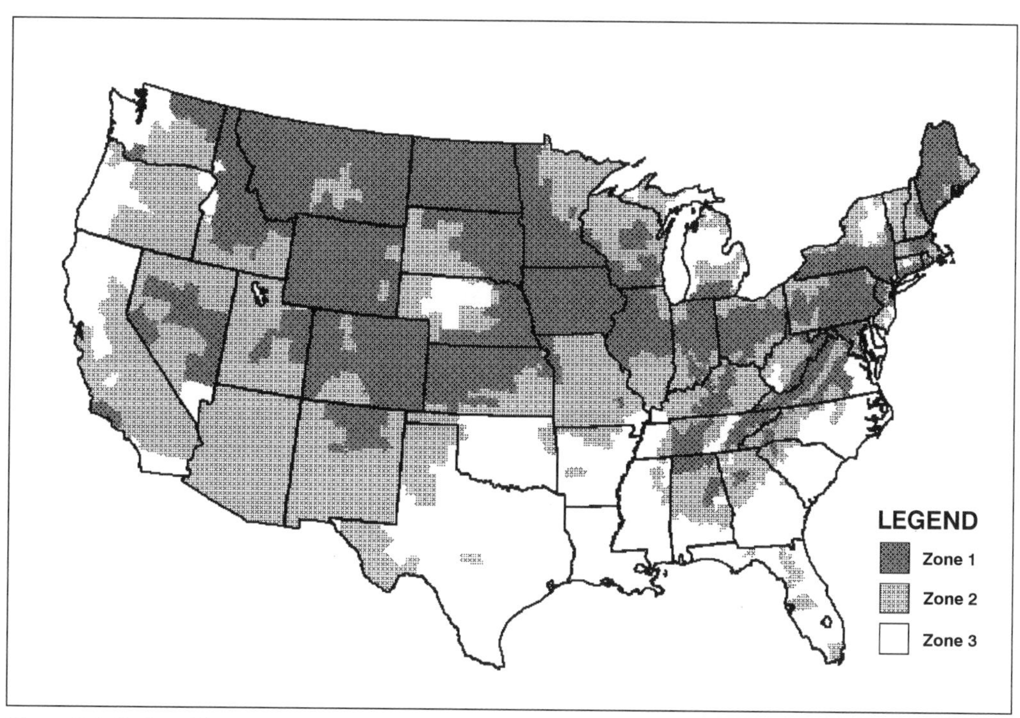

Figure 5.6 Radon risk zones in the United States. This map was developed to help agencies target radon program activities and resources. Areas in zone 1 have a predicted indoor radon level greater than 4 picocuries/liter, zone 2 levels are predicted to be 2 – 4 picocuries/liter, and zone 3 less than 2 picocuries/liter. (*Source:* Environmental Protection Agency, Washington, D.C.)

lines require a seven-day measurement. Finnish regulations require that measurements be taken for two months and, recognizing that radon accumulation changes with the season, that the measurements be taken during specified months of the year.

Radon enters buildings from the ground, water, and to a lesser extent, in construction materials. Although building materials such as granite, concrete that contains phosphate slag and fly ash, and phosphogypsum wallboard can be contaminated with radon, they are not considered important sources. Its migration through the ground depends on local soil conditions, which may vary substantially over distances of just a few meters. Changes in porosity, the presence of cracks, and other irregularities influence the rate and direction of radon gas seepage. A variety of methods have been used to estimate and map the risk of radon contamination (see, for example, the U.S. EPA's map of radon zones, Figure 5.6, and the discussion of radon risk mapping in Finland in Voutilainen and Mäkaläinen 1993).

Buildings should be tested for elevated concentrations of radon gas, especially in areas with soils and geological formations known to be radon sources. However, radon contamination in buildings is unpredictable. Buildings situated in zones that are mapped as low risk may develop high radon concentrations. Although radon is more likely to accumulate in floors below ground and in buildings with low rates of outside air exchange, it can be carried to upper floors by the ventilation system, so samples should also be taken from floors above ground. Elevated radon concentrations have been reported as high as the twenty-third floor (Lyons 1994).

Eliminating radon from the indoor atmosphere requires finding and closing the points of entry of the gas and increasing air exchange rates to reduce existing concentrations and prevent future buildups. All cracks and joints in the concrete foundation and basement areas should be sealed (e.g., sump pump openings and French drains — trenches filled with loose stones and covered with earth). These measures will usually be sufficient, but more sophisticated and expensive steps may be necessary if high radon concentrations persist. For example, special ventilation systems may be installed to vent radon gas directly to the outside from beneath floor slabs and around basements and foundations (see, for example, Swedjemark et al. 1989). Estimates by the EPA suggest that the cost-effectiveness of programs to measure indoor radon levels and the associated mitigation activities compare favorably with other environmental risk-reduction programs (Guimond, Malm, and Rowson 1990). Since 1980 Sweden has set limits for radon levels in buildings. Experience there indicates that acceptable indoor radon concentrations can be attained even in high radon risk zones if appropriate building design and construction techniques are applied (Swedjemark 1990).

Sulfur Dioxide (SO_2)

Sulfur dioxide is a by-product of many industrial processes and is produced in the combustion of heating oil and coal. Since high levels of particulate matter and other sulfur compounds are also produced by these processes, it is difficult to separate their individual health effects. There is some evidence that the particulate matter that normally accompanies the generation of sulfur dioxide accentuates its toxic effect, further complicating the assessment of its toxicity alone.

Because sulfur dioxide dissolves easily in water, it is almost entirely expelled from the body. Its presence will aggravate the symptoms of asthmatics and those with chronic bronchitis and cardiovascular diseases. Of greater danger is that it reacts with water to form sulfuric acid — a highly corrosive acid that damages human tissue and also accelerates the deterioration of building materials.

Sulfur dioxide is very difficult to control. Charcoal filters can help to keep concentrations below the generally accepted limit of 0.05 parts per million.

Volatile Organic Compounds (VOC)

Volatile organic compounds are a class of chemicals that contain carbon, hydrogen, and oxygen and that exist in the vapor phase at room temperature. The term *VOC* is broadly defined, and researchers differ in the compounds they choose to include in this category. Technical definitions are generally based on chemical composition and boiling point. VOCs are commonly subdivided into the categories very volatile organic compounds, volatile organic compounds, and semivolatile organic compounds, as shown in Table 5.2. Ketones, alcohols, phenols, aldehydes, and epoxides are some of the many classes of VOCs often found in indoor air.

VOCs are emitted by most of the furnishings, equipment, and supplies used in offices. Sealants, adhesives, solvents, paints, particleboard, fabrics, carpet, tape, foam, felt markers, carbonless paper, and many cleaning solutions are common sources. Consumer products such as hair spray, cosmetics, and dry-cleaned clothing also emit VOCs.

Emission rates tend to decrease over time as materials age. So it is not surprising that VOC concentrations are usually highest in new and recently renovated buildings. Studies suggest that VOC emissions from new building materials tend to decline and then reach a more or less stable level after about one year (Baldwin and Farant 1990). However, many sources, such as cleaning solutions and office supplies, are continually replaced, so the contribution of VOCs from these sources remains more or less constant unless alternative products with lower emission rates are used.

Air quality studies have shown that the office environment generally contains low concentrations (on the order of parts per trillion to parts per million) of 50 to 300

Table 5.2 Classification of volatile organic compounds. (*Source*: Adapted from Mølhave 1990.)

Description	Boiling point range (°C)
Very volatile (gaseous) organic compounds (VVOC)	< 0°C to 50 – 100°C
Volatile organic compounds (VOC)	50 – 100°C to 240 – 260°C
Semivolatile organic compounds (SVOC)	240 – 260°C to 360 – 400°C

different VOCs. The risks from individual compounds and tolerance limits are constantly revised as more studies are done. However, the combined health effects of multiple VOCs are largely unknown (Mølhave 1990).

The health effects of the VOCs found in offices range from headaches and dizziness to nausea, acute allergic reactions, and life-threatening diseases such as cancer. The effects of specific compounds depend on the concentration, length of exposure, and presence of other stressors in the environment. Many VOCs once thought to be safe, such as benzene, are now known to be carcinogenic.

Establishing the health risk of VOCs to office occupants is difficult because they are exposed to relatively low doses over very long periods of time. It may take years before illness symptoms develop, and it is then very hard to reliably prove that a specific chemical was the cause. There are so many different chemical and biological agents that cause headaches, eye and nose irritation, and increased susceptibility to infections such as colds that it is difficult and impractical to test all but the most obviously problematic VOCs. Furthermore, the virtually infinite combinations of VOCs that could occur in indoor air make the investigation of synergistic effects a daunting task. Studies such as those by Kjaergaard, Mølhave, and Pedersen (1990) and Koren et al. (1990) have found that mixtures of VOCs can cause eye irritation, decreased psychological performance, and inflammation of the upper airways and generally contribute to sick building symptoms.

The pragmatic approach that is usually adopted to assess VOCs in offices is to measure the concentration of specific compounds suspected to be problematic in a given building as well as to estimate the total load of VOCs. It is impractical to identify and quantify every one of the hundreds of VOCs that could be present in normal indoor air. The **TVOC** (total VOC) measurement is an indicator of the total mass concentration of VOCs present in the sample. It is a considerable simplification. Since specific chemicals are not identified, the TVOC does not take into account the different toxicity and health effects of the specific VOCs that are present. Nonetheless, in practice, the TVOC value has been used to assess whether a VOC-related air quality problem is likely to exist.

Current research indicates that at TVOC levels less than about 0.2 milligram/cubic meter, occupants should not experience irritation or discomfort (Table 5.3). At levels of 0.2 – 3.0 milligrams/cubic meter, some occupants may experience irritation and discomfort, depending on individual sensitivities, synergistic effects of the specific chemicals present, and interactions with other stressors such as temperature or fatigue that can increase an individual's sensitivity. At TVOCs of 3.0 – 25.0 milligrams/cubic meter, headaches and other weak neurotoxic effects commonly occur after relatively short exposures (within a few hours). Toxic effects become generally prevalent at TVOC levels above 25.0 milligrams/cubic meter (Mølhave 1990).

Increasing the outside air fraction in the ventilation supply can reduce the indoor VOC concentration by dilution. However, the physics of dilution is much less effective for contaminants at the very low concentrations at which VOCs are generally

Table 5.3 Dose-response relations of total volatile organic compound levels. (*Source:* Adapted from Mølhave 1990.)

Total concentration (Milligrams/cubic meter)	Response
< 0.2	No irritation or discomfort
0.2 – 3.0	Possible irritation and discomfort, depending on exposure to other chemicals or stressors, and how they interact
3.0 – 25.0	Probable exposure effect and headaches
> 25.0	Headaches and possibly other neurotoxic effects

found in offices (see the subsection "Improving Indoor Air Quality" and Figure N5-8 later in this chapter). Filters of charcoal, carbon, or aluminum can also help in reducing the VOC level. But the most effective way to reduce VOC concentrations is to control or eliminate the indoor sources.

AIRBORNE PARTICLES

Both outdoor and indoor air contain suspended solid matter generally referred to as **airborne particles.** Dust, dirt, and biological materials such as pollen, spores, and microorganisms (discussed below) are brought into buildings with the outdoor air. In addition, building materials, furnishings, and the occupants themselves produce particulate residues. Bits of plaster, asbestos, and cellulose from paper products; fibers from carpets, clothing, and fabrics; hair, dead skin, and manmade mineral fibers (MMMF) such as fiberglass all add to the load of particulate matter that is airborne or accumulates on furniture, in service equipment, or in hard-to-clean areas.

The health effects of inhaling airborne particles depend on their size and shape, the site within the respiratory system where they are deposited, and their chemical composition. Some particles pose serious health risks, even in low concentrations. Accumulations of dust and dirt, particularly organic material, provide breeding sites for organisms such as fungi and dust mites and can also damage electronic office equipment. Dust bridges have caused electrical shorts, telephone switch failures, and computer disk crashes (Weschler and Shields 1991).

In the course of their activities, people stir up settled particles and, in effect, surround themselves with their own dust cloud. As a result, occupants can be exposed to dust levels four to five times higher than the ambient load of airborne particles. Studies have shown a higher prevalence of sick building symptoms in offices that have large areas where particulate matter accumulates, such as open shelving, storage areas, fabric furnishings, and spaces that are difficult to clean. Not surprisingly, improved office cleaning has been shown to reduce sick building symptoms (Raw, Roys, and Whitehead 1993; Skov, Valbjørn, and DISG 1987).

Airborne particles may be a fraction of a micron to tens of microns in size (a micron is one thousandth of a millimeter). For measurement purposes, particle sizes of less than 10 microns are considered respirable (i.e., will be inhaled). However, many airborne irritants such as pollen are larger (Figure 5.7).

Particle concentration is generally measured as the mass of respirable particles per cubic meter of air. The Japanese mandatory indoor environment limit is 150 micrograms/cubic meter (Potter 1988). Current research suggests that in

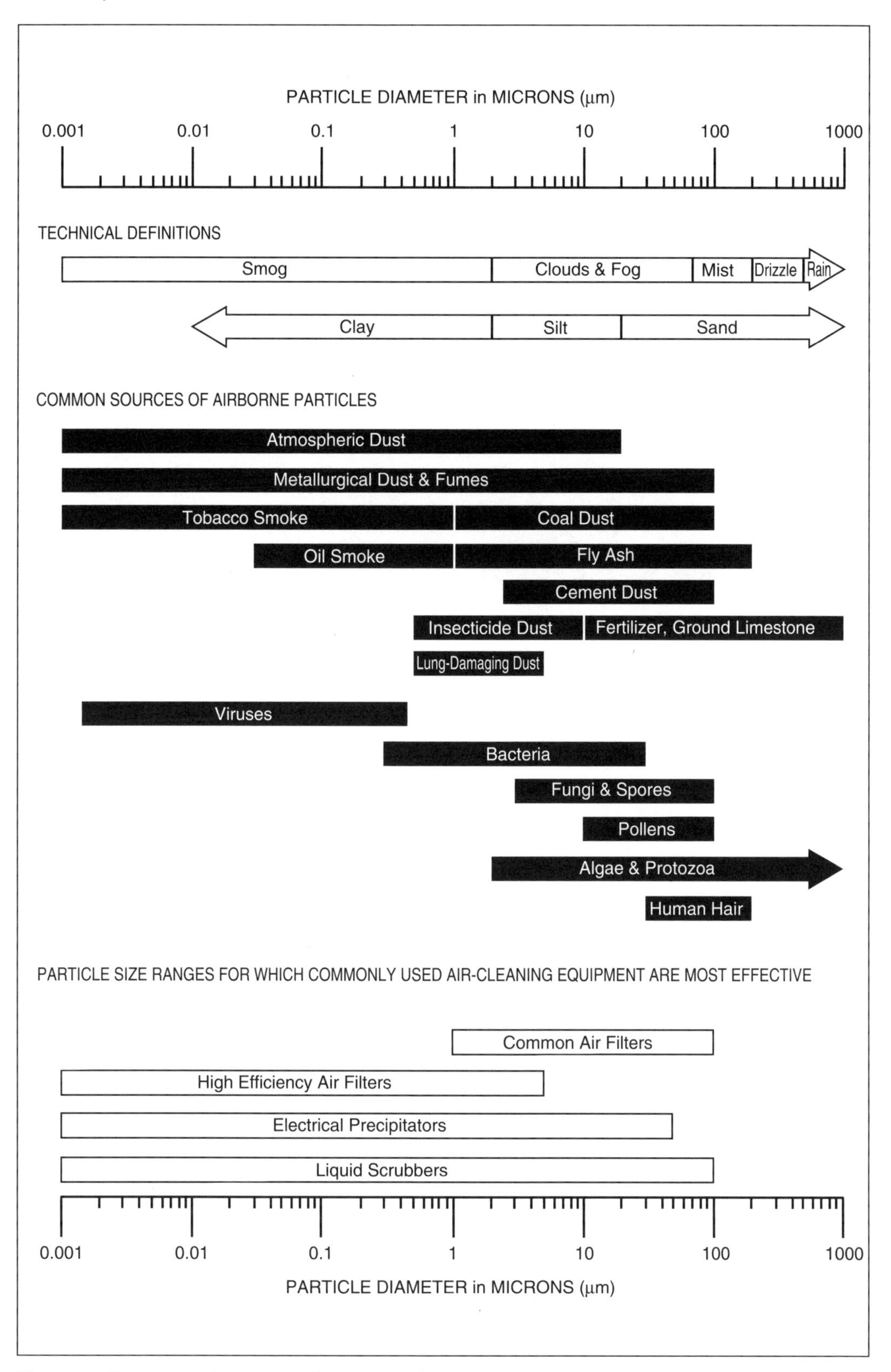

Figure 5.7 Size ranges of common airborne particulate matter and the types of air-cleaning equipment effective for their removal. (*Sources:* Godish 1991, Steele and Brown 1990, Woods 1988b.)

Figure 5.8 This photograph, taken from inside a 1.3 meter by 1 meter (4 feet by 3 feet) air duct, shows the accumulation of dirt on the inside walls. One batt is partly detached (at arrow) and hangs down, impeding the air flow. (*Source:* Place and Associates, Ottawa.)

general office environments, respirable mass concentrations should be limited to 50 micrograms/cubic meter or less. A characteristic of man-made mineral fibers is that they break repeatedly into shorter and shorter pieces to form dust that can cause skin irritation and lung diseases. Recommended exposure levels range from 1 to 3 fibers/milliliter.

The particles most likely to be retained by the human body measure 1 micron or less. These can penetrate the alveoli — the smallest air passageways in the lung. Respirable particles from smoking tobacco products and many other indoor air pollutants are mostly in the small size range of less than 0.5 micron. So by removing the larger particles, the overall respirable mass concentration can be lowered, but the concentration of small particles, those most likely to cause illness symptoms, remains unchanged. Also, the concentration measure does not take into account the chemical makeup of the particles. An asbestos particle is a much greater health risk than a clay particle. The respirable mass concentration is therefore not a reliable indicator of the health risk of airborne particles.

In office buildings, filters and electrostatic devices are most commonly used to remove airborne particles. Filtration systems force air through a material that traps particles larger than the openings. Finer filters trap smaller particles. HEPA filters and electrostatic air cleaners can remove smaller particles than conventional filtration systems but are more expensive. Electrostatic devices use a high voltage to attract particles to a collector element. In general, the smaller the size of particles to be removed, the more expensive the system.

To control airborne particle levels requires the effective cleaning and maintenance of both the air-handling system and the office in general. The more dirt and dust in carpets, and on furniture and equipment, the more particles there are to become airborne as people move around. Air-handling systems must be regularly cleaned, serviced, and the filters replaced (Figure 5.8). Using low-quality filters or replacing them less frequently than required is commonly the cause of excessive levels of airborne particles indoors.

Asbestos

Asbestos, an inflammable mineral fiber, was used for many years as insulation and as a fireproof covering. Unfortunately, when the material is handled or subjected to abrasion or vibration, it readily releases fibers small enough to be suspended and carried in the air. When asbestos fibers lodge in the lung, they cause *asbestosis* (a lethal lung disorder) and cause or aggravate lung cancer, *mesothelioma* (a rare tumor), and other chronic obstructive lung diseases.

Today, the health hazards of asbestos are well documented and widely known. But it was only after innumerable studies and decades of use that its dangers were recognized and finally accepted. As a result, asbestos is present in many older buildings. Over time, aging asbestos used in duct linings and HVAC system plenums breaks apart, releasing fibers that are then carried by the ventilation air into the occupied spaces. Exposure limits are strictly regulated and are set at 0.1 fiber/cubic centimeter of air (OSHA 1994). Filters are very effective in removing these airborne fibers.

Removing asbestos from buildings is not only expensive, but the procedure itself poses a health risk because large quantities of asbestos fibers are released. In many cases, it is less dangerous to encapsulate asbestos-containing materials with a bonding agent or sealer rather than to remove them. A liquid sealer can be sprayed into small spaces that would be difficult to reach, and because the material is not being handled, the process does not generate airborne asbestos fibers.

MICROORGANISMS

Microscopic-size plants and animals are everywhere in the outdoor and indoor environments. The microbiological particulate matter found in office buildings includes viruses, bacteria, fungi, protozoa, and mites, as well as the substances they produce, such as excrement, spores, and pollen. They may cause unpleasant odors, allergic reactions, or disease.

In some cases, it is chemicals in the debris created by a microorganism rather than the organism itself that causes disease or an allergic response. Symptoms may include recurrent persistent coughs, shortness of breath, asthma, fever, fatigue, a lowered resistance to disease, chills, inflammation of the eyes, and nausea. Once microorganisms are in a building, the forced-air ventilation system efficiently distributes potential disease-causing organisms and biological irritants throughout the occupied spaces. Hence, microorganisms are implicated in most cases of sick building syndrome.

Although a number of studies have reported a higher incidence of illness symptoms in offices equipped with HVACs than in naturally ventilated buildings, the cause is generally considered to be the foreign materials that collect on the equipment rather than the equipment itself (Burge 1992; Mendell 1993). Components of the air-conditioning system, particularly those that are moist, can support high levels of bacteria and fungi, as can other building components where dirt or water accumulate (e.g., ceiling tiles, carpets, and areas wetted by accidental flooding or roof leakage).

Some microorganisms occur only in specific types of building equipment, whereas others colonize wherever dirt and debris accumulate. Fungi and their related spores almost always originate from outdoor air that is brought into the building as part of the fresh air intake. Cooling towers, evaporative condensers, and humidification equipment are particularly attractive environments for microorganisms. Dirt and organic material on the building exterior can also harbor infectious microorganisms. For example, the fungus *Aspergillus fumigatous,* found in the droppings of pigeons and other birds, can penetrate poorly maintained air filtration systems. The fungus primarily affects individuals whose immune system is weakened by illness or age.

The occupants themselves are a major source of disease bacteria. The very nature of the office setting promotes the transmission of disease. Not only are people in close proximity; they also interact frequently and with many different individuals. They exchange files, reports, and other items that pass through many hands. They cough and sneeze, producing germ-laden water droplets that are suspended in the air and fall on objects nearby. The dedicated "troopers" who put in a full day of work while suffering from the flu all too easily pass the illness to their coworkers.

Chicken pox, measles, mumps, and various colds and flus are commonly spread in the spray of water droplets produced by sneezing. On the order of a few microns in size, these droplets can remain airborne for some time — long enough to enter the air-handling system. Studies have shown that the incidence of common cold increases with the number of people who work together in a room (Jaakkola, Heinonen, and Seppänen 1990). Encouraging employees to stay home with a cold instead of coming to work may be an effective way to reduce an organization's sick leave work losses.

Dust mites have adapted well to the built environment and exist in most dwellings worldwide. Mite excrement is especially fine, readily mixing with the ambient air and inhaled. It causes allergic responses in susceptible individuals. The allergy-producing substances can persist in dust for years (Bischoff 1989). Though dust mites are normally considered an issue only for residences and schools, sick building symptoms were lower in offices cleaned by a process that eradicated dust mites than in those cleaned using methods that could not. Promoting health through cleanliness is as important in the office as it is at home. Occupants in cleaner offices report fewer work-related illness symptoms (Raw, Roys, and Whitehead 1993).

There are no numerical guidelines for exposure to microorganisms. A tremendous variety of microbiological materials can exist in indoor air, and people vary widely in their sensitivity to them. As well, the relationship between building characteristics, microorganism concentrations, and the incidence of illness is not well understood. Isolating specific disease-causing microorganism commonly requires sophisticated and expensive testing. Indoor concentrations of microorganisms are generally considered to be acceptable if they are lower than outdoor levels. A higher count indoors may indicate that breeding zones are present within the building.

In most cases, the indoor concentration of microorganisms and their by-products can be readily controlled to safe levels by proper maintenance and cleaning of the general office area and the building services (e.g., the ventilation system and air filters). Standing bodies of water are likely to develop large populations of microorganisms unless the equipment is regularly and thoroughly cleaned. Maintenance can be easier and more effective if components are made of durable materials with surfaces that can be readily accessed and cleaned. Small, odd-shaped nooks and crannies that are difficult to clean readily become sources of microorganisms.

Operation of the building systems can also affect the incidence of infection. Organisms differ in the conditions that promote their growth. Indoor climate settings can be chosen that are least favorable to the growth of organisms. A relative humidity of 40% to 60% generally offers an optimal balance (Figure 5.9). Since disease transmission is favored by a high relative humidity, there is a health benefit to setting the level at the low end of this range or as low as occupants find comfortable.

Legionnaires' Disease and Pontiac Fever

Legionnaires' disease is perhaps the most widely known building-related illness caused by airborne microorganisms. It is named after a 1976 epidemic of pneumonia among a group of American Legion conventioneers in Philadelphia. The dis-

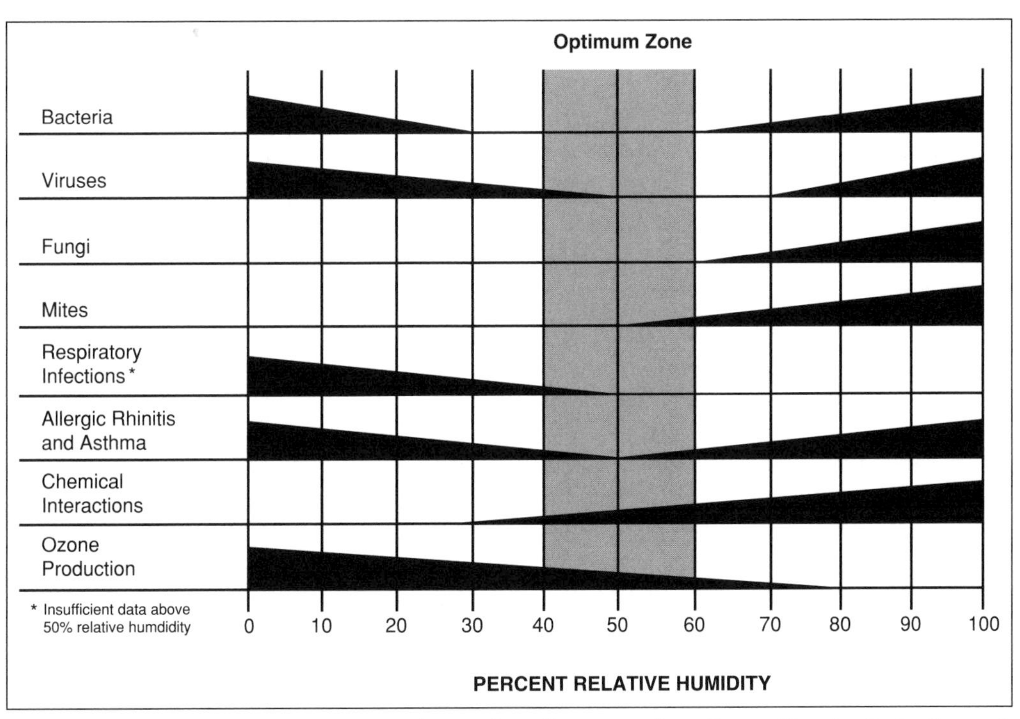

Figure 5.9 Effect of relative humidity on factors that affect air quality. (*Source:* Theodor D. Sterling and Associates, Vancouver.)

ease infected 149 Legionnaires and 72 other people who were in or near the hotel where the convention was held. Thirty-four people eventually died. At the time, the cause of the illness was unknown. The disease organism was later found to be the bacterium *Legionella pneumophila* (Shands and Fraser 1980).

Legionnaires' disease and Pontiac fever are both caused by species of *Legionella* bacteria but are quite different. Legionnaires' disease causes pneumonia symptoms and affects 1% to 4% of those exposed. It is the more serious disease, with a mortality rate of about 15% of those affected. Individuals whose resistance to disease is impaired by age, lung disease (such as pulmonary disease from cigarette smoking), asthma, or suppression of the immune system are more likely to succumb. Between 50,000 and 70,000 cases of Legionnaires' disease are thought to occur each year in America (Hodgson and Hess 1992).

Pontiac fever is a nonfatal disease with symptoms similar to the flu — chills, fatigue, fever, headache, and muscular pain. It does not cause pneumonia symptoms. About 95% of those exposed develop the illness within one or two days. Antibiotic treatment is not required, and symptoms generally subside in two or three days (Barbaree 1991; Friedman et al. 1987; Morris and Shelton 1991). Because the disease is mild and the symptoms are common to many ailments, there are no reliable estimates of the overall incidence of Pontiac fever.

Legionella bacteria occur naturally in surface waters and survive in low numbers after routine water treatment. In buildings, they can become established in components of air-conditioning systems (particularly cooling towers, evaporative condensers, and humidifiers) and in the hot-water plumbing systems of hospitals and hotels (see, for example, Bornstein et al. 1986; Memish et al. 1992). People become infected by ingesting contaminated water or breathing droplets from showers, whirlpools, or other sources.

A number of epidemics of Legionnaires' disease and Pontiac fever have been clearly linked to the presence of high concentrations of *Legionella* in the ventilation system (Finnegan and Pickering 1986; Shands and Fraser 1980). As with other microorganisms, the bacteria become airborne in fine water droplets, which are then carried by a forced-air ventilation system throughout the building.

Humidifier Fever

Humidifier fever is a flulike illness precipitated by exposure to air from contaminated humidifiers. The illness appears to be an allergic response to antigens produced by microorganisms in the humidifier water. There is disagreement about the specific organism involved. It may be an amoeba (a single-celled protozoan).

The symptoms of humidifier fever vary considerably, ranging from mild headaches and malaise to high fever, muscle and joint aching and pain, dry cough, shivering, and shortness of breath. Due to the variable clinical features of this disease, it is often misdiagnosed.

Humidifier fever tends to occur after a period when the humidifier is not used, such as the first day after a weekend or holiday. Symptoms occur 4 – 8 hours after initial exposure and are typically preceded by a feeling of cold, often with shivering. It usually resolves without treatment within 24 hours, allowing a return to work the following day. Despite this continuing exposure, the disease does not recur until after the next extended absence. The disease is most severe after people have had a long absence from the environment (Finnegan and Pickering 1986; McSharry, Anderson, and Boyd 1987). Exposure may therefore be producing a short-term measure of immunity. Humidifier fever can be prevented by regular cleaning of humidification equipment.

Control of Microorganisms

The primary measure to control the growth of microorganisms in ventilation systems is regular maintenance, cleaning, and inspection. Where the control of microbial growth is difficult, treatment with biocides or hyperchlorination may also be required. *Legionella* have been successfully eradicated from hot-water supply systems by superheating — raising the water temperature above 60°C (140°F) for 72 hours and flushing water outlets with hot water for 30 minutes (Best et al. 1983).

ODORS

The human olfactory system, our sense of smell, continuously samples the air. Although objectionable odors may be annoying, they serve to warn people of potential harm. Attractive odors confirm that a visually appealing meal will indeed be good to eat; foul odors warn that the food might best be left alone.

Olfactory information is transmitted to several areas of the brain, particularly those associated with memory formation and retrieval, emotional response, and the regulation of neuroendocrine function (e.g., the hypothalamus). For this reason, an odor may remind someone of specific events or emotions for which an association has developed. In affecting neuroendocrine function, odors can cause physical reactions by triggering the release of hormones or other responses. For example, an odor could prompt the recall of a fearful memory and cause a person to begin sweating.

People assess the quality of indoor air largely on the basis of its odor and on their perception of the associated health risks. Although offensive-smelling air is not necessarily unhealthy, the sheer unpleasantness of the odor can bring about symptoms such as nausea, vomiting, dizziness, lethargy, headaches, and loss of appetite. In some cases, odors from insecticides, cleaning solutions, tobacco smoke, dry-cleaned clothing, paint, or perfume cause serious physical illness such as allergic or asthmatic reactions (Figure 5.10) (Shim and Williams 1986). But harmful contaminants, such as carbon monoxide and

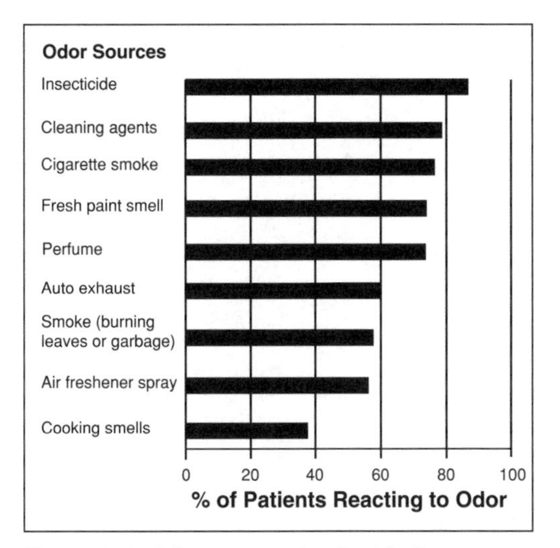

Figure 5.10 Odorants associated with the aggravation of asthma. (*Source:* Data from Shim and Williams 1986.)

many airborne bacteria and fungi, are often odorless. The maximum exposure levels specified by occupational safety standards for many airborne chemicals are well below the concentrations at which their odors are detected (Amoore and Hautala 1983; Billings and Jonas 1981).

Odors in the office environment result from the mix of chemicals in the air. Constituents may interact, masking or amplifying individual odors. For this reason, determining the cause of an objectionable odor can be quite difficult.

Foul outdoor air containing industrial effluents, smog, and general pollution raises the indoor odor level. As well, fumes from vehicle exhaust or garbage bins around a building can be sucked into air intakes located at ground level and lead to occupant complaints (Figure 5.11). (It is accepted practice to place air intakes at ground level in order to reduce the risk of pulling smoke into the building during a fire.)

The major indoor contributors to objectionable odors are volatile organic compounds (e.g., released by building materials, cleaning products, carpet glues, and paint solvents), certain office supplies (e.g., marking pens and printing ink), air fresheners and deodorizers, and plant and animal sources (e.g., molds and animal excrement). In addition, occupants' body odor, tobacco smoking, and consumer products brought into the office can be significant odorant sources. (In the nineteenth century, many people believed that substances given off by the human body were harmful. For this reason, early research on indoor air quality tended to focus on preventing body odors from reaching objectionable levels.)

Deodorizers and air fresheners are used to mask objectionable odors, particularly in washrooms. Paradichlorobenzene, a constituent of mothballs and commonly used in commercial deodorizers, is a carcinogen. It is estimated that the indoor air exposures to this compound create a population-based risk of 83 cancer deaths per million. Among VOCs, only benzene and chloroform are estimated to pose a greater cancer risk (Cone and Shusterman 1991).

Very little is known about the toxicity of the chemicals in perfumes at the concentrations normally encountered in indoor air. The most commonly reported health effects are allergies, but perfumes are also a frequent exacerbating agent of asthma.

Inorganic chemicals are generally odorless at the concentrations in which they are normally found in offices, with the exception of ozone and compounds that contain sulfur. Organic chemicals with higher molecular weights (over 300) are generally odorless as well. Other organic compounds usually have perceptible odors, some detectable at concentrations as low as 1 part per trillion.

Odors from biological sources are often indicative of poor hygiene or incorrect operation of building systems. Plumbing problems such as inadequate venting of waste pipes and washroom soil stacks can force sewage gases into occupied areas. Condensation on air-conditioning coils or on certain metals and their coating materials can also produce irritating odors. Food, cooking, decomposition of animal and vegetable matter, and the improper disposal of these items are also common sources. Animal residues from rats, mice, and bats are odorous as well as being a health hazard. Distributing poisons to

Figure 5.11 Air intakes near ground level, such as this one, easily draw vehicle exhaust and fumes from garbage bins into a building, degrading the indoor air quality.

eliminate these pests sometimes results in animals' dying within the walls, ductwork, or other difficult-to-reach spaces. Their decaying bodies can produce pungent odors until they are either removed or become dried out. Odors from decomposing animal bodies indicate that problematic microorganisms are probably being released into the airstream.

There is no standard for office odors. It is generally assumed that providing the minimum recommended ventilation rate will be sufficient to dilute odors. The ASHRAE minimum ventilation rate for offices where cigarette smoking is not permitted is 8 liters/second/person (15 cubic feet/minute/person) (ASHRAE 1989; Cone and Shusterman 1991). Odors can also be reduced by adsorption with activated charcoal or other materials and the use of chemicals to mask the odors, reduce their intensity to an acceptable level, or destroy them by chemical reaction.

Some odor-producing substances such as cigarette smoke and coffee oils are readily absorbed by fabrics and adhere to surfaces making them difficult and expensive to eliminate. The odors can remain long after the activity that produced them has ceased. Emission rates for common office materials such as cotton, wool, rayon, and porous wood that absorb odors are decreased with lower levels of temperature and humidity. Where the material itself is the odor's source (e.g., linoleum, paint, rubber, and upholstery), lower relative humidity alone reduces the release of odor. Although emission rates are higher with increased temperature and humidity, human *perception* of odor is reduced. A general guideline is that maintaining a relative humidity of between 45% and 60% is optimal for the control of indoor odor levels.

No given odor is always appropriate. An odor considered appealing in one context may be objectionable in another; one that attracts some people may nauseate others. Because all odors become unpleasant at high levels of perceived intensity, it is best to keep odor levels low.

NEGATIVE AIR IONS

The existence of charged particles in gases was discovered in the late nineteenth century. They were named **ions,** the same term used to describe charge carriers in liquids. Ever since their discovery, air ions have been the subject of research, much of it focused on their effects on human health. As early as 1939, published reports claimed that raising the indoor concentration of negative air ions enhanced human health, well-being, and comfort (Kröling 1985).

During the 1950s, negative air ions were promoted as effective in the treatment of human ailments ranging from constipation to cancer. Despite the lack of medical evidence to support these claims, the sale of air-ion generators to the public soared. The U.S. Food and Drug Administration eventually intervened and restricted the advertising and distribution of the machines. As a result, scientific interest in air ions and funding of research dropped sharply. Then, in the 1980s, concern about the health effects of indoor air led researchers to measure every constituent of the air, *including* air ions. In some studies, beneficial and significant correlations were found between the concentration of negative air ions and health. Other studies did not find significant effects. Because the issue of negative air ions remains so controversial, it is treated here in greater detail than would otherwise be merited.

What Are Air Ions?

Air ions occur naturally in the environment and are formed by the collision of high-energy particles with neutral air molecules. The most common natural sources of high-energy particles are radioactive elements (e.g., uranium and radon), cosmic rays, and ultraviolet light. Free electrons can also be produced by vigorous mechanical forces such as the shearing of water droplets in waterfalls or the rapid flow of large volumes of air over land masses.

Air molecules that lose electrons when they collide with high-energy particles become positively charged and are termed **positive air ions.** If the freed electrons attach to a neutral air molecule, it forms a **negative air ion.** Air ions are attracted to ions of opposite charge and to objects that can absorb or neutralize their charge, such as walls and furniture.

Air ions are divided into three classes according to their mobility and size: fast, slow, and intermediate. The smaller the size, the greater the mobility. Fast ions are small, highly mobile, and short-lived (from 50 to 250 seconds). These fast negative ions are purported to have beneficial effects on human health and well-being (Dolezalek 1985). Slow ions are longer-lived and may last several days. Slow and intermediate ions are formed primarily by the collision of a fast ion and an **aerosol** (an airborne liquid or solid particle).

Controversial Benefits of Negative Air Ions

A number of investigators found that humans exposed to relatively high negative air-ion concentrations, under either natural or experimental conditions, reported changes in mood and psychological performance as well as relief from a variety of discomfort symptoms such as headache, nausea, insomnia, and elevated levels of tension and anxiety (e.g., Hawkins 1981; Morton and Kershner 1990; Sulman 1984; and Tom et al. 1981). High positive ion concentrations have been reported to aggravate discomfort symptoms and lower performance. However, many comparable studies have failed to demonstrate any significant effects (e.g., Fletcher 1988; Hedge and Collins 1987; Hedge and Eleftherakis 1982; Kröling 1985). Hawkins found a significant effect in one study and none in another (Hawkins 1981; Hawkins and Morris 1984).

One issue about which there is no controversy is that negative air ions remove airborne particles. Many household and commercial air cleaners use them for this purpose (Household air cleaners 1992). Negative ions can attach to large dust particles as well as minute microorganisms, making them one of the few agents that can remove the tiny particles in cigarette smoke. Unfortunately, the newly formed negatively charged particles are then deposited as a dust film on virtually every exposed surface in the room, whereas filters or an electrostatic precipitator incorporated into a building's HVAC system traps and collects airborne particulate matter so that it can be conveniently removed.

Much of the controversy surrounding negative ions may lie in the difficulty of distinguishing the benefits of improving the indoor air quality by removing airborne particles from other purported health benefits. For example, people with allergies to dust, mold, pollen, and microorganisms will feel better when the air they breathe is free of these irritants — whether they are removed by an ion generator or by some other type of air cleaner. Wyon (1992) found that negative ion generators installed in a hospital improved perceptions of the air quality and reduced physical illness symptoms. He used a positively charged collector plate to gather charged airborne particles and demonstrate the air-cleaning effect of the negative ion generators. He concluded that it was the air-cleansing effect of the negative ion generators that produced the beneficial results he reported. However, people suffering from allergies or illness symptoms are better advised to seek medical attention than to depend on negative ion generators for relief.

Until recently, ion-generating devices also produced considerable quantities of ozone and nitrous gases. Nitrous gases can irritate the eyes, nose, and throat. Ozone is recognized as causing acute and chronic health effects, as discussed earlier in this chapter. The toxic and chemically active characteristics of ozone eliminate odors by oxidizing the offending molecules. Thus, ozone can kill microorganisms and give air a subjectively "fresh" smell. Regardless, ion-generating devices that produce ozone should not be used.

Another controversial mechanism proposed to explain how negative air ions could affect human health is its effect on the production of **serotonin** — a hormone believed to affect the body's metabolism, circulatory system, and endocrine functions. Elevated levels can produce an allergic type of reaction similar to that produced by histamines. Several investigators believe that negative air ions inhibit the production of serotonin and that positive ions promote its release.

Sulman (1984), in reviewing the impact of weather on health, asserted that air ions influenced serotonin production in humans. He estimated that some 30% of the population had weather-sensitive discomfort complaints such as headaches, migraines, heightened irritability and anxiety, insomnia, and depression. He considered these symptoms to be the result of increased production of serotonin and found that antiserotonin drugs provided relief. Sulman asserted that high positive air-ion concentrations caused elevated serotonin production and that negative air ions could counteract this effect. This relationship between negative air ions, weather patterns, and human health is disputed in the scientific literature (see, for example, Fletcher 1988; Kröling 1985; and Reiter 1985).

Commercial negative ion generators are designed to produce a stream of negatively charged, fast ions to raise the negative ion concentration in an enclosed space. However, Daniell, Camp, and Horstman (1991) found that some devices did not produce any measurable increase. The high negative ion levels used in laboratory experiments are commonly 10–1,000 times those found in nature (Kröling 1985). Such concentrations would be difficult to produce in an office setting.

The negative ion concentration in indoor air depends on the type of ventilation system, the building materials (e.g., trace amounts of radioactive elements will raise the count), and the concentration of aerosols. Even small amounts of aerosols, such as the smoke produced by one cigarette, will reduce the negative ion concentration in a moderate-size office to nearly zero (Kröling 1985). So it is unlikely that experimental findings could be replicated in a working office.

The extensive publicity on indoor air quality — its risks and possible solutions — has created an expectation that negative ion generators can improve the air people breathe and reduce sick building symptoms. Strongly held beliefs increase the likelihood that people will experience the expected effect. Experimental subjects who believed they were surrounded by negative ions reported improvements in air quality and a reduction in sick building symptoms, even though *no* negative ions were generated by the devices they were given — evidence that reported beneficial effects may be more psychological than physical (Daniell, Camp, and Horstman 1991). As such, intense publicity can be a major confounding factor when investigating controversial and emotionally charged issues such as negative ions.

Conclusion for Negative Air Ions

The only negative ion effect for which there is clear evidence and general consensus is the elimination of particles from the air. Although this can improve human health, there are other more effective air-cleaning methods. The other health benefits claimed for negative ions are disputed in the scientific literature. Many rigorously controlled studies have not shown beneficial effects from high negative ion concentrations, and some studies have demonstrated a placebo effect (i.e., subjects perceived an effect simply from being told that negative ions were present).

However, it is undisputed that clean air, free of particles as well as chemical contaminants, is a significant health benefit. There are many definitive steps that can be taken to design and maintain the air supply systems of offices to improve the occupants' health. Rather than focusing attention on whether individual devices (such as ion generators) do or do not provide health benefits, the focus should be on addressing indoor air quality from a total building performance perspective.

There should be a rationale for selecting the level of indoor air quality to be achieved and a well-defined procedure to assess conformance. Then indoor air quality can be addressed in a comprehensive manner, and the relative merits of specific devices should be judged in the context of all available courses of action that would contribute to satisfying the defined performance objectives. From this perspective, highest priority should be given to activities most likely to deliver the greatest ben-

Table 5.4 Successful approaches to avoid indoor air quality problems and sustain healthy indoor air.

- Prevent the entry of pollutants
- Reduce or eliminate indoor pollutant sources
- Eliminate, isolate, or restrict polluting activities
- Schedule activities to minimize occupant exposure
- Improve performance of the air-handling system
- Increase dilution by increasing the outside air fraction
- Monitor building operation and document occupant observations
- Raise occupants' awareness of how their actions affect indoor air quality
- Control other environmental stressors

efit for their cost. Debating the benefits of negative ion generators should not become an issue until other options more likely to deliver greater benefits at less cost have been exhausted.

Improving Indoor Air Quality

There are ways to improve indoor air quality during the design, commissioning, and operation of a building. Once a building is occupied, both the indoor and outdoor conditions need to be monitored for changes that may increase the pollutant load or reduce the overall indoor air quality. Occupants reporting illness symptoms such as runny eyes and nose, headaches, coughing, dry or sore throat, and frequent respiratory infections may be an indication of indoor air quality problems. Such problems may be temporary. They may be associated with changes in the seasons, unusual weather, a renovation, or new work activities. Regardless of their cause, occupant complaints must be addressed promptly and rigorously. Some fundamental approaches used to avoid air quality problems and sustain healthy indoor air are discussed in the following sub-sections and are summarized in Table 5.4.

PREVENT THE ENTRY OF POLLUTANTS

It is less expensive and more effective to eliminate contaminant sources than to depend on mechanical or chemical measures to remove or dilute contaminants once they are dispersed in the indoor environment. So the first line of defense is to avoid mixing contaminated outdoor air with the building's supply. If the outside air is highly polluted with smog, industrial waste gases, or vehicle exhaust, standard conditioning may not be adequate and more rigorous conditioning and cleaning systems may be required to make the air quality suitable for the office facility.

Finding and eliminating the routes contaminants take to infiltrate offices from underground parking structures or across the building enclosure can be daunting. Virtually any crack in the structure, caulking that has dried and fallen off, or openings for service runs (such as for electrical conduits or plumbing) are potential pathways for fumes to enter office areas (Figure 5.12). Problems most commonly arise at locations where different materials or components meet and have been poorly fitted or the sealant used to fill gaps has shrunk or not adhered.

Preventing the unwanted intake of outdoor pollutants generally requires removing their source, moving the air intake (which can be prohibitively expensive), or regulating activities. The vicinity of air intakes should be kept clear of materials and activities that produce odors and airborne contaminants (e.g., garbage bins, idling vehicles). Even then, local wind patterns can direct pollution into the building's air intake from outdoor sources

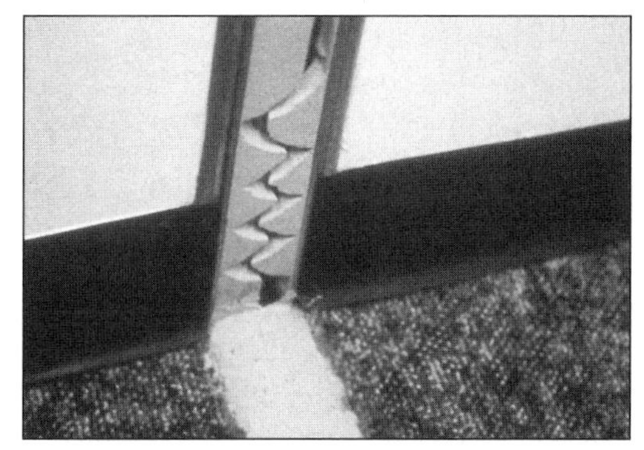

Figure 5.12 This crack in an interior wall extends into an expansion joint. Airborne chemical contaminants can migrate along such structural elements and enter the interior office space, far from their source.

5 – 10 meters (15 – 30 feet) away or more (Figure 5.13). For this reason, air-handling systems should be inspected at several different times during the day and under a variety of weather conditions. The hours that trash is collected and compactors are operated can be restricted to periods when the building is unoccupied. Not permitting vehicles to idle at loading docks, changing times when deliveries and shipments are made, and relocating or eliminating collection booths in underground garages (which force vehicles to stop and idle) can also be effective solutions. The operation of the air-handling system can be modified to minimize the intake of known pollutants. For example, outdoor ozone levels tend to peak at midday. The air-handling system can be set to draw a higher fraction of outdoor air in the early morning and late afternoon and less during the midday peak ozone hours.

REDUCE OR ELIMINATE INDOOR POLLUTANT SOURCES

Many indoor contaminants are produced by furnishings, equipment, and work activities. Choosing products with lower emission rates or changing procedures to eliminate the need for them goes a long way to avoid introducing pollutants. However, if an alternate product is less durable, it may need more maintenance or regular replacement. Even if it pollutes less, the frequent maintenance or replacement may offset the initial higher emission rate of the original product.

Figure 5.13 Local wind patterns can redirect and concentrate pollutants from outdoor sources in unexpected ways. The particular combination of surrounding structures and prevailing wind patterns at this location caused exhaust from vehicles idling in this alleyway to be drawn into the air intake (at arrow) — even though it was located on the roof!

Over the past 45 years, the number and kind of pollutant sources have increased dramatically with the introduction of new construction materials, finishes, equipment, and consumer products. For example, solid wood sheets have been replaced by composite wood products such as particleboard and plywood that contain wood fiber, binders, adhesives, and other chemical additives. Until recently, these composites all contained urea-formaldehyde resins that emitted vapors known to provoke illness symptoms. Some manufacturers are developing and marketing alternative resins free of formaldehyde. Water-based paints and those containing less organic solvents generally produce less odor. They **offgas** (emit contami-

Figure 5.14 Portable humidifiers, such as this one, tend to be cleaned infrequently, increasing the risk they will develop high levels of bacteria and fungi that can cause air quality problems.

nants) more slowly and produce less total emissions. In some cases, surface coatings can be used to reduce emissions; for example, varnish coatings on particleboard can lower formaldehyde emissions (Levin 1993b; Godish, Rouch, and Guindon 1989).

New carpeting is a strong emitter of chemical contaminants. Rolling out the carpet in a well-ventilated warehouse for several days prior to installation can reduce offgassing after the material is installed. Studies have shown that carpeting can increase illness symptoms (see, for example, Norbäck and Torgén 1989) and can elevate the concentration of some chemical contaminants for more than a year (Rothweiller, Wäger, and Schlatter 1992). Low-emitting adhesives are now available for installing floor products such as tiles and carpeting. It is important, however, to ensure that these adhesives are not used to fill surface irregularities. The thicker deposits of adhesive will continue to offgas for months, negating their low offgassing characteristics.

Many sources of volatile organic compounds such as paints, adhesives, and other building materials show reduced emission rates with aging. **Building-bakeout** is sometimes promoted as a way to accelerate the aging process. This technique involves exposing the building interior to elevated temperatures for several days. Indoor temperatures as high as 32°C (90°F) are typically maintained for three to five days. However, the bakeout results in very low humidity that can damage wood, fine furniture, artwork, and some building materials. What's more, exposing building interiors to abnormally high temperatures may accelerate the deterioration of some materials. For this reason, building-bakeout is no longer a recommended practice. Some authorities recommend very high rates of ventilation for extended periods to achieve the same benefits.

Equipment and furnishings that attract or collect dirt become sources of airborne contaminants. They can also become breeding areas for microorganisms such as molds and bacteria. Standing water and moist surfaces (associated, for instance, with the use of portable humidifiers) are especially liable to harbor fungi, bacteria, and other microbes that can be transported in circulating air and cause illness or allergic reactions (Figure 5.14). Some types of furnishings are more difficult to clean. Fabrics, for example, tend to hold odors and trap dirt. There is evidence to suggest that fabric materials increase the risk of allergy symptoms and nose and throat irritation (Jaakkola et al. 1991; Raw, Roys, and Whitehead 1993). Judicious cleaning of office areas is thus important for the maintenance of indoor air quality.

ELIMINATE, ISOLATE, OR RESTRICT POLLUTING ACTIVITIES

It is less expensive to eliminate or control a pollutant at its source than to remove it after dispersal. Tobacco smoke is difficult

Figure 5.15 An organization can continue to work in its office building while renovations are under way. However, equipment downtime, work disruptions, and the exposure of employees to construction debris, noise, dust, and fumes can exact a high cost in productive time lost.

to contain or remove once it has been absorbed by furnishings. The most effective and least expensive way to control this pollutant is to ban smoking in the entire building, and that's what many organizations have done.

Less harmful pollutant sources can be isolated. For example, photocopiers, laser printers, coffee machines, and other equipment can be grouped in areas that are separated from the general office space by walls or dividers. Locally venting these areas to the outside would reduce their contribution to the indoor pollutant load. Photographic and other laboratories and printing equipment can also be isolated in this way.

Some activities generate toxic or irritating air pollutants but are essential to the organization and cannot be eliminated. For example, a small company that designed computer boards did soldering to build prototypes for testing. The fumes infiltrated into the air-handling system and created an air quality problem. Isolating the activity, providing direct air exhausted to the outside, and restricting the hours when soldering was permitted resolved the problem. In extreme cases, it may be necessary to move the offending activities to a separate structure, specifically designed to safely accommodate them.

SCHEDULE ACTIVITIES TO MINIMIZE OCCUPANT EXPOSURE

Serious illness symptoms caused by indoor air can occur when a new building is first occupied or during renovations. The pollutant emission rates from carpets, carpet adhesives, paint, wallpaper, caulking, new furniture, and other furnishings are highest when they are new or when liquid-based materials are drying. Occupant exposure to these pollutants can be minimized by staggering construction and office work activities and by providing maximum dilution with outside air.

Whenever possible, renovations should be scheduled at times when the office is unoccupied, such as during nights, weekends, and holidays (Figure 5.15).

Table 5.5 Frequency of physical deficiencies in buildings known to have indoor air quality problems. (*Source:* Adapted from Woods 1989.)

Problems Rooted in *Design*	Physical Cause	Frequency
Building systems	Insufficient mixing of outdoor air	75%
	Inadequate airflow to occupied areas	75%
Service equipment	Inadequate filtration of supply air	65%
	Inadequate drain lines and drain pans	60%
	Contaminated ductwork or duct linings	45%
	Malfunctioning humidifiers	20%
Problems Rooted in *Operation*		
Service equipment	Inappropriate control strategies	90%
	Inadequate maintenance	75%
	Changing thermal and contaminant loads	60%

Renovation areas should be sealed off from the rest of the building that is still in use to prevent dust, dirt, and fumes from entering occupied spaces. This typically requires that air diffusers and return air registers be sealed and other precautions taken to prevent contaminants from entering the air-handling system.

The period of time needed for new materials to stabilize is different for every building. Temperature, humidity, airflow rate, and the specific contaminants all influence the rate of stabilization. After the initial high release of volatile compounds subsides and the proportion of outdoor air is reduced, the concentrations of contaminants known to cause illness symptoms and the incidence of illness symptoms among the occupants should be monitored. If illness symptoms begin to increase, mitigation measures should be taken, such as inspecting for contaminant sources, increasing the outside air fraction, or periodically flushing the building with outside air.

IMPROVE PERFORMANCE OF THE AIR-HANDLING SYSTEM

A mechanical system that is properly designed, installed, and operated can provide a healthy and comfortable work environment (see, for example, Burge et al. 1987). The higher incidence of indoor air problems found in mechanically rather than naturally ventilated buildings (Potter 1988; Woods 1989) generally stems from deficiencies in the design and/or maintenance of the ventilation systems (Burge, Jones, and Robertson 1990; Robertson 1988; Woods 1988a). The National Institute for Occupational Safety and Health (NIOSH) estimates that about half of all sick building complaints were the result of inadequate ventilation and dirty or contaminated air-conditioning systems. Incorrect design, improper installation, inadequate maintenance, and poor operating procedures were common problems. Poor-quality outdoor air, inadequate air distribution to the occupied spaces, inferior maintenance, and inappropriate control strategies occurred in 75% or more of the cases reported by Woods (1988a) (Table 5.5). Many of these deficiencies can be mitigated or eliminated by more frequent and rigorous cleaning and maintenance of the air-handling system, ensuring adequate outdoor air ventilation rates, and improved training of those who operate these systems.

The contaminant loads in office air are so variable that no general ventilation guideline could ensure adequate indoor air quality in all cases. Air-handling systems must be designed to provide sufficient outdoor air to dilute the expected pollutant loads or isolate them, as required for the specific building. Similarly, the air filtration system will provide satisfactory service only if it is capable of removing the contaminants of concern and if it is properly maintained.

Occupants in mechanically ventilated buildings commonly complain of insufficient air movement. Although the recommended rate of airflow may be met, the distribution of supply air is not uniform throughout a building. The location of air diffusers and the layout of walls, office furniture, and acoustic dividers all influence the direction and rate of airflow through the occupied space. In open plan offices, small areas that do no have an overhead diffuser and are surrounded by high screens and furniture can become dead air spaces with substantially less air circulation than the average ventilation rate. Air circulation can usually be increased by rearranging or removing screens. In some cases, adding a ceiling diffuser or providing a desk fan may be warranted.

The capacity of an HVAC system is specified to maintain the desired temperature and humidity levels in an energy-efficient manner. To satisfy thermal comfort needs or optimize energy consumption, HVACs are sometimes operated with levels of outdoor air exchange that are now considered insufficient to provide for adequate indoor air quality. This practice is less common now that the health consequences are better understood. In some cases, the capacity of the HVAC in older buildings may not be sufficient to maintain the desired outdoor air fraction during extreme weather conditions. In the late 1970s and early 1980s, it was accepted practice to design for a lower minimum outside air fraction. (The influence of outside air fraction on indoor air quality is discussed further in the following subsection.)

Studies have shown that the potential energy savings from this practice are low or insignificant. For example, Eto and Meyer (1988) reported that even in severe climates, increasing minimum ventilation rates fourfold from 2.5 to 10 liters/second/person (5 to 20 cubic feet/minute/person), would increase the annual energy cost of operating a typical office building by only 5%. Researchers at the Bonneville Power Administration confirmed that such an increase in ventilation rates would not cause major increases in overall energy costs. For large office buildings, the expected increase was less than 0.5%, and for small offices, it was about 10% (Steele and Brown 1990). Manufacturers have responded to changing air quality requirements by developing HVAC systems that employ heat recovery systems to reduce energy consumption while at the same time adding plenty of outside air.

INCREASE DILUTION BY INCREASING THE OUTSIDE AIR FRACTION

The concentration of indoor pollutants largely depends on the rate at which they are diluted by the addition of air that is free of those contaminants. In most situations, the outside air is considered for practical purposes to be "contaminant-free" because the chemical contaminants generated inside office buildings usually occur outdoors in very low concentrations. Dilution with outside air can normally be expected to lower the concentration of indoor air contaminants. Dilution will obviously be less effective or even detrimental if the outside air is unusually polluted, as may occur during unfavorable weather conditions, such as temperature inversions, that can impede the normal dispersion of urban smog and other airborne contaminants.

The rate of outdoor air exchange in mechanically ventilated buildings depends on the rate of air circulation (i.e., the rate at which air is moved through the building) and on the proportion of outside air that is added (i.e., the **outside air fraction**). The rate of airflow in a room is generally measured as the number of *outside* air changes per hour or the rate of *outside* airflow per unit area or per person.

The number of **air changes per hour (ach)** is the volume of air that flows into a room over a one-hour period divided by the volume of the room itself. If the volume of air flowing into a room in one hour

Table 5.6 Effect of ceiling height on delivered outside air exchange. (*Source:* Adapted from Levin 1993b.)

Outside air changes/hour/square foot for a supply air ventilation rate of 1 cubic foot/minute/square foot.

Percentage outside air	Ceiling height in feet 8	10	12
10	0.75	0.60	0.50
20	1.50	1.20	1.00
30	2.25	1.80	1.50
40	3.00	2.40	2.00
50	3.75	3.00	2.50
60	4.50	3.60	3.00
70	5.25	4.20	3.50
80	6.00	4.80	4.00
90	6.75	5.40	4.50
100	7.50	6.00	5.00

Outside air changes/hour/square meter for a supply air ventilation rate of 5 liters/second/square meter.

Percentage outside air	Ceiling height in meters 2.5	3.0	3.5
10	0.72	0.60	0.51
20	1.44	1.20	1.03
30	2.16	1.80	1.54
40	2.88	2.40	2.06
50	3.60	3.00	2.57
60	4.32	3.60	3.09
70	5.04	4.20	3.60
80	5.76	4.80	4.11
90	6.48	5.40	4.63
100	7.20	6.00	5.14

is equal to half the volume of the room, the number of air changes per hour is 0.5. The **outside air exchange rate** or **outside air change rate** is calculated as the volume of *outside* air flowing into a room over a one-hour period divided by the volume of the room. Only when the ventilation supply air is comprised entirely of outside air (i.e., an outside air fraction of 100%) will the outside air exchange rate and the total air exchange rate be equal. If the outside air fraction is 50%, then the outside air exchange rate will be 50% of the total air exchange rate. Unfortunately, in the literature, the term *outside air exchange rate* is sometimes shortened to simply *air exchange rate,* assuming the reader to be aware that the reference is to the outside air component.

The **outside air ventilation rate** is the rate at which outside air is supplied — that is, the volume of *outside* air per unit of time. It is generally quoted in reference to area or to occupants. The units commonly used are liters per second per square meter (L/s/m²) or cubic feet per minute per square foot (cfm/ft²) in reference to area, and liters per second per person (L/s/p) or cubic feet per minute per person (cfm/p) in reference to occupancy. Here, too, there is often confusion when the term *ventilation rate* is used.

Simply increasing the rate at which air is moved through a building will not dilute airborne contaminants. Only by expelling indoor air and taking in outside air will contaminant concentrations be reduced.

In new or recently renovated buildings, the dilution of indoor air contaminants can be significantly accelerated by operating the ventilation system at a 100% outside air fraction for several weeks before the facility is occupied and then for several weeks afterward. The cost of flushing a building in this way can be minimized by scheduling this increased outside air ventilation rate at a time of year when the outdoor temperature and humidity are most similar to those required indoors. Not only will flushing the building reduce existing air contaminant concentrations; it also accelerates the release of volatile compounds so that emission rates will decrease more quickly.

Current ventilation standards recommend 8 liters/second/person (15 cubic feet/minute/person) for general offices, a higher minimum of 10 liters/second/person (20 cubic feet/minute/person) for open plan areas, and a rate of at least 18 liters/second/person (35 cubic feet/minute/person) in areas where smoking is permitted (ASHRAE 1989). However, this is a general guideline and does not take into account the unique characteristics of individual buildings or differences in pollutant loads. It may therefore be necessary to increase the out-

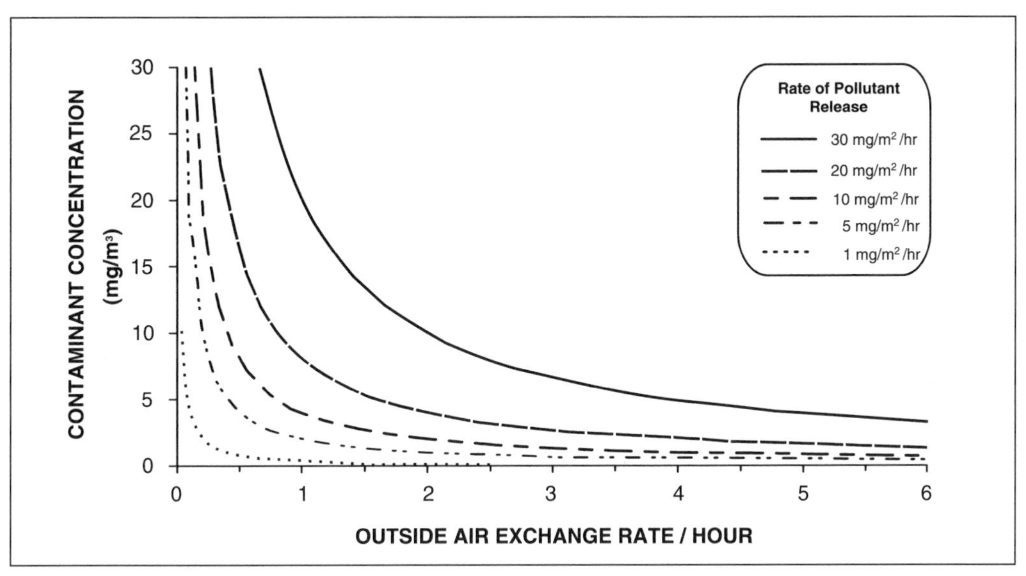

Figure 5.16 Effect of ventilation rate and source strength on indoor air pollutant concentrations. (*Source:* Adapted from Levin 1993b.)

side air fraction in order to achieve an acceptable level of air quality at every work setting.

The effect of the outside air fraction on the outside air exchange rate is illustrated in Table 5.6. The values given in this table are for a supply air ventilation rate of 5 liters/second/square meter for the section in metric units and 1 cubic foot/minute/square foot for the section in imperial units. The air exchange rate values are quoted in air changes per hour in both sections. However, the values are different because the supply air ventilation rate and ceiling heights are not equivalent. The air change rate per unit area is given for ceilings of 2.5 meters, 3.0 meters, 3.5 meters (8 feet, 10 feet, and 12 feet) and for outside air fractions ranging from 10% to 100%. For example, at an air fraction of 100% in a room with an 8-foot ceiling, the outside air exchange rate is 7.5 air changes/hour/square foot. But if the ceiling is 2 feet higher, the rate is only 6.0 air changes/hour/square foot, and at 12 feet it is 5.0 air changes/hour/square foot. A higher ceiling increases the volume of a space and thus reduces the outside air exchange rate. Reducing the air fraction reduces the outside air exchange rate as well.

A given HVAC system can provide a range of outside air fractions. This range is limited by the physical design of the system and its conditioning capacity. If the outside air is too cold or too hot, the HVAC system may not have sufficient heating or cooling capacity to condition the air to the desired temperature. Thus, when selecting an HVAC system, it is critical to evaluate the outside air fraction that can be provided at the extremes of environmental conditions that are expected to occur.

The outside air fractions used in office buildings range from 10% to 100%. However, some buildings, mostly older large office buildings, have system limitations that restrict the maximum outside air fraction to 10% to 20%. It is generally recommended that HVAC systems be capable of supplying no less than 20% outside air under all climatic conditions.

Figure 5.16 illustrates the impact on indoor air quality of the outside air exchange rate and the strength of an air pollutant source (i.e., the rate at which a source emits contaminants). The curves on the graph represent air pollutant sources releasing contaminants at different rates. Not surprisingly, because stronger contaminant sources have higher emission rates, more air is needed for dilution, so a higher ventilation rate is required to achieve a given contaminant concentration in the indoor air. A weaker source requires much less ventilation to achieve the same level of air quality.

The graph also demonstrates clearly that increasing the outside air exchange rate sometimes increases dilution dramatically but at other times has little effect. The range in which the curves change sharply from near-vertical to near-horizontal is where changes in the ventilation rate will have the greatest effect on indoor air quality. This occurs in the 0.5 to 1.5 air changes/hour range. Most buildings operate within this range for much of the time they are occupied. For example, an open plan office environment with the minimum recommended outside air exchange rate of 10 liters/second/person (20 cubic feet/minute/person), with an average of 13 square meters/person (140 square feet/person) and a ceiling height of 3 meters (about 9 feet), delivers 0.85 air changes/hour of outside air.

Thus, the range of ventilation rates at which buildings are currently operated is such that small changes in ventilation rate can be expected to significantly affect indoor air quality. But as the outside air exchange rate is increased beyond 1.5 air changes/hour, improvements in air quality diminish rapidly (Levin 1993b). So for buildings that have indoor air quality problems but already have a high rate of outside air exchange, methods other than dilution are needed to reduce air contaminant concentrations. This highlights the importance of controlling pollutant sources.

Finding the optimum rate of outside air exchange is an inexact procedure at best. It is good practice to err on the side of caution and minimize the buildup of air pollutants by periodically flushing office buildings with 100% outside air whenever weather conditions are favorable (i.e., when the outside temperature and relative humidity are about the same as are required indoors). This procedure is incorporated into the "economizer" cycle that many HVAC systems now offer.

MONITOR BUILDING OPERATION AND DOCUMENT OCCUPANT OBSERVATIONS

Eliminating known contaminants does not in itself ensure that the air will not cause illness symptoms. Since the health effects of many compounds and mixtures of chemicals are unknown, a detailed analysis of indoor air samples may not reveal the cause of an air quality problem. For this reason, it is important to monitor the operation of the air-handling system and the health of the occupants.

The use of monitoring to adjust system operation is a valuable means of improving air quality. The causes of an air quality problem may not be completely known, but it is possible to determine which changes tend to improve air quality and which tend to degrade it.

An increase in occupant air quality complaints, incidence of illness symptoms, or in the rate of absenteeism may indicate that the indoor air quality has deteriorated. By using appropriate procedures to record and evaluate these indicators, many air quality problems can be recognized and remedied early, before people become seriously ill or the problems become politicized.

In a monitoring program, specific information about the outside weather conditions, building operation, occupant perceptions, and absenteeism due to illness are collected at regular intervals, in addition to the usual logging of occupant complaints. These data should then be used to determine which factors improve or degrade air quality in that specific facility so that the building's operation can be optimized. The monitoring system also provides a means to gauge the effects of changes in operation. For example, increasing the outside air fraction may or may not improve air quality. Monitoring provides a way to recognize whether such a change in building operation produces any noticeable improvement and, if it does, provides a means to determine the level at which there is no further improvement. In this way, monitoring provides the information that enables the facility manager to use a more adaptive approach to building operation — to be more responsive to unpredictable, fluctuating, or changing office conditions.

Monitoring occupant satisfaction documents changes in occupants' perception of office conditions. In fact, some practitioners maintain that occupant satisfaction should be used to *define* the level of air quality to be maintained. Fanger (1990) suggests defining "high," "standard," and "minimum" levels of air quality when 90%, 80%, and 70% of occupants are satisfied. This approach assesses acceptability directly and eliminates the problem of trying to predict the physical conditions that occupants will perceive as satisfactory. It also eliminates the need to assume that outdoor air is free of pollutants or to make assumptions about the major sources of indoor air contamination in order to calculate a quality rating. It is fundamentally an adaptive management approach that seeks to optimize occupant satisfaction and assess performance by direct measurement. It does not, however, offer protection from the many toxic pollutants that occupants do not sense.

For buildings with acceptable indoor air quality, a monitoring system is a means to recognize whether conditions are beginning to deteriorate. As grievances, claims, and litigation become more common, records of system operation and indoor air quality inspections can give the building owner legal protection. Should the issue of legal liability arise, a well-documented monitoring program and records of any mitigative measures undertaken demonstrate that management acted responsibly to identify and address office environment issues — that is, that management had demonstrated *due diligence*.

Computer-based automated building control systems are currently used to provide integrated operation of complex building systems. Environmental sensors distributed throughout the building supply a constant stream of data that are used to optimize building operation (see the subsection "Automated Control of Building Services" in Chapter 4). As the health effects of indoor air become better understood, computer programs could be developed that would allow these systems to optimize air quality in the same way that they optimize other building operating parameters today. This approach has been attempted using carbon dioxide as the indicator. The more people in a space, the more carbon dioxide they exhale. It was thought that adjusting the ventilation rate to maintain a low carbon dioxide level would ensure an adequate level of air quality. However, this simple measure was insufficient because the concentration of many contaminants is unrelated to occupancy (see the subsection "Carbon Dioxide" earlier in this chapter). For this reason, several different indicators would be needed in order for such a monitoring system to perform adequately.

RAISE OCCUPANTS' AWARENESS OF HOW THEIR ACTIONS AFFECT INDOOR AIR QUALITY

Building owners, facility managers, and office occupants alike need to become more aware of the ways in which their actions affect the overall indoor air quality. Personal-use items such as hair spray, nail polish, and dry-cleaned clothing emit chemical contaminants to which some people may be highly sensitive. The addition or removal of partitions, relocation or addition of air vents, and other modifications to the office can alter airflow patterns and reduce air exchange rates in some locations. These areas are then more likely to develop indoor air quality problems.

Those who select products for offices — from construction materials and furniture to office equipment, supplies, and cleaning solutions — should compare the contaminant emission rates of alternative products and select those less likely to degrade air quality.

CONTROL OTHER ENVIRONMENTAL STRESSORS

Poor indoor air quality imposes a physical stress on individuals. In the same way that people weakened by fatigue are more susceptible to illness, sensitivity to indoor air pollutants can be increased by exposure to other environmental stressors such as uncomfortable humidity or temperature, drafts, poor illumination, noise, and ergonomically poor furniture arrangements. Work-related pressures add to people's stress and further lower their tolerance for environmental stressors (see the "Human Response to Stress" and "Stress and the Work Environment" sections in Chapter 7). Addressing the total workplace environment that occupants experience increases the likelihood that corrective measures will produce noticeable as well as lasting improvements rather than shifting attention to another unresolved deficiency.

Conclusion for Air Quality

Airborne contaminants exist in the office setting as they do elsewhere. However, the forced-air ventilation systems now used in most office buildings disperse and continue to recirculate airborne contaminants throughout the facility. Thus, contaminant sources are not just a problem for those in the immediate vicinity; they affect all occupants.

Indoor air quality problems arise from excessive levels of chemical pollutants, particulate matter, and microbial contaminants in the air. The most effective and energy-efficient means to sustain healthy indoor air is to eliminate or reduce the sources of these materials. A lower contaminant load reduces the outside air fraction needed for dilution, thereby reducing energy consumption while maintaining satisfactory indoor air quality. Sources can be controlled by removing toxic products, substituting less polluting ones, encapsulating sources so the offending chemicals are not released into the air, or isolating and directly venting emissions. Maintaining a high standard of cleanliness and reducing the areas where dirt or water can collect also improve air quality and lower the incidence of sick building symptoms.

Current scientific knowledge is inadequate to identify the degree of risk associated with most (more than 90%) of the chemicals and biological substances in the office environment (National Research Council 1984). As the relationship between specific concentrations of indoor air contaminants and health is better understood and the ability to monitor low concentrations of airborne contaminants improves, the list of harmful constituents of indoor air will likely increase.

In the absence of reliable estimates of safe exposure levels for many indoor air pollutants, and given the lack of information about synergistic effects, it is prudent to err on the side of safety. Occupant health and complaint reports should be monitored for early indications of air quality-related health problems. If there is an increase in ailments associated with poor air quality, efforts should be made to identify and eliminate pollution sources, adjust building operations, or take other actions to reduce the incidence of symptoms to acceptable levels.

ACOUSTICS

Acoustic concerns in offices relate to noise and vibration. **Noise** is sound that is unwanted by the listener. Unlike the concept of noise in electronics, it is not classified by specific physical characteristics of the source, such as frequency or intensity. Rather, it is defined solely on the basis of the listener's subjective reaction. As such, sounds enjoyed in one context may be annoying noises in another.

Rapid back-and-forth motion (**vibration**) can produce audible sound or low-frequency vibrations that cannot be heard but produce physiological effects.

Figure 5.17 This sign in downtown Taipei publicly displays the level of street noise — which at 84 decibels is high. The noise level, together with the vehicle emissions, congestion, and heat, is not only uncomfortable for those outside; it degrades the quality of the indoor environment of the buildings nearby.

Vehicular traffic is the main source of noise and vibration external to buildings (Figure 5.17). Internal sources are the building services — elevators, fans, motors, compressors; and to a lesser degree, the office equipment — impact printers, photocopiers, paper shredders, refrigerators, water coolers; and of course, the occupants — their speech and activities.

Humans perceive sound when changes in air pressure cause the eardrum to vibrate. Nerve impulses generated by the inner ear are interpreted by the brain as the sensation of sound. Sounds can trigger an alarm response, one of the brain's many subconscious functions. This leads to an alert reaction in which the body is activated — disturbing sleep and interrupting concentration so that people are prepared to react to possible danger. In offices, noise distracts people from their work and is an additional stressor that they must expend effort to overcome. The more energy people expend to cope with their physical environment, the more quickly they fatigue (Wohlwill et al. 1976).

Office workers consistently report noise distraction to be one of the most troublesome obstacles to their performance (Harris 1991; Sundstrom et al. 1994). When noise becomes a barrier to work, it exacts a productivity cost from the organization. People make more mistakes and work more slowly. They also tend to use more simplistic problem-solving methods. Thus, as noise distraction becomes more troublesome, people not only work less effectively; they think differently, imposing a quality cost.

A noisy setting causes frequent breaks in concentration, making it more difficult to perform tasks that require continuous attention. It is not surprising, then, that noise distraction causes more errors in complex tasks than in simple ones. Noise interferes with the ability to distinguish between pertinent and unimportant aspects of a task. In affecting the judgment of relevance, noise distraction does not simply reduce the speed of performance; it changes the way people choose to do a task (Boggs and Simon 1968; Davidson, Hagmann, and Baum 1990; Dornic, Ekehammer, and Laaksonen 1991; Jones 1979; Kahneman 1973). Broken concentration reduces people's ability to make the creative leaps that distinguish solutions that are merely acceptable from those that are truly innovative. DeMarco and Lister (1987) found that computer programmers who worked in a quieter environment were significantly more likely to recognize a subtle but significant shortcut in the programming task they were given. Noise not only degrades the performance of complex tasks at the time it occurs, its negative effects persist for some time after the noise has ended (Sundstrom 1986).

People differ in their ability to tolerate noise. Noise is more acceptable if its occurrence can be predicted and there is some control of volume and duration. Several studies have compared the performance of subjects working under noisy conditions with a similar group working under the same conditions but given the power to turn the noise off. Even though the option of turning off the noise was never exercised, those given the control consistently performed better. Simply knowing when the noise would occur reduced stress and improved performance (Glass and Singer 1972; Trice 1987), whereas working under uncontrollable noise conditions has been shown to induce depressive moods that bias judgments toward more negative choices (Jones and Broadbent 1979; Willner and Neiva 1986).

Noise tolerance is also influenced by an individual's attitude and his or her past experience. Studies have shown that people who have grown up under crowded and noisy conditions (e.g., in a large family or high density residential areas) are more tolerant of noise. Under noisy conditions, their performance of complex tasks shows less degradation than that of subjects who grew up in quieter surroundings (Nagar, Pandy, and Paulus 1988). People are generally quite tolerant of self-generated noise. Sounds associated with activities of which they approve or people they like are generally more tolerable than sounds associated with disapproved activities or disliked people.

Disruption of speech communication and distracting background noise are not the only characteristics of sound that cause annoyance. Intensity, duration, sharpness (how quickly it reaches its maximum level), and complexity (single tone or multiple tones) also contribute to a sound's degree of annoyance. Unexpected, intermittent, and irregular sounds are generally more distracting. High-pitched sounds tend to be more annoying than low-pitched ones.

Noise can degrade performance by sensory overload, add to other sources of job-related stress, and contribute to stress-related illness (Karacek and Theorell 1990). Not surprisingly, noise disruption is associated with lower employee satisfaction with their job and physical work environment (Sundstrom et al. 1994). As such, noise can exact multiple penalties. Not only can the quality and quantity of an individual's output be reduced; worker satisfaction also suffers, perhaps to the point of increasing employee turnover.

Resolving Office Noise Complaints

There are fundamentally three approaches to reducing noise in the office environment: reduce or eliminate noise sources, modify the acoustic properties of the office space, and protect the individual. In short, mitigation measures address the sound source, the path, or the receiver — the person affected.

Distracting sounds can be avoided by providing alternative work areas, such as quiet places for tasks requiring concentration. Acoustic problems may also arise from organizational policies that fail to recognize the cost of noise distraction. Short-term savings secured by allowing overcrowding (even temporarily) or requiring employees to answer their own telephones may create numerous interruptions that, in the long run, lead to higher costs due to reduced productivity.

Because it is the individual's *perception* of sound that determines its distracting effect, complaints can best be addressed by defining needs and exploring ways to better accommodate occupants. It is a process complementary to other successful management approaches that seek to build employee commitment and involvement by responding to employees' needs. However, people cannot consistently define their acoustic requirements and more often report symptoms and perceptions rather than actual problems (Figure 5.18). A qualified acoustician is often required to interpret occupant perceptions, find the root causes of problems, and design effective solutions.

REDUCE OR ELIMINATE NOISE SOURCES

The most obvious way to mitigate noise problems is to eliminate sound sources and reduce sound intensity. The build-

Figure 5.18 Well-intentioned office workers placed acoustic ceiling tiles around this noisy equipment in hopes of reducing the overall noise level. Unfortunately, the tiles covered too small an area to be effective, and the paper notices posted on them covered the open-pore surface, undermining the materials' sound absorbing quality.

ing's systems generate considerable noise and vibration, which are readily conducted through the building structure, plumbing, and ventilation servicing. Wherever possible, major noise sources such as fans, motors, and elevator equipment should be acoustically separated from actively used areas. Measures to dampen sound and vibration are incorporated into the design of mounting hardware and enclosures. However, they deteriorate with age, leading to problems with noise and vibration. Some types of office equipment can also be troublesome vibration sources. (Vibration is discussed separately later in this chapter.)

The noise generated by office equipment can be significant. In many cases, noisy equipment can be replaced with quieter models. For example, computer equipment and many other electronic office devices have cooling fans, which differ significantly in the level of noise they generate. In fact, some manufacturers expend considerable engineering effort to reduce the noise level of their equipment (Figure 5.19). In some designs, the fan may be eliminated by using passive airflow and selecting components that generate less heat. Though the fan in a single piece of equipment may not be of concern, dozens or hundreds in an automated open plan office can generate quite a din. Impact printers, one of the most annoying and loudest components of computer equipment, can be replaced by laser or ink-jet models that employ a virtually silent printing technology. Many of the newer impact printers are quieter. Alternatively, printer hoods can be used. Constructed of sound-absorbing materials, they completely surround a printer to contain its noise. However, these bulky housings are awkward to use and are often rendered less effective by users who leave the hoods open.

Figure 5.19 Measuring the characteristics of the noise produced by impact printers can lead to improved design of the equipment and effective dampening solutions. (*Source:* Institute for Research in Construction, National Research Council Canada, Ottawa.)

Some noise sources can be readily shielded or moved to a separate room. Frequently the best solution is to locate troublesome machines away from the activities they disturb or group them together in a separate room. Photocopiers, printers, fax machines, paper shredders, and other equipment can often be housed in a suitably soundproofed and conveniently located room. In an open plan office, it may be acceptable to surround the cluster of equipment with sound-absorbent screens.

When separating a noisy activity from a quiet one, suitable buffering needs to be provided. Acoustic benefits are seriously compromised if the door into a noisy room must frequently be opened, such as by workers getting their printouts. The door's location is necessarily a compromise between convenient access and noisy interruptions.

Meeting and group work areas can be especially troublesome noise sources. The sounds are predominantly human speech. The pitch and loudness vary with the speaker and the emphasis and excitement he or she projects. The sounds are also intermittent — burst of applause, laughter, or animated discussion. All these characteristics — speech, variation in pitch and loudness, and intermittence — make this source of background sound particularly disruptive to others. Meeting areas therefore need to be located and constructed to provide an adequate buffer from incompatible activities. Some meetings might best be held off-site — recognizing that there are time, cost, and disruption considerations to that solution as well.

In general, the more people working in an area, the louder will be the background noise level. Placing workstations farther apart and reducing the overall population density of an office area reduces the number of human and equipment noise sources and offers more buffer space between people. Where space is available, this is a successful approach to managing office noise. However, office space is expensive, and the trend is toward providing smaller work areas, accommodating positions below middle management in less than 10 square meters (110 square feet) (IFMA 1994). This underscores the importance of proper acoustic design to compensate for higher occupant densities.

Most people who need quiet for focused concentration require it for only a portion of their activities. It is often impractical to assign them a full-time work space that has the high level of acoustic privacy they occasionally need. Some organizations have set aside quiet office areas that individuals can use when they need to work undisturbed. Without telephones or other distracting noises, these areas provide a haven from the bustle of the general workplace. Providing a range of spaces with different acoustic characteristics acknowledges that no one setting can support the full range of activities needed for creative and productive work. An organization's investment in multiple work settings depends on the makeup of its workforce. Research-oriented groups would likely use such quiet areas more than staff doing routine tasks.

Intermittent sounds, such as ringing telephones, can be extremely disruptive, especially if the individual has little control over them. The creative use of technology can often eliminate such troublesome sources, especially when the technology's overall impact is well thought through so new problems are not introduced. Most telephone calls are less important than the work they interrupt (McMillen 1992). Even "quiet" or silent "light-only" phones break a person's concentration, though they distract nearby workers less. Traditionally, a secretary would screen phone calls or deliveries. More recently, calls are forwarded to an answering machine, voice mail, or electronic mail (E-mail), which sends messages by computer to the recipient's electronic mailbox to be read at his or her discretion. A feature of some systems is that they indicate when a new message has been received, sometimes flashing a light on the computer screen until the message is read. Unfortunately, this defeats one of the major benefits of E-mail — to receive a message without being interrupted. Other technological advances such as voice-interactive computers and videoconferencing from a desktop computer will soon be widespread in offices. Their smooth introduction will, in part, depend on how disruptive they are to the surrounding occupants.

An effective and often neglected way to control noise sources is to convince people

Figure 5.20 In an open plan office it can be difficult to find a socially acceptable way to be left alone. One occupant used a rice-paper screen to barricade the entrance to his work area and posted a note that read, "Sorry, I'm busy. Free at 10:30" (translated from French, "Désolé, occupé. Libre 10:30".)

to change their behavior. For example, drop-in visits serve important social functions, build camaraderie and team spirit, and encourage an exchange of ideas. But they can also be tremendously disruptive when there is no socially acceptable way to be left alone (Figure 5.20). A greater awareness of the disturbance effects of common activities like unscheduled visits and conversations (regardless of the topic) in the midst of open plan work areas can go a long way to reduce noise distraction.

Noise problems can rarely be solved by quieting a single offending source. Effective acoustic designs address all the sources, their setting, and the activities they might disrupt. Solutions are then integrated with other environmental requirements of the workplace (e.g., thermal comfort, air quality, aesthetics) and the best set of trade-offs is used.

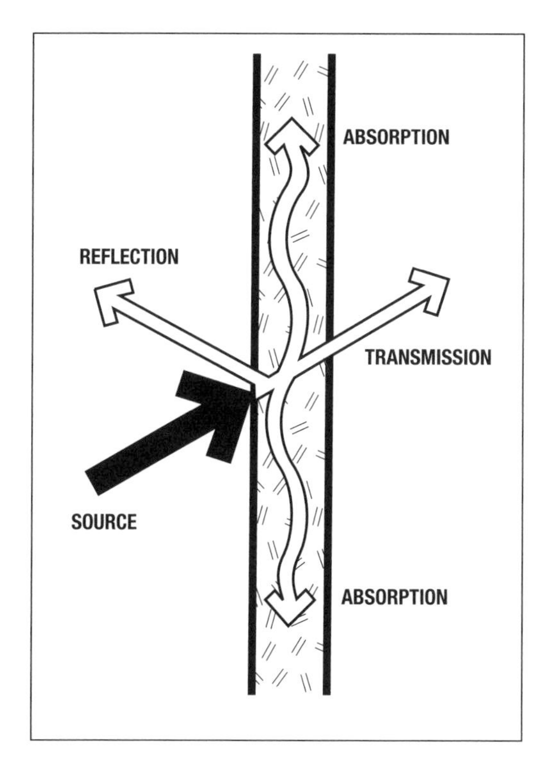

Figure 5.21 Reflection, absorption, and transmission of sound.

MODIFY THE SPACE TO SUIT ACOUSTIC NEEDS

The acoustic characteristics of the office space and its furnishings directly affect the sound levels that will be propagated by a noise source. Once generated, sound is absorbed, reflected, and transmitted until the energy of the air pressure wave is dissipated (Figure 5.21). Sound is **absorbed** if the energy of the air pressure wave is dissipated within the object. Soft materials, such as fabric-covered walls, tend to absorb sound. Acoustic ceiling tiles and dividing screens are specifically designed for this purpose. If the air pressure wave passes through openings in a barrier, or if it causes the material itself to vibrate (e.g., a rigid screen, wall, or the glass of a closed window), generating an air pressure wave on the opposite side, the sound will be heard on the other side and is said to be **transmitted.** Materials that are hard but light enough in weight to vibrate tend to transmit sound well. The sound-insulating property of a wall is easily lost if services such as plumbing and electrical outlets create openings through which sound can pass to the adjacent room. Materials that are hard and dense, such as concrete walls, block sound well because they are massive. But they are also good sound **reflectors** (i.e., the air pressure wave bounces off the wall and back into the room).

The treatment of office space to improve acoustic performance usually focuses on the dissipation of sound energy as quickly and completely as possible. Surfaces that absorb sound well reduce sound reflections and lower the effective background noise level. In general, hard surfaces — such as windows, concrete walls, bare floors, and drywall or concrete ceilings — reflect sound well. Soft surfaces absorb more sound and reflect less. They can significantly reduce the level of background noise if they are of sufficient bulk. Heavy fabric coverings such as draped curtains, tapestries, and acoustic ceiling tiles absorb noise effectively. Carpeting dampens the sound and vibration of footfalls, a noise source that can be transmitted to adjacent rooms and the floor below as well as being a local annoyance. However, sheer draperies, thin fabric coverings, or wallpaper applied directly to hard surfaces provide virtually no sound absorption.

Fabric furnishings collect dust and dirt and are more difficult to clean than smooth surfaces. There is a higher incidence of SBS, allergy, and asthma symptoms in offices with large areas of fabric surfaces and other dust accumulation sites (see the subsection "Airborne Particles" earlier in this chapter). This can be countered with regular and thorough cleaning or by substituting, in lieu of fabric furnishings, materials with smooth, easily cleaned surfaces designed specifically for acoustic control.

There is a wide selection of materials and construction techniques that can be used to improve the acoustic performance of walls, doors, and ceilings. Within the office, the principal concern is to maximize the acoustic insulation of work areas

Figure 5.22 Acoustic furniture panels are constructed of multiple layers of materials that together produce its sound-absorbing and sound-blocking properties. (*Source:* Steelcase, Grand Rapids, Mich.)

(i.e., to reduce sound transmission between spaces, reduce reflection within a space, and increase sound absorption) Cellulose fiber or glass wool quilt are the materials commonly used to absorb sound. When handled correctly, they do not significantly increase the level of indoor particles.

The size, shape, and finish of office furnishings also affect the way sound will behave in a space. Large, dense objects (e.g., a row of filing cabinets) can block sound effectively, and if they have an acoustically absorptive surface, they will not increase the noise level in front of them by reflecting sound. For this reason, the design and placement of office furnishings are not only a matter of functionality and aesthetics; they affect acoustic performance as well. Sometimes decor has to be compromised to meet acoustic needs.

In an open plan office, acoustic furniture panels are used to divide space and create more or less enclosed workstations. In general, the more enclosed an area, the greater will be its protection from sounds generated outside and the better it will absorb the sounds generated within. Sound propagates around an obstacle, and so freestanding panels used as sound barriers block sound more effectively the larger they are. In addition to size, the sound-absorbing and sound-blocking properties of an acoustic panel depend on its internal design and the materials of which it is constructed (Figure 5.22). Panels that offer better noise reduction are generally more expensive. The final decision regarding selection and placement of panels should also take into account environmental factors other than acoustics such as thermal comfort, air quality, and lighting. In general, acoustic panels should not be higher than 1.6 meters (62 inches) to avoid undue interference with other environmental factors.

Contrary to popular belief, an enclosed office does not necessarily guarantee acoustic privacy. Walls and doors of lightweight materials and hollow-core construction readily transmit sound to adjacent rooms. To provide acoustic privacy, their internal construction must be designed for adequate noise reduction. Openings in the wall for electrical, heating, and ventilation services can compromise acoustic performance to the point that conversations in one room can be clearly heard in adjacent spaces. Packing sound-absorbing material around the openings for building services and behind electrical outlets and switches can alleviate this problem as long as it is done consistently and with a high level of workmanship. Details important to acoustic performance are often hidden and inaccessible as construction proceeds, so on-site supervision of the work must be scheduled at appropriate times. Ensuring that tradespeople appreciate the importance of sealing *every* small gap goes a long way toward realizing the benefits of the acoustic design specified in the plans.

Ensuring that the walls have proper acoustic insulation still may not contain the sounds of an enclosed office. Most offices use suspended ceilings, in which acoustic tiles rest on a support grid hung from the underside of the floor above (see the subsection "Ceilings" in Chapter 4). This provides a continuous space, called

Figure 5.23 Sound will travel along any available path — which, in offices, includes through the ceiling plenum (*A*), through walls and partitions (*B*), and through the space beneath a raised floor (*C*). As well, sounds, such as footfalls from the floor above (*D*), can be transmitted through the building structure. This highlights the importance of consistency in the application of an acoustic design as well as the value of highly absorbent ceiling tiles that prevent sound from entering the plenum.

the **ceiling plenum,** in which to house services such as lighting and the ventilation system. Unfortunately, the ceiling plenum contains machinery, ductwork and the floor overhead — all of which have hard surfaces and readily reflect or transmit sound through the plenum to adjacent rooms (Figure 5.23). In making the ceiling plenum a more or less continuous open space by not extending walls or partitions through it to the floor above makes it easier to install and maintain the building servicing it houses. Unfortunately, sound is also able to travel unimpeded throughout the space.

To resolve this problem, a room's sound insulation must be continued through the suspended ceiling and plenum to the underside of the floor above. This is usually done by extending upward the acoustically insulated office walls and sealing their junction to the floor above. Alternatively, using highly absorbent ceiling tiles limits the amount of sound that enters the plenum, thereby lessening its overall impact. The sound absorbance of ceiling tiles is expressed in terms of their absorption coefficient. If a ceiling tile has an absorption coefficient of 0.9, 90% of the sound is absorbed and 10% is reflected back into the space. However, the light fixtures incorporated in the suspended ceiling usually have hard surfaces that reflect sound and tend to reduce the effective acoustic insulation of the ceiling as a whole.

The human hearing system is particularly sensitive to speech. People engrossed in conversation amid the din of a noisy cocktail party are easily distracted if they overhear their names mentioned — a phenomenon commonly termed the *cocktail party effect*. It illustrates that even when people's attention is focused elsewhere, they are monitoring the conversations going on around them. It is not surprising, then, that intelligible speech is more distracting than meaningless sounds of the same intensity. Studies have confirmed that it is the information content of conversation, not its loudness or pitch, that makes speech more distracting. Thus, if conversations can be rendered less intelligible, they should be less distracting.

Sound systems that do just that have been developed for offices. Termed **sound masking,** these devices generate random sounds, primarily in the human voice range, similar to that of rushing air, a waterfall, or waves washing ashore. These sounds are different from "white noise," "pink noise," or piped-in music (which is tonal and can be distracting). Adding background sound to the office environment raises the threshold of audibility. Although the overall background sound level is raised, speech becomes less intelligible and its distracting effect is reduced.

A well-designed sound-masking system is carefully tuned to augment the naturally occurring background sounds and mask annoying ones as unobtrusively as possible. To use sound masking, a space must have adequate sound absorption. The acoustic ceilings and screens commonly used in open plan offices are generally adequate. However, sound masking is not suitable for areas occupied by people with hearing impairments. Because sound masking raises the level of background noise, it can make hearing more difficult for the hearing impaired and interfere with the functioning of hearing aids. Experience has shown that successful installations with satisfied clients have used a single supplier for the design, installation, tuning, and maintenance of the system. This arrangement ensures the supplier's long-term interest in the proper functioning of the system. Unfortunately, few firms offer this full service (Clunis 1992).

Still, the fact remains that sound masking increases the background noise level. Even subtle background noise can be a stressor. The quiet sound of air passing through a ventilation grille may be hardly noticed. But when the sound suddenly stops and the room is quieter, people commonly feel a release of tension. For tasks that demand focused concentration, sound masking is still more stressful than a quiet setting. Studies have shown that sound masking improves performance compared with unmasked distracting noise, but performance is best in the absence of both noise and sound masking (Loewen and Suedfeld 1992).

PROTECT THE PERSON

The apparent loudness of a sound depends on its frequency and intensity. Frequency is measured in units called **hertz** (Hz). A hertz represents one pulse or cycle per second. The human ear detects frequencies from about 20 to 16,000 hertz and is most sensitive in the 2,000 – 5,000 hertz range (Figure 5.24). (A piano's fundamental notes span the range from 27 – 4,186 hertz. However, the complex combination of associated higher frequencies — termed harmonics — that give the instrument its characteristic sound extend to the higher frequencies of the audible range.) Below about 16 hertz, the ear perceives the air pressure wave as individual beats rather than as a tone.

Sound is normally measured in terms of its pressure using a logarithmic scale in units of **decibels** (dB). The scale represents the sound's energy, regardless of its frequency. A weighting scale (known as the dB(A) scale) was developed to provide a unit of measure that approximates a person's perception of sound (Figure 5.25).

Occupational health and safety standards specify sound exposure limits to prevent physical hearing impairment (see, for example, ASHRAE 1991; COSHR 1991). These bodies develop regulations that specify the maximum allowable sound intensity levels, the signage required to identify high-noise areas, and mandatory employee training in the hazards of routine exposure to high sound levels, and the correct use of hearing protection devices.

Noise levels in general office areas are well below the limits set by regulation or the levels that cause hearing loss. However, offices have noisy areas that ordinarily only a few people use (e.g., mechanical rooms, specially ventilated computer rooms, loading docks with motor vehicles). These spaces must comply with the regulations, which generally set 84 dB(A) as the allowable limit above which investigations must be done and actions taken to protect the workers.

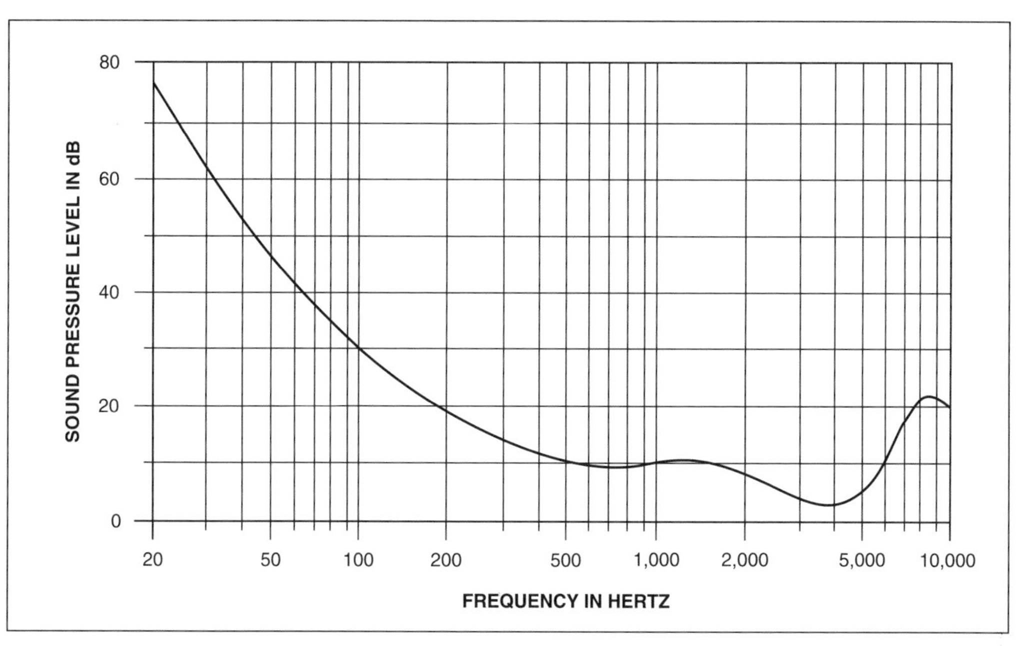

Figure 5.24 This graph shows the way the sensitivity of the human ear to sound varies with frequency. Sound levels along the curve are perceived to be of equal loudness. For example, a sound with a frequency of 100 Hz at an intensity of 30 dB will be perceived to be as loud as a 1,000 Hz sound at 10 dB. The sound pressures in this graph are measured in decibels above a reference sound level of 2 x 10^{-5} newtons/square meter. (*Source:* Adapted from Szokolay 1980.)

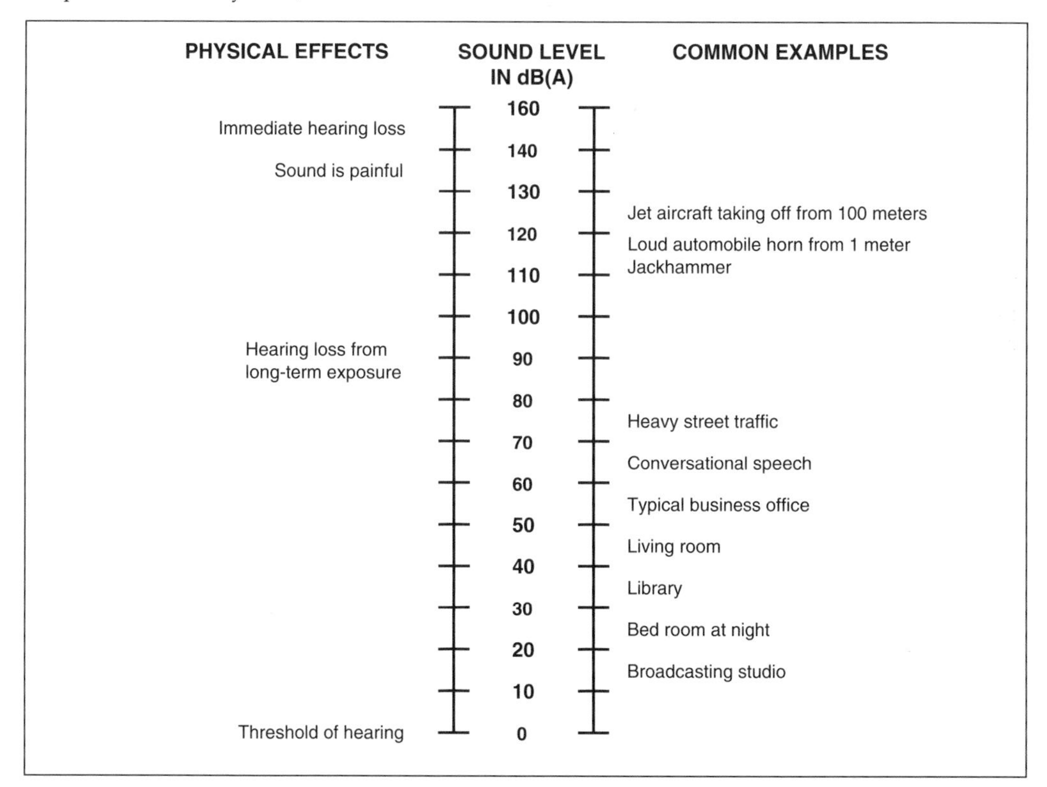

Figure 5.25 Some commonly encountered sound levels. The background sound level in offices generally ranges from 35 to 55 dB(A), well below regulated noise limits. Long-term exposure to levels above 90 dB(A) will cause permanent hearing loss. Levels of 120 dB(A) are painful, and at 150 dB(A) there is immediate loss of hearing. (*Source:* Adapted from Osborne 1987.)

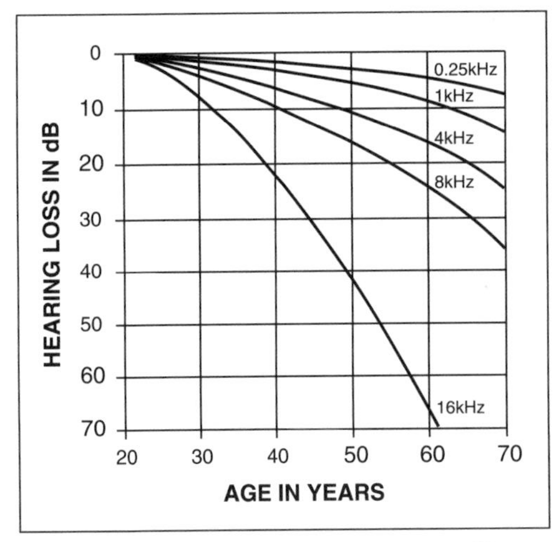

Figure 5.26 Age-related hearing loss in men. (*Source:* Szokolay 1980.)

Simply providing ear protectors does not assure that individuals will be safeguarded. Too often, protective measures are ineffective because workers do not follow recommended procedures or simply wear the headphones around their necks instead of over their ears. Using ear protection in offices is generally considered unacceptable, yet inadvertently it is actually in common use. People doing routine work, like data entry, often wear headphones to listen to music or the radio. This sound does not interfere with their ability to do that task, and the combination of the sound and the headphones reduces the distracting effect of office noises.

With age, there is a gradual loss of hearing acuity (the ability to distinguish sounds of similar frequency) as well as sensitivity (the sound intensity needed to hear clearly). Age-related hearing loss is more pronounced in men than women. Sensitivity to high frequencies generally declines more rapidly than sensitivity to low ones (Figure 5.26). To compensate for reduced sensitivity, a higher sound volume is needed. But the reduction in acuity makes it more difficult to understand speech in the presence of background noise. Thus, simply amplifying all the sounds is not sufficient. A greater difference between the loudness of the speech and the background noise is also needed. Background noise levels are generally lower in enclosed spaces than open plan or shared layouts. Private offices may partially compensate for age-related hearing loss among the senior employees who usually occupy them.

The background noise levels appropriate for a specific office will depend on the activities. Listening to speech is a special hearing task that demands keen discriminating ability. It is more than just the perception of sound levels and tones. The sounds must be sufficiently distinct from background noises for the message to be understood. Consonants, for example, are more difficult to distinguish than vowels. In general, when the sound level of speech is 10 decibels or more above the background level, it is easily understood. If verbal communication involves an unfamiliar topic with difficult new words, then the human voice should be about 20 decibels above the background. The confidential nature of discussions may demand that there be no annoying sounds at all — a sound level below about 35 dB(A) and that speech not be overheard outside the room. However, in team work areas, designed to encourage verbal communication, higher levels of background noise can be tolerated — about 45 dB(A). Of course, there are some tasks, such as in a busy reception area, that by their nature must be performed in the midst of noise.

Office occupants' acoustic concerns most often center on two issues: freedom from distraction and privacy. The preceding discussion has addressed ways to prevent noise distraction. Privacy, however, is highly subjective. It depends on individual needs, attitudes, and perception as well as on the nature of the work activities. People feel their privacy needs are met when their desire not to be viewed or overheard by others is balanced with their need for social contact and recognition. The management of noise in offices involves balancing these individual needs with the organization's need to supervise work and control facility costs.

Figure 5.27 Noise and vibration from the mechanical equipment on the roof are readily transmitted through the glass window into this work space. In addition to the disruption, this view has little appeal.

Vibration

Vibration is the motion produced by the movement of an object about a fixed point. It can be regular, such as the motion of a weight on the end of a spring, or it can be random. In the office setting, the major sources of vibration are motors, fans, or compressors. Inaudible low-frequency vibrations can produce severe physiological effects. Acting on the balance-sensing organ of the inner ear, vibration can cause disorientation, nausea, dizziness, vision problems, and fatigue.

Building services machinery generally have powerful motors and are potentially troublesome sources of noise and vibration. HVAC systems use large fans to circulate air and heavy-duty compressors for air-conditioning, and elevators are also operated by sizable machinery. The strong vibrations from these sources are readily conducted through the building structure, plumbing, and ventilation servicing to reach the occupants (Figure 5.27). The trend toward using higher-powered machinery and lightweight structures in new construction exacerbates this problem.

It's easier and less expensive to control noise at its source than after it has traveled some distance. In particular, with mechanical equipment, the sound's source is often some rotating element that is less than perfectly balanced. Then the machine's housing vibrates, amplifying the problem. Materials used to dampen the vibration deteriorate with age and become less effective. This, however, can be addressed by routine inspection, maintenance, and replacement of parts as needed. Wherever possible, such major noise sources should be acoustically separated from actively used areas. Though these issues are more in the realm of mechanical engineering than facility management, being aware of these root sources and taking proactive mitigative measures can resolve acoustic problems before occupants are severely affected.

Although it is commonly assumed that the equipment used in offices generates so little vibration that measures to control its transmission are unnecessary, many types of office equipment can generate troublesome levels of vibration. Impact printers, photocopiers, and other office equipment placed near work surfaces are common sources. Less obvious are compressor motors in refrigerators and water coolers that can transmit their vibrations to the floor and become bothersome to people seated nearby. In some cases, the activities of the occupants themselves can be a troublesome source of vibration (Figure 5.28).

In most cases, transmission of the low-intensity vibrations generated by office equipment can be easily controlled by setting the offending equipment on a vibration-absorbing material instead of directly on the floor. The vibration-generating equipment can also be moved so that it is as far as possible from where people are working.

Figure 5.28 The vibration caused by an aerobics class is being measured on this instrumented platform. Activities such as this can be a troublesome source of noise and vibration if they are carried through the building's structure. (*Source:* Institute for Research in Construction, National Research Council Canada, Ottawa.)

CONCLUSION

Occupants typically report a similar set of symptoms for environmental problems (e.g., headaches, sore muscles, general malaise), regardless of the nature of those problems — uncomfortable temperatures, distracting noises, or poor air quality. This compounds the difficulty of isolating the specific cause of a problem and developing corrective procedures and remedial actions. For those charged with improving a facility's performance or resolving environmental complaints, the situation is always unique. No matter how clearly the facts are understood or how many examples of similar cases are reviewed, success depends on the definitive actions taken to address the particular characteristics of the specific facility. The people involved, the context within which the issue has arisen, the history of how it has been handled, and the time and resource constraints will be as important as the technical aspects.

Whether the issue is controversial or banal, a substantial measure of good judgment is always required. Fundamentally, decisions about the office environment involve trade-offs — between individual concerns and organizational needs, between expensive and inexpensive measures, between addressing an issue now or at a future date. Perhaps most important, judgment determines the context within which an issue will be addressed.

Often, the publicity surrounding an office environmental issue creates a situation in which it is more important that something *visible* be done than that any measurable improvement be achieved. The need to defuse a crisis often demands that an issue be handled somewhat in isolation (see the section "Psychosocial Response to Health Risks in the Office Setting" in Chapter 7). If potentially controversial issues are addressed before they become politically charged, a wider range of options will be available to resolve them, it is more likely that real and sustainable improvements will be achieved, and the financial as well as emotional cost will be less. What's more, proactive measures to improve the office environment can generate positive and well-deserved benefits by demonstrating an organization's commitment to its employees. By viewing occupant concerns in the larger context of the performance of the total workplace, they can be addressed in a more comprehensive, and ultimately more successful manner.

LITERATURE CITED: ACOUSTICS

ASHRAE. 1991. Sound and vibration control. *ASHRAE handbook of fundamentals.* Atlanta: American Society of Heating, Refrigerating and Air-Conditioning Engineers.

Boggs, D. H., and J. R. Simon. 1968. Differential effect of noise on tasks of varying complexity. *Journal of Applied Psychology* 52:148–153.

Bradshaw, V. 1985. *Building control systems.* New York: John Wiley & Sons.

Clunis, G. 1992. Sound masking systems: A guideline. *Canadian Acoustics* (Toronto). 20(4):17–18

COSHR. 1991. Levels of sound. Canadian Occupational Safety and Health Regulations. Labour Canada. Part VII. July.

DeMarco, T., and T. Lister. 1987. *Peopleware: Productive projects and teams.* New York: Dorset House Publishing.

Davidson, L., J. Hagmann, and A. Baum. 1990. An exploration of a possible physiological explanation for stressor aftereffects. *Journal of Applied Social Psychology* 20(11, part 2):869–880.

Dornic, S., B. Ekehammer, and T. Laaksonen. 1991. Tolerance for mental effort: Self-ratings related to perception, performance, and personality. *Personality and Individual Differences* 12(3):313–319.

Glass, D. C., and J. E. Singer. 1972. *Urban stress: Experiments on noise and social stressors.* New York: Academic Press.

Harris, L. 1991. *The office environment index 1991: Summary of worldwide findings.* A study conducted for Steelcase by Louis Harris and Associates, New York.

IFMA. 1994. *Benchmarks II.* Research report 13. Houston: International Facility Management Association.

Jones, D., and D. Broadbent. 1979. Side-effects of interference with speech by noise. *Ergonomics* 22(9):1073–1081.

Jones, D. M. 1979. Stress and memory. In *Applied problems in memory,* edited by M. Gruneberg and P. Morris. London: Academic Press.

Kahneman, D. 1973. *Attention and effort.* London: Prentice-Hall Ltd.

Karacek, R., and T. Theorell. 1990. *Healthy work: Stress, productivity, and the reconstruction of working life.* New York: Basic Books.

Loewen, L., and P. Suedfeld. 1992. Cognitive and arousal effects of masking noise. *Environment and Behavior* 24(3):381–395.

McMillen, P. 1992. Computers, phones converge. *Computing Canada* 18(11):30.

Nagar, D., J. Pandey, and P. B. Paulus. 1988. The effects of residential crowding experience on reactivity to laboratory crowding and noise. *Journal of Applied Social Psychology* 18(16, part 2):1423–1442.

Osborne, D. P. 1987. *Ergonomics at work.* London: John Wiley & Sons.

Sundstrom, E. 1986. *Work places: The Psychology of the physical environment in offices and factories.* New York: Cambridge University Press.

Sundstrom, E., J. P. Town, R. W. Rice, D. P. Osborn, and M. Brill. 1994. Office noise, satisfaction, and performance. *Environment and Behavior* 26(2):195–222.

Szokolay, S. V. 1980. *Environmental science handbook for architects and builders.* New York: John Wiley & Sons.

Trice, A. 1987. Informed consent: IV. The effects of the timing of giving consent on experimental performance. *Journal of General Psychology* 114(2):125–128.

Willner, P., and J. Neiva. 1986. Brief exposure to uncontrollable but not to controllable noise biases the retrieval of information from memory. *British Journal of Clinical Psychology* 25(2):93–100.

Wohlwill, J. F., J. L. Nasar, D. M. De Joy, and H. H. Foruzami. 1976. Behavioural effects of a noisy environment: Task involvement versus passive exposure. *Journal of Applied Psychology* 61:67–74.

LITERATURE CITED: AIR QUALITY AND INTRODUCTION

Amoore, J., and E. Hautala. 1983. Odor as an aid to chemical safety: Odor thresholds compared with threshold limit values and volatiles for 214 industrial chemicals in air and water dilution. *Journal of Applied Toxicology* 3:272–290.

Aris, R. M., D. Christian, P. Q. Hearne, K. Kerr, W. E. Finkbeiner, and J. R. Balmes. 1993. Ozone-induced airway inflammation in human subjects as determined by airway lavage and biopsy. *American Review of Respiratory Disease* 148:1363–1372.

ASHRAE. 1989. Ventilation for acceptable indoor air quality. ASHRAE standard 62-1989. Atlanta: American Society of Heating, Refrigerating, and Air-Conditioning Engineers.

Baldwin, M., and J. Farant. 1990. Study of selected volatile organic compounds in office buildings at different stages of occupancy. In *Indoor air '90, proceedings of the 5th International Conference on Indoor Air Quality and Climate.* 2:665–670. Ottawa: Canada Mortgage and Housing Corporation.

Barbaree, J. M. 1991. Controlling *Legionella* in cooling towers. *ASHRAE Journal* (June):38–42.

Best, M., V. Yu, J. Stout, A. Goetz, R. Muder, and F. Taylor. 1983. Legionellaceae in the hospital water-supply. *Lancet* (2):307–310.

Billings, C., and L. Jonas. 1981. Olfactory thresholds in air as compared to threshold limit values. *American Industrial Hygiene Association Journal* 42:479–480.

Bischoff, E. 1989. Sources of pollution of indoor air by mite-allergen-containing house dust. *Environment International* 15:181–192.

Bornstein, N., C. Vieilly, M. Nowicki, J. Paucod, and J. Fleurette. 1986. Epidemiological evidence of Legionellosis transmission through domestic hot water supply systems and possibilities of control. *Israel Journal of Medical Science* 22(9):655–661.

Burge, P. S. 1992. The sick building syndrome: Where are we in 1992? *Indoor Environment* 1(4):199–203.

Burge, P. S., P. Jones, and A. S. Robertson. 1990. Sick Building Syndrome. In *Indoor air '90, proceedings of the 5th International Conference on Indoor Air Quality and Climate.* 1:479–484. Ottawa: Canada Mortgage and Housing Corporation.

Burge, S., A. Hedge, S. Wilson, J. Bass, and A. Robertson. 1987. Sick building syndrome: A study of 4373 office workers. *Annals of Occupational Hygiene* 31(4a):493–504.

Cone, J., and D. Shusterman. 1991. Health effects of indoor odorants. *Environmental Health Perspectives* 95:53–59.

Epstein, S. S. 1978. *The politics of cancer.* San Francisco: Sierra Club Books.

Eto, J., and C. Meyer. 1988. The HVAC costs of increased fresh air ventilation rates in office buildings. *ASHRAE Transactions* 94(part 2). Atlanta: American Society of Heating, Refrigerating, and Air-Conditioning Engineers.

Fanger, P. O. 1990. New principles for a future ventilation standard. In *Indoor air '90, proceedings of the 5th International Conference on Indoor Air Quality and Climate.* 5:353–363. Ottawa: Canada Mortgage and Housing Corporation.

Feron, V., R. Woutersen, J. Arts, F. Cassee, Fl. De Vrijer, and P. van Bladeren. 1992. Indoor air, a variable complex mixture: Strategy for selection of combinations of chemicals with high health hazard potential. *Environmental Technology* 13:341–350.

Finnegan, M. J., and C. A. C. Pickering. 1986. Building related illness. *Clinical Allergy* 16:389–405.

Fisk, W. J., M. J. Mendell, J. M. Daisey, D. Faulkner, A. T. Hodgson, M. Nematollahi, and J. M. Macher. 1993. Phase 1 of the California Healthy Building Study: A summary. *Indoor Air* 3:246–254.

Friedman, S., K. Spitalny, J. Barabaree, Y. Faur, R. McKinney. 1987. Pontiac fever outbreak associated with a cooling tower. *American Journal of Public Health* 77(5):569–572.

Godish, T. 1991. *Air quality.* Chelsea, Mich.: Lewis Publishers.

Godish, T., and C. Guindon. 1990. Formaldehyde emissions from U-F resin finish coatings. In *Indoor air '90, proceedings of the 5th International Conference on Indoor Air Quality and Climate* 3:689–691. Ottawa: Canada Mortgage and Housing Corporation.

Godish, T., J. Rouch, and C. Guindon. 1989. Control of residential formaldehyde levels by source treatment. *Environment International* 15:609–613.

Godish, T., T. Zollinger, V. Konopinski. 1986. Dose-response relationship between symptom severity and formaldehyde exposure in a self-referred population. In *Proceedings of the 79th Annual Meeting of the Air Pollution Control Association.* Pittsburgh: Air Pollution Control Association. .

Green, G. H. 1985. Indoor relative humidities in winter and the related absenteeism. *ASHRAE Transactions* 91(part 1B):643–651. Atlanta: American Society of Heating, Refrigerating, and Air-Conditioning Engineers.

Hedge, A., P. Burge, A. Robertson, S. Wilson, and J. Harris-Bass. 1989. Work-related illness in offices: A proposed model of the sick building syndrome.

Environment International 15:143–158.

Hodgson, M. J. and C. A. Hess. 1992. Doctors, lawyers, and building-associated diseases. *ASHRAE Journal* (February):25–32. Atlanta: American Society of Heating, Refrigerating, and Air-Conditioning Engineers.

Jaakkola, J., O. P. Heinonen, and O. Seppänen. 1990. The occurrence of common cold and the number of persons in the office room. In *Indoor air '90, proceedings of the 5th International Conference on Indoor Air Quality and Climate.* 1:155–160. Ottawa: Canada Mortgage and Housing Corporation.

Jaakkola, J., O. P. Heinonen, and O. Seppänen. 1991. Mechanical ventilation in office buildings and the sick building syndrome: An experimental and epidemiological study. *Indoor Air* 2:111–121.

Jaakkola, J., K. Komulainen, P. Tuomaala, and O. Seppänen. 1991. Textile surface materials and the sick building syndrome in office workers. *Architecture and Environmental Health* 46(3):181.

Kjaergaard S., L. Mølhave, and O. Pedersen. 1990. Changes in sensory reactions, eye physiology, and performance when exposed to a mixture of 22 indoor air volatile organic compounds. In *Indoor air '90, proceedings of the 5th International Conference on Indoor Air Quality and Climate.* 1:319–325. Ottawa: Canada Mortgage and Housing Corporation.

Koren H., R. Devlin, D. House, S. Steingold, and D. Graham. 1990. The inflammatory response of the human airways to volatile organic compounds. In *Indoor air '90, proceedings of the 5th International Conference on Indoor Air Quality and Climate.* 1:325–330. Ottawa: Canada Mortgage and Housing Corporation.

Lenvik, K. 1992. Sick building syndrome symptoms: Different prevalences between males and females. *Environment International* 18(1):11–17.

Levin, H. 1993a. EPA classifies ETS as a human carcinogen. *Indoor Air Bulletin* 2(8):7–10.

Levin, H. 1993b. The myth of energy conservation and IAQ. *Indoor Air Bulletin* 2(8):1–7.

Levin, H. 1994. Personal communication. Hal Levin and Associates, Santa Cruz, Calif.

Lippman, M. 1989. Health effects of ozone: A critical review. *JAPCA (Journal of the Air and Waste Management Association)* 39:672–695.

Lippy, B., and R. Turner. 1991. Complex mixtures in industrial workspaces: Lessons for indoor air quality evaluations. *Environmental Health Perspectives* 95:81–83.

McSharry, C., K. Anderson, and G. Boyd. 1987. Serological and clinical investigation of humidifier fever. *Clinical Allergy* (17):15–22.

Memish, Z., C. Oxley, J. Constant, and G. Garber. 1992. Plumbing system shock absorbers as a source of *Legionella pneumophila*. *American Journal of Infection Control* 20(6):305–309.

Mendell, M. J. 1993. Non-specific symptoms in office workers: a review and summary of the epidemiological literature. *Indoor Air* 3:227–236.

Mølhave, L. 1990. Volatile organic compounds, indoor air quality, and human health. In *Indoor air '90, proceedings of the 5th International Conference on Indoor Air Quality and Climate.* 5:15–33. Ottawa: Canada Mortgage and Housing Corporation.

Morris, G. K., and B. G. Shelton. 1991. *Legionella in environmental samples: Hazard analysis and suggested remedial actions.* Technical bulletin 1.3. Norcross, Ga.: Pathogen Control Associates.

National Research Council. 1984. *Toxicity testing.* Washington, D. C.: National Academy Press.

Norbäck, D., and M. Torgén. 1989. A longitudinal study relating carpeting with sick building syndrome. *Environment International* 15:129–135.

OSHA. 1994. *Federal Register.* August 10. U.S. Occupational Safety and Health Administration.

Pennebaker, J. W. 1982. *The psychology of physical symptoms.* New York: Springer-Verlag.

Potter, I. N. 1988. *The sick building syndrome: Symptoms, risk factors, and practical design guidance.* Technical note 4/88. Bracknell, Berkshire, U.K.: Building Services Research and Information Association.

Putnam, V., J. Woods, and D. Rask. 1990. A comparison of carbon dioxide concentrations and indoor environmental acceptability in commercial buildings. In *Indoor air '90, proceedings of the 5th International Conference on Indoor Air Quality and Climate* 3:365–370. Ottawa: Canada Mortgage and Housing Corporation.

Raw, G. J., M. S. Roys, and C. Whitehead. 1993. Sick building syndrome: Cleanliness is next to healthiness. *Indoor Air* 3:237–245.

Robertson, A. S., K. T. Roberts, P. S. Burge, and G. Raw. 1990. The effect of change in building ventilation category on sickness absence rates and the prevalence of sick building syndrome. In *Indoor air '90, proceedings of the 5th International Conference on Indoor Air Quality and Climate* 1:237–242. Ottawa: Canada Mortgage and Housing Corporation.

Robertson, G. 1988. Sources, nature, and symptomology of indoor air pollutants. In *Proceedings of healthy buildings 88,* 3:507–516. Stockholm: Swedish Council for Building Research.

Rothweiller, H., P. Wäger, and C. Schlatter. 1992. Long term emissions from two glued carpets with different backings measured in indoor air. *Environmental Technology* 13:891–896.

Shair, F. H. 1981. Relating indoor pollutant concentrations of ozone and sulfur dioxide to those outside: Economic reduction of indoor ozone through selective filtration of the make-up air. *ASHRAE Transactions* 87(part 1):116–139.

Shands, K. N., and D. W. Fraser. 1980. Legionnaires' disease. *Disease-a-Month* 26(3):1–40.

Shim, C., and M. Williams. 1986. Effect of odors in asthma. *American Journal of Medicine* 80:18–22.

Skov, P., O. Valbjørn, and DISG. 1987. The "sick" building syndrome in the office environment: The Danish town hall study. *Environment International* 13:339–349.

Spektor, D. M., M. Lippman, G. D. Thurston, P. J. Lioy, J. Stecko, G. O'Connor, E. Garshick, F. E. Speizer, and C. Hayes. 1988. Effects of ambient ozone on respiratory function in healthy adults exercising outdoors. *American Review of Respiratory Disease* 138:821–828.

Steele, T., and M. Brown. 1990. Energy, cost, and program implications. Portland, Oreg.: Bonneville Power Administration.

Sterling, E. M., A. Arundel, and T. D. Sterling. 1985. Criteria for human exposure to humidity in occupied buildings. *ASHRAE Transactions* 91(part 1B):611–621.

Sundell, J., T. Lindvall, and B. Stenberg. 1992. The importance of building and room factors for sick building syndrome and facial skin symptoms in office workers. In *Proceedings of the ASHRAE IAQ '92 Conference.* Atlanta: American Society of Heating, Refrigerating, and Air-Conditioning Engineers.

Weschler, C. J., and H. C. Shields. 1989. Indoor ozone exposures. *JAPCA (Journal of the Air and Waste Management Association)* 39(12):1562–1568

Weschler, C. J., and H. C. Shields. 1991. The impact of ventilation and indoor air quality on electronic equipment. *ASHRAE Transactions: Symposia* (part 1):455. Atlanta: American Society of Heating, Refrigerating, and Air-Conditioning Engineers.

Woods, J. E. 1988a. Recent developments for heating, cooling, and ventilating buildings: Trends for assuring healthy buildings. In *Proceedings of healthy buildings 88* 1:99–107. Stockholm: Swedish Council for Building Research.

Woods, J. E. 1988b. Sources of indoor air contaminants. *ASHRAE Transactions: Symposia* (part 1B):462-495. Atlanta: American Society of Heating, Refrigerating, and Air-Conditioning Engineers.

Woods, J. E. 1989. Cost avoidance and productivity in owning and operating buildings. *Occupational Medicine: State of the Art Reviews 1989*. Philadelphia: Hanley & Belfus.

LITERATURE CITED: NEGATIVE AIR IONS

Daniell, W., J. Camp, and S. Horstman. 1991. Trial of a negative ion generator device in remediating problems related to indoor air quality. *Journal of Occupational Medicine* 33(6):681–687.

Dolezalek, H. 1985. Remarks on the physics of atmospheric ions (natural and artificial). *International Journal of Biometeorology* 29(3):211–221.

Fletcher, R. J. 1988. "Föhn illness" and human biometeorology in the Chinook area of Canada. *International Journal of Biometeorology* 32:168–175.

Hawkins, L. H. 1981. The influence of air ions, temperature, and humidity on subjective well-being and comfort. *Journal of Environmental Psychology* 1:279–292.

Hawkins, L. H., and L. Morris. 1984. Air ions and the sick building syndrome. In *Proceedings: Indoor air* 3:197–200. Stockholm: Swedish Council for Building Research.

Hedge, A., and M. D. Collins. 1987. Do negative air ions affect human mood and performance? *Annals of Occupational Hygiene* 31(3):285–290.

Hedge, A., and E. Eleftherakis. 1982. Air ionization: An evaluation of its physiological and psychological effects. *Annals of Occupational Hygiene* 25(4):409–419.

Household air cleaners. 1992. *Consumer Reports* (October):657–662.

Kröling, P. 1985. Natural and artificially produced air ions — a biologically relevant climate factor? *International Journal of Biometeorology* 29(3):233–242.

Morton, L. L., and J. R. Kershner. 1990. Differential negative air ion effects on learning disabled and normal-achieving children. *International Journal of Biometeorology* 34:35–41.

Reiter, R. 1985. Frequency distribution of positive and negative small ion concentrations based on many years' recordings at two mountain stations. *International Journal of Biometeorology* 29(3):223–231.

Sulman, F. G. 1984. The impact of weather on human health. *Reviews on Environmental Health* 4(2):83–119.

Tom, G., M. F. Poole, J. Galla, and J. Berrier. 1981. The influence of negative air ions on human performance and mood. *Human Factors* 23(5):633–636.

Wyon, D. P. 1992. Sick buildings and the experimental approach. *Environmental Technology* 13:313–322.

LITERATURE CITED: RADON

Axelson, O. 1991. Occupational and environmental exposures to radon: Cancer risks. *Annual Review of Public Health* 12:235–255.

Guimond, R., S. Malm, and D. Rowson. 1990. Radon in the United States: Accomplishments and future challenges. In *Indoor air '90, proceedings of the 5th International Conference on Indoor Air Quality and Climate* 5:287–296. Ottawa: Canada Mortgage and Housing Corporation.

Lyons, W. 1994. Personal communication. Fort Collins, Co.

Morgera, R. V. 1992 Radon: Health implications in Rhode Island. *Rhode Island Medicine* 75:317–319.

Swedjemark, G. 1990. Swedish perspectives on radon. In *Indoor air '90, Proceedings of the 5th International Conference on Indoor Air Quality and Climate* 5:297–305. Ottawa: Canada Mortgage and Housing Corporation.

Swedjemark, G., H. Wahren, A. Mäkitalo, and W. Tell. 1989. Experience from indoor radon-daughter limitation schemes in Sweden. *Environment International* 15:253–260.

Turner, S., and P. Binnie. 1990. An indoor air quality survey of twenty-six Swiss office buildings. *Environmental Technology* 11:303–314.

Voutilainen, A., and I. Mäkeläinen. 1993. Radon risk mapping using indoor monitoring data - A case study of the Lahti area, Finland. *Indoor Air* 3:369-375.

LITERATURE CITED: THERMAL COMFORT

ASHRAE. 1992. Thermal environmental conditions for human occupancy. ASHRAE standard 55-1992. Atlanta: American Society of Heating, Refrigerating, and Air-Conditioning Engineers.

ASHRAE. 1993. Physiological principles and thermal comfort. Chapter 8 in *ASHRAE handbook of fundamentals*. Atlanta: American Society of Heating, Refrigerating, and Air-Conditioning Engineers.

Brill, M. 1984. *Using office design to increase productivity*. Buffalo, N.Y.: Buffalo Organization for Social and Technological Innovations (BOSTI).

Fanger, P. O., and N. K. Christensen. 1986. Perception of draught in ventilated spaces. *Ergonomics* 29(2):215–235.

Garland, H. O. 1985. Altered temperature. In *Variations in human physiology*, edited by R. M. Case and D. E. Evans, 111–133. Manchester, U.K.: Manchester University Press.

Grandjean, E. 1980. *Fitting the task to the man: An ergonomic approach*. London: Taylor & Francis.

Green, G. H. 1985. Indoor relative humidities in winter and the related absenteeism. *ASHRAE Transactions* 91(part 1B):643–651. Atlanta: American Society of Heating, Refrigerating, and Air-Conditioning Engineers.

Harris, L. 1991. *The office environment index 1991: Summary of worldwide findings*. A study conducted for Steelcase by Louis Harris and Associates, New York.

Int-Hout, D. 1993. Total environmental quality. *ASHRAE Transactions: Symposia*. (part 1):960–967.

Atlanta: American Society of Heating, Refrigerating, and Air-Conditioning Engineers.

Palonen, J., O. Seppänen, and J. K. Jaakkola. 1993. The effects of air temperature and relative humidity on thermal comfort in the office environment. *Indoor Air* 3:391–397.

Potter, I. N. 1988. *The sick building syndrome: Symptoms, risk factors, and practical design guidance.* Technical note 4/88. Bracknell, Berkshire, U.K.: Building Services Research and Information Association.

Schaefer, O., J. A. Hildes, P. Greidanus, and D. Leung. 1974. Regional sweating in Eskimos compared to Caucasians. *Canadian Journal of Physiology and Pharmacology* 52:960–965.

Schiller, G. 1990. A comparison of measured and predicted comfort in office buildings. *ASHRAE Transactions* (part 1):609–622. Atlanta: American Society of Heating, Refrigerating, and Air-Conditioning Engineers.

Schiller, G., E. Arend, F. Bauman, C. Benton, M. Fountain, and T. Doherty. 1988. Thermal environments and comfort in office buildings. *ASHRAE Transactions* 94(part 2). Atlanta: American Society of Heating, Refrigerating, and Air-Conditioning Engineers.

Stephenson, L. A., and M. A. Kolka. 1988. Effect of gender, circadian period and sleep loss on thermal responses during exercise. In *Human performance physiology and environmental medicine at terrestrial extremes,* edited by K. Pandolf, M. Sawka, and R. Gonzalez, 267–304. New York: Benchmark Press.

Sterling, E. M., A. Arundel, and T. D. Sterling. 1985. Criteria for human exposure to humidity in occupied buildings. *ASHRAE Transactions* 91(part 1B):611–621. Atlanta: American Society of Heating, Refrigerating, and Air-Conditioning Engineers.

Sundstrom, E., J. P. Town, R. W. Rice, D. P. Osborn, and M. Brill. 1994. Office noise, satisfaction, and performance. *Environment and Behavior* 26(2):195–222.

Wenger, C. B. 1988. Human heat acclimatization. In *Human performance physiology and environmental medicine at terrestrial extremes,* edited by K. Pandolf, M. Sawka, and R. Gonzalez, 153–197. New York: Benchmark Press.

Young, A. J. 1988. Human adaptation to cold. In *Human performance physiology and environmental medicine at terrestrial extremes,* edited by K. Pandolf, M. Sawka, and R. Gonzalez, 401–434. New York: Benchmark Press.

Chapter 6

COMPUTERS IN THE OFFICE SETTING

The computer has rapidly and profoundly changed the way office work is done and the work settings needed to support it (Figures 6.1 and 6.2). It has also highlighted how the office environment impacts occupants' health and productivity. This chapter summarizes current ideas and recommendations for computers in the office setting and presents background information upon which they are based. By understanding why computer work may cause or aggravate illness and injury, steps can be taken to mitigate and largely eliminate these problems. The field of ergonomics is presented first to provide a context for the discussion of specific issues. Then vision and office illumination, workstations appropriate for computer use, cumulative trauma disorder, and radiation are addressed. Although these issues also affect noncomputer tasks, they have received greater public attention in connection with office computer use.

At the time the IBM personal computer was introduced in 1981, few office workers had access to computers. After little more than a decade, it is now common in offices for every desk to be equipped with a computer screen and keyboard, together termed a **video display terminal** (**VDT**) or **video display unit** (**VDU**). In a 1991 survey, more than 80% of office workers in the United States, Canada, and the European Community reported using a computer in their jobs for three to four hours per day. Heavy VDT use of five or more hours per day was less common (20% to 30%) but had increased steadily compared with previous surveys (Harris 1991).

As with any new technology, unforeseen problems arose when computers were introduced and widely used in the general office setting. The impact of intensive computer use on human performance, health, and quality of work life was not

Figure 6.1 The widespread introduction of computers into the office workplace has profoundly changed the work setting. Typing pools, typical of the 1960s and 1970s (photo shown here) have been replaced in the 1980s and 1990s by groups of computer workstations that have larger areas to lay out work materials and room illumination designed to minimize screen glare (photo on facing page). (*Source:* Chris Lund, National Archives of Canada, PA144836)

well understood. Little was known about how working at a computer differed from other office tasks. Some people readily embraced the new technology; to others, it was a major psychological and physical challenge.

Initially, there were no guidelines for accommodating computer work areas. VDTs were installed in existing office space with little or no modification to the physical environment. Unlike purpose-built computer rooms staffed by specialists, the migration of computers into the general office involved placing this equipment in a setting designed for paper-based work and having it operated by people with little or no computer experience.

It soon became apparent that the computer equipment itself affected the physical office environment (Table 6.1). The heat it produced was an added load for which building air-handling systems had not been designed. Where buildings lacked the necessary cooling capacity, room temperatures increased and offices became warm and stuffy. Desk fans became commonplace as occupants tried to cope. The new equipment added a background din of electronic beeps, the clicking of keyboards, the whirr of cooling fans, and the loud, erratic drone of impact printers. The diverse array of equipment,

Figure 6.2 Office computer stations, typical of the 1990s. (*Source:* Steelcase, Grand Rapids, Mich.)

arranged as space would permit, created hard-to-clean areas that collected dirt and dust, raising the level of airborne particulate matter and degrading indoor air quality. Some equipment released irritating odors and chemical contaminants.

Overhead illumination and bright window areas produced glare on computer screens, making them difficult to view. VDTs often had low scanning frequencies that produced perceptible screen flicker. Difficult viewing conditions precipitated discomfort and illness symptoms such as tired or burning eyes, frequent headaches, and blurred vision.

Existing office furniture, designed for paper-based work, was not well suited to computer use. Work surfaces were too small to accommodate reference documents and other work materials together with a monitor, keyboard, and often the computer itself. The furniture and the general office area could not accommodate the myriad of computer cables, so wires spilled over work surfaces and onto floors. The result was a cramped and clut-

Table 6-1 Effects of computers on building systems and office occupants.

Computer Component	Building System	Human System	Human Effects
Display screen	Lighting	Vision Posture	Visual fatigue from glare Muscle fatigue from constrained positions
Keyboard	Furnishings: chair, work surface, keyboard support	Posture	Ailments caused by awkward repetitive motions
Electronic equipment: fax, computers, printers	HVAC, acoustics, air quality, aesthetics	Hearing, vision, thermal comfort, posture	Reduced productivity from disruption Fatigue from cramped, cluttered work spaces Stress caused by poor office environment
Cables	Service runs	Safety	Injury from tripping over wires Potential safety hazard Lost work time due to power interruptions or overloaded circuits

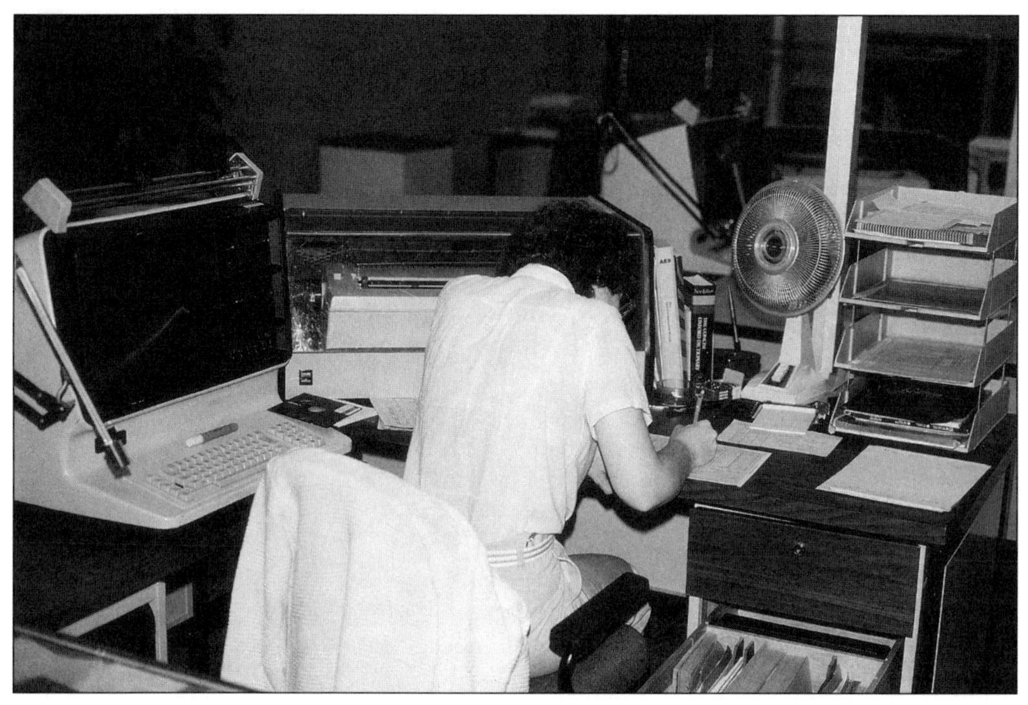

Figure 6.3 Office automation brought an array of sophisticated equipment into general office space ill suited for that purpose. Accommodating bulky computer equipment in a small area made work spaces cramped and cluttered. The concentration of computers in this work space generated more heat than the mechanical system could remove. The occupant added a desk fan to provide some cooling air movement.

tered work space with a variety of obstacles that could easily trip the unwary occupant or visitor (Figure 6.3).

Tabletops were too high for comfortable keyboard use. Keyboards were commonly attached to the monitors and so could not be moved to an appropriate typing position. Chairs did not provide sufficient support or adjustability for a person to work at a computer for long periods. Screens could not tilt or swivel, and their placement was determined more by the space available than by optimum viewing position to avoid troublesome glare and poor postures.

Noise disruption, uncomfortable temperatures, and poor air quality were stressors that increased the physical and mental effort needed to accomplish work tasks. The more effort people had to expend to overcome such stressors, the more quickly they fatigued and the less energy was available for productive work.

People responded to the ergonomic limitations of their office setting by working in awkward and constrained positions. Many developed chronic neck, shoulder, and back pain when they sat for extended hours in chairs with poor back support or when they craned their necks to view the monitor or to see around a glare spot. The added strain on the wrists and fingers from using computer keyboards introduced an illness to the office, now known as cumulative trauma disorder or repetitive strain injury (discussed later in this chapter). These ailments made typing and other arm and hand motions painful. The array of computer-related complaints has proved to be costly, both in lost work time and in compensation payments. The costs and liability of these illnesses prompted intensive research efforts to better understand how computers could cause or aggravate illness and injury and to develop effective measures for prevention and control (Pascarelli and Quilter 1994; Patkin 1990).

Computers dramatically changed the work process. People are more sedentary when they work at a VDT than when they perform other types of office jobs. They shift their bodies less frequently and have less need to reach for documents, to walk to get files, to change typewriter paper, or to write with pen and paper. People can be so still while working at their computers that automated occupancy sensors switch off the overhead lighting because no motion is detectable (Dirks 1993). With computers, office workers could perform more tasks without leaving their seats, or even taking their hands off their keyboards. In fact, part of the efficiency gain in automating office work has been to improve convenience by having ever more information and communications power at the desktop.

Working at a computer is much more intense than conventional paper-based office jobs. Operators maintain fairly static postures for relatively long periods of time. The monitor is at a fixed position, and so the operators unvaryingly look in one direction and maintain a constant viewing distance. The staring gaze causes them to blink less frequently, making the eyes dry and more likely to become sore. Staring at a fixed distance for long periods is itself fatiguing to the eye.

It is not only the mechanics of work that has changed; the pace has increased as well. A large part of the productivity gain from automating clerical tasks depends on a continuous and rapid work rate. Office automation technology is designed to eliminate unnecessary motions; however, in so doing, the variety of motions was reduced and their repetitiveness increased.

Early reports of muscle discomfort and vision problems among VDT operators were greeted with skepticism. Managers and supervisors as well as medical professionals found it difficult to believe that VDT use could be related to such wide a range of complaints as headaches, vision problems, and nonspecific pain and soreness in the wrists, arms, back, neck, and shoulders. Those who complained were often considered to be lazy, unmotivated, dissatisfied, or suffering from psychological problems (see, for example, Reid, Ewan, and Lowy 1991).

It is now well established that VDT use can lead to a number of temporary and permanent physical ailments, and a great deal has been learned about reducing these health risks. Media coverage has increased public awareness and concern. It has also led to increased litigation, stronger provisions in union agreements, and a greater willingness on the part of regulatory agencies to fine companies that ignore ergonomic-related occupational injuries. Workers routinely seek compensation for such injuries through union grievance procedures and government regulatory agencies such as the U.S. Environmental Protection Agency (EPA) and the U.S. Occupational Safety and Health Administration (OSHA). Standards governing VDT use in public and private sector offices are being developed or have been instituted in the United States, Canada, and Europe.

Recognizing the serious health risks involved, many organizations have voluntarily introduced policies to improve the ergonomic quality of computer workstations, work schedules, and task designs. It is now common to provide alternative work for employees who fear they are at high risk, such as those with a past history of musculoskeletal injury, those who have vision difficulties, and pregnant women. Furniture and computer equipment manufacturers have modified and improved their products to address user concerns. Workstation furniture that permits independent adjustment of the height and angle of the keyboard, work surface, and monitor is now readily available. Ergonomically appropriate chairs offer good support for the variety of postures people assume in performing computer-based and paper-based work. Lighting systems can be designed to illuminate computer work areas so as to avoid screen glare problems. Low-radiation monitors are available and have dropped steadily in price.

Even well-designed equipment, furniture, and office environments cannot eliminate all the physical and psychological stresses associated with VDT work. The issue of cumulative trauma disorders among computer users demonstrated that the resolution of workplace deficiencies must address more than the design of furniture and equipment. The work process, job design, and overall office environment to which an individual is exposed also contribute to the incidence and severity of computer-related complaints. The way that computer equipment is used can substantially reduce unwanted effects. Improving keyboard techniques, increasing task variety, reducing the length of VDT sessions, and controlling job-related stress reduce the incidence of computer-related ailments.

Although most ergonomic-related injuries and litigation among office workers involve cumulative trauma disorders, noncomputer work settings can also be inadequate, causing discomfort, injury, and diminished human performance. The expense of absenteeism, workers' compensation claims, and increased insurance rates has substantially altered cost-benefit assessments of improvements to the office environment. The issue of addressing ergonomic as well as other deficiencies in the office environment has become too costly to ignore in terms of human pain and suffering, lost productivity, and employer liability.

ERGONOMICS

Ergonomics is the study of work. It is a field dedicated to understanding how the human body reacts to the physical stresses and strains of work activities and how tools, machines, and procedures can be designed to minimize operator fatigue and injury.

Ergonomics is a young field. It developed during the 1930s, when specialists in physiology and preventive medicine were hired by progressive manufacturing companies to improve assembly line working conditions. Their efforts focused on assessing human physical capabilities and finding ways to maximize the amount of work an individual could produce without injury or increased absenteeism. The primary motivation was to increase production.

The current practice of ergonomics emerged during World War II, when the design of products for human use and the study of the body's mechanical capabilities were combined to optimize a number of production and combat-related tasks. The entry of large numbers of women into the factory labor force during the war brought a new urgency to the design of tools, machines, and factory conditions suited to the workers' physical and mental capabilities. There was generous government funding of ergonomic research not only to improve the efficiency of ammunition and weapons production but also to make war machines more functional. Complex environments, such as the cockpits in airplanes and tanks, were redesigned so they could be operated more efficiently and were easier to learn.

The driving motivation in these ergonomic efforts was quite narrowly defined — to help win the war. Although working conditions in factories and hastily set up offices were rudimentary, they were willingly tolerated within the societal context of wartime sacrifice (Figure 6.4).

Conditions in today's workplaces are considerably better than in the factories and offices of the 1940s. The context of the office workplace is considerably different as well. Office work is not part of a desperate struggle to win a war. In addition to the financial reward, people want their work to offer opportunities for successful accomplishment, professional development, social support, and other personally satisfying benefits.

The practice of ergonomics still retains its original mission to fit the tools, equipment, and setting to the worker, but the objectives have broadened and the priorities have changed. Office workers expect to be accommodated in a reasonably safe and comfortable environment. There is

Figure 6.4 Cramped and rudimentary work spaces were willingly tolerated within the societal context of wartime sacrifice. (*Sources:* John F. Mailer, National Archives of Canada, PA169637; Chris Lund, National Archives of Canada, PA144871.)

greater emphasis on the individual's health, well-being, and quality of work life.

The involvement of ergonomists in the design of office furniture and equipment has also extended to the engineering and evaluation of work settings, office layouts, and job descriptions (i.e., the set of tasks that comprise an individual's job responsibilities). But the issue that has highlighted the importance of their work and has more critically tested their design skills has been the widespread introduction of computers into the general office setting.

Office Settings for Computer-Based Work

Operating a computer is not an inherently dangerous or difficult activity. Rather, injuries are more likely to occur because the work is physically demanding and postures are constrained. Paper documents are easily moved around a workstation surface to accommodate different sitting or standing positions. Computer monitors, however, remain in the same spot, and keyboards can be repositioned to only a limited degree.

Computer work tends to be done for longer uninterrupted periods, to be more intense, and to involve more repetitive motions than paper-based office tasks. An uncomfortable chair, awkward posture, and problematic lighting can be tolerated for short periods. But when they must be endured for hours at a time, on a daily basis, the consequences become more severe.

Most VDT-related health problems result from vision difficulties or ergonomically poor work settings that force people to bend in awkward positions and reach or twist in ways that strain muscles. Fundamentally, the problems are caused by excesses. As long as there is sufficient time for the body to fully recover from physical strain, the effects are not cumulative. But when computers are integral to work activities, there rarely is sufficient time to recover from even minor strain. Thus, a disruptive or uncomfortable work setting exacts a double performance cost — faster to fatigue and slower to recover.

In addition, it takes longer to rest and recover from fatigue when the body must also cope with physical or psychological stressors. Anxiety about work or personal life can sap a person's energy as much as physical stressors. The computer has made it easy to monitor work activity and measure individual productivity. Excessive monitoring can itself become a significant stressor, contributing to work-related health problems (Westin 1992).

How people feel about their work can also have a powerful effect on their health. Job satisfaction and supportive coworkers make it easier to cope with stress. High job demands with little control over work scheduling and unsupportive or antagonistic coworkers and supervisors create an unhealthy, high-stress work environment. Headaches, ulcers, sleep disorders, and cardiovascular disease are common stress-related disorders. In taxing the body's resources, stress aggravates other physical ailments as well (see the section "Human Response to Stress" in Chapter 7).

There are fundamentally three ways to prevent computer-related injuries: reduce the strain of an activity, reduce its duration, or reduce its intensity. The most effective approach is to use all three methods.

REDUCE TASK STRAIN

The physical strain of computer work is greatly reduced by providing an ergonomically appropriate work setting. The combination of chair design, height and size of work surfaces, and arrangement of computer screen, keyboard, and mouse can encourage good posture that makes computer-based work less fatiguing and less likely to cause injury. Appropriate lighting, background noise level, temperature, relative humidity, and air quality reduce interruptions, discomfort, and stress caused by the physical environment.

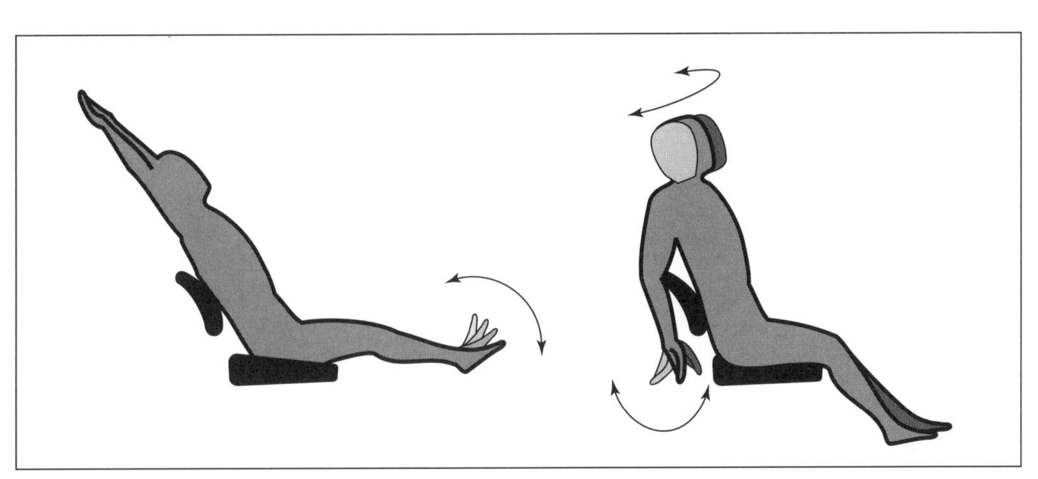

Figure 6.5 Stretching to relax constricted muscles gives the body a chance to recover.

Movement is important. Muscles fatigue quickly when the body is held rigid in any position. For this reason, it is easier to walk than to stand still for more than a few minutes. When working at a computer, the head, torso, and arms are held in constrained positions for long periods. The strain on the body can be reduced by periodic movement — shifting in the chair, stretching, leaning back, or standing up (Figure 6.5). Changing positions frequently increases blood circulation and shifts the work of holding the body upright to different muscles, giving them a chance to rest.

REDUCE TASK DURATION

The length of time that people spend continuously at computers can often be substantially reduced by breaking long work sessions into shorter periods and alternating them with noncomputer tasks. In some cases, jobs that are entirely computer-based can be redesigned to include other types of work or can be rotated among a group of people. Dividing computer tasks over more people reduces the maximum computer workload to which an individual is exposed. Overtime work and incentive programs based on the speed of input often were inadvertently the cause of injuries. When people push themselves beyond their physical limits they are more likely to overtax muscles already tired and overused after a normal workday.

Taking a few minutes every hour to stretch and look away from the screen serves to relax the eyes and give the body a chance to recover. For those who find it difficult to periodically stop keyboard work, there are computer programs that time each work session and signal when to take a break.

REDUCE TASK INTENSITY

Stress exacerbates many physical symptoms. Tight deadlines and the frustration of having little control over the schedule or work methods is associated with increased incidence of computer-related injuries. Jobs that are closely monitored, have an intense pace of work, or involve pressure for high accuracy, speed, and productivity tend to cause high levels of mental stress. The incidence of cumulative trauma disorders is much higher in these jobs (e.g., among journalists and telephone operators) than for other office workers who use computers the same amount of time but in less stressful work environments.

Perseverance under adverse and uncomfortable circumstances is often the key to career success. However, in the case of computer use, it frequently leads to injury and productivity loss. If people can control their schedule and have adequate time to complete their work so they are not unduly pressured, they can sustain their output by choosing less demanding tasks when they fatigue.

Injuries can also be caused by the force with which a person works. Though computer keyboards only require a light touch, some operators develop the habit of pounding on the keys. As keyboards have become quite large, it is common for users to overextend the reach of their hands and fingers. Hitting keys harder than necessary and excessive stretching of the hands increases the risk of injury. Other poor keyboarding techniques are malpositioning of the wrists and thumbs and excessive mobility of the fingers (Pascarelli and Kella 1993).

Using a mouse can also cause injuries if it is gripped too tightly or operated with excessive force. Similarly, the wrist and finger motions needed to operate trackballs can be troublesome. These motions increase the risk of cumulative trauma disorders and can be prevented by modifying typing techniques. For example, some key combinations can be reached with less stretching by using different fingers or software routines (called **macros**) to perform the function (Pacarelli and Quilter 1994).

VISION

Vision is involved in virtually every office task. The process of seeing requires numerous muscular as well as nerve functions. Reading demands on the order of 10,000 eye movements per hour. It is not surprising, then, that the eyes are often a major source of fatigue and illness symptoms among office workers.

Office work that includes daily VDT use is a more strenuous visual task than traditional paper-based jobs. Studies have shown that people who use a VDT for several hours a day are more likely to encounter vision-related ailments — notably, headaches, blurred or double vision, itching and burning eyes, tension, and eye fatigue. Compounding this problem is that people tend to blink less often when staring at a VDT screen, which causes their eyes to feel dry. This can be par-

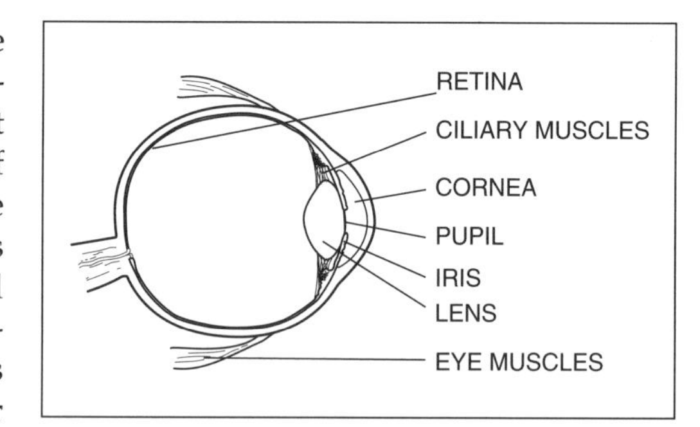

Figure 6.6 Anatomy of the human eye.

ticularly troublesome for those who wear contact lenses. Vision problems can also cause pain or stiffness in the back, shoulders, and neck when people assume awkward postures as they strain to see screen images that are unsteady, unsharp, or obscured by glare (AOA 1992; Sheedy and Parsons 1990).

Visual discomfort among VDT users commonly results from uncorrected vision problems, improper office lighting, glare, a poor-quality screen image, and inappropriate workstation design or layout. The concentrated nature of VDT work tends to intensify vision problems that may be tolerated for other tasks.

How the Eye Sees

For people to see clearly, a sharp image must be projected onto the eye's retina (Figure 6.6). The cornea and lens together focus the incoming light rays to form a sharp image on the retina. The retina consists of light-sensitive cells that convert light energy to nerve impulses. The iris regulates the amount of light reaching the retina by varying the size of the opening in its center — the pupil. To bring objects at varying distances into crisp focus, the shape of the lens is changed by contraction of the muscles that surround it, a process known as **accommodation.** When these muscles are relaxed, distant objects are distinct. For the eye to focus on near objects, the muscles must contract. The nearer the object, the greater the contraction effort. VDT work demands that a near object (i.e., the screen) be kept in focus for extended periods. This is an inherently more fatiguing task than viewing distant objects (on the order of 7 meters or 20 feet away).

The viewing distance between the operator's eyes and the VDT is an important factor associated with vision complaints (Schleifer et al. 1990). **Farsightedness** is a condition in which far objects are seen more clearly than close ones. Though the farsighted condition may not be severe enough for an individual to require corrective lenses for reading, it may be sufficient to cause blurred vision and discomfort when using a VDT. The eyes tire from the extra effort needed to focus close-up for long periods.

Nearsightedness is a condition in which near objects are seen more clearly than far ones. It usually appears before 25 years of age. Seeing close objects more clearly than far ones tends to be less of a problem for office work.

Astigmatism is a vision defect in which portions of the visual field are focused less sharply. This blurring of vision occurs at all distances. It may also be more troublesome when viewing a computer monitor than when performing other visual tasks.

The **near-point distance** is the shortest viewing distance at which an object can be brought into sharp focus. With age, the lens of the eye loses its elasticity, and the near-point distance increases (Table 6.2). When the near-point distance has increased beyond 25 centimeters (10 inches), the reduced elasticity of the lens renders close vision gradually more strenuous, a condition known as **presbyopia**. The onset of this condition is generally at 40–45 years of age. Presbyopia makes VDT work more difficult because it increases the muscular effort needed to focus at a close distance. The eye fatigues more quickly, and the screen may appear blurred because it is too close to be sharply focused. Most of these conditions can be treated with prescription corrective lenses or vision therapy, such as eye exercises. Changing the work schedule, doing difficult visual tasks in shorter multiple sessions instead of one long one, varying visual tasks more frequently, and better adjusting the work setting for optimal viewing provide significant benefits as well (AOA 1987).

Table 6.2 Average near-point viewing distances at different ages. (*Source:* Grandjean 1987.)

Age (years)	Near Point Distance (centimeters)	(inches)
16	8	3
32	12	5
44	25	10
50	50	20
60	100	40

The lack of proper corrective lenses is a common cause of vision problems among VDT users. Many people with small degrees of nearsightedness, farsightedness, or astigmatism see well enough not to require eyeglasses for everyday use. But the added effort of viewing a VDT for long periods can aggravate visual deficiencies to the point that vision problems occur (Sheedy 1992).

Many VDT users who already wear corrective lenses for reading have difficulty viewing a VDT for long periods. Reading glasses are designed to give a sharp focus at about 40 centimeters (16 inches), a normal reading distance. VDTs are placed anywhere from 35 to 80 centimeters (14 to 30 inches) from the user, and the eye muscles must work to compensate for this difference in viewing distance. Corrective lenses specifically designed to focus at the viewing distance of the VDT can resolve this vision problem. In a survey of 1,300 optometrists, 40% gave patients prescriptions specifically for VDT work (Sheedy 1992). These eyeglasses can also be polarized with an antireflective coating to help reduce screen reflections.

Some VDT-related vision problems can progress over time if left untreated. For this reason, VDT users should have comprehensive eye examinations periodically to identify and correct vision conditions.

Figure 6.7 The receptionist's eyes must constantly adjust between the bright, sunlit lobby and the darker area at the work surface — a situation that contributes to visual discomfort and fatigue. Moreover, the lobby is so bright that the lights on the telephone consol — which indicate an incoming call or a line in use — cannot be seen. This receptionist attached a calendar to the console as a shading device.

The Eye's Response to Varying Light Levels

Illumination has a critical effect on the eye's ability to focus. At low light levels, focusing becomes more strenuous because contrast is reduced and sharpness is diminished making it harder to see. Since focusing becomes more difficult after the age of 40, poor illumination is more troublesome for older individuals.

The muscles of the iris control the size of the pupil, enlarging or reducing the opening to regulate the brightness of the image projected on the retina. Effort is needed only to change the size of the opening, not to maintain it. As soon as the pupil has reached the required size, the muscles of the iris can relax. For this reason, repeatedly viewing objects that have widely different brightness levels is more strenuous than viewing objects of about the same brightness. The muscles of the iris must work harder to adjust repeatedly to the changing light levels.

Brightness contrasts that fluctuate frequently are even more disturbing than static ones. Some familiar examples of this are work that requires the operator to alternately glance at bright and dark areas, such as from a bright page to a darker computer screen or to see indicator lights in very bright surroundings (Figure 6.7). For this reason, viewing moving parts of a machine, the headlights of oncoming cars, or flashes of sunlight reflected off of passing traffic are also difficult vision tasks. The pupil and retina of the eye cannot respond fast enough to accommodate fluctuating brightness levels. As a result, the

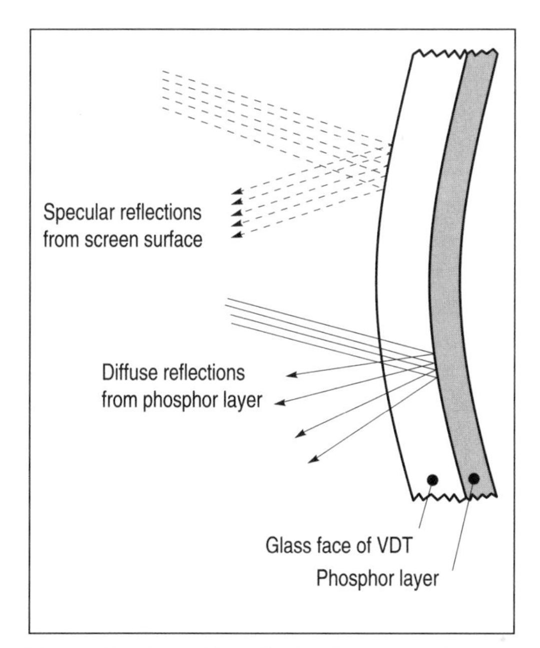

Figure 6.8 A double reflection image can be produced on a VDT monitor when separate reflections are produced from the outside and inner surfaces of the screen. (*Source:* Adapted from Grandjean 1987.)

retina is under- or over-exposed for much of the time, causing eye fatigue. This mechanism also contributes to the discomfort caused by VDT screens and fluorescent lighting that have a perceptible flicker.

These characteristics of the eye's response highlight two important ergonomic principles: to minimize visual fatigue, all objects in the visual field should be of similar brightness; and there should be no rapid fluctuation in illumination level because the eye cannot respond quickly enough to adapt.

Glare

Glare is the effect of excessive brightness in the field of view that causes discomfort and interferes with vision. **Direct glare** occurs when the light source is in the field of view. **Reflected glare** occurs when the light source is bounced off a surface, as when the reflection of overhead lighting forms a bright spot on a computer screen. Shiny finishes on the frame of the VDT screen, furnishings, work surfaces, glossy paper, and even the operator's clothing or jewelry are common glare sources that should be avoided. Reflective surfaces often can be treated or refinished to give them a matte finish.

Under certain conditions, computer screens can produce a reflection from the outside surface and a second one from the phosphor-coated inner surface (Figure 6.8). This can be particularly fatiguing because the eye may try to fuse the two images into a single one, the way the images of the left and right eye are fused to give a sharp image and the perception of depth. Unfortunately, this double image causes eye fatigue because it cannot be fused.

Glare impairs performance by making vision more difficult and therefore more fatiguing. It is also distracting because the eye tends to be attracted to the brightest part of the visual field. Glare can indirectly cause various musculoskeletal injuries, such as to the neck and back, as a result of the awkward postures that people adopt to compensate for a screen that is difficult to view.

The most effective way to control glare is at its source. Providing window coverings (either interior curtains or shading devices on the building's exterior), shielding light sources, and changing the orientation of VDT screens are effective measures. Windows offer a welcome view to the outside but are troublesome sources of glare. Adjustable vertical blinds can be angled to compensate for different sun angles throughout the day while still allowing a view to the outside. As well, computer screens should be oriented perpendicular to windowed areas or shielded from their glare by acoustic panels, dividing screens, or other furnishings.

A hood on the top and sides of a monitor can offer a simple but effective way to reduce screen reflections. Such hoods can be purchased or constructed of cardboard and tape (a black matte finish works best).

When it is not possible to eliminate glare sources, glare filters can be used. **Hard glare filters** are made of glass or plastic and have a reflective coating.

Some are attached to the VDT housing and stand away from the surface; others can be applied directly to the screen surface. These filters tend to work better the closer they are positioned to the screen face. **Mesh filters** consist of a loosely woven screen that allows light to pass out from the monitor while absorbing light hitting the filter at an angle. They are particularly effective to remedy bright light reflecting off the screen surface. However, they tend to reduce the sharpness and brightness of the screen image more than hard filters and can reflect light coming from extreme angles into the viewer's eyes. Whichever type of filter is used, it must be cleaned regularly to avoid the buildup of dust that degrades image quality.

Alternatively, screens may be treated with an antireflective coating. Silica coating and etching are relatively inexpensive treatments that diffuse light falling on the screen face. However, they noticeably reduce image contrast and sharpness. Although costly, optical coatings similar to those applied to camera lenses significantly reduce glare while permitting maximum light transmission.

Although glare filters can be effective in reducing screen reflections, when a filter is placed between the eye and the image to be viewed, some characteristics of the image are invariably compromised. There is generally some loss of contrast and sharpness as well as some reduction of image brightness. So it is preferable to eliminate glare without the use of filters or coatings.

Characteristics of the VDT Monitor

The quality of the VDT screen image directly affects the visual effort needed to view it and thus the length of time it can be viewed without fatigue or visual discomfort. A sharp, bright image; large characters; and high contrast between characters and background make viewing easier. For tasks that involve detailed graphic images with fine lines or small icons, a larger display may be needed. The user should be able to adjust the brightness and contrast to optimize legibility. There should be no perceptible jitter or flicker in the image, as an unsteady image can cause headaches and other vision-related problems. Since the electric field of a monitor attracts dust to the screen, regular cleaning helps to maintain good image quality.

The monitor should be mounted on an adjustable stand or other device so that it can be tilted or swiveled to a comfortable viewing angle that minimizes glare from surrounding light sources. Screens vary in their curvature. A flatter screen generally gives fewer reflection problems.

Text can be displayed as light letters on a dark background or the reverse, with dark letters on a bright background (often termed **reverse polarity**). Debate continues about which polarity is preferable; however, there is general agreement that reflected glare is less apparent when reverse polarity is used.

The number of times the screen image is redrawn each second is termed the **vertical scan rate.** A 60 hertz display redraws the entire screen image 60 times each second. The higher the vertical scan rate, the less likely there will be perceptible screen flicker. Some displays interlace the redrawing of the screen, refreshing every second line in the first pass and the remaining lines in a second pass. It enables a less expensive technology to be used but does not provide as steady an image.

Individuals differ in their sensitivity to screen flicker. At slower vertical scan rates (e.g., 50–60 hertz), most people can see a perceptible flickering of the screen in large bright areas, such as the background in reverse polarity images. At higher scan rates of 72 hertz or more, there is generally no perceptible screen flicker.

VDT use is a strenuous visual activity. As with other strenuous physical activities, periodic rest breaks will help to avoid overtaxing the body. Looking away from the screen or paper documents and focusing on distant objects, 7 meters (20 feet) away or more, blinking, and massaging the eyes gives them a rest. The National Institute for Occupational Safety and Health (NIOSH) in the United States recommends that full-time VDT users take a 10-minute break from VDT work every hour and that part-time users take a 10- to 15-minute break every two hours.

Illumination for Computer Work

Good lighting is essential for good vision. But lighting requirements vary according to the task and the individual. Older people need more light to see clearly than younger people. More light is desired for paper-based work than to view a computer screen. In fact, high light levels increase vision problems with computer screens. But most computer work also involves reading reference documents. Thus, illumination of computer work areas is usually a compromise to satisfy the demands of different activities.

Light levels on the order of 300–500 lux are generally recommended for VDT work areas. In non-VDT office areas, light levels are generally 700–1,000 lux. (The lux is the metric unit of light measurement. It is equal to 0.0929 footcandle.) Where more light is needed, task lighting at the work setting can be used.

Avoiding glare is the principal challenge in providing illumination for VDT work areas. A VDT screen is oriented more or less vertically and is positioned higher than traditional desk work like reading, writing, and conventional typing. Instead of looking down at the work surface, the VDT users' glance is forward and slightly down. Overhead lights, task lights, and other bright objects are more likely to be in their field of view causing direct glare or to be reflected in their screen from behind (Figure 6.9). Eyeglass wearers can be bothered by light sources behind them that are reflected in their glasses even though there is no reflection on the computer screen (Kaplan and Aronoff 1989).

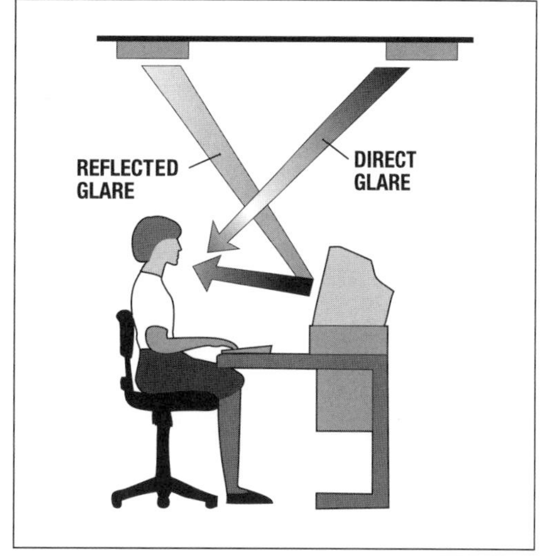

Figure 6.9 In working with VDTs, the users' line of sight is forward and slightly down. Glare can be caused by bright objects directly in their field of view or reflected in their screen from behind.

Figure 6.10 The overhead direct lighting is reflected in the computer screens causing troublesome glare. These fixtures were supposed to be installed with the bulbs facing the ceiling (i.e., semi-indirect lighting). However, the electricians were unfamiliar with these fixtures and simply installed them the way they usually oriented lights, with the bulbs facing down.

Direct overhead lighting systems cast about 90% of their illumination downward. Unshielded, this lighting casts harsh shadows, creating sharp contrasts. The light sources are readily reflected in computer screens, producing troublesome glare (Figure 6.10). To counter this prob-

Figure 6.11 This parabolic lens on these ceiling light fixtures was designed to eliminate glare on computer screens. When viewed at a distance (top photo) the lamps appear to be well shielded. Upon closer examination (center photo) the lenses are not tightly fitted in their frames. The same view, in a darker photograph, highlights these gaps (bottom photo) and shows the bright linear features that would be reflected in computer screens.

lem, the light sources are usually shielded with louvers or low-glare lenses. The parabolic louver (often referred to as an "egg-crate" louver) is one of the more common designs. Shielding devices must fit snugly in the frame, otherwise gaps will create distracting bright spots (Figure 6.11).

Ceiling light fixtures should be installed to the sides of VDT users, aligned perpendicular to computer screens so that the operators' lines of sight are between the luminaries. The illumination from ceiling fixtures should be directed principally downward. Light sources should be shielded and positioned high enough in the field of view (at an angle of 45 degrees or more above the horizontal). Where there are too many workstations in an area for them to be positioned for suitable illumination, an indirect lighting system may be more appropriate. **Indirect lighting** systems cast 90% or more of their light onto the ceiling and walls. When properly designed, they produce a bright, even illumination with practically no shadows.

Brightness contrast is the ratio of two brightness levels. When one object is three times brighter than another, they are said to have a 3:1 brightness contrast. **Reflectance** is the ratio of the light reflected from a surface to the light falling upon it. The reflectance and brightness contrast determine whether objects in the field of view will be distracting or visually fatiguing.

Experts differ on the level of brightness contrast that should be acceptable. Ideally, work materials should all be of about the same brightness to minimize visual effort. In general, contrast ratios of about 3:1 between the task area and the immediate surroundings are acceptable. Work surfaces with a reflectance of about 30% work well, giving an acceptable level of contrast with both white paper documents and the VDT screen (assuming background light levels are within the 300–500 lux range). More distant surfaces within the field of view should be no more than ten times brighter or darker than the task area. Bright walls (white or dark-colored) contrasting with dark floors, furniture, work surfaces, or equipment are common sources of excessive visual contrast in the office that should be avoided (Grandjean 1987). Table 6.3 presents commonly recommended reflectance values for VDT and non-VDT work areas.

From the standpoint of visual comfort, it is the *reflectance* of the surface that is critical, not its color. However, saturated bright colors like red and orange can be

Table 6-3 Recommended reflectance values for office elements (*Source:* Adapted from Grandjean 1987.)

Item	RECOMMENDED REFLECTANCE	
	Areas with no VDT use	Areas with VDT use
Ceiling	80–90%	70%
Blinds, curtains	50–60%	50%
Walls behind VDT screen	50–60%	40–50%
Walls opposite VDT screen	50–60%	30–40%
Furniture	25–40%	40–50%
Flooring	20–40%	20–40%

visually distracting. Eye-catching effects such as sharp black-white contrasts or bold graphic designs on walls should be avoided. They produce excessive brightness contrasts and are visually distracting. (Other physiological and psychological factors that affect vision are presented in the "Aesthetics" subsection in Chapter 4.)

VDT WORK SETTINGS

The design and adjustment of chairs, desks, office equipment, and background environmental conditions all affect the ergonomic performance of a work setting. Poorly designed or incorrectly adjusted work settings increase the physical strain on an individual, causing fatigue, impairing performance, and increasing the risk of injury.

Workstations intended for computer use are commonly of modular construction. Work surfaces, shelves, and storage cabinets can be mounted at a range of heights tailored to individual needs. However, the benefit of adjustability is severely compromised unless the users are shown how to adjust their furniture and where to position their computer equipment and work materials to minimize strain. They should also be made aware of the early signs of a developing injury and the procedure for having it corrected. There is no single, ideal work configuration, but any arrangement that frequently demands awkward postures or excessive twisting and stretching is likely to cause injury.

Chairs and the Seated Posture

A proper seated posture aligns the skeleton so that muscles do not strain to hold the body erect. Experts do not agree on the optimum seated posture. Current thinking is that individual comfort should guide seating position and that furniture should be sufficiently adjustable to offer support and comfort for the range of tasks people perform. Office chairs in particular should be chosen to fit the user, as no *one* design will suit all physiques or styles of working. People sit in different positions for the various activities they do during a workday (Table 6.4). As indicated at the bottom of the table, most office workers are active sitters (i.e., they shift their seated position frequently). However when doing computer-based work most people are considerably less active than when doing other types of office work.

The posture most widely recommended for computer work is an upright position with ears in line with the shoulders and hips, as shown in the left illustration of Figure 6.12. Yet whenever the work permits, VDT operators can be seen leaning back with their arms and hands slightly raised and resting on a support or the work surface itself. Many stretch out their legs as well (right illustration). It is a posture very similar to that used when operating a car, which is not surprising since driving is also a task that requires manual operations in a seated position for long periods of time.

Table 6.4 Sitting activity of office workers. Sample size: USA n=2045; Europe n=274. (*Sources:* Herman Miller Inc. 1991; Dowell 1994.)

Proportion of time spent on different work day activities

Activities	USA	Europe
Away from office/ out of chair	19%	19%
Reading	12%	13%
Writing	17%	18%
Talking-telephone/ person	21%	17%
Working on computer or typewriter	31%	38%

Division of sitting positions for different work day activities

Activity	USA	Europe
Reading		
sit forward	42%	54%
sit upright	11%	8%
recline	47%	38%
Talking		
sit forward	20%	26%
sit upright	15%	12%
recline	65%	62%
Writing		
sit forward	68%	76%
sit upright	11%	14%
recline	22%	10%
Typing		
sit forward	17%	21%
sit upright	37%	37%
recline	46%	42%

Overall sitting activity level

Activity level	USA	Europe
Active sitter	65%	65%
Quiet sitter	24%	20%
Neither	11%	15%

Some ergonomists favor a slightly reclining posture, leaning backward about 20 degrees to 30 degrees. With a well-supported and high chair back, this posture reduces the load on the back and shoulder muscles. As well, the greater angle between the thighs and trunk increases blood circulation to the lower limbs (Grandjean 1987).

A relaxed posture with the trunk bent slightly forward holds the weight of the body in balance with itself. It is the posture people commonly adopt when they are taking notes or reading because it is relaxing and minimizes strain on the back muscles (Grandjean 1987). A forward-leaning posture of about 15 degrees has been promoted for computer work as well (Mandal 1981). Periodically shifting between forward- and backward-leaning positions moves the sitting effort to different muscle groups, thereby reducing fatigue. Shifting positions is also beneficial for the intervertebral discs.

The **intervertebral discs** work like cushions between the vertebrae of the spine, giving the back its flexibility. Sitting postures differ in the pressure they generate on the discs, particularly those of the lower back, or **lumbar region** (Figure 6.13). The higher the disc loads, the greater the risk of backaches and disc injuries. Activities and postures that generate increased loads on the discs, such as lifting heavy weights and bad seating, can cause or aggravate these ailments and accelerate disc deterioration. With the development of sophisticated techniques to measure the pressure inside a disc it became possible to make quantitative comparisons of the disc pressures generated by different postures (Figure 6.14).

Disc pressure is greater when sitting than when standing. This is because the single-curved spine of the seated position (*A* in Figure 6.15) generates more pressure within the discs than the normal S-curved spine of the standing position (*B* in Figure 6.15). Because an upright seated posture with a good support for the lower back closely approximates the S-curve of the

Figure 6.12 Upright and reclining postures for operating a VDT. In the upright posture, the head is positioned with ears in line with shoulders, elbows at the side, and forearms about horizontal. This posture was considered optimal for typing and is often recommended for VDT work (left illustration). It is common for VDT operators to sit in a reclining posture, similar to the position used when driving a car (right illustration).

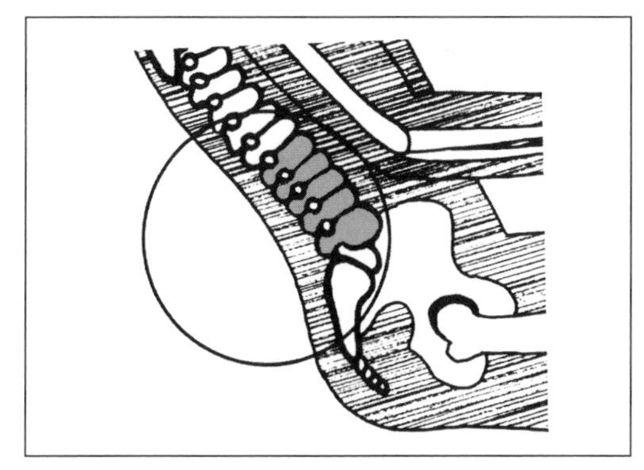

Figure 6.13 The lower part of the back, termed the lumbar region. (*Source:* Herman Miller Inc., Zeeland, Mich.)

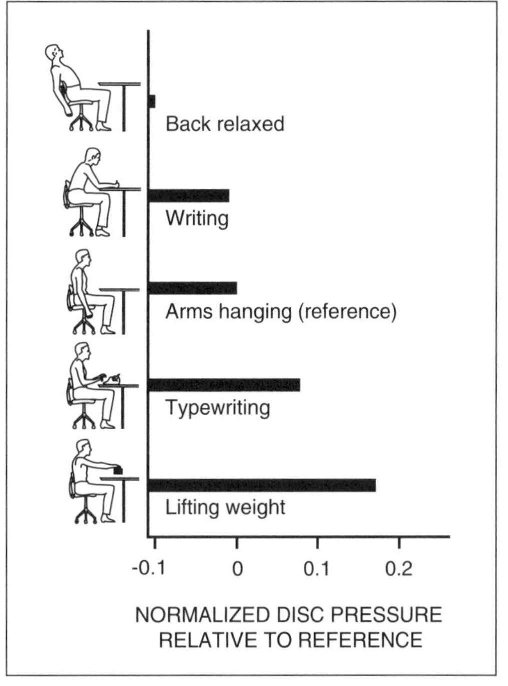

Figure 6.14 Effect of sitting position on disc pressure. The pressure on the disc between the third and fourth vertebrae of the lumbar region is shown for different sitting positions. (*Sources:* Adapted from Grandjean 1987; data from Andersson and Ortengren 1974.)

standing posture, it was thought to be the optimum sitting position.

But disc pressure is not the only stress on the body. Several muscle groups must exert static force to hold the trunk in a seated position. During **static effort,** muscles are contracted and remain in a state of heightened tension even though outward signs of exertion may not be apparent. In **dynamic effort,** such as walking, muscles successively contract and relax. Blood is repeatedly squeezed out of the muscles during compression, and a fresh supply is received during relaxation. For this reason, the flow of oxygen and nutrients to the muscles and removal of waste products are greater during dynamic effort. Not surprisingly, dynamic effort at a suitable pace can be carried on for much longer periods of time than a similar level of static effort.

When a person is working at a comput-

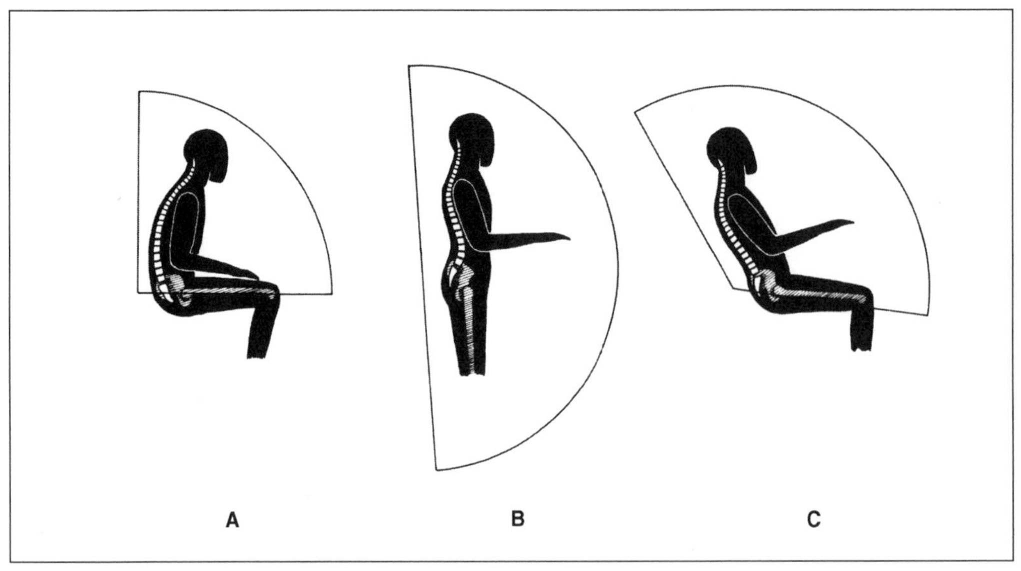

Figure 6.15 Curvature of the spine when changing from a sitting to a standing position. (*A*) Sitting down on an unsupported surface causes a backward rotation of the pelvis. The normal reverse curve of the lower back is flattened. (*B*) Normal S-curved position of the spine in the standing position. (*C*) A chair with a lumbar support can restore the reverse curve of the lower back. (*Source:* Herman Miller Inc., Zeeland, Mich.)

er, the shoulders, arms, and trunk do mainly static work to hold the hands and head in place. In reclining, a significant portion of the upper body's weight is transferred to the backrest, thereby reducing the strain on the discs and muscles.

Activity measurements of the muscles used in sitting have shown that in a properly supported chair, much greater static effort is required to maintain the upright seated posture than to maintain a slightly forward leaning or backward reclining position. Orthopedic studies have also shown that by reducing static loads, the reclining position generally produces less fatigue and fewer musculoskeletal problems. Thus, the seated posture that minimizes disc pressure is different from the one that minimizes muscle fatigue, and the most *comfortable* compromise is not an upright position.

The position shown to minimize both disc pressure and static muscular effort is reclining with the chair back at an angle of about 110 degrees to 120 degrees from the horizontal as shown at C in Figure 6.15 (Grandjean 1987). Thus, any work in which it is possible to lean back will benefit from a chair with an adjustable backrest. However, to reduce the risk of cumulative trauma disorders, an upright posture is preferred because it allows the arms and hands to be held in a better position for typing (Pacarelli and Quilter 1994).

Though there is disagreement about upper body position, there is consensus about the importance of supporting the lower back, the lumbar region. To reduce pressure on the discs, chair backs should be contoured to maintain the S-curve of the spine or have an adjustable lumbar pad about 5 centimeters (2 inches) thick for this purpose.

There is no seated posture optimal for all the activities performed at a computer-equipped work setting because many tasks do not involve computer use. People also read, speak on the phone, or take rest breaks — activities that are better performed in a variety of other positions (Figure 6.16). Chairs that are to be employed for intensive computer work must offer proper support for the postures used in that activity, but they must also be sufficiently adjustable to support the postures used during other tasks. However, when chairs are used for only short periods at a time, less sophisticated and less expensive models may be sufficient.

Figure 6.16 People assume a variety of seated postures — often over the course of just a few minutes. Changing positions frequently is beneficial. It increases blood circulation to the muscles and shifts the work of holding the body upright among different muscle groups, periodically giving each a chance to rest. (*Source:* Herman Miller Inc., Zeeland, Mich.)

The following are general guidelines for selecting office chairs. Because the ergonomic performance of a chair is in part dependent on correct positioning of the work surface with which it is used, these components should be selected together.

• The chair height should be adjustable so the elbow can be bent at about a 90 degree angle when the hands are at their normal working position (in the case of VDT work, this is generally taken to be with the fingers resting on the home row of the keyboard and the wrists flat). Controls should be conveniently located and easy to use from a seated position; otherwise, it is unlikely that they will be adjusted to suit different tasks. The upper leg should be horizontal and the lower leg vertical, with the feet resting on the floor or on a footrest. If the feet are not supported (i.e., are hanging), the blood supply to the lower leg will be constricted. Footrests should be inclined and have a nonskid surface.

• Armrests should be padded and positioned close enough to the person so they can be leaned on comfortably. They should adjust vertically and not hit the work surface, preventing the operator from sitting close enough to comfortably use the keyboard and view the monitor (Figure 6.17 on page 242).

• The seat pan should be padded and contoured for comfort and support. To prevent cutting off blood circulation to the legs, the front edge should curve downward, and the seat should not be so long that it touches the leg below the knee.

• To reduce twisting motions of the torso, the chair should swivel. A five-branch base provides greater stability than a four-branch design. Casters permit the chair to roll in any direction, making it easier to shift position while seated and to move closer instead of straining for items just out of reach.

Work Surfaces

Work surfaces for VDT tasks need to be large enough to accommodate both the computer equipment and reference documents. Since computer users frequently rest their arms on the edge of the work surface, it should have a rounded or flexible edge to support the forearms without impeding blood circulation to the hands (Figure 6.18). As a general rule, the primary work surface should have a length of at least 120–150 centimeters (4–5 feet) and a depth of at least 75–90 centimeters (2.5–3 feet). It should be wide enough for

Figure 6.18 A soft, contoured edge is more comfortable than a hard, right-angle edge and does not constrict blood flow to the hands when the wrists or arms are rested on the work surface. (*Source:* Herman Miller Inc., Zeeland, Mich.)

Figure 6.17 The armrests built into this chair can be adjusted vertically and rotate horizontally to suit the user. (*Source:* Allseating, Mississauga, Ontario.)

documents to be laid open to one side, particularly if references are often used or documents are spread out to both sides of the computer.

A commonly used guideline is for items in constant use to be placed no more than about 40 centimeters (16 inches) to the side and 30 centimeters (12 inches) in front of the user. Frequently used items should be within easy reach — about 60 centimeters (24 inches) to the sides and 50 centimeters (20 inches) to the front whereas materials that are needed only occasionally can be stored further away (Figure 6.19). As with any guideline, judgement is needed in applying them to a specific situation. A

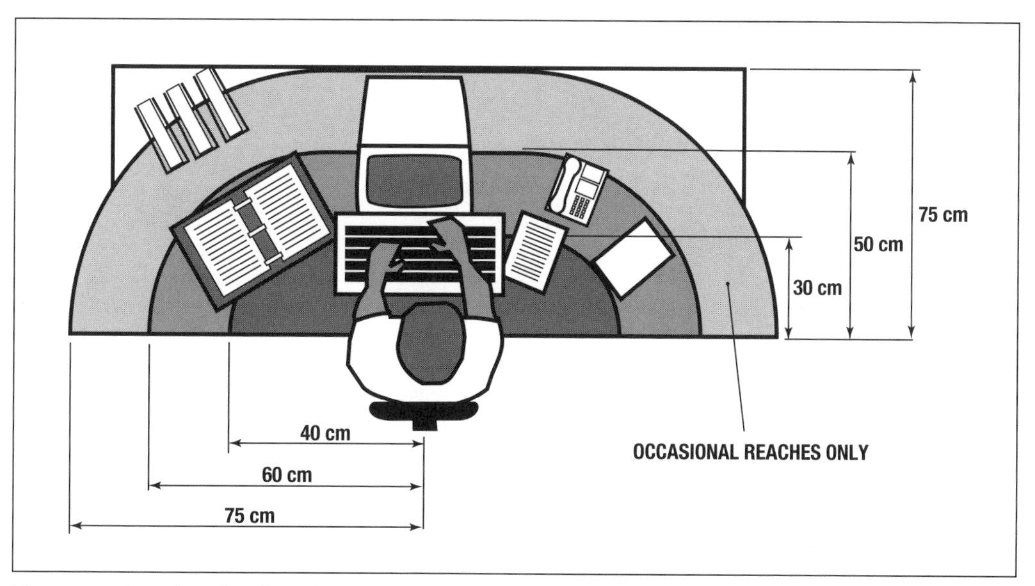

Figure 6.19 A work surface should be designed to accommodate work materials so that frequently used items can be reached easily without physical strain. The guidelines indicated in this illustration are discussed in the text.

Figure 6.20 Examples of height-adjustable work surfaces, operated by crank handles. *Left:* Work surface has a vertical travel of 20 centimeters (8 inches) and a tilt of 0 degrees to 45 degrees. *Middle:* Platform for the computer monitor has a vertical travel of 15 centimeters (6 inches). The surrounding tabletop remains at a fixed height. The recessed keyboard tray can be adjusted 13 centimeters (5 inches) above or below the fixed work surface. *Right:* Tabletop has a vertical travel of 20 centimeters (8 inches) with a recessed keyboard tray that has a vertical range of 13 centimeters (5 inches). Both keyboard trays are shown with wrist rests. (*Source:* Teknion Furniture Systems, Downsview, Ontario.)

Figure 6.21 The work surface shown here has a vertical travel of 50 centimeters (20 inches) so that it can be used from either a sitting or standing position. An electric drive mechanism allows for easy adjustment to suit different work postures. (*Source:* Herman Miller Inc., Zeeland, Mich.)

very small person, for example, may need their materials to be closer than these general recommendations suggest.

In general, for manual tasks performed in front of the body, maximum performance is achieved by keeping the elbows down at the sides and bent at about a 90 degree angle. A work surface that is too high will cause the shoulder lifting muscles to become painfully fatigued. One that is too low restricts leg movement. There should be sufficient space below the work surface for legs to be stretched out and moved to the side, preferably enough to cross the legs at the knees. This makes it easier to shift sitting positions reducing muscle fatigue.

A keyboard should be positioned at a lower height than a work surface used for paper-based tasks. Placing the keyboard on a separate support is one solution for work surfaces that are the wrong height (see the subsection "The Mouse and Keyboard" later in this chapter).

Some work surfaces are adjustable and can be raised and lowered using a hand crank or power lifting mechanism (Figure 6.20). Alternatively, the chair can be raised or lowered so that a 90 degree elbow angle is attained so long as the feet rest on the floor or on a footrest of appropriate height. A standing work posture can offer welcome relief from long periods of sitting, and some manufacturers have introduced a workstation that supports both sitting and standing positions (Figure 6.21).

Positioning the VDT Screen

The VDT screen should be positioned to accommodate the resting or *normal* line of sight which is 10 degrees to 15 degrees below the horizontal. Eye movement is comfortable within about 15 degrees above and below this line of sight (Figure 6.22) (Grandjean 1987). Positioning the top of the monitor at or slightly below eye level generally works well. For some types of VDT work, a lower screen position may be preferred, such as when reference documents are placed on the work surface (Hill and Kroemer 1986). This reduces the amount of repetitive head motion and eye fatigue from refocusing between reference documents and the computer monitor (Figure 6.23). However, the head and neck should not be bent forward more than about 15 degrees to pre-

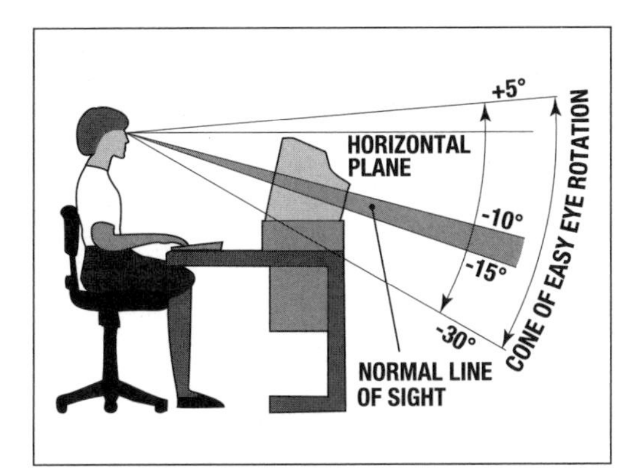

Figure 6.22 The normal line of sight falls within a viewing angle of 5 degrees above and 30 degrees below the horizontal plane. It is the field of view that can easily be accommodated by rotation of the eyes or slight inclination of the head. (*Source:* Adapted from Grandjean 1987.)

vent straining neck and shoulder muscles (Grandjean 1987). Alternatively, work surfaces can be split into two surfaces that can be raised and lowered separately. The computer monitor can then be placed on the rear surface and raised or lowered independently of the front work surface supporting the keyboard.

The VDT screen should be positioned at a viewing distance of 35–50 centimeters (14–20 inches). Very large screens may need to be placed farther away. The monitor should tilt and swivel on its base so that it can be oriented for comfortable viewing and to avoid glare.

Figure 6.23 When reference materials must be laid on the work surface, a lower screen position can reduce the amount of repetitive head motion and the eye fatigue from refocusing when glancing between the reference documents and the computer monitor. (*Source:* NOVA Office Furniture, Effingham, Ill.)

The Mouse and Keyboard

Working at a computer commonly requires intensive use of a keyboard or a mouse. Full-time operators, such as data-entry clerks, will type 10,000 to 20,000 keystrokes an hour. The health risks of strenuous computer work can be reduced by ensuring that the placement of the keyboard and mouse enable the forearms and hands to be correctly positioned. For this reason, the keyboard should be separate from the monitor.

The forearm, wrist, and hand should be held flat for keyboard work. Typing with the wrist bent upward to reach the keyboard increases the risk of developing cumulative trauma disorders. Wrist bending can be reduced by physically lowering the upper rows of keys. Keyboards and keyboard trays that tilt downward 10 to 20 degrees away from the user have recently been introduced.

For those who rest the palms of their hands on the work surface while typing, a thinner keyboard produces less upward bending of the wrist and so reduces the risk of injury (Grandjean 1987). Wrist and palm supports can help maintain proper wrist and hand position. However, some experts recommend that the wrists and hands not be rested on any support while typing because it encourages bad typing habits (e.g., overstretching fingers rather than moving the whole hand), it transfers loads that are normally carried by the shoulder joints and muscles to the small tendons of the fingers, and the pressure of the support on the wrist increases the risk of inflammation of tendons (Pascarelli and Quilter 1994).

A keyboard should have good tactile feedback to indicate when a keystroke is accepted so the user is less inclined to pound on the keys. The point of acceptance should be about half the downward travel of the key. Scooped keys make it easier to keep fingers in the proper position. Key size and spacing are also a consideration. People with large hands may find the smaller keyboards on laptop computers difficult to use.

The conventional rectangular flat keyboard forces the wrists into an unnatural position, palms down (*pronation*), and wrists rotated outward (*ulnar deviation*) to align the fingers on the home row of the keyboard. If the palms are rested on the work surface while typing, the hand is also bent upward at the wrist (*dorsiflexion*). Not everyone can hold a palms-down position comfortably for extended periods.

A number of alternative keyboards have been designed to reduce the strain of typing and offer greater comfort (Figure 6.24). Some keyboards are split, and the spacing between the two halves is adjustable, so the outward rotation of the wrist can be reduced. In some cases, the center of the keyboard is raised so the hand does not have to be rotated to a fully palms down position. An alternative keyboard concept eliminates finger stretching by assigning only one key to each finger. By simultaneously pressing multiple keys, termed **chord-keying**, the full range of characters is produced.

Computer users, even those who touch-type, tend to glance frequently at their keyboards. Since the eye refocuses with each glance, there will be less eye fatigue if the keyboard is the same viewing distance as the VDT screen and reference documents.

Keyboard trays were introduced as an ergonomic improvement that could be attached to existing furniture. These supports allow the keyboard to be positioned in front of the work surface at the desired height and swung beneath it when not in use. Unfortunately, these devices can often create ergonomic problems. They can be too narrow to accommodate adjustable palm supports and other ergonomic aids and too flimsy to offer a solid support. They may restrict leg room beneath the work surface, making it more difficult to shift sitting positions. They also force the operator to sit farther away from the work surface, which may be too far to comfortably view the monitor and reference documents. If a mouse is used, there

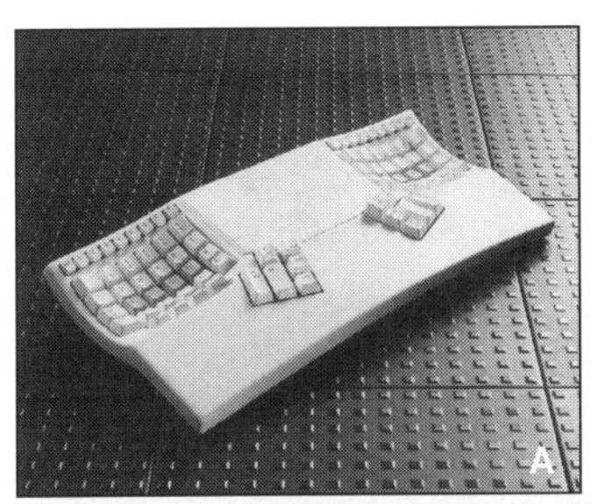

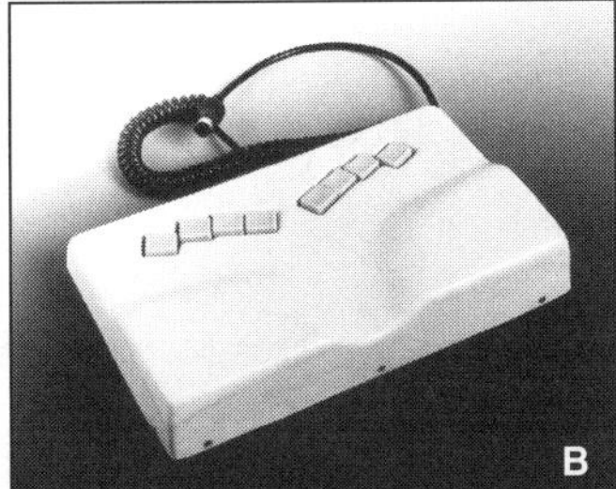

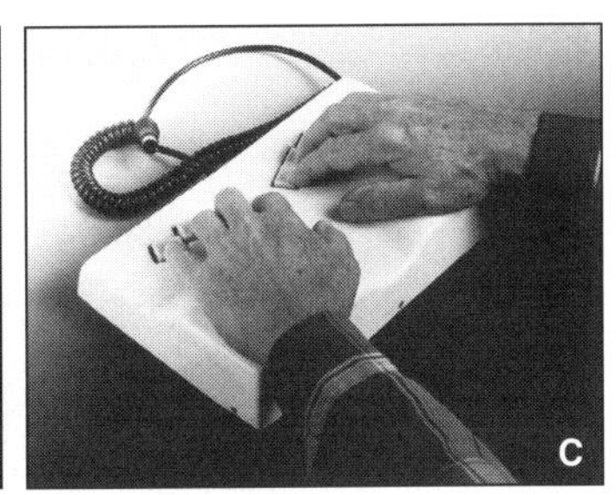

Figure 6.24 Alternative keyboard designs can offer a more comfortable hand position. (*A*) Fixed keyboard with dished keypads. This keyboard is elevated toward the center with a dished keypad for each hand. (*Source:* Kinesis Corp., Bothell, Wash.) (*B* and *C*) Chord-key keyboard. This keyboard has eight keys, each being operated by one finger. The full range of characters is produced by simultaneously pressing multiple keys, termed chord-keying. (*Source:* Vatell Corp., Blacksburg, Va.) (*D*) Split keyboard. This keyboard can be split in half and the separation between the two segments can be adjusted and locked. The segments can also be raised in the center. (*Source:* Maxi Switch, Tuscon, Ariz.) (*E*) This design brings the keyboard to the hands by mounting a keypad on each arm of an ergonomic chair. (*Source:* Workplace Designs, Stillwater, Minn.)

needs to be space for it on the keyboard support or the user will have to stretch forward to operate it. Working with a mouse on a work surface at a different height than the keyboard can also be problematic.

A pullout keyboard tray that slides on rails attached beneath the work surface is the simplest design. It can work well if it is solid and at the correct height. Cantilevered keyboard supports are more adjustable, but they take up more space under the work surface and are more prone to bounce. For many users, the most comfortable and sturdy location for the keyboard is on the work surface.

Document Holders

Document holders or copy stands can improve the ergonomics of a computer work setting by allowing reference materials to be positioned adjacent to the screen. With the screen and reference documents positioned at the same viewing distance and in the same direction, repetitive head motions and refocusing of the eyes are minimized when glancing between the screen and the documents. However, such holders are only of benefit if they are used.

Computer users are often unable or unwilling to use document holders. Sometimes it is because the documents are too large or it is necessary to write on them. For items that are used only briefly, as in some data-entry work, it may be inconvenient to place them on the holder. If several documents must be used at the same time, placing one on the copy stand and the others on the work surface can cause greater visual fatigue than having them all

Figure 6.25 A nineteenth-century advertisement for corsets to reduce back and shoulder pain. These braces were a poor solution. They restricted movement and did not address the principal source of the problem — desks that were too low forced workers to stoop.

lying flat on the work surface. In that case, there needs to be sufficient space on the work surface to accommodate these materials. Ideally, they should be positioned at the same distance from the eye as the screen.

CUMULATIVE TRAUMA DISORDER

Cumulative trauma disorder (**CTD**), also known as **repetitive strain injury (RSI)**, is a collective term for a range of physical ailments characterized by discomfort or persistent pain in muscles, tendons, and other soft tissues. As the term is commonly used, it refers to disorders of the upper body. Medically, these disorders are included in the more general class of ailments called "musculoskeletal disorders," or more specifically, "upper-extremity musculoskeletal disorders" (Stock 1991). The terms **repetitive trauma disorder** and **repetitive motion illness** are also used. Since these disorders are caused by multiple factors, it is more correct to use the term **upper-extremity musculoskeletal disorders,** which refers to the symptoms alone, not the possible causes. However, that term is rather cumbersome and has not been widely adopted. In this book, this group of ailments is referred to as **cumulative trauma disorder.**

CTDs are not new illnesses. In the nineteenth century, doctors described cases of occupation-related cramps among writers and craftsmen with symptoms similar to the repetitive strain injuries reported in the 1980s (Figure 6.25) (Quintner 1991). *Carpenter's elbow, writer's cramp, bricklayer's shoulder,* and *washerwoman's thumb* are names for different types of CTDs. In the early 1900s, telegraph operators reported a painful arm and elbow condition they termed *glass elbow* similar to the symptoms now reported by computer operators doing intensive data-entry work.

CTDs have long been common among factory workers performing repetitive motions in auto assembly, the garment

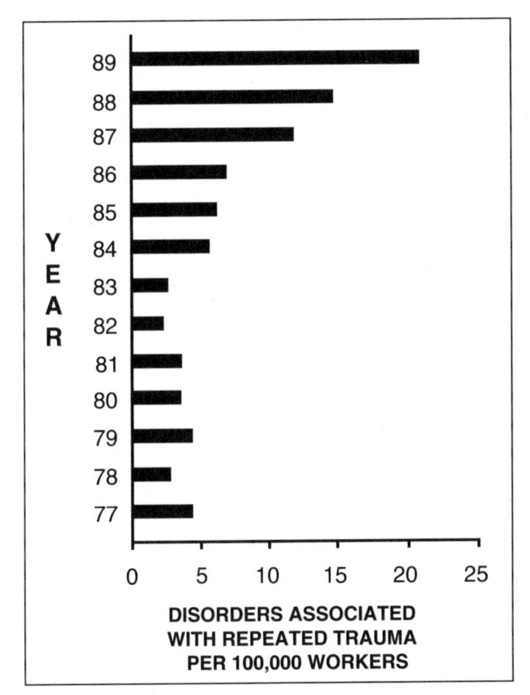

Figure 6.26 The incidence of disorders associated with repeated trauma has increased dramatically in recent years. (*Source:* U.S. Bureau of Labor Statistics 1990.)

industry, and food-processing jobs especially meatpacking. Although they occur more frequently in these strenuous occupations, CTDs also occur in less demanding occupations such as among pianists and hairdressers. What has been remarkable is the dramatic increase in CTDs among office workers.

In the United States, the incidence of CTDs has increased more than threefold over the past ten years, accounting for 61% (223,600 cases) of all reported occupational diseases in 1990 (Figure 6.26). These statistics from the U.S. Bureau of Labor Statistics include CTDs within the more general category "disorders associated with repeated trauma." This category includes other ailments associated with repeated motion, pressure, or vibration, such as noise-induced hearing loss. But most cases in this category (e.g., 95% in 1991) are CTDs (U.S. Bureau of Labor Statistics 1992). This increase has coincided with the rapid computerization of scores of office jobs. Telephone operators, secretaries, writers, and other groups who worked at computer keyboards for extended hours experienced a rise in CTD problems. This increased incidence is attributable not only to the widespread use of computers in offices but also to more accurate reporting, greater awareness, and improved diagnosis of CTDs.

At first, CTDs were viewed with skepticism because the symptoms are mostly subjective — the presence of pain. There commonly is no observable physical damage. So CTD sufferers were sometimes considered to be lazy and unmotivated or branded as chronic complainers. Studies have now shown that there has been a statistically significant increase in CTDs among computer users and that the intensity of computer use and the quality of workstation design are contributing factors (see, for example, Gerr, Letz, and Landrigan 1991; a study of 1,545 clerical workers by Rossignol et al. 1987; and a study of 1,032 office workers by Stellman et al. 1987). NIOSH has conducted a number of studies confirming the link between computer use and the increased incidence of CTDs among office workers (NIOSH 1990, 1992, 1993).

CTD Symptoms

The specific type of CTD a person develops and the progress of the illness will vary widely, depending on the nature of the individual's activities and physical make-up. Although the symptoms are mostly subjective and develop gradually over time, some can be objectively measured. For example, to diagnose carpal tunnel syndrome, damage to the median nerve can be assessed by electromyography.

Early symptoms are mild and may not at first be linked to work activities if discomfort occurs only during the night, long after leaving the job. Initially, there is aching and tiredness of the affected limb at night and/or during the work shift, but physical signs are not present. As the illness progresses, symptoms become more intense during the work shift and do not resolve overnight. Among office workers, the most common symptoms are numbness or shooting pains in the hands, wrists, and arms and chronic pain in the neck and shoulder. Eventually, the ability to hold, grasp, and manipulate objects is impaired (Armstrong 1983).

If the condition remains untreated, both the offending repetitive work motions as well as other nonrepetitive movements will trigger chronic aching, fatigue, and weakness. At this stage, physical signs are usually present, and the symptoms persist despite resting the affected limbs. Without treatment, the condition may then last for months or years. In some cases, nerve damage can be so severe that the affected arm and hand cannot be rehabilitated. Some computer users afflicted with CTDs have been unable to work at a keyboard again (Browne, Nolan, and Faithfull 1984; Guidotti 1992).

Cumulative trauma disorders are difficult to treat, and success rates are lower the longer the condition is permitted to develop. Patients typically require weeks or months to recover from a serious CTD. Pain control, stress management counseling, and emotional support may also be needed during convalescence (Guidotti 1992). If patients then return to their old jobs without ergonomic improvements to their work settings, their symptoms commonly reappear and they have to find alternative work. But with appropriate ergonomic aids, many can resume their former jobs.

Work-Related Risk Factors

CTDs are caused or aggravated by repetitive and/or forceful movements and awkward postures sustained for long periods without adequate rest breaks. Exposure to cold and vibration increases the risk. Since treatments can be difficult and are often unsuccessful, the best approach to manage CTDs in the office workplace is prevention.

Factors associated with an increased incidence of CTDs among computer users include the number of hours spent typing, the number of hours working on deadlines, infrequent rest breaks, and awkward constrained postures resulting from ergonomically inappropriate or incorrectly adjusted furniture. An individual's style of work is another risk factor. Certain arm and hand positions and certain keyboard techniques predispose the operator to develop CTDs.

The psychosocial setting has also been shown to be a contributing factor. High job stress — such as excessive work pressure, heavy and unpredictable workloads, poor relations between management and employees and among coworkers, and the pressure of electronic performance monitoring (e.g., monitoring keystrokes per hour or the number of telephone inquiries handled) — is significantly associated with CTD incidence (NIOSH 1992, 1993; Smith, Cohen, and Stammerjohn 1981; Westin 1992). For example, in the telecommunications industry, CTDs are widespread among workers who are not heavy computer users but have high-stress jobs. In a recent three-year study at U.S. West, NIOSH (1992) found that 22% of the directory assistance operators had medically verified CTDs, even though the ergonomic conditions were considered to be acceptable.

That stress should be an important contributing factor is not surprising. It is common for people under stress to unconsciously tense the muscles of the shoulder and neck or clench and grind their teeth. When muscles remain tensed for prolonged periods, they fatigue, become painful, and are more susceptible to injury. What's more, if those muscles must also perform repetitive motions, the tension is an added workload that hastens fatigue. Periodic rest breaks provide an opportunity for muscles to relax and recover but are less effective if stress causes them to remain tensed.

Thus, CTDs are caused by multiple factors. It is the combination of these factors, their intensity, and the unique characteristics of the individual that determine whether a

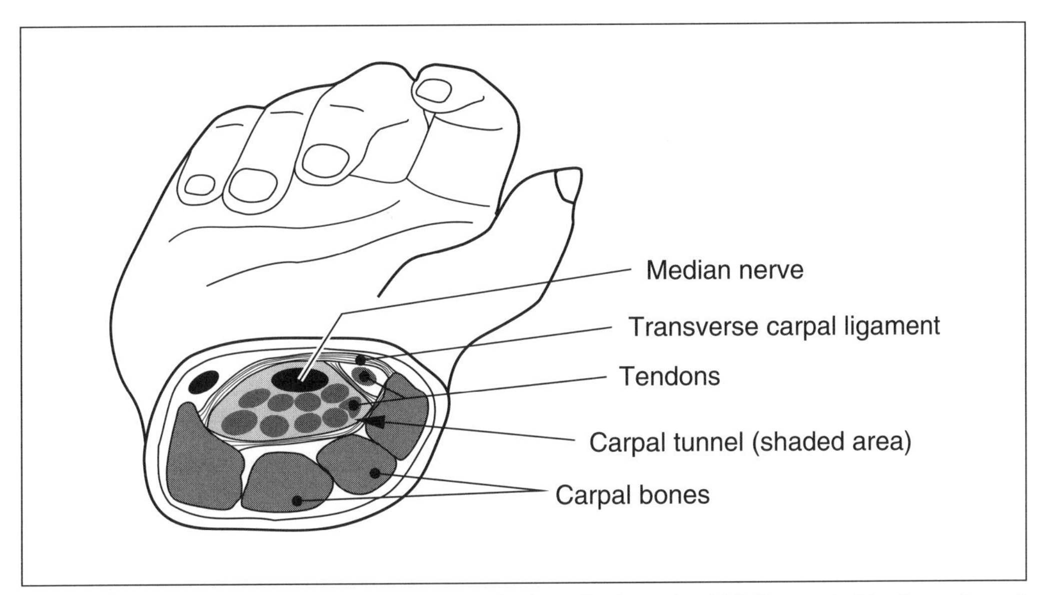

Figure 6.27 The carpal tunnel is a narrow passage in the wrist through which ligaments, blood vessels, and the median nerve pass. Carpal tunnel syndrome is a painful condition caused by compression of the median nerve when the ligaments or nerve sheath swell within the confined space of the carpal tunnel.

CTD disorder will develop, where it will occur, and how severe it will be. For this reason, CTDs commonly afflict only a portion of workers performing a given task. Some cases develop as well-defined ailments, whereas others are less specific and poorly defined problems. Of the well-defined medical disorders, *tendinitis, epicondylitis, tenosynovitis,* and *carpal tunnel syndrome* are CTDs commonly diagnosed among office workers.

Tendinitis refers to inflammation of a tendon, a fibrous cord that joins muscle to bone or to another muscle. Workers are susceptible to shoulder and forearm tendinitis. **Epicondylitis** is the inflammation of a tendon at the elbow. It can be caused by work activities and is also a common sports injury known as "tennis elbow." **Tenosynovitis** is the irritation of a tendon sheath. Tendons often pass through a protective sheath where they curve around bones or change directions. The inner wall of the sheath secretes a lubricating substance, allowing the tendon to slide easily. Excessive movement of the tendon can cause irritation, and if the friction continues, the resulting overproduction of lubricating fluid causes inflammation. Tenosynovitis associated with keyboard use can cause severe pain in the thumb and fingers (Pascarelli and Quilter 1994).

Carpal tunnel syndrome is a specific disabling condition of the hand caused by compression of the median nerve in the wrist. There, the nerve passes through a narrow opening between the carpal ligament at the base of the hand and the wrist bones beneath, known as the carpal bones (Figure 6.27). Excessive use can cause swelling of the tendons, inflammation of the sheath around the nerve, or tightening of the carpal ligament, all of which can compress the median nerve, causing pain. Once the condition is diagnosed, the initial treatment is to immobilize the wrist. Steroid injections may provide relief, but if the condition persists, the pressure on the median nerve can be relieved surgically (Weiss and Akelman 1992).

The most important occupational risk factor for carpal tunnel syndrome is highly repetitive hand motions, particularly those that require greater hand force (Silverstein, Fine, and Armstrong 1987). Awkward hand postures, vibration, and cold temperatures may also contribute (Armstrong 1983). Carpal tunnel syndrome is a common ailment of cashiers, assembly workers, seamstresses, machinists, meat packers, bricklayers, and those who use computers (Pascarelli and Kella 1993). There is disagreement within the medical community over whether heavy use of computer keyboards can actually *cause* carpal tunnel syndrome. Professionals who specialize in these ailments (e.g., occupational physicians, hand surgeons, and neurologists) generally support this cause-effect link (Stephens 1993); others disagree. However, there is consensus within the general medical community that once carpal tunnel syndrome has begun to develop, it will be aggravated by repetitive activities of the hand and wrist, including keyboard use. Carpal tunnel syndrome can also be caused by congenital defects, acute trauma, pregnancy, drug side effects, and disease (Armstrong 1983; Mascola and Rickman 1991).

CTD Costs and Liability

There have now been many well-publicized outbreaks of CTDs among computer users in large organizations. The injury became a national concern in Australia during the early 1980s when there was a sudden and dramatic increase of cases among office workers (Hopkins 1990). In New South Wales, the number of CTD compensation cases (at that time termed repetitive strain injuries) rose from 980 in 1978 to 4,490 in 1983, with settlements as high as A$350,000 (US$250,000). A 1985 study of government employees in western Australia found that 19% of word-processing operators, 22% of data-processing operators, and 22% of court reporters reported CTD complaints (Gerr, Letz, and Lendrigan 1991; Kiesler and Finholt 1988).

Recent statistics suggest that the incidence of CTDs in Australia peaked in 1985 and has since decreased rapidly. Telecom Australia, a large telecommunications company, reported that for the 1981–1985 period, the incidence of new CTD cases was 284 per thousand among clerical workers and 343 per thousand among telephonists. The average absence from work was 24 days per case. The reporting of CTDs peaked at 600 new cases per thousand workers in the last quarter of 1984 and declined to less than 25 cases in the last quarter of 1988, about the same number as in 1981 before the sharp increase occurred (Gerr, Letz, and Lendrigan 1991). The reasons for the decline are not well understood, but are likely due, in part, to the introduction of mitigative measures and more accurate diagnoses.

The United States has also witnessed a steep rise in the frequency of CTDs in the workplace, coinciding with the rapid computerization of office jobs. For example, in the finance, real estate, and insurance industry category, a computer-intensive white-collar industry group, the incidence of CTDs increased tenfold over a five-year period, growing from 0.5 to 5.6 cases per 10,000 between 1985 and 1990 (Figure 6.28) (Betts 1992; U.S. Bureau of Labor Statistics 1990). If it follows the same course as in Australia, there is the potential for CTDs to cost billions of dollars in lost productivity, compensation claims, and medical treatment. The National Council on Compensation Insurance in the United States estimates the average compensation at US$29,000. A recent study by Liberty Mutual Insurance Company found that its average compensation payments were about US$8,000 per case and estimated the annual compensable cost in the United States to be US$563 million (Webster and Snook 1994).

The high incidence of CTDs among computer users has sparked union action to improve working conditions, investigations by health and safety regulatory agencies, and numerous lawsuits against employers and computer manufacturers. A number of workers' compensation cases and lawsuits have been successfully filed against employers.

In 1987, OSHA cited U.S. West when 225 of its 500 workers filed claims against the company for CTDs. The company eventually settled for lifetime medical care of some 20 workers, and OSHA mandated

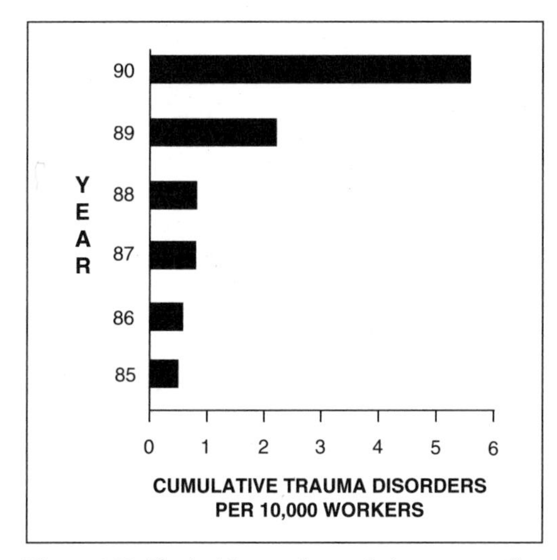

Figure 6.28 The incidence of cumulative trauma disorders has increased rapidly among white-collar workers. These data illustrate the growing incidence of CTDs in the finance, insurance, and real estate industry group. (*Source:* U.S. Bureau of Labor Statistics 1990.)

the redesign of the two directory assistance offices where the outbreaks had occurred. A 1992 survey by the Communications Workers of America (CWA) indicated that after making improvements to both the ergonomics of the workstations and job design, U.S. West had improved conditions to the point that its workers had the lowest incidence of CTDs among CWA members (LeGrande 1993).

Newsroom reporters and editors work continuous hours under pressure to meet tight deadlines. CTDs began to appear in newsrooms in the 1980s as the journalism industry computerized. The New York newspaper *Newsday* became one of the more widely publicized examples of severe and widespread CTDs in the office workplace. At first, the reporters tried to ignore the aches and pains and continue working, but CTDs are aggravated and become more severe if the offending motions are continued. As more people were affected and their symptoms became more debilitating, there were demands to investigate the problem. A six-month study by researchers at NIOSH and the University of Michigan found that 331 (40%) of the 834 employees surveyed reported CTD symptoms (NIOSH 1990). Those who spent many hours typing and typed very fast were at greatest risk. About 100 required medical treatment.

At *Newsday,* a management-worker committee was formed to resolve CTD problems. With the assistance of government health authorities and an ergonomics consultant, modifications were made to the physical work setting, the design of work tasks, and supervisory policies. The newspaper spent US$3 million on chairs, desks, headsets, armrests, and other specialized equipment. Typists were hired to take dictation from those reporters no longer able to type their own work. With a greater awareness of the risks and consequences, workers are now encouraged to stop working and get help at the early stages of CTD. There have since been other similar cases in the newspaper industry in which employees received compensation (Gerr, Letz, and Landrigen 1991; NIOSH 1990, 1993; Roel 1990).

Conclusion for CTD

Cumulative trauma disorders have become an occupational risk of office work. There is some risk associated with most jobs. What has made CTDs a particularly sensitive issue among office workers is that their workplace has traditionally been considered a safe environment.

Steps can be taken to minimize CTD risk in the office, but it cannot be entirely eliminated. Even in an ergonomically sound workplace, occupational illnesses will occur. They may be the result of temporary changes such as extended work hours, new equipment, or inattention to early warning symptoms. Some individuals are more likely to contract the disorder as a result of their work techniques or physical characteristics. A growing body of research has provided a better understanding of these disorders and the steps that can be taken to prevent them. Organizations need to monitor the incidence of CTDs to identify problematic activities or equipment, promote safe work techniques, and take effective action when symptoms first appear.

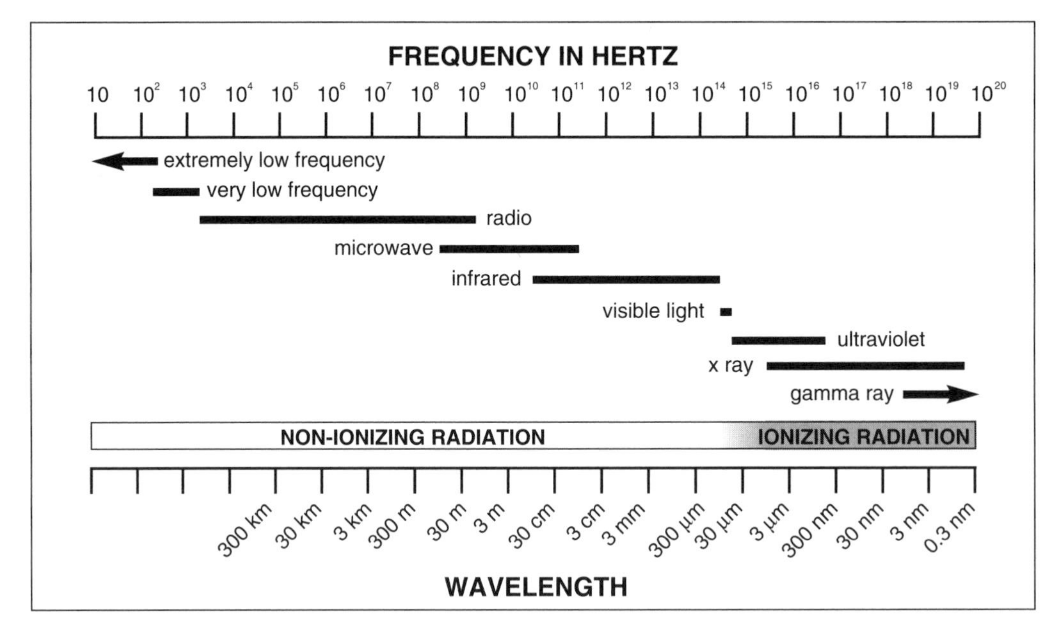

Figure 6.29 The electromagnetic spectrum. Abbreviations: km – kilometer; m – meter; cm – centimeter; mm – millimeter; µm – micron (one thousandth of a millimeter); nm – nanometer (one millionth of a millimeter).

ELECTROMAGNETIC FIELDS AND HUMAN HEALTH

For the past 15 years, there has been growing public concern about the health effects of weak electromagnetic energy emitted by power lines, household wiring, and electrically powered devices that are used close to the body, such as electric blankets and computer monitors. At issue is the extremely low frequency (ELF) electromagnetic fields they produce.

Some studies suggest that long-term exposure to these emissions increases the risk of miscarriages and certain types of cancer. Other studies have not found statistically significant risks. Within the medical and scientific community, there has not yet been sufficient evidence to reach a consensus one way or the other.

Electromagnetic energy spans a wide range of frequencies from the extremely low frequencies of household electric current, through radio waves and visible light, to X rays and gamma rays at the very high frequencies (Figure 6.29). The names used to describe different frequency ranges derive from their characteristics. Since the properties of waves change gradually, the boundaries are somewhat arbitrary and differ slightly according to the application. For this reason, there is some overlap between named frequency ranges, as show in the illustration. Higher frequencies are more energetic. X rays, gamma rays, and higher frequencies are termed "ionizing radiation." They are considered hazardous to human health because their energy level is high enough to break chemical bonds and cause biological damage. Computer equipment generates electromagnetic energy in a wide range of frequencies from the very low frequency (VLF) and extremely low frequency (ELF) to the microwave region of the spectrum. The frequencies and intensities of electromagnetic energy that a specific computer monitor emits depends on its internal design — the circuitry, placement of components, and shielding.

The ELF emissions associated with electrically powered devices and power distribution facilities had always been assumed to be too weak to pose any health risk. Then, in 1979, a landmark study of Colorado schoolchildren found that those who lived near a power line had two to three times as great a chance of developing cancer. This correlation seemed so unlikely that power companies paid to have the study repeated. It was expected that the results would be negative. Surprisingly, the second study supported the findings of the original work (Bates 1991; Savitz 1986, 1987; Wertheimer and Leeper 1979, 1982).

Many more studies have been conducted since. A recent large-scale study by Thériault et al. (1994) examined the incidence of cancer among 223,000 male electric utility workers in France and Canada in relation to their estimated lifetime occupational exposure to ELF electromagnetic fields. A significant association was found between their cumulative exposure to ELF magnetic fields and certain types of leukemia. The study also illustrated the tremendous difficulties in obtaining reliable information on long-term exposure and the sophisticated statistical interpretation required to wrestle with the many confounding factors that could bias this type of research.

The public is increasingly aware of and concerned about the health risks of ELF electromagnetic fields. The issue has been dramatically portrayed by the media and in such books as *Currents of Death: Power Lines, Computer Terminals, and the Attempt to Cover Up Their Threat to Your Health* by Paul Brodeur (1989). In reviewing the scientific and political controversy surrounding the health effects of ELF electromagnetic fields, Brodeur asserted that power utilities and other vested interests were obstructing scientific inquiry and the dissemination of information.

Power utilities, equipment manufacturers, employers, and employees all have high stakes in this issue. With both public concern and the potential costs so high, any research on the subject receives intense political as well as scientific scrutiny. Work that is funded by organizations with vested interests is viewed with considerable suspicion.

There is also a political dimension to the scientific inquiry itself. Scientists and practitioners often contest the validity of methods used by researchers in disciplines other than their own. Physics, engineering, medical research, and epidemiology encompass different, though overlapping, knowledge areas. As a result, they each address this issue from inherently different perspectives.

The core principles of a scientific discipline, its laws and theories, define a particular perspective on the way the natural world is expected to behave. Scientists' points of view are invariably influenced by that of the discipline in which they were trained. What researchers expect to find determines how they will design their research and, to a large extent, the kind of answers they are likely to uncover. It is as true in scientific research as it is in other human endeavors.

This difference in perspective is of more than academic interest. Scientific debate is frequently colored by the disdain with which some practitioners view the methods of other disciplines. See, for example, the highly charged editorial by George Moore in the journal *Cancer,* questioning not only the research on electromagnetic fields and human health but also the value of epidemiological methods in general, the response by Richard Stevens and David Savitz, and Moore's rebuttal (Moore 1991, 1992; Stevens and Savitz 1992).

Biological Effects of ELF Electromagnetic Fields

Electromagnetic fields are comprised of two components — an electric field and a magnetic field. ELF sources, such as electrical power supplies, can induce very small electric and magnetic energy fields close by. But there is an important difference between the two types of fields. Electric fields are easily shielded by conducting materials such as a building, a wall, or a person. Magnetic fields, however, pass through most materials. For this reason, it has been assumed that the magnetic component is more likely to pose a health risk, and research has focused on the biological effects of weak magnetic fields.

Much of the controversy surrounding electromagnetic energy and human health arises from differences in the assumptions made about the mechanism by which they could affect living organisms. Initially, most research was based on the assumption that if ELF electromagnetic fields were a health hazard, they would have a **toxic effect.** That is, at some dosage, a particular type of electromagnetic energy would cause illness, and higher intensities would increase the incidence and severity of illness. This classic dose-response relationship is observed for toxic substances like lead and cyanide that are foreign to living organisms. Experiments to test the toxicity hypothesis tended to focus on the effects of high dosage, with little regard for subtle differences in signal characteristics such as modulation and frequency.

But electromagnetic fields are not foreign to biological systems. Living organisms are in fact complex electrochemical systems that depend on electromagnetic energy for critical communication and control processes. Nerve function, cellular communication, protein synthesis, and the release of hormones are mediated by very weak electromagnetic signals that trigger biochemical processes (Frey 1993).

Living organisms demonstrate highly evolved adaptations to electromagnetic energy. For example, the visual system is exquisitely adapted to the portion of the electromagnetic spectrum termed "visible light." The eye and skin possess filtering systems for protection against the harmful effects of ultraviolet radiation. Weak magnetic fields on the order of 500 milligauss, about that of the earth's magnetic field, can be sensed by organisms as primitive as bacteria and as complex as marine mammals. (The gauss is a unit of measurement for magnetic field strength. A milligauss (mG) is one-thousandth of a gauss.)

Living organisms evolved in the presence of the earth's weak magnetic field. The earth's magnetic field is effectively static and has a field strength of 200–700 milligauss depending on geographic latitude (Reiter 1992). Industrialized societies are today immersed in a complex mixture of man-made electromagnetic energy emanating from power lines and the myriad electrical appliances and items of communication equipment upon which our way of life depends. It is a far more complex electromagnetic environment than the one in which organisms, including humans, evolved.

Instead of a toxic effect, some of these recently introduced forms of electromagnetic energy may be producing an **interference effect,** whereby disturbance of a biochemical process depends not only on the intensity of a field but also on its frequency, modulation, and other subtle characteristics. A useful analogy is that of a radio. The electronic circuits of a radio produce sound by selectively responding to electromagnetic energy (in this case, radio waves) that have specific characteristics — a particular frequency and modulation. The radio waves detected are very weak and exist in the presence of those produced by other radio stations. A radio is designed to be sensitive only to signals that are at the frequency to which it is tuned and that have a specific type of modulation (e.g., 800 kilohertz on the AM [amplitude modulation] band). The presence of other signals, even much stronger ones, does not disrupt reception unless they have characteristics very similar to the signal to which the system (in this case, the radio) is tuned. But radio reception is easily disrupted by a very weak signal if the signal has the same characteristics as the one to which the radio is tuned (e.g., a signal of the same frequency and modulation).

In a similar way, very weak electromagnetic fields with the specific characteristics to which biological systems respond may interact with electrochemical processes in living organisms. They could alter critical cell functions — speeding them up, slowing them down, or changing their nature. In recent years, this line of research has produced fruitful results (Frey 1993).

WEAK ELECTROMAGNETIC FIELDS AND HUMAN HEALTH

The weak magnetic fields associated with electrical power are on the order of 10 to 100 times less intense than the earth's magnetic field. Background magnetic fields in homes are about 1-30 millegauss (Kaune et al. 1987). However, these magnetic fields are fundamentally different: those associated with electrical power are alternating fields, whereas the earth's magnetic field is static.

Alternating magnetic fields have been shown to produce different biological effects than static ones of the same intensity. For example, production of the hormone *melatonin* is suppressed by a weak alternating magnetic field but is unaffected by a static magnetic field of the same intensity (Lerchl et al. 1991; Liburdy et al. 1993; Richardson et al. 1993). Many of the demonstrated biological effects of weak electromagnetic fields are related to their influence on the production and release of melatonin by the pineal gland (discussed in the following subsection).

Weak alternating electromagnetic fields have been shown to affect cancer growth, nerve function, cell signaling, pineal gland function, and the immune system. Many of these effects are interrelated. For example, the disruption of communication between transformed cells and normal cells is involved in the rate of cancer growth. In some cases, electromagnetic fields accelerate but do not initiate a process. For example, they have been shown to significantly enhance the effect of a chemical tumor promoter in stimulating the growth of cancer cells, even though the tumor growth was not accelerated in the presence of the electromagnetic fields alone (Frey 1993).

Low-intensity pulsed electromagnetic fields have been shown to increase the rate of bone formation and to affect neural function, development, and repair. In fact, weak electric fields have been used to promote nerve repair and the healing of bone (Frey 1993).

THE PINEAL GLAND AND MELATONIN

The **pineal gland** is an endocrine organ near the center of the brain. **Melatonin,** the chief hormone it produces, is involved in a number of important physiological processes, including day-night activity rhythms and immune response.

In humans, the level of melatonin in the bloodstream is low during the day. Visible light sensed by the eyes inhibits its production. At night, melatonin levels in the pineal gland and bloodstream begin to increase shortly after the onset of darkness, reaching a concentration about ten times that of daytime levels. Exposure to light during the normal dark cycle causes a precipitous drop in melatonin (Wilson, Stevens, and Anderson 1989).

Disturbance of the normal cyclic variation in melatonin levels causes subtle changes that can disrupt a person's biological clock, producing a "jet-lag" kind of fatigue, mood disturbances such as depression, endocrine and reproductive malfunctions, and immunodeficiency (Reiter 1992; Wilson, Stevens, and Anderson 1989).

ELF electromagnetic fields, such as those associated with 50 hertz and 60 hertz alternating current used in Europe and North America for power distribution, have been shown to disrupt pineal melatonin production (Wilson, Stevens, and Anderson 1989; Wilson et al. 1990). There is evidence that certain ultraviolet wavelengths produce this disruptive effect as well (Reiter 1992).

Melatonin has important inhibiting properties against leukemia, breast cancer, prostate cancer, and melanoma (Frey 1993). Epidemiological studies have associated these cancers with weak electromagnetic fields. Laboratory studies conducted on breast cancer cells found that ELF magnetic fields acted at the cellular level to enhance the rate of cancer proliferation by blocking the natural cancer-inhibiting action of melatonin. A 60 hertz magnetic field of 11.95 milligauss has been shown to block melatonin's ability to inhibit the growth of breast cancer cells, whereas a weaker magnetic field of 2.53 milligauss did not block its cancer-inhibiting action. This suggests that there is a threshold level between these two field strengths at which the action of melatonin is blocked. Since the experiment was conducted in cultured cells, not in living organisms, the reduction of melatonin's cancer-fighting action was not simply the result of suppressed melatonin production by the pineal gland. It suggests there is a direct interaction at the cellular level between ELF magnetic fields, breast cancer cells, and melatonin (Liburdy et al. 1993).

A number of biological mechanisms have been proposed to explain how ELF magnetic fields could affect the cell surface and subsequent gene expression events such as DNA synthesis and cell proliferation. Jacobson (1992, 1991) has proposed a mechanism to explain the physics by which weak magnetic fields may affect protein synthesis and the transmission of genetic information at the cellular level.

Further evidence that weak alternating ELF magnetic fields produce significant biological effects in humans is provided by positive results from research into their therapeutic uses. Weak alternating ELF magnetic fields have been used experimentally in the treatment of Parkinson's disease, epilepsy, and multiple sclerosis (Sandyk and Anninos 1992; Sandyk 1992, 1993).

There is considerable evidence that disturbing the daily rise and fall of melatonin can have significant effects on health and that it may increase the risk of serious illnesses such as cancer. The risk to human health posed by weak ELF electromagnetic fields remains controversial. However, the burden of evidence now clearly indicates that they have biological effects on immune response processes known to inhibit the growth of cancer cells.

Uncertainties about which exposure factors to measure and the crudeness of those measures would tend to mask any health effects that were present. It is perhaps remarkable that some studies detected a significant risk at all. For this reason, if a causal relationship is eventually proved, the true risk factors will likely be appreciably higher than those reported in the recent research.

Health Risks of VDTs

Some early studies on the health risks of VDTs found an increased incidence of miscarriage among VDT operators (e.g., Goldhaber, Polen, and Hiatt 1988), whereas others did not find a significant association (e.g., Bryant and Love 1989). Nonetheless, many organizations now offer women the option of being reassigned to non-VDT jobs during their pregnancies. If an association between VDT use and miscarriage does exist, it may be that factors other than exposure to electromagnetic fields are involved. For example, VDT operators may experience greater work-related stress and are more sedentary, both of which are factors that could make a pregnancy more difficult.

Research by the Finnish Institute of Occupational Health (Lindbohm et al. 1992) suggests why some studies of VDT use have found a significant association with miscarriages but others have not. Their study looked at 585 pregnant women who performed clerical work on VDTs in offices throughout Finland from 1975 to 1985. Of those, 191 suffered miscarriages and 394 had live births. The intensity of the ELF magnetic field was measured for each of the 23 types of VDTs used. The VDTs were then divided into three groups — low-ELF (less than 4 milligauss), moderate-ELF (4–9 milligauss), and high-ELF (more than 9 milligauss).

When all the subjects were considered together, there was no significant correlation between hours of VDT work and miscarriage risk. However, when the data were grouped according to the intensity of ELF emissions from their monitors, the subjects who used VDTs with high-ELF emissions showed a statistically significant higher rate of miscarriages — 3.5 times that of the low-emission group. The high-emission monitors were older models. All the VDTs of recent manufacture have emissions less than 9 milligauss.

The study showed clearly that when VDT use was assessed without evaluating the ELF magnetic field produced by the monitor, negative results could be obtained when in fact a positive association existed. Studies of VDTs and miscarriages generally have not measured the magnetic fields produced by the VDTs that the subjects used. This may explain why many of those studies did not find significant associations.

There is not yet sufficient information to definitively set a minimum safe level for ELF magnetic field exposure. However, the Swedish Board for Measurement and Testing (usually abbreviated *MPR*, its initials in Swedish) established a standard for evaluating electromagnetic emissions from equipment, including computer monitors. The original standard is called MPR. MPR II is a more recent version of the standard covering a wider range of frequencies. Those monitors that meet the MPR II emission standards have ELF magnetic fields less than 2.5 milligauss, well below the level for which miscarriage risks were reported in the Finnish study. The MPR II emission guidelines have been widely accepted, and for consumers in North America, they have become the *de facto* standard for a monitor to be considered low-emission.

A third standard was developed by the TCO, the Swedish office workers' union. It includes many of the elements in MPR II and sets more stringent limits on levels of ELF emissions. It requires that emissions be measured closer to the screen where the fields are stronger and specifies energy conservation requirements such as software that shuts down the display when it is not in use.

Increased production and competition among manufacturers, as a result of the burgeoning demand for low-emission MPR II–compliant VDTs, have led to substantially reduced prices. However, low-emission monitors are still about double the price of standard monitors with comparable features.

There are no guidelines for the spacing of VDT units. In high-density office layouts, people may be seated immediately next to the VDT of an adjacent work setting. Electromagnetic emissions are higher to the back and sides of a VDT than in front of the screen. Office walls and the acoustic panels used in open plan layouts afford little or no shielding from the magnetic component of electromagnetic fields. Some experts advise seating people no closer than 90 centimeters (3 feet) from the sides and back of a VDT, a standard that the World Health Organization has adopted.

A growing body of evidence indicates that weak ELF electromagnetic fields have significant biological effects and can adversely affect human health. However, the ELF magnetic fields produced by VDTs, particularly low-radiation monitors that comply with the Swedish MPR II specification, are on the order of one-tenth to one-hundredth the level of exposure to the same types of fields produced by common household electrical appliances. They can produce magnetic field strengths on the order of 100 milligauss and are devices that also may be used for long periods of time close to the body. Based on our current knowledge, it appears that if weak ELF electromagnetic fields are found to cause health problems, it will be devices other than VDTs that will pose the greatest risk.

VDT-RELATED LEGISLATION AND LIABILITY

No state in the United States or province of Canada has enacted comprehensive safety standards for VDT use. Some local American governments attempted to establish laws, but all have been defeated.

In 1988, Suffolk County, New York,

established requirements for VDT installations including performance requirements for workstations and chairs, and mandatory provision of antiglare screens. The legislation also specified the frequency and duration of work breaks for VDT operators to reduce the risk of CTDs. Businesses were slated to pay 80% of the cost for employees' annual eye exams and eyeglass purchases and to provide educational programs on VDT safety. The law would have affected the users of 12,000 VDT terminals at 170 firms in the eastern portion of Long Island. However, the law was invalidated in a 1989 action backed by computer manufacturers. It was overturned largely on the grounds that workplace regulations are the domain of the state and federal levels of government, not the county.

In 1989, Maine passed a law that has stood but is fairly innocuous. It requires employers with more than 25 terminals to provide their computer users with annual safety training to minimize VDT-related health risks.

In January 1991, a San Francisco ordinance went into effect that imposed stiff regulations on VDT use in the workplace. That law required companies with more than 15 employees to provide adjustable chairs with armrests, wrist rests, and footrests if requested by workers who spend more than half their time operating VDTs. As well, VDTs were required to have detachable keyboards and be free of glare problems, and operators were to have a 15-minute break from keyboard work every two hours. This ordinance was overturned a year later on similar grounds as the Suffolk County legislation.

Although stringent VDT laws have been overturned in court, the problems that prompted them have not disappeared. Other legislative and regulatory efforts are under way, and a number of state and federal agencies are preparing recommendations. For instance, California is developing statewide ergonomic regulations that would apply to VDT operators. At the federal level, OSHA is writing general ergonomic regulations that would apply to both offices and industrial workplaces. In Canada, the federal government has defined standards for ergonomic furniture. The International Standards Organization is producing a VDT standard that the European Community is expected to adopt as a basis for standardization among its member nations. There are indications that these organizations will harmonize their efforts, building on each other's recommendations.

Employees suffering from VDT-related injuries have joined with their unions to launch liability suits against computer hardware manufacturers, distributors, and resellers. Compensation is sought on the grounds that suppliers were negligent in having designed equipment that would foreseeably cause injury. In New York State alone, more than 44 product liability suits were filed against computer manufacturers (Betts 1992).

Workers' compensation statutes generally render employers immune from workplace liability. However, this immunity does not apply if the employer endangers workers through negligence, malicious conduct, or fraudulent concealment of injury — all of which are difficult to prove. One case in which the employer was found at fault was the asbestos-poisoning liability suit against Johns-Manville Corporation. Prosecutors presented incriminating memos that proved the employer knew that workers were being exposed to hazardous materials (Rauber 1991).

There is still uncertainty about the health effects that VDTs may present. As a result, it is difficult to establish that an employer knowingly exposed workers to hazardous conditions simply by having them work at VDTs. Failing to mitigate VDT risks may then be considered unintentional, thereby preserving the employer's immunity from liability suits. But if the evidence for VDT health risks increases, then at some point, a failure to mitigate those risks will be seen as negligence and the employer might face a liability suit (Owen 1994).

There are already cases in which employers have been fined by regulatory agencies for inadequately addressing occupational injuries related to VDT use, as noted previously in the discussion of cumulative trauma disorder.

The advent of the Americans with Disabilities Act of 1990 may also make it more difficult for employers in the United States to ignore VDT-related health risks, especially those that involve cumulative trauma disorders. The act prohibits employers from discriminating against the disabled in hiring or firing and includes CTDs in its broad definition of disability. This law will make it much more difficult to fire employees with long-term CTD disabilities even if they become unable to use a keyboard. The act also requires employers to make reasonable accommodations for the physical and mental limitations of otherwise qualified employees. This was the case with some newspaper employees who developed serious CTDs and were given voice-activated computers or assigned typists in order to accommodate their disabilities (Betts 1991).

Computer-related illness is a major concern of the office workforce. The increased awareness of VDT risks has led workers to organize. The VDT Coalition, a group of unions and individuals concerned about the health and safety of VDT operators, was formed in 1978. The coalition keeps members apprised of current research, lobbys government, and sponsors courses and information sessions not only on VDT issues but also on strategies and tactics to successfully influence public and private sector organizations (Baker, Stock, and Szudy 1992). It is an indication of the level of concern among workers and the risk to employers who choose to ignore VDT-related health issues.

The health risk of VDTs has become a prominent union concern and has prompted regulatory agencies to investigate and, if necessary, impose fines and mandatory changes in the workplace. Many public and private sector organizations have responded by purchasing low-emission VDTs and ergonomically appropriate furniture, implementing programs to prevent VDT-related injury, and offering alternative work to those who develop computer-related ailments or believe they are at risk (e.g., pregnant women). It is clear that the trend is toward more stringent regulation of the office workplace.

SUMMARY OF RECOMMENDATIONS FOR COMPUTERS IN THE OFFICE SETTING

Preventing computer-related injuries in the office involves more than supplying appropriate furniture and high-quality computer equipment. Many factors affect the overall match between individuals, their activities, and the office work environment. Eyestrain, headaches, stress, fatigue, backaches, and cumulative trauma disorders can be reduced and sometimes eliminated if chairs, work surfaces, light sources, and VDT screens are correctly positioned, work breaks are taken, and work tasks are varied. Providing employees with a well-designed computer work area requires coordination between the furniture buyer, the facilities manager, and the information systems manager. The selection of the computer equipment will influence the size and features of the work setting, which, in turn, will be affected by the space available for each workstation.

Some organizations have ergonomists on staff to monitor and improve work techniques. Key ergonomic considerations for computer workstations were discussed in this chapter and are summarized below. Beyond these guidelines, a qualified ergonomist should be consulted to resolve specific work setting deficiencies that may be reducing productivity or causing injuries.

Ergonomically Appropriate Workstations. Orthopedically correct chairs and office furniture allow employees to work in a comfortable and healthy posture. The ergonomics of the entire workstation should be reviewed periodically to ensure that the separate elements — chair, work surfaces, keyboard, footrest, palm supports, and other ergonomic aids — are correctly adjusted and properly used.

The workstation design and layout should not require awkward or difficult physical movements in order to perform work tasks. For VDT work, the workstation should be sufficiently adjustable for elbows to be at the person's side, with the lower arms at about a 90 degree angle to the upper arms. Wrists should be held straight. It is recommended that palm and wrist supports be used when the hands are resting but not when typing (Pascarelli and Quilter 1994). Knees should be at the level of the hips or slightly higher, and a footrest should be used if necessary.

Workstation elements should be positioned so the viewer's head looks downward at a comfortable angle (no more than about 15 degrees below the horizontal). The viewing distance to the screen and reference materials should be the same (to minimize refocusing) and the screen and reference materials should be placed as close together as possible (to minimize repetitive head motion).

There should be adequate space on the work surface for reference documents and other work materials to be viewed and used. Sufficient space is needed under the work surface for people to stretch their legs and shift their posture. This relieves strain on the back and gives different muscle groups a chance to rest.

These general ergonomic principles apply to all VDT workstations. However, since every person's physical characteristics are unique, other configurations may be required to meet special needs.

Appropriate Illumination. The characteristics most important for comfort and good visual performance are a suitable level of illumination, fairly uniform brightness for all objects in the visual field, the absence of rapidly changing light levels, and avoidance of glare. The optimum level and quality of light depend to some extent on the nature of the task and the vision capacity of the individual. Objects in the center of the visual field should have brightness contrasts of 3:1 or less, and the contrast between the center of view and the peripheral visual field should be 10:1 or less. Excessive contrasts tend to be more troublesome at the sides than at the top of the visual field. Large surface areas in the visual field, such as work surfaces, should have neutral colors, matte finishes, and a reflectance of about 30%.

Room lighting for VDT work areas should provide an even shadowless illumination between 300 to 500 lux. No light source should be directly visible within the operator's field of view and overhead light sources should be shielded. Task lamps should be provided where higher light levels are needed for paper-based work.

Antiglare Screens. Any filter placed in front of the screen will degrade the sharpness of the image to some extent. It is better to provide background lighting that does not produce screen glare, thereby eliminating the need for antiglare filters. Where reflected glare is a problem, antiglare filters should be provided. Filters made of glass degrade the image less than mesh designs.

Radiation Shielding. Current research suggests that monitors with emissions low enough to satisfy the Swedish MPR II standard are not associated with radiation health problems (Lindbohm et al. 1992). Although there are no standards for seating distances, several organizations specify that people sit no closer than 90 centimeters (3 feet) to the back or sides of a VDT.

Noise and Clutter. Computer equipment and peripherals can generate distracting and stress-producing noise. Inadequate space to accommodate the various components makes workstations cramped and inefficient. Areas must be large enough that there is sufficient work surface, leg room, and storage space after the equipment has been installed. Wiring should be secured out of the way and not left to trip the unwary. For this reason, it may be necessary to modify space and furniture standards, allowing floor area assignments and furniture expense to be determined more by the requirements of the task than by the status of the position.

Thermal Comfort. Computers and other equipment in the automated office can add substantially to the heat load. Office ventilation systems must have sufficient capacity to maintain a comfortable work environment given the maximum amount of people and equipment that might be accommodated and under adverse climatic conditions.

Indoor Air Quality. Symptoms such as runny eyes, headaches, or sore throats may indicate the presence of an indoor air quality problem. Although the causes may not appear to be directly related to computers in the office, their possible contribution should be examined.

Accommodating Physiques outside the Design Norms. People whose physiques are outside office furniture design norms are more likely to experience discomfort and injuries caused by an ergonomically poor fit of the work setting to their needs. Many people are taller, shorter, larger, or smaller than the range of body sizes for which most office furnishings are optimized. Despite the flexibility of today's office furniture, very small and very large people are at an ergonomic disadvantage. When too many factors stress the body at the same time, the individual is more likely to experience difficulty. Multiple minor stressors can together create a significant physical problem, even though separately they would be tolerable.

Work Techniques. Much can be done to alleviate the ill effects of VDT use by changing work techniques. There are often alternative ways to perform the same task, one of which is physically much easier than the others. By understanding why certain movements cause strain, VDT users are better able to prevent injuries.

Regular Work Breaks. Data-entry clerks and other full-time computer operators should be encouraged to take a ten-minute break from typing at least every hour. Rest breaks, along with some simple stretching exercises, help reduce muscle fatigue, eye fatigue, and the risk of cumulative trauma disorders. Exercises designed specifically for VDT operators may also be beneficial (see, for example, Lee et al. 1992; Pacarelli and Quilter 1994).

Work Design. Wherever possible, the work process should be designed so that VDT users periodically do nonkeyboard tasks to relieve the repetitive motions of VDT work and the associated physical stress. Psychological stress has also been shown to contribute to VDT-related illnesses. Tight deadlines, heavy workloads, and electronic monitoring can be sources of employee stress and a drain on productivity.

Training. User training is the key to benefiting from ergonomically superior furniture and equipment, more varied job content, and greater operator discretion over task scheduling. Most computer users are never shown how to adjust their work settings and correctly position their equipment. It is imperative that all employees be shown appropriate working postures that minimize fatigue. They also need to be aware of the early symptoms of work-related illnesses such as cumulative trauma disorders and be encouraged to seek prompt medical attention.

User Awareness. Individuals need to be alert to those work techniques that cause fatigue or discomfort so they may stop and correct problematic situations. Everyone's body is physically unique and functions somewhat differently. People with long fingers or large hands may easily press some key combinations that are a difficult stretch for those with smaller hands. In a cluttered work space, people tend to endure an awkward posture for a short time rather than cleanup the area. But it is surprising how easily a "short time" can extend to an hour or more. Once muscles have become fatigued by an awkward posture, they are less able to support normal work activities. Being aware of the risks encourages the development of better work habits. Individuals must play an active role to ensure that their work assignments, job design, and physical work setting are ergonomically appropriate and that they are used in a proper manner.

LITERATURE CITED

Andersson, B. J. G., and R. Ortengren. 1974. Lumbar disc pressure and myoelectric back muscle activity during sitting. 1. Studies on an office chair. *Scandinavian Journal of Rehabilitation Medicine* 3:104-135.

AOA. 1987. *Vision and lifestyles.* St. Louis, Miss.: American Optometric Association.

AOA. 1992. *VDT user's guide to better vision.* St. Louis, Miss.: American Optometric Association.

Armstrong, T. J. 1983. *An ergonomics guide to carpal tunnel syndrome.* Akron, Ohio: American Industrial Hygiene Association.

Baker, R., L. Stock, and B. Szudy. 1992. Hardware to hard hats: Training workers for action. *American Journal of Industrial Medicine* 22(5):691–701.

Bates, M. N. 1991. Extremely low frequency electromagnetic fields and cancer: The epidemiologic evidence. *Environmental Health Perspectives* 95:147–156.

Betts, M. 1991. Ergonomic experts say IS should be part of the team fighting repetitive strain injuries. *Computerworld,* September 21.

Betts, M. 1992. Keyboard injuries provoke lawsuits. *Computerworld,* June 15.

Brodeur, P. 1989. *Currents of death: Power lines, computer terminals, and the attempt to cover up their threat to your health.* New York: Simon & Schuster.

Browne, C. D., B. M. Nolan, and D. K. Faithfull. 1984. Occupational repetition strain injuries. *Medical Journal of Australia* 140:320–332.

Bryant, H. E., and E. J. Love. 1989. Video display terminal use and spontaneous abortion risk. *International Journal of Epidemiology* 18:132–138.

Dirks, G. 1993. Liability issues and facility management: Clearing up some of the issues. IFMA and Steelcase broadcast. November 2.

Donkin, S. W. 1987. *Sitting on the job.* Boston: Houghton Mifflin.

Dowell, B. 1994. Personal communication. Zeeland, Mich.: Herman Miller Research & Design.

Frey, A. 1993. Electromagnetic field interactions with biological systems. *The FASEB Journal* 7:272–281.

Gerr, F., R. Letz, and P. Landrigan. 1991. Upper-extremity musculoskeletal disorders of occupational origin. *Annual Review of Public Health* 12:543–566.

Goldhaber, M. K., M. R. Polen, and R. A. Hiatt. 1988. The risk of miscarriage and birth defects among women who use visual display terminals during pregnancy. *American Journal of Industrial Medicine* 13:695–706.

Grandjean, E. 1987. *Ergonomics in computerized offices.* London: Taylor & Francis.

Grandjean, E., W. Hünting, and M. Pidermann. 1983. VDT workstation design: preferred settings and their effects. *Human Factors* 25:161–175.

Guidotti, T. L. 1992. Occupational repetitive strain injury. *American Family Physician* 45(2):585–592.

Harris, L. 1991. *The office environment index 1991: Summary of worldwide findings.* A study conducted for Steelcase by Louis Harris and Associates, New York.

Herman Miller, Inc. 1991. *Work chair handbook.* Zeeland, Mich.: Herman Miller, Inc.

Hill, S. G., and K. H. E. Kroemer. 1986. Preferred declination of the line-of-sight. *Human Factors* 28(2):127–134.

Hopkins, A. 1990. Stress, the quality of work life, and repetition strain injury in Australia. *Work and Stress* 4(2):129–138.

Jacobson, J. I. 1991. A look at the possible mechanism and potential of magneto therapy. *Journal of Theoretical Biology* 149:97-119.

Jacobson, J. I. 1992. Exploring the potential of magneto-recrystallization of genes and associated structures with respect to nerve regeneration and cancer. *International Journal of Neuroscience* 64:153–165.

Kaplan, A., and S. Aronoff. 1989. Lighting assessment, St. John's Taxation Centre. Internal report for Revenue Canada Taxation.

Kaune, W. T., R. G. Stevens, N. J. Callahan, R. K. Severson, and D. B. Thomas. 1987. Residential magnetic and electric fields. *Bioelectromagnetics* 8:315–335.

Kiesler, S., and T. Finholt. 1988. The mystery of RSI. *American Psychologist* 43(12):1004–1015.

Lee, K., N. Swanson, S. Sauter, R. Wickstrom, A. Waiker, and M. Magnum. 1992. A review of physical exercises recommended for VDT operators. *Applied Ergonomics* 23(6):387–408.

LeGrande, D. 1993. Personal communication. Coordinator, Occupational Safety and Health. Communication Workers of America, Washington, D.C.

Lerchl, A., K. O. Honaka, and R. J. Reiter. 1991. Pineal gland "magnetosensitivity" to static magnetic fields is a consequence of induced electric currents (eddy currents). *Journal of Pineal Research* 10:109-116.

Liburdy, R. P., T. R. Sloma, R. Sokolic, and P. Yaswen. 1993. ELF magnetic fields, breast cancer, and melatonin: 60 Hz fields block melatonin's oncostatic action on ER+ breast cancer cell proliferation. *Journal of Pineal Research* 14:89–97.

Lindbohm, M., M. Hietanen, P. Kyyronen, M. Sallmen, P. von Nandelstadh, H. Taskinen, M. Pekkarinen, M. Ylikoski, and K. Hemminki. 1992. Magnetic fields of video display terminals and spontaneous abortion. *American Journal of Epidemiology* 136(9):1041–1051.

Mandal, A. C. 1981. The seated man (*homo sedens*). The seated work position. Theory and practice. *Applied Ergonomics* 12(1):19–26.

Mascola, J. R., and L. S. Rickman. 1991. Infectious causes of carpal tunnel syndrome: Case report and review. *Review of Infectious Diseases* 13(5):911–917.

Moore, G. E. 1991. The emperor's magnetic clothes. *Cancer* 68(3):455–457.

Moore, G. E. 1992. Reply to Stevens and Savitz. *Cancer* 69(2):606–607.

NIOSH. 1990. Hazard evaluation and technical assistance report: Newsday, Inc. Report HHE 89-250-2046. National Institute for Occupational Safety and Health. Washington, D.C.: Department of Health and Human Services.

NIOSH. 1992. Health Hazard Report: U.S. West Communications. Report HETA 89-299-2230. National Institute for Occupational Safety and Health. Washington, D.C.: Department of Health and Human Services.

NIOSH. 1993. Health Hazard Report. Los Angeles Times. Report HETA 90-013-2277. National Institute for Occupational Safety and Health. Washington, D.C.: Department of Health and Human Services.

Owen, R. D. 1994. Carpal tunnel syndrome: A products liability prospective. *Ergonomics* 37(3):449–476.

Pascarelli, E. F., and J. J. Kella. 1993. Soft-tissue injuries related to use of the computer keyboard. *Journal of Occupational Medicine* 35(5):522–532.

Pascarelli, E. F., and D. Quilter. 1994. *Repetitive strain injury: a computer user's guide.* New York: John Wiley & Sons.

Patkin, M. 1990. Neck and arm pain in office workers: Causes and management. In *Promoting health and productivity in the computerized office,* edited by S. L. Sauter, M. J. Dainoff, and M. J. Smith. London: Taylor & Francis.

Quintner, J. 1991. The RSI syndrome in historical perspective. *International Disability Studies* 13(3):99–104.

Rauber, P. 1991. New life for white death. *Sierra,* September–October, 63–65, 104, 105, 110, 111.

Reid, J., C. Ewan, and E. Lowy. 1991. Pilgrimage of pain: The illness experiences of women with repetition strain injury and the search for credibility. *Social Science and Medicine* 32(5):601–612.

Reiter, R. J. 1992. Alterations of the circadian melatonin rhythm by the electromagnetic spectrum: a study in environmental toxicology. *Regulatory Toxicology and Pharmacology* 15:226–244.

Richardson, B. A., K. Yaga, R. J. Reiter, and P. Hoover. 1993. Suppression of nocturnal pineal *N*-Acetyltransferase activity and melatonin content by inverted magnetic fields and induced eddy currents. *International Journal of Neuroscience* 69:149–155.

Roel, R. E. 1990. Cause of typing injuries unclear. *Newsday,* January 26, 43.

Rossignol, A. M., E. P. Morse, M. S. Summers, and L. D. Pagnotto. 1987. Video display terminal use and reported health symptoms among Massachusetts clerical workers. *Journal of Occupational Medicine* 29:112–118.

Sandyk, R. 1992. Successful treatment of multiple sclerosis with magnetic fields. *International Journal of Neuroscience* 66:237–250.

Sandyk, R., and P. A. Anninos. 1992. Attenuation of epilepsy with application of external magnetic fields: A case report. *International Journal of Neuroscience* 66:75–85.

Sandyk, R. 1993. Weak magnetic fields antagonize the effects of melatonin on blood glucose levels in Parkinson's disease. *International Journal of Neuroscience* 68:85–91.

Savitz, D. A. 1986. Human health effects of extremely low frequency electromagnetic fields: Critical review of clinical and epidemiological studies. *Proceedings of the IEEE Power Engineering Society 1986 Winter Meeting.* New York: Institute of Electrical and Electronics Engineers.

Savitz, D. A. 1987. Case control study of childhood cancer and residential exposure to electric and magnetic fields. Final report. New York State Power Lines Project. Wadsworth Center for Laboratories and Research, Albany, N.Y.

Schleifer, L., S. Sauter, R. Smith, and S. Knutson. 1990. Ergonomic predictors of visual system complaints in VDT entry work. *Behaviour and Information Technology* 9(4):273–282.

Sheedy, J. E. 1992. Vision problems at video display terminals: A survey of optometrists. *Journal of the American Optometric Association* 63(10):687–692.

Sheedy, J. E., and S. D. Parsons. 1990. Vision and the video display terminal: Clinical findings. In *Promoting health and productivity in the computerized office,* edited by S. L. Sauter, M. J. Dainoff, and M. J. Smith. London: Taylor & Francis.

Silverstein, B. A., L. J. Fine, and T. J. Armstrong. 1987. Occupational factors and carpal tunnel syndrome. *American Journal of Industrial Medicine* 11:343–358.

Smith, M. J., B. G. Cohen, and L. W. Stammerjohn Jr. 1981. An investigation of health complaints and job stress in video display operations. *Human Factors* 23(4):387–400.

Stellman, J., S. Klitzman, G. C. Gordon, and B. R. Snow. 1987. Work environment and the well-being of clerical and VDT workers. *Journal of Occupational Behavior* 8:95–114.

Stephens, R. 1993. Personal communication. Director, Office of Ergonomic Support. Washington, D.C.: Occupational Safety and Health Administration.

Stevens, R. G., and D. A. Savitz. 1992. Is electromagnetic fields and cancer an issue worthy of study? *Cancer* 69(2):603–606.

Stewart, T. 1985. Ergonomics of the office. *Ergonomics* 28(8):1165–1177.

Stock, S. R. 1991. Workplace ergonomic factors and the development of musculoskeletal disorders of the neck and upper limbs: A meta-analysis. *American Journal of Industrial Medicine* 19:87–107.

Thériault, G., M. Goldberg, A. B. Miller, B. Armstrong, P. Guénel, J. Deadman, E. Imbernon, T. To, A. Chevalier, D. Cyr, and C. Wall. 1994. Cancer risks associated with occupational exposure to magnetic fields among electric utility workers in Ontario and Quebec, Canada, and France: 1970–1989. *American Journal of Epidemiology* 139(6):550–572.

U.S. Bureau of Labor Statistics. 1990. Survey of occupational injuries and illnesses, 1977–1989. Washington, D.C.: U.S. Department of Labor.

U.S. Bureau of Labor Statistics. 1992. Occupational injuries and illnesses in the United States by industry, 1990. Bulletin 2399. Washington, D.C.: U.S. Department of Labor.

Webster, B., and S. H. Snook. 1994. The cost of compensable upper extremity cumulative trauma disorders. *Journal of Occupational Medicine* 36(7):713–717.

Weiss, A. P., and E. Akelman. 1992. Carpal tunnel syndrome: A review. *Rhode Island Journal of Medicine* 75(6):303–306.

Wertheimer, N., and E. Leeper. 1979. Electrical wiring configuration and childhood cancer. *American Journal of Epidemiology* 109:345–355.

Wertheimer, N., and E. Leeper. 1982. Adult cancer related to electrical wires near the home. *International Journal of Epidemiology* 11(4):345–355.

Westin, A. F. 1992. Two key factors that belong in a macroergonomic analysis of electronic monitoring. *Applied Ergonomics* 23(1):35–42.

Wilson, B. W., R. G. Stevens, and L. E. Anderson. 1989. Neuroendocrine mediated effects of electromagnetic-field exposure: Possible role of the pineal gland. *Life Sciences* 45:1319–1332.

Wilson, B. W., C. W. Wright, J. E. Morris, R. L. Buschbom, D. P. Brown, D. L. Miller, R. Sommers-Flannigan, and L. E. Anderson. 1990. Evidence for an effect of ELF electromagnetic fields on human pineal gland function. *Journal of Pineal Research* 9:259–269.

Chapter 7

PSYCHOSOCIAL FACTORS AND INDIVIDUAL ENVIRONMENTAL CONTROL

An organization's ability to adapt and compete in a rapidly changing business environment depends on the commitment and drive of its workforce. Employees committed to their organization and motivated to promote its success are a valuable source of ideas and a potent force in implementing change. No one understands the intricacies of a job better than those who do it. Encouraging people to apply that knowledge, to find better ways of structuring the job and the organization itself, can reap rich rewards — for the organization and individuals alike. Efforts to reengineer an organization to improve performance depend on eliciting the support and participation of its people.

Organizational management has shifted dramatically from traditional "command and control" orientations to approaches that focus on building employee commitment and motivation. Management experts like Peter Drucker have promoted the delegation of authority and responsibility as a means of fostering employee initiative and creativity. Today, these qualities are seen as the foundation of a productive organization.

People want to feel that they make a difference — that their thoughts and ingenuity, the way they do their jobs, and the ideas they contribute are important and are recognized by their employer and their peers. *In Search of Excellence* by Peters and Waterman (1984), one of the more popular books promoting this management approach, examined organizations that have benefited from a management style supportive of individual initiative, innovation, and effective teamwork. Such organizations are driven by corporate cultures that are well suited to their particular style of management and that communicate clearly their commitment to and expectations of their workforce.

A corporate culture is communicated in many ways. It is expressed in an organization's management approach — the way priorities are set and decisions are made. It is expressed in the psychosocial environment of the workplace — the way people feel and the way they interact, work together, speak to each other, and support coworkers. An organization's attitude toward its people is also expressed in a very visible manner by the design of the facilities and work settings provided for its workforce. The size of the work space, the quality of the furnishings, the degree of control over noise distraction and interruptions, thermal comfort, and access to a view outside are all indicators of an individual's rank in the organization and a recognition of his or her contribution.

A wide range of techniques have been developed to create management environments that promote individual initiative as well as effective group collaboration. Central to them all is a recognition that for organizations to build lasting employee loyalty, they must demonstrate a continuing commitment to their workforce — and devote considerable time, effort, and expense to doing so. The physical work setting exerts a powerful, though often subtle, influence on interpersonal relations, motivation, and productivity. As such, improving the work environment so as to better support office occupants and their work activities can complement broader management initiatives.

An organization may introduce a more open and responsive style of management to motivate its workforce and enhance performance. Managers may be encouraged to show greater concern and flexibility in dealing with individuals' personal needs. For example, it is now common to adjust work hours and work locations to accommodate family responsibilities and other personal commitments.

The more consistently such policies are applied to every aspect of the work environment, the stronger will be their effect. The physical office setting is an ever-present and visible expression of an organization's attitude toward its people. Maintaining rigid control of furnishings, office layout, and other aspects of the work space that employees use conveys a strong message of authoritarian leadership. It's difficult to believe that an organization is truly dedicated to supporting innovative efforts to enhance productivity if critical work resources such as space, equipment, and freedom from distraction cannot be changed.

People need to be able to adjust their work settings to suit the tasks they perform. Choosing how to do a job, and optimizing procedures and techniques, requires that individuals be given a measure of control not only over their time and activities but also of the physical resources needed to carry out their work. Providing individuals with controls for their physical work environment is as much a part of employee empowerment as giving them the responsibility for when and how to complete a task.

This chapter examines the way the physical workplace influences psychological and social processes within the office setting. Also discussed are the ways that people respond to perceived environmental health hazards and the factors that influence occupant behavior under such conditions. The technology now exists to offer office workers greater control of their own physical work environment. The value of providing such controls and the benefits they can produce are examined in the larger context of the corporate culture that an organization wishes to foster.

EFFECTS OF THE PHYSICAL OFFICE SETTING ON PSYCHOSOCIAL BEHAVIOR

The physical work setting exerts a strong influence on people's social and psychological behavior. People react consciously and subconsciously to their surroundings. The brightness of lights, degree of crowding, perception of odors, sensation of air movement, and diversity of colors all affect the way people feel in a space.

Office settings can promote certain behaviors and reduce the likelihood of others. The impact tends to be cumulative because physical settings affect the pattern of people's experiences over time rather than control specific events. When people who work well together are relocated far apart, the greater physical distance won't necessarily reduce their ability to collaborate, but it will increase the likelihood that over time they will spend less time together.

Although the theoretical importance of physical environments has long been acknowledged, it has received more attention since automation placed greater demands on the office facility and the people who work in them. Research on occupational stress has traditionally focused on **psychosocial factors** — the individual's psychological characteristics and perceptions and the nature of his or her social relationships.

More recently, studies from the fields of organizational psychology and environmental psychology have found that physical environmental factors such as temperature, ventilation, lighting, and work space design significantly influence employee attitudes and behavior. Job satisfaction, job turnover, comfort at work, and similar measures of employee attitude are not direct measures of health, but they are considered to be good indicators of stress-related health effects. That is, people who are more dissatisfied with their job are more likely to experience health problems (Klitzman and Stellman 1989). (See the "Human Response to Stress" and "Stress and the Work Environment" sections later in this chapter.)

Just as the work setting influences job satisfaction, the converse interaction also occurs. Job satisfaction influences occupants' perceptions of the physical work environment (see, for example, Zalesny, Farace, and Kurchner-Hawkins 1985). An extreme example of this was seen in the diagnosis of an office facility where one group of managers were dissatisfied with a diverse range of physical factors including the lighting, ventilation, and visual privacy. Yet other respondents working next to them in the open plan office rated these factors positively. Upon further analysis, it was found that this group were all in the same department and were the only managers who did not have enclosed offices. An enclosed office was perceived as higher in status than an open plan work space. The managers' exceedingly low rating of their physical office space reflected their dissatisfaction with the lack of recognition implied by their work setting more than any physical problem with the building services (Kaplan 1989).

Klitzman and Stellman (1989) found significant correlations between physical working conditions and psychological well-being. In their study, the factors most strongly associated with psychological well-being were air quality, ergonomic factors, noise, and privacy. Although physical and psychosocial working conditions are related, they found that worker assessments of the physical environment are distinct from their assessments of general working conditions such as workload, decision-making latitude, and relationships with coworkers. That is, people who reported problems with their physical environment were not simply dissatisfied employees who tended to complain about every aspect of their working conditions.

The correlation of physical and psychosocial working conditions arises because many aspects common to both spring from the same source. For example, a higher rank within an organization generally brings with it greater autonomy, more control of work methods and task scheduling, as well as higher pay. The work tends to be performed in offices with greater privacy, fewer noise distractions, comfortable furniture, and in general, more control over the physical environment. Thus, occupational status largely determines both physical and psychosocial working conditions (Becker 1981; Klitzman and Stellman 1989; Sundstrom,

Figure 7.1 Personalization of the work space is a visible expression of an individual's identity, interests, and ownership. This worker is obviously a baseball fan.

Town, Brown, Forman, and McGee 1982; Zalesny, Farace, and Kurchner-Hawkins 1985).

The Individual Within the Collective

People want to be recognized. They want to be treated as individuals — not just as nameless, faceless members of an organization. Their uniqueness and personal style contribute to their sense of identity. People at a cocktail party will look up when their names are spoken, even though they are engrossed in a different conversation. Subconsciously, they are constantly monitoring the din of background conversation, and at the first indication of acknowledgment, their conscious attention is grabbed.

Both individuals and groups benefit from a strong sense of identity. They tend to be better able to focus their efforts. People are energized when they feel part of a group with a central identity, a sense of purpose, and activities that are directed toward a common goal. The benefits of fostering individual identity include improved morale, more effective communication, a greater sense of commitment to the task and the organization, and lower staff turnover.

Workplace design, building layout, and facility regulations directly affect identity. Most people have a location where they regularly work, and one of the first things they do is personalize it (Figure 7.1). They display pictures and mementos of their friends and family, their social network. Awards and diplomas confirm their achievements. Cartoons and quotes present their point of view. The choice and arrangement of furniture, the presence of plants, and the selection of color can all be visible expressions of individual identity and ownership. Similarly, the physical setting can enhance a group's identity and promote a sense of team cohesion by physically grouping their work spaces, walkways, and shared facilities; giving their area a distinctive style of furnishings and color schemes; or by highlighting their identity with a sign.

Organizations differ in their official and unofficial tolerance of personalizing work spaces. In general, greater power is accompanied by greater freedom to personalize. Though there may be few explicit regulations, there are often strict informal rules. Violating them may be taken as an indication of a lack of professionalism, a challenge of authority, or a general lack of respect for the traditions of the organization.

There is a tendency for rules about personalizing work spaces to be more restrictive than is necessary to ensure a suitably professional appearance and for the convenient maintenance and operation of the facility. The more detailed the rules, the less judgment is needed to monitor compliance, and the less risk that subjective assessments will be seen as expressions of personal bias.

Unfortunately, such tight regulation runs counter to people's need to express their identity and ownership. Overregulation of the work setting can foster resentment and an unwillingness to cooperate with management. A more constructive approach is to minimize control over work space personalization, ensure that there is a consistent rationale for the regulations that exist, and clearly define a procedure to address complaints. There also needs to be a relatively easy way to change or eliminate regulations that have outlived their usefulness.

BOUNDARIES AND PERSONAL TERRITORY

Boundaries are features that denote territorial divisions within a space. In defining a border between spaces that differ in ownership or function, they help to control the pattern of space usage, but they can also have dramatic effects on social interactions. This dual nature of boundaries in the office can precipitate unexpected controversy when space-planning and facility management objectives conflict with human behavior.

Boundaries may be physical, such as doors, walls, and partitions; cultural, like not entering a washroom for the opposite sex; or symbolic — a change in decor that defines a reception area. The placement of screens physically defines the traffic ways within an open plan office layout. Changes in the color of screen dividers or floor coverings and well-defined passageways may also serve as symbolic boundaries. The significance of boundaries as symbolic statements often exceeds their intended function of separating spaces.

Boundaries affect the way people interact, the flow of information within an organization, the perception of status, and the exercise of power. Providing a work group with a clearly defined area can build team spirit. Boundary features are important in defining a person's territory — his or her personal space. The boundaries of a person's work space are defined by the chair and work surfaces, walls, screens, bookcases, filing cabinets, plants, and other furnishings over which they claim ownership. The amount and quality of work space that an individual controls affects his or her status. For this reason, the greater the similarity among work spaces, the more important small differences can become. Better access to a window view or a location farther from a busy corridor can become important indicators of status to those within a group, yet not recognized by others — even the facility manager. Thus, seemingly minor changes to the type of boundary and its location can generate considerable dissension as occupants attempt to defend their space.

WORK SPACE LOCATION AND VISIBILITY

The location and visibility of people's work settings directly affect whom they are likely to meet and with whom they will build working relationships and friendships. People whose work spaces are closer to each other tend to be more aware of each other's interests, more likely to share information and experiences, and more willing and able to help each other on short notice.

The location and visibility of a work space also affects the perceived power of its occupant. A work space close to the key decision-makers is assumed to be reserved for those whose opinions are highly valued by the organization. There is also more opportunity to interact with and perhaps influence them. A posh office is not always an indicator of political power. A senior executive might be given the trappings of power without having any real influence on events. It is a way to move someone out of a decision-making position without their losing face. Proximity to superiors can also be stressful when people feel their every action is closely monitored.

The space-planning process has traditionally sought to locate work groups that need to interact frequently close together. When the office work process involved the physical movement of paper documents through a sequence of processing steps, there was an efficiency gain in minimizing distances. However, when information resides on a computer instead of on paper documents the different people who work with it need not be located in the same city, let alone in adjacent work areas.

Since the work process no longer dictates physical adjacencies, some organizations have adopted the opposite approach to the placement of work groups. Since groups that must work together interact frequently anyway, work groups can be placed so as to encourage new channels of communication that might not otherwise develop within the organization. So groups that rarely work together are located in adjacent spaces in the hope that chance meetings will promote exchanges of skills and perspectives, and lead to productive collaboration and innovation.

Competing Space Demands and Accommodation Objectives

The allocation of office space must balance a number of competing demands: the minimum space required for a work activity and the space that would be optimal; the social and psychological costs of a crowded work area and the overhead expense of space; the need for the quality of a work space to suit the occupant's status versus work tasks that require more space than a person's job classification entitles them to claim.

Office accommodation is a significant expense, easily written off in good times but one of the first targets for cutbacks when money is tight. The trade-off between the size and cost of work settings is often reduced to fitting the most people into the smallest area. There is a strong financial incentive to use high-density open plan layouts. However, people in cramped quarters find it more difficult to work. They interfere with each other's activities. The overcrowding also causes psychological stress. So high work space densities can readily lower people's productivity.

As discussed in Chapters 3 and 5, savings in accommodation costs can be shortsighted (see the calculation in Table 3.3). Because of the relatively high cost of labor in industrialized nations, any savings in facility costs are readily negated by even a small loss of productivity.

The amount of space people need to feel comfortable is in part culturally determined and in part set by tradition. The minimum living and working space is much less in countries like Japan and China than in Canada and the United States. The amount of space that a North American office worker expects differs with the industry and the age of the company. People are more tolerant of constraints in young, start-up companies, especially when they have a stake in the success of the business. In established enterprises such as banks and law offices, even new recruits expect their work areas to be furnished with all the trappings of a mature and stable company. Expectation is thus an important determinant of satisfaction.

The open plan office has been controversial since its introduction some 30 years ago (as discussed in Chapter 2). Early promoters touted improved communication among workers and the greater flexibility of layouts as major benefits. But to the North American organizations that adopted open plan layouts, cost reduction was generally the most attractive advantage. Floor space could be used more efficiently if it was one large open space instead of many separate offices with immovable or difficult-to-move walls. The overall cost of accommodating an employee was less in an open plan arrangement than in enclosed offices.

Despite the glowing predictions of those who promoted the open plan arrangements, many studies have documented that occupants are generally less satisfied in an open plan office than an enclosed one. The reasons lie primarily in a real and perceived lack of environmental control. Occupants in open plan offices complain of higher noise levels, loss of privacy, increased visual distraction, lower air quality, and poorer thermal comfort (see, for example, Becker 1981; Block and Stokes 1989; Brookes 1972; Brookes and Kaplan 1972; Hedge 1982; Leaman 1992; Sundstrom, Herbert, and Brown 1982). The features of the open plan work setting that occupants find most objectionable invariably arise from a lack of control of the local environment, particularly at the individual work setting. Giving occupants of open plan offices more control of their physical environment can improve their level of satisfaction as well as their productivity.

But enclosed offices are no panacea. They would appear to offer greater acoustic and visual privacy. Occupants can close the door when they don't want to be disturbed. However, the acoustic privacy is sometimes more perceived than real. Offices commonly are not well soundproofed, and conversations can easily be overheard in adjacent rooms.

In enclosed offices, occupants generally have more freedom to arrange furnishings and adjust the lighting and temperature to suit their comfort. Here, too, the expected level of control may not be provided. For example, temperature may be controlled by a thermostat *outside* the room — an unfortunate arrangement that commonly results when an open plan office area is converted to multiple enclosed offices.

Enclosed offices tend to be allocated more floor area than open plan workspaces. In part, this may be a matter of tradition — more senior people are deemed to be entitled to additional space. The structural grid of a building imposes some restrictions on the placement of partitions. This may force an office to be larger so the partitions align with the columns. As well, for there to be enough room to open the door and move around, more space is generally needed to house a given set of furnishings in an enclosed office than in the open plan.

Commonly the mix of office activities is best accommodated by a range of work settings. The open plan and enclosed office are but two of many possibilities. Office layouts should be chosen and space allocated to optimize the facility for the activities it is to accommodate.

THE POLITICS OF SPACE

The allocation of office space, furnishings, and equipment is a politically sensitive issue. Disagreements about work space assignments easily become highly polarized "turf battles." Few aspects of organizational life can reduce otherwise calm and rational employees to enraged defenders of such apparent trivialities as an additional bit of office space or an extra chair. Such disputes may be stated in terms of practical needs when the true source of dissension typically revolves around issues of status, influence, and power. Many executives have lost their jobs after managing a reassignment of work space or coordinating a company move simply because they misread the political implications of their space allocation decisions and offended too many people (Binder 1988).

Figure 7.2 The large size of this office, the commanding view, and high-quality furnishings reflect the power and success of its occupant. (*Source:* Photo by Tony Fouhse, Ottawa.)

A work setting should be suitably equipped and of sufficient size to accommodate the activities for which it is to be used. But the size of an individual's office or of a group's work area is also perceived as an indicator of the status, authority, and power of the occupant(s). The larger the space, the more desirable the location, and the more sumptuous the appointments, the greater the power (Figure 7.2).

In subtle ways, office accommodation can influence the respect and support received from coworkers and, as a consequence, access to resources and opportunities for career advancement. Access to and control of prized work spaces can affect a person's access to people in authority. Less desirable work settings may impose inconvenient constraints. A lack of privacy makes it more difficult to have a confidential discussion. For this reason, practical considerations such as the area needed to perform a task or how frequently a work space is occupied are often overshadowed by politically motivated interests. Unfortunately, the need to display status can consume valuable facility resources — space, equipment, and funds that might otherwise support more productive work activities.

Space Standards: Providing Equity Amid Diversity

In general, conflicts over space are less likely to become serious when the overall quality of the office facility is good, occupants are given reasonable leeway in personalizing their work spaces, and the method of space allocation is perceived to be fair.

Space standards define for each job classification the amount of floor space, style of enclosure, and type and quality of furnishings and equipment to which an employee is entitled. In a recent survey of North American companies, almost 40% reported that they consistently use formal, written space standards (Figure 7.3). The other 60% grant exceptions to their standards or allocate space on a situational basis (IFMA 1994).

Space standards reinforce lines of authority — higher positions have better-quality work spaces. They legitimize the unequal allocation of floor area and equipment across organizational levels while ensuring equity within ranks.

But strictly applied, space standards can easily become counterproductive. One amusing example involved a government security agency responsible for protecting a prominent political figure. The person lived in an apartment, and the agency rented the unit next door so that security officers could provide round-the-clock protection. Though the rented apartment was furnished with wall-to-wall carpeting, the agency had it removed because the officers on duty were not of high enough rank to be entitled to carpeted office space. The agency reluctantly had to replace the carpeting when the resident of the apartment beneath the rented one complained of the noise caused by the officers' hard boots on the bare floors and vowed to publicize the address of the person being protected!

Well-defined space standards strive to provide visible equity and acknowledgment of status so that all employees feel they are dealt with fairly. The easiest way to ensure equal treatment is for everyone at a similar level in the organization to be given the same accommodation, and this has been the traditional approach to space standards. But it is questionable whether such standards actually create equity.

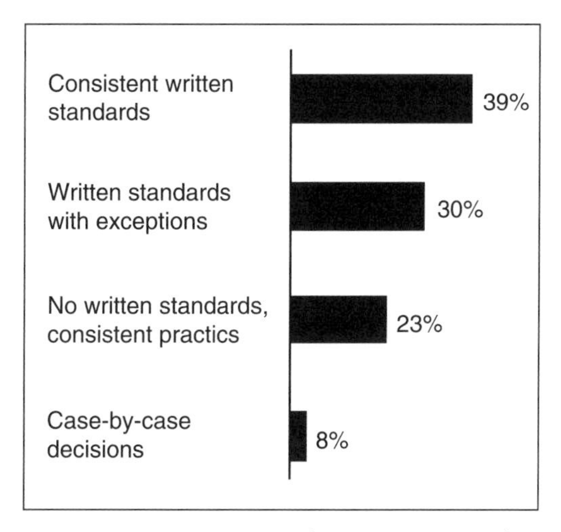

Figure 7.3 Almost 40% of the 274 companies that completed the survey reported having formal, written standards for space planning that were used on a consistent basis. The majority of companies, 60%, reported that they used a mix of explicit and casual space standards, granted exceptions, or allocated space on a case-by-case basis. (*Source:* IFMA 1994.)

MATCHING THE WORK SETTING TO THE INDIVIDUAL

In setting space standards, a fundamental assumption is made that employees in a given job classification all have about the same intellectual and physical abilities. In practice, managers and supervisors recognize individual differences among their staff and apportion time and resources to each accordingly. A new employee might be given extra supervision and support while he or she learns the job. More competent individuals may be delegated more responsibility, resources, and discretion. Good managers are able to tailor their supervision and assistance to derive the greatest benefit for their effort.

In the same way, there is a benefit for work settings to be tailored to individual needs. Such characteristics as vision, hearing, and tolerance of noise disruption vary widely among office workers. Many physiological attributes deteriorate with age, such as visual acuity and the ability to distinguish speech from background noise. The fine details on a high-resolution computer monitor may be easily seen by young eyes, but an older user may need a much larger screen to see the same features.

Characteristics that reduce people's productivity can be partly offset by enhancements to their work settings. People with poor eyesight can benefit from prescription eyeglasses for VDT work or larger computer screens. People with back ailments may need more expensive ergonomic chairs to compensate for their weaker backs.

Many work setting features designed to compensate for disabilities — such as deafness, blindness, or restricted use of limbs — are appreciated by all users. The more sensitive designs that permit disabled people to enter and work in office buildings commonly make access easier for everyone.

To individual employees, equity is largely determined by the degree to which their expectations and needs are met. The relative importance of salary, benefits, level of responsibility, intellectual challenge, and other aspects of a job are different for each person. So, too, is the importance of different elements of their work setting.

When standards that prescribe the same physical setting for everyone in a job category are rigidly applied, the opportunity to account for individual differences is lost. Such standards may ensure that everyone receives the same equipment, but it is unlikely that everyone will receive equal benefit. A work setting will invariably be better suited to some people than to others. When individual differences are recognized, the physical work setting can be used to compensate for individual strengths and weaknesses and thereby improve the performance of the office workforce as a whole.

HEALTH AND SAFETY STANDARDS

Until recently, employers have been relatively free to set office standards as they saw fit because there has been no consensus within the scientific community about the office setting's effects on human health and well-being. Occupational health and safety is controlled by government regulatory agencies. These bodies provide standards to regulate conditions in industrial workplaces where acute risks such as exposure to toxic chemicals, explosion, injury from heavy equipment, or the collapse of man-made structures can cause serious injury and loss of life. Conditions within offices are generally much less severe than those encountered in industrial settings. Not surprisingly, office environments, even in buildings known to cause illness, almost always satisfy established standards.

In the United States, the Americans with Disabilities Act stipulates the removal of physical barriers that prevent people with disabilities from engaging in a full office career. The intent is to go beyond simply providing reasonable physical accommodation — such as ramps and grab bars — to include psychological accommodation for persons with mental difficulties. However, there is little experience and information to support the latter objective.

Office health risks tend to be chronic and, at least initially, less severe than industrial hazards (see Chapters 5 and 6). Nonetheless, they can be serious and debilitating (e.g., cumulative trauma disorders). Widely publicized health risks of the office setting have spurred regulatory bodies, unions, and public lobby groups to develop office quality regulations. Stricter guidelines are being introduced that set minimum standards for everything from ergonomically appropriate work arrangements to indoor environmental quality (e.g., air, temperature, lighting, acoustics). This trend will likely improve the worst office settings, typically occupied by employees in the lowest echelons. Raising their standards will also tend to reduce the differential in workplace quality within the organizational hierarchy.

CHANGING WORK STYLES

Perhaps the strongest force in narrowing the differences in office quality between the highest and lowest ranks has been an increase in collaborative work (Figure 7.4).

Figure 7.4 There is a trend for work to be increasingly collaborative and to involve members from multiple levels of the organization. It is common for team members to work together at one of their work areas. But the physical layout of a work setting designed for a single person may be awkward for two or more to use. (*Source:* Industry, Science and Technology Canada, Ottawa.)

It is easier to maintain a wide discrepancy in office standards between levels in an organization when there is minimal contact between individuals and groups. The more closely that people of different levels work together, the more likely that major differences in the quality of their work settings will be resented. Employees can be quite ingenious in finding ways to circumvent unpopular space policies, channelling productive energy into disruptive efforts that can undermine an organization's activities.

Tough economic times have also pressured organizations to modify work space policies. When the recent recession forced organizations to reduce their ranks, a result was fewer managers and fewer management levels. Fewer levels meant that people at the bottom of the hierarchy were closer to those at the top. Downsizing, restructuring, and the move to more collaborative work groups have people from different levels working together more and also having their work spaces physically closer.

When people work in closer proximity, especially in an open plan arrangement, it is less feasible to have major differences in background environmental quality. Everyone within an open plan area is exposed to essentially the same ambient conditions such as background lighting, thermal comfort, and noise disruption. Lower-echelon employees have tended to benefit by working closer to those in higher positions who expect better-quality work settings.

In an effort to bolster productivity and competitiveness, some organizations have sought to enhance their office quality standards, particularly for lower-echelon employees. At the same time, they limited expenditures on richly appointed executive suites, reflecting both a commitment to fiscal responsibility and the realities of the need to reduce spending. Together, these trends have tended to make work settings within an organization progressively more uniform.

Overall, the office setting can make a greater contribution to an organization's productivity the more it can be tailored to the needs of the individual occupants. Flexible work space policies are more difficult to administer because each office occupant is given more choice and facility managers must exercise a greater degree of judgment in assessing work space requests. But the payoff of improved worker performance and morale can be substantial.

PSYCHOSOCIAL RESPONSE TO HEALTH RISKS IN THE OFFICE SETTING

The public has learned to be suspicious of assurances from government regulators and managers of private and public sector organizations that their health and safety are secure. And for good reason. There have been too many cases in which the public's health and safety were known to be at risk and their well-being was compromised to advance hidden private agendas. For decades, there was "insufficient evidence" to prove that smoking was a health hazard. The public was assured that asbestos was safe long after the serious health problems of workers in that industry had been recognized. The Canadian government offered financial incentives for homeowners to add urea-formaldehyde foam insulation (known as UFFI) to their houses even though studies had already identified it to be a health risk and its use had been banned in countries such as the Netherlands. It was later banned in Canada as well, but only after thousands of people found that the addition of UFFI caused the value of their homes to plummet, and many discovered that the chemical caused them to feel ill in their homes.

The confidence of office workers in the safety of their workplace has been severely shaken. In recent years, health concerns have been raised about indoor air, radiation from VDTs, and simply typing at computer keyboards. Individuals must deal with the uncertainty that their work environment may pose a health risk. Some employers take steps to address these issues, but management is often seen as unresponsive or intent on denying that health risks exist. Office workers frequently feel abandoned and discounted by those responsible for their well-being.

For example, when office workers first complained that indoor air made them feel unwell or that uncomfortable workstations gave them hand and wrist injuries, their grievances were dismissed. They were treated as lazy workers or chronic complainers. Eventually, their ailments were shown to be all too real, and health risks of the office setting are now taken seriously. But it took years to overcome the suspicions. During that time, few preventive steps were taken, and the victims received little support.

Many health risks in the office setting are controversial. There is uncertainty about the existence of some problems and whether their causes lie in the workplace or people's lifestyles. It is often unclear how they can best be addressed, whether preventive measures will be effective, and whether remedial action will deliver lasting results.

Successfully mitigating workplace health risks involves much more than scientific investigations and technological or medical solutions. All too often, the publicity surrounding these issues creates such vehement confrontations that prompt action — *any action* — becomes more important than developing effective solutions. Then, after the hysteria has died down and the issue is no longer in the public eye, the situation reverts back to the way it was. If solutions were chosen more rationally, on the basis of their probable effectiveness, the resources directed at addressing these issues would more likely produce lasting and beneficial results.

People react emotionally as well as intellectually to health risks. In general, the greater the risk and the greater the uncertainty, the more emotional will be the response. For example, when residents became concerned about the health effects of chemical leakage from a toxic waste dump at Love Canal in New York State, the health commissioner announced a plan to remedy the problem and protect the residents. He believed he was acting in a responsible and professional manner, but after presenting the plan, he was jeered by shouts from the audience, "You're murdering us!" (Levine 1982).

These emotional reactions seem irrational and counterproductive, and frustrate scientists and engineers trying to assess environmental problems and mitigate the damage they cause. As with other environmental concerns, efforts to resolve workplace health issues all too often become highly polarized emotional confrontations rather than the rational assessments and effective responses that both management and employees profess to want. In part, this is due to the psychosocial context within which environmental health risks appear.

People differ in their psychosocial response to health and safety risks. Information that readily alleviates concern and uncertainty in one situation exacerbates it in others. Parents' anxiety is immediately resolved when a phone call notifies them that their child has arrived safely at his or her destination. Even if an imagined danger is found to be real, once the uncertainty is removed, people begin the process of coping instead of worrying about an ill-defined and ever-expanding universe of imagined possibilities.

But health risks arising from the office environment are often complex, and so explanations cannot be as straightforward. As well, many of the combined and chronic effects are unknown or controversial (see Chapters 5 and 6). In this context, information intended to reduce uncertainty may escalate the problem — confusing the issue further and increasing the doubt that surrounds it. To avoid exacerbating such situations, information must be presented in a language that listeners understand and within a context they appreciate. It is more likely they will believe what they are told if the messenger is someone they feel is trustworthy.

The Stress of Uncertainty

The stress of uncertainty affects the way people react to health risks. The more vague the conditions, the more likely it is that people will respond in emotional and seemingly irrational ways. Some people, by their nature, respond more emotionally to stressful situations than others. Yet this fails to explain why, when faced with potential health risks, many people who normally use rational, deductive-reasoning processes for problem solving suddenly adopt emotionally charged extreme positions unsupported by the available evidence or their own observations. Such has often been the reaction to workplace health concerns.

When people question risks to their health and don't trust the experts appointed to reassure them, they take action to reduce their exposure — just in case a suspected hazard turns out to be real. On the morning of March 28, 1979, one of two nuclear power generating units at the Three Mile Island plant experienced an odd sequence of equipment failures and human errors that caused several puffs of radioactive steam to escape. Public authorities considered the event to pose a significant health risk. The governor of Pennsylvania issued a calm and measured advisory suggesting that pregnant women and young children within five miles of the plant might want to evacuate. Those within ten miles were advised to take shelter in their homes. The advisory was recommending that some 3,500 people living near the plant should leave the area and everyone else should stay put. Instead, some 200,000 people were sufficiently alarmed to relocate an average of 100 miles. It was the widest imbalance on record between the scale of an advisory and the magnitude of the subsequent evacuation (Erikson 1991).

The form of a public response is not indicative of its validity. Objections voiced in a highly emotional way are sometimes quite justified. Reasonable people at one time presented unemotional, logical arguments supported by scientific studies that showed tobacco smoke, asbestos, and DDT posed no threat to human health. They deemed their opponents to be emotional alarmists. But those "alarmists" were eventually proved correct. The emotional fervor with which a position is stated has more to do with the degree of distrust and technical uncertainty surrounding a situation than with the position's validity.

The public has been sensitized by discoveries of long-abandoned toxic waste dumps and other contamination conditions to which people were unexpectedly exposed. The health hazards of those encounters are often unknown and might only become apparent years after the event. For example, a rumor began in Memphis that a residential area was built on what had once been a toxic waste dump. Neighborhood residents flocked to their physicians complaining of various maladies that they attributed to the dump beneath their homes. Eventually, it was determined that the dump had in fact never existed (Schwartz 1985).

In 1979, government workers moved into a large, new office complex in Hull, Quebec. Many occupants felt unwell whenever they were inside the building. Their concerns were answered by unequivocal assertions that the building was not the source of their problems — a complete denial that a problem existed. The situation rapidly escalated because so many people feared their health was at risk.

Two opposing factions quickly emerged, each asserting that the other's perception of the situation was completely false. Suspicions of hidden motives and agendas were rampant. The social dynamics became increasingly emotional and confrontational. Each side came to assume that all information provided by the other side was biased to advance its position rather than to disclose the truth. Not surprisingly, the situation rapidly escalated into a highly polarized confrontation culminating in a one-day walkout of some 5,000 office workers. Their vociferous complaints, publicity (e.g., protest buttons, information materials), and media attention were successful in forcing an evaluation of the building (Figure 7.5).

Figure 7.5 Office workers concerned about poor indoor air quality gained media attention by walking off the job, distributing information pamphlets, and wearing these protest buttons. At first reticent, management eventually agreed to have the office building tested.

Numerous studies were conducted over the years, and various deficiencies were identified and corrected. Yet some people still develop sick building symptoms when they work in that complex. Among the occupants and public alike there remain lingering doubts about the safety of working in that structure.

If an office health risk that occupants perceive to be potentially serious is poorly handled, the memory of that incident can scar an organization long after the issue has officially been laid to rest. For this reason, office health concerns need to be dealt with in a manner that builds occupant confidence. Social and psychological considerations must be addressed as well as physical injuries. By understanding the psychosocial processes at work, organizations can choose more effective courses of action to limit the emotional escalation and resolve real or perceived health risks.

Psychosocial Stressors and Workplace Health Risks

The seepage of toxic chemicals through the soil of a residential neighborhood or the presence of airborne contaminants in an office do not destroy buildings. But they disrupt, in a fundamental way, people's confidence in their environment. What is safe and what is dangerous, who can be trusted and who cannot, become uncertain.

Though many nonoffice workplaces pose far greater risks, the health concerns associated with an office setting are **involuntary risks.** Occupants perceive them to be human-produced, preventable risks that a workplace should not impose.

In the office workplace, health concerns that involve a great deal of uncertainty tend to become the most polarized and emotional and are the most difficult to resolve. They commonly involve some form of contamination. Exposures to asbestos fibers, environmental tobacco smoke, radiation, and a mix of airborne chemicals are familiar examples.

Health risks associated with ergonomically inappropriate work settings do not involve contaminants but are associated with a high degree of uncertainty and apprehension. They can precipitate illnesses such as cumulative trauma disorders. It is not known in advance whether a particular work setting will cause illness in a particular individual. Some people may be severely affected while others, using the same equipment, are not affected (see Chapter 6).

The principal factors that determine how stressful health concerns in the office environment will be to the occupants are uncertainty of exposure, uncertainty of risk, differential effects, vested interests, and absence of consensus.

Uncertainty of exposure. For many health risks of the office environment, people cannot sense whether they are being exposed, and their physical symptoms do not clearly indicate the cause. Symptoms such as headaches, fatigue, and sore eyes can be the result of any number of factors that may or may not be related to the office environment.

Uncertainty of risk. Experts disagree on the degree of risk that known irritants in the office environment pose to human health. As well, there are serious gaps in the existing knowledge about the combined health risk of multiple stressors, such as job pressures, electronic monitoring of performance, and exposure to mixtures of chemical contaminants.

Differential effects. When the physical office environment is the source of a health problem, it rarely affects everyone exposed. There are usually some people who are completely unaffected. When the physical harm that people experience is so different, opposing beliefs readily develop, and social interactions can become antagonistic. Those unaffected often find it difficult to believe that illnesses they do not personally experience are real. For example, it may be hard to believe that one person develops a severe headache every afternoon when people seated nearby do not.

Vested interest. The intense media coverage of sick building syndrome has sensitized office workers to the types of health problems that can arise and the cover-ups that have occurred. There is usually a strong incentive for employers to understate health concerns related to the office environment — a motivation that directly conflicts with the occupants' health and safety interests. So there is a natural reluctance to blindly accept an organization's internal assessment of contentious office quality issues.

Absence of consensus. So long as there is disagreement about the reality of a health risk, what may appear to some as a measured and responsible course of action may be perceived as inadequate, dangerous, or unethical by others.

Taken together, these stressors tend to promote fear of the risks that might eventually surface and suspicion that the whole truth is not being told. What's more, the tendency for only a minority of those exposed to experience any physical effects can readily lead to socially divisive behavior, the polarizing of opinion, and a confrontational climate. These conditions and the resulting psychosocial responses are characteristic of a class of emergency events known as "chronic technological disasters." Kroll-Smith and Couch (1991) found close parallels between the way people respond to chronic technological disasters (such as pollution and radiation) and the response of office occupants to workplace health risks.

Human Behavior in Chronic Technological Emergencies

The occurrence of **natural disasters** has changed little over the centuries. Tornadoes, hurricanes, floods, and droughts strike with regularity. However, the capability to predict these events has advanced considerably. Early detection allows time for evasive actions that may control the damage and remove people from the danger. These types of emergencies may be severe, but unlike technological disasters, they do not drag on for years amid uncertainties about how serious the health risks might be, who is affected, who should be held responsible, and what action should be taken.

Technological disasters are crisis events that are largely the outcome of human decisions and actions. They often pollute and contaminate rather than merely destroy. Often, as in the case of dioxin and ionizing radiation, people cannot sense whether they are being exposed, and it is unknown what doses are definitely safe. The emergency condition lasts for a long period of time. There is no concrete, attention-grabbing event to mark its onset or its final dissipation. There is no clearly defined point at which the danger is unequivocally perceived to be passed. As a result, the stress of apprehended danger and uncertainty may persist indefinitely, effectively becoming a chronic condition. Soil contaminated with toxic wastes may remain hazardous for decades, with no well-defined point in time when it is no longer harmful.

Technological accidents involve human action. Even if they are precipitated by a natural event — such as a storm that causes an oil tanker to run aground and pollute the shoreline — the event tends to be perceived as preventable if only appropriate human action had been taken. It is not surprising, then, that technological accidents provoke anger and a search for guilty parties. There is a psychological need to place blame. Common targets are those who are believed to have caused the event or who could have taken action to prevent it. Public officials may be blamed for inadequate safety legislation, lax inspections, or not responding quickly enough to minimize human suffering.

During the twentieth century, the incidence of chronic technological disasters has increased dramatically in both number and scale, particularly over the last twenty years. Perrow (1984), in his now classic book *Normal Accidents,* attributes this increase to the technological systems upon which our society has become dependent. He asserts that the more complex a technological system and the more tightly coupled its components, the greater the risk that unexpected chance events will precipitate a failure of crisis proportions.

Elaborate safety systems and continuous monitoring procedures may prevent many or most failures from becoming crisis events. But in analyzing the causes of technological failures, ranging from nuclear power plant disasters such as Chernobyl to marine and aircraft crashes, they are invariably found to be caused by a combination of technological system failure and human error.

Human error is normal in crisis situations because of the inherent limitations of the human nervous system. Emotional

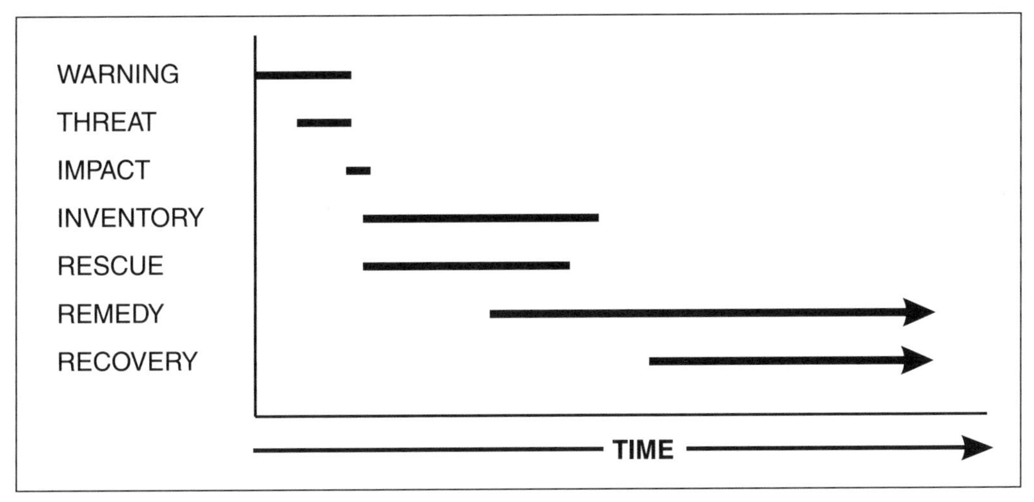

Figure 7.6 The seven-stage standard disaster model, showing the sequence of events and a general indication of their relative duration.

stress and time urgency impair performance and compromise the rationality of decision making in both individuals and groups (Frankenhaeuser 1992). Under conditions of severe stress, it is normal for human attention to become narrowly focused, for perceptions such as time duration to be distorted, for people to exhibit mental inflexibility and fluctuations in their vigilance. Yet technological systems are commonly designed with the assumption that human performance will remain intact in a crisis situation.

In a natural disaster, people generally progress through a fairly predictable sequence of behaviors, often termed the "standard disaster model" (Figure 7.6). There are seven more or less distinct stages, beginning when normal routines are first disrupted, continuing through the period of disruption caused by the disaster event, and eventually ending with the emergence of a new stable routine (see, for example, Baker and Chapman 1962; Kroll-Smith and Couch 1993).

During the "warning" stage, there is apprehension that a calamity may occur. By the "threat" stage, there are unequivocal signs of the approaching disaster. The "impact" stage is the most intense point, when the flying debris, walls of fire, or torrential floods destroy any last vestiges of normal life. After this, there may be considerable pain and grief, but the destruction is over.

The "inventory" and "rescue" stages follow immediately. Survivors begin to piece together what has happened, assess or inventory their losses, and start to comprehend the impacts of the disaster event. Survivor groups spontaneously emerge and begin the rescue process — treating the wounded, freeing trapped victims, and extinguishing fires.

With the "remedy" stage, relief agencies take control of the disaster scene and impose a formal structure on people's inventory and rescue stages. During the "recovery" stage, the disaster environment is replaced by reestablishing the old structure or beginning a new pattern of life.

Natural disasters tend to be episodic. The entire process may take place in a matter of minutes, or it may develop over an extended period of time, but the extreme environment is usually a short-lived event. It is a horrendous period bounded before and after by periods of stability. For example, the eruption of Mount Saint Helen's in Washington State had been anticipated for weeks before it occurred. But less than an hour passed between the extended threat stage, the actual impact, and commencement of the inventory and rescue.

By contrast, many technological emergencies become chronic conditions. This is particularly true of contamination events such as the escape of radioactive gases from a nuclear power plant or toxic pollutants in the soil or water. Such contamination events have social impacts fundamentally different from those of natural disasters. They scare people and evoke a dread that cannot readily be calmed by coolheaded, logical reasoning. By its very nature, the crisis is generally unbounded, and there is little, if any, experience in dealing with the specifics.

It may take years from the time a hazardous substance is discovered in the environment to the time people realize that most of the damage has already been done. The warning and threat stages of the impending hazard can be so long and drawn out that they become a more or less permanent way of life. There is no brief, terrifying event followed by a relatively longer period of inventory, rescue, remedy, and recovery, as occurs with natural disasters. Instead, the stress of an apprehended but uncertain danger persists — often for years, becoming a chronic condition.

Chemicals leaching invisibly through the ground may give indications that danger is present, but the signals are often vague and open to dispute. The apprehension of residents near Love Canal in New York lasted for years until they were permanently moved out of the area. The 1986 explosion at the Chernobyl nuclear power plant in the Ukraine dispersed radioactive particles over a wide geographic area, extending from Scandinavia to Greece and into northern Asia (Figure 7.7). But the fallout was invisible, and the level of radiation varied greatly over the affected area.

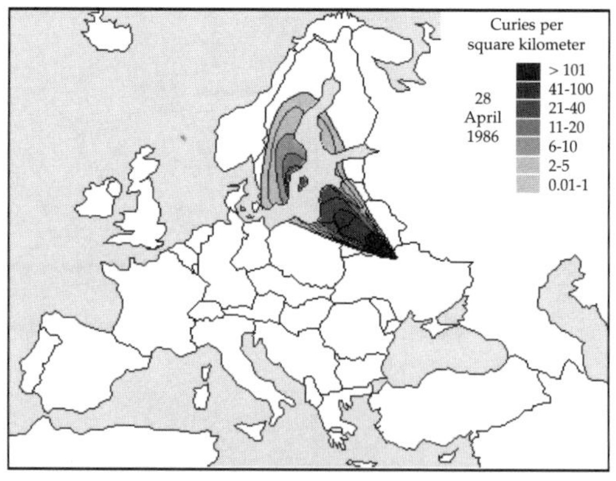

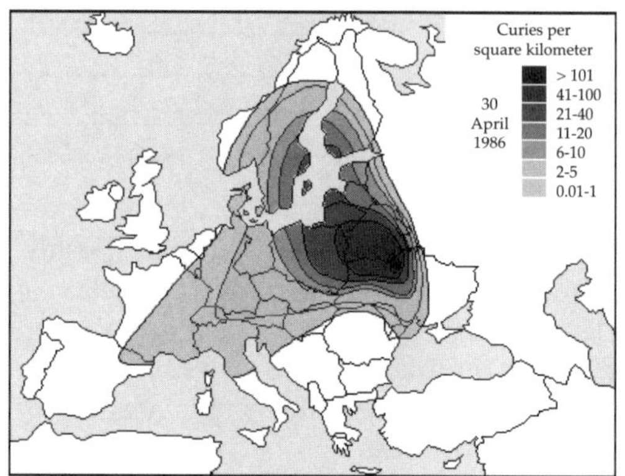

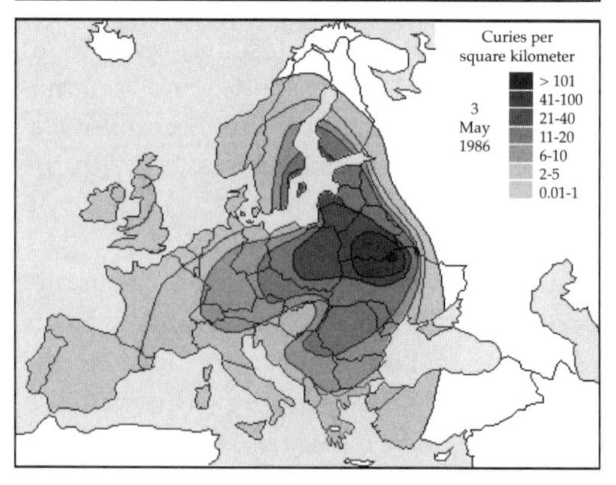

Figure 7.7 Spread of the radioactive cloud from the 1986 explosion at the Chernobyl nuclear power plant. This series of maps shows the rate of spread and coverage of the radioactive cloud that moved across Europe immediately following the accident. (*Source:* David W. Hulse, University of Oregon. Original animation by Elena Bukvareva, Moscow.)

At high exposures, the health effects of radiation occur quickly, but at lower levels, symptoms may take a long time to appear. It is much more difficult to link illnesses to an event long ago because the individual could have been exposed to so many other causal factors. Cancers such as leukemia might only manifest themselves after years or decades and numerous environmental pollutants have been implicated as causative agents. Estimates of future deaths from the Chernobyl disaster range from a few thousand to tens of thousands (Miller 1991). It took months for some consensus to develop about which areas were safe to live in, where people should be evacuated, what level of contamination was safe, or what food could be eaten. The period of apprehension for those affected by Chernobyl will be long indeed.

Extended warning and threat stages strain the coping abilities of a community, particularly if only some members are affected. When just a few people experience a chronic cough, always feel tired, or develop repeated upper respiratory infections, it is unclear whether there is a real health threat. Alternative explanations are possible and reasonable. The scattered individual incidents can be treated as personal problems rather than as a threat that demands community action. Workplace health issues commonly occur in this way. The technological hazards are rarely so severe that everyone is affected. Instead, only a small proportion of office occupants develop illness symptoms.

A long period of ambiguous warning and threat destabilizes established patterns of social interaction and relationships. There is disagreement on reality — some people claim to be in grave danger, whereas others see the situation as less serious or no threat at all. This disagreement on the fundamental reality of the situation further increases the level of uncertainty and makes it more difficult for people to cope. They turn to neighbors or coworkers for support and are uncertain of receiving a sympathetic response. So they tend to seek out people who are prepared to see the situation as they do, people who share their beliefs.

In natural disasters, all segments of a community tend to move through disaster stages at the same time, and there is a tendency for shared experience to increase cooperation. But in chronic technological disasters, there is not the same agreement about the nature and severity of the problem. There may not even be consensus on whether the feared event has occurred. This is particularly true of hazards that pollute the soil, air, or water. There is commonly a high degree of confusion and uncertainty about which areas are contaminated, whether there is a health risk, and what action should be taken.

Without a shared understanding of the event, individuals, organizations, and experts working to mitigate the problem respond on the basis of their unique assessments of the situation. As a result, the actions of one group may appear inappropriate or even dangerous to those who interpret the circumstances differently. The greater the perceived risks and the longer the uncertainty persists, the greater the social conflict that is generated.

As well, the coping mechanisms normally used by groups and individuals to deal with invisible and uncertain health threats may exacerbate the psychological stress. Coping behavior can itself become a cause of illness. As the level of uncertainty increases and the danger is perceived to be more severe, people's form of coping tends to shift from predominantly rational deductive-reasoning processes to the acceptance of emotional beliefs that are backed by a supportive group. Under these conditions, beliefs are psychologically more satisfying because they provide a desperately needed sense of predictability. There isn't sufficient information for a satisfying course of action to be deduced by reasoning alone.

BELIEFS AND PERCEPTIONS

People facing an invisible and uncertain health threat tend to develop belief systems about the nature of the threat. Instead of thinking in terms of probabilities and alternative possibilities, belief systems offer assertions of certainty. It is asserted with confidence that the soil *is* contaminated, the indoor air *causes* illness, and the computers *trigger* miscarriages. These assertions are often accompanied by equally confident pronouncements of what should be done and how people should be compensated.

The more uncertainty that exists, the greater the psychological need to construct a belief system that defines the scope and the seriousness of the danger. It is a means of coping with a potentially serious but poorly defined risk by asserting that the hazard and the correct course of action are known. Beliefs confer certainty on reality and thereby reduce the stress of acute uncertainty. Technical experts may disagree over the presence of dioxins in the soil or the health risk of pesticide residues on food, but believers are certain that the chemicals are present and the risks are severe. Certainty has a psychologically reassuring and calming effect that relieves the stress of excessive ambiguity and fear.

Beliefs are social phenomena. They are constructed through a process of communication among people who share a common understanding about their world or certain aspects of it. There is a consensus understanding about what is dangerous, what is safe, and what is sacred. This collective agreement exerts a strong hold on believers. To violate a belief is to risk censure and disapproval. So in being a believer, there is an implied moral obligation to conform with the shared understanding of the group. For this reason, once a shared belief system has formed, little supporting evidence is needed to confirm it, but extraordinary amounts of contrary evidence are required to refute it. It is far more difficult to resolve a technological problem, such as a workplace health issue, once polarized belief systems have developed.

Perceptions, on the other hand, are more personal. People perceive by becoming aware of something directly through their senses. Perceptions are easier to revise in response to new information because there is no group conformance to be maintained. But perceptions are more tentative, more subject to change, and therefore less reassuring. Beliefs offer the comfort of certainty. To individuals coping with what they perceive to be an ambiguous and potentially dangerous threat to their health and safety, beliefs offer considerably more psychological and social support than perceptions.

Beliefs provide definitive answers, but only for some people. Not everyone is affected to the same degree, and not everyone shares in those beliefs. An indoor air quality problem generally affects only a portion of the office occupants. Those unaffected can only imagine what the victims claim to experience and may choose not to become committed believers. Chronic contamination events typically exhibit this characteristic. For example, the seepage of contaminants through soil is influenced by local topography and soil characteristics that can divert the flow away from one home and concentrate it at the adjacent one. So, to one homeowner, the problem is real and threatening while his or her neighbor may be unaffected and remain unconcerned.

Similarly, vehicle exhaust can migrate from an underground parking garage through an expansion joint in the building structure and emerge at only a few locations in the office space. For some, the threat of contamination may be remote or nonexistent while their neighbors may become ill. One segment of a community or one group of office occupants may see their environment as a health risk whereas others do not.

Thus, the formation of belief systems tends to be a socially divisive process. For this reason, victims of chronic technological hazards tend to lose their normal support networks within their communities or peer groups. Those who disagree with the victims' claims tend to avoid them. In turn, the victims respond by forming groups of their own, comprised of other victims or those who fear becoming victims. Together, they tend to affirm each other's fears.

Groups that emerge around a threat-belief system move quickly to the impact stage and focus on the possibility of suffering, fear, or death. Firmly believing themselves to be victims of contamination, they make assertions that are likely to be emotionally charged, placing moral demands on friends, coworkers, and others to accept their claims that adverse effects are occurring and immediate action is necessary.

People who regard the problem as less serious or nonexistent are likely to begin viewing believers as threats to their property values or their jobs. Those who do not interpret the environmental cues as cause for extreme concern may see themselves as victims of a fictitious or at best exaggerated crisis. Their assertions may also evolve into a competing belief system.

What then emerges are competing views of the same local world. The social consensus that normally supports individuals' trust in their perception of their world has instead become a source of social conflict. It is not a conflict based on verifiable information. Instead, it becomes a dispute between people who see their antagonists as unwilling to cooperate in a realistic assessment of the threat. As a result, they are defined as persons with special motives to make false claims. Opposition is explained away as greed, hysteria, fear, or with other negative labels that heighten the emotional intensity of the conflict and adversely affect the psychosocial stability of the participants. Resolution of the dispute becomes all but impossible so long as each side maintains its belief system to be the reality upon which any course of action must be built, and efforts at dialogue become endless cycles of blaming, condemnation, and censure.

To address concerns about uncertain health risks of the office setting, there must be a psychosocial environment within which effective action can be taken. It is important to prevent an escalation from rational, perception-based reasoning processes to the more emotional and confrontational belief system reasoning processes that are dominated by social support group dynamics.

Addressing Uncertain Health Risks in the Office Setting

Health concerns about the physical office environment have important psychosocial dimensions as well as technical and medical ones. Even if the technical and medical issues can be resolved, a residue of antagonism and distrust may remain that compromises commitment and cooperation within the organization.

In the office setting, the management environment existing before a health issue arises is probably the most important determinant of how successfully workers' concerns can be resolved. Organizations that build and maintain a trusting relationship with their employees and have well-established and considerate approaches to safety are best able to respond to a potential emergency or crisis situation. Where a high level of trust exists within the organizational culture, health issues can much more readily be resolved through rational discussion processes. Once a crisis situation has developed and becomes emotional and polarized, it is very difficult to start building trust.

Where the level of trust within an organization is poor, fear of a workplace health risk causes people to communicate with each other and behave in ways that distort perceptions and encourage the emergence of hostile groups committed to nonnegotiable positions. Offering objective scientific data in such a confrontational setting may do little but fan the fire. The destructive confrontational dynamics must first be arrested before conditions conducive to cooperative problem solving can be created. To do so may require the intervention of specialists in the art of conflict resolution and consensus building (Kroll-Smith 1993).

The greater the perceived severity of a health risk, the more readily the confrontational dynamics can escalate. Unfortunately, the rush to allay people's fears has sometimes been at the expense of accuracy. Once information has been presented and is perceived to misrepresent reality, the damage done to whatever trust existed is very difficult to repair. For this reason, hasty efforts to downplay health risks are often counterproductive and may backfire.

However, a strategy of revealing little information in an effort to protect an organization is generally self-defeating as well. It calls into question the very legitimacy the organization is trying to preserve. It's difficult to persuade occupants that their interests are truly being served so long as information they consider vital is being withheld.

The more quickly uncertainty is reduced, the less stressful the issue will be for those affected. Effective action needs to be initiated rapidly, and perhaps of greater importance, the response must be *perceived* as rapid. It must address both the technical and psychosocial challenges presented. All too often, the situation is seen as a purely technical problem — only technical measures are taken, and important psychosocial factors are ignored.

Open recognition by management that people are worried and actions that demonstrate a commitment to resolve occupant concerns are both positive steps toward controlling the escalation of a crisis. People have a psychological need to hear their organization acknowledge that there *may* be a technical problem, that people are anxious, and that steps will be taken in good faith to address both the technical and psychosocial aspects of the situation.

Not everyone will perceive an issue in the same way. For example, when a new carpet was installed on one floor of an office building, some people became ill from the chemicals it released into the air. Employee reaction was divided. One group, comprised of individuals who did not become ill, disclaimed the hazard. A second group, comprised primarily of those affected, believed the problem to be serious, vehemently demanded action, and proclaimed their entitlement to compensation. There was also a third group, who adopted an intermediate position. Their view was that a problem might or might not exist but they believed that a safe environment was a worker's right. By openly identifying the different ways that people feel, there is the opportunity to build a shared perception that everyone is hurting in some way. Even those who did not become ill were dissatisfied with the deterioration of the *social* setting of their work environment. Building upon shared perceptions is a particularly effective way to reduce group polarization so that conflicts can be resolved (Kroll-Smith 1993).

When people are exposed to uncertain threats to their health and well-being, as many sick building syndromes are perceived to be, their response may be shaped less by objective information than by subjective beliefs. They do not behave as dispassionate evaluators of all the facts, rationally deducing the degree of threat posed to them. Typically, all the facts are not known. What facts there are may not be communicated in a way that those affected can understand. Presented with ambiguous information and the high stress of uncertainty in the face of a serious but invisible threat to their health, people commonly behave in what appears to be an irrational manner. But when viewed in the context of the social setting and its cultural norms, their behavior is not only more comprehensible; it can be seen as an expected reaction, well within the normal range of human behavior. By recognizing both the psychosocial and technical dimensions of a problem, a more comprehensive approach can be taken to resolve it and to prevent the formation of deep and lasting distrust within the organization.

HUMAN RESPONSE TO STRESS

Everyone experiences stress. Moderate levels of stress can improve performance. Tasks that challenge a person's abilities and encourage the learning of new skills, enhance achievement and stimulate productivity. Successful completion of a challenging task is an important source of personal satisfaction. However, when a situation is so challenging that it is perceived to be overwhelming, the resulting stress may cause discomforting feelings of anxiety and frustration that impair performance — behavior becomes inefficient and overreactive, and the ability to recover from the additional physical and mental effort is retarded. If excessive stress conditions occur frequently or for prolonged periods, the body's resources are progressively depleted and the risk of physical and psychological disorders increases. Excessive levels of stress that cause pain or injury are often referred to as **strain** or **distress.**

Stress is a complex psychological and physiological response to external demands. The demands may be physical, such as a need for intense physical exertion; emotional, as caused by acute embarrassment or fear; or environmental, like noise distraction or drafts. Stress can affect people's physical reaction to the office environment as well as their perception of it.

Agents that precipitate stress are termed **stressors.** Stressors typically impose multiple demands. For example, people who have an allergic reaction to an airborne contaminant (an environmental demand) and feel ill will probably work less effectively. If they are trying to meet a tight deadline, their slower progress can impose an added emotional demand about whether the work can be completed on time. The illness symptoms of their allergic reaction also impose additional physical demands on their body so they fatigue more quickly.

Stress is not a specific physical dimension of the environment, a particular behavior, or a single pattern of physiological responses. Some predicaments are inherently stressful to most people. But the level of stress that a particular situation will cause depends on the way individuals perceive it, their physiological response, and their personality. It is the interaction of the objective characteristics of a situation and people's subjective perception and response that determines how stressful it will be (Frankenhaeuser 1991; Selye 1976). Stress responses are therefore highly individual. A situation that is very stressful to one person may be mildly stressful or not stressful to someone else. Some people are terrified to speak in public; others relish the attention.

When people are exposed to stressful conditions, extra mental and physical effort is mobilized to address the challenge. People also take steps to reduce their stress level, a behavior known as **coping.** Coping may involve changing behavior to adapt to a situation, modifying the situation to better suit the individual, or both. For example, the stress of a heavy workload can be reduced by obtaining additional resources (e.g., more staff, time, or money) or by finding a more efficient method to do the work. Physical activity has been shown to moderate the effects of high-stress conditions, so taking periodic breaks for some exercise can be an effective way to cope with a high-stress work assignment.

Coping behavior is generally beneficial. When stress levels are too high, performance is impaired. So in controlling stress, a person is able to respond more effectively to a situation. However, coping behavior can be maladaptive. For example, one way to cope with a fear of public speaking is to always avoid it. But if one's career is dependent on an ability to address audiences, avoidance is going to compromise job advancement.

Physiological Response to Stress

Stress precipitates a number of physiological changes that alter a person's physical state, abilities, and perception. Under moderate stress, these changes are largely beneficial. They cause hormonal control systems, commanded by the brain, to prepare the body to act. The body's response to stress is largely regulated by the pituitary and adrenal glands. They trigger responses such as increased heart rate, secretion of stomach acids, and constriction of blood vessels.

The principal hormones by which the body's stress response is controlled are catecholamines (one of which is adrenaline) and cortisol. When the concentration of these hormones in the bloodstream suddenly increases in response to stress, a number of body functions are affected. Muscles tense. Heart rate, blood pressure, and respiration increase, as does the blood sugar concentration. These short-term effects produce a surge of energy and a heightened level of arousal often termed the "fight or flight" response. But if the body is exposed to this heightened level of preparedness frequently or for prolonged periods, stress becomes a chronic condition and the effects become harmful.

People become less attentive, their error rates and risk of injury increase, and they are more likely to develop illnesses. The specific effects of chronic stress vary widely among individuals. Chronic stress can precipitate frustration, anxiety, and depression. Headaches, sleep disorders, irritability, emotional and physical fatigue, and feelings of helplessness are common symptoms. Chronic stress impairs performance. Long-term exposure to stress with inadequate opportunities to recover can lead to cumulative fatigue, reduced attention span, withdrawal, and passivity (also termed "learned helplessness") (Cohen et al. 1986).

Chronic stress compromises health in two fundamental ways — physiologically and behaviorally. It depletes the body's resources and disrupts normal physiological functions, reducing the body's capacity to tolerate additional demands. As well, the body's ability to fight disease can be inhibited, increasing susceptibility to illness. Chronic stress can initiate or aggravate coronary heart disease, high blood pressure, arteriosclerosis, gastrointestinal disorders such as peptic ulcers, and a range of psychological disorders.

The link between chronic stress and heart disease is well known. Elevated levels of adrenaline and cortisol have been shown to promote cardiovascular disease, and high catecholamine levels have been associated with hypertension, changes in blood clotting, and acceleration of arteriosclerosis (Frankenhaeuser and Johansson 1986; Johansson and Aronsson 1991; Karacek and Theorell 1990).

Chronic stress may also encourage behaviors that are unhealthy, such as increased smoking, excessive alcohol consumption, overeating, drug abuse, reduction in physical exercise, and inability to relax.

The apparent absence of physical illness does not in itself guarantee that a stressful work environment is not exacting significant hidden costs. People are quite resilient and can learn to cope with considerable levels of stress in their environment, but coping demands effort. This additional effort expended on coping with the work setting is a form of **adaptation cost**. Adaptation costs exact a performance toll in the form of reduced work quality, a slower pace of work, and more rapid fatiguing.

Chronic stress also intensifies the impact of the physical setting on individual performance. Stress is cumulative. The intellectual demands of work, the physical strain of tasks (e.g., visual, muscular), environmental stress (e.g., tolerating distractions or physical discomfort), and psychosocial pressures (e.g., interactions with coworkers) together form the individual's total stress load. The greater the total stress load, the more likely that performance and health will be impaired (Gaillard 1993; Karacek and Theorell 1990).

Chronically stressed people fatigue more quickly and are less able to tolerate minor annoyances in the physical work environment or their interactions with coworkers. For this reason, features of the office environment that are not ordinarily noticed, such as background noise or air movement, may suddenly become intolerable when an individual is under a high stress load. Psychological stress caused by a heavy workload and tight deadline, physical stresses such as suffering from illness, or environmental stresses such as feeling too cold all contribute.

If the physical environment is close to a person's physiological tolerance limit for air quality, thermal comfort, or other factors, under the additional load of chronic stress, he or she is more likely to experi-

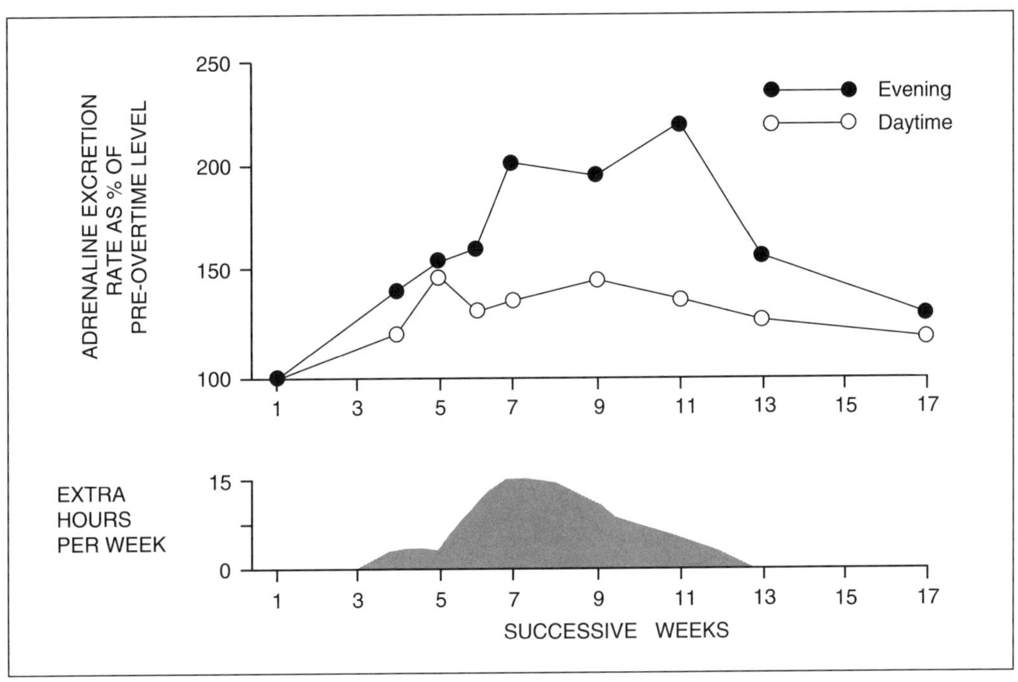

Figure 7.8 Relationship of adrenaline levels in office workers to the hours of overtime worked. (*Sources:* Adapted from Frankenhaeuser and Johansson 1986; and Rissler 1977.)

ence illness symptoms. Taken together, the effects of chronic stress reduce the ability of office occupants to cope with their work environment by reducing their physiological and psychological tolerance.

The Lingering Effects of Stress at Work

The effects of stress at work extend into leisure-time hours. Work that demands intense adaptive effort, such as high-stress jobs or overtime hours, increases the time required for the body to recover. For example, office workers who spent long hours doing attention-demanding but highly regimented work, such as computer-based data-entry tasks, took longer to recover or "unwind" after work than those whose jobs were less stressful (Frankenhaeuser and Johansson 1986). **Unwinding** was defined as the period of time required for the body to reach baseline physiological conditions after stress conditions ceased. This "slow unwinding" or delayed recovery effect was particularly evident in overtime workers.

The study results shown in Figure 7.8 illustrate the effect of daily overtime work on the level of unwinding or recovery that office workers had reached by the evening. An average of 73 hours of overtime work per employee was spread over two months, but most of it occurred within a four-week period. The adrenal hormone *adrenaline* was used to measure arousal levels in the study participants.

Adrenaline is easily measured using blood or urine samples. In this study, all values were calculated as a percentage of the individuals' preovertime baseline readings. Separate daytime and evening baselines were used. Thus, values greater than 100 indicate stress levels higher than the baseline level.

As shown in the figure, adrenaline levels were elevated throughout the period when overtime work was done. Surprisingly, these levels were higher in the evening, after work, than during the day. The pronounced elevation of adrenaline secretion in the evenings, which were spent relaxing at home, was accompanied by markedly elevated heart rates as well as feelings of irritability and fatigue.

The effects of the overtime workload extended into leisure hours and accumulated gradually. The highest rate of overtime work occurred during week seven of the study, but the peak daytime adrenaline level occurred about two weeks later, and the peak evening adrenaline level occurred four weeks later. Complete physiological resolution of this stress did not occur for several weeks after the overtime work had ceased. Some four weeks after all overtime had stopped, adrenaline levels still had not returned to their pre-overtime baseline values (Frankenhaeuser and Johansson 1986; Rissler 1977).

This study demonstrated that the peak physiological impact of work overload occurs sometime after the peak demand, such as in the evening, after the workday is done. So the effects of work overload extend into leisure hours. What's more, the stress of work overload and its effects can be cumulative, lengthening the time needed for complete physiological recovery. Thus, factors that affect the stress level of office work, such as job design and work scheduling, have impacts that extend well beyond the workday.

Subsequent studies have identified a number of factors that influence the speed of the recovery process. Being physically and mentally fit improves the speed of recovery after a stressful task. Job content has a strong effect — recovery from work experienced as repetitious and boring tends to be slower. Lundberg et al. (1993) found that recovery was slower after monotonous data-entry work than after more stimulating learning tasks.

The demands of nonwork activities also can significantly impair a person's opportunity to relax and recover after work. For example, family responsibilities and other personal maintenance tasks are commonly a major contributor to overload stress, and because they are work that must be done upon returning home, they reduce or eliminate the time available to unwind (Frankenhaeuser 1991).

These studies suggest that the stress of extended periods of overtime work and job designs that are intense but have low task diversity and are intellectually undemanding impose an increased physiological load on the body. They can create conditions of cumulative fatigue in which the body becomes progressively more rundown. By recognizing the factors that contribute to stress and the psychosocial conditions that may serve as buffers, steps can be taken to protect office workers from harmful stress effects while achieving high levels of productivity.

The Cost of Stress

The cost of job-related stress is high. It has been estimated that stress-related diseases such as coronary heart disease, ulcers, and psychological disorders together with the losses from stress-related accidents, substance abuse, and absenteeism cost U.S. industry some $150 billion a year (OTA 1985).

Heart disease is the leading cause of death in the United States. It is estimated that 3% to 16% of the risk of heart attack and 28% of the risk for all serious stress-related illnesses could be attributed to job strain (Karacek and Theorell 1990). In 1984, the costs of cardiovascular illnesses in the United States were estimated at $64.4 billion in treatment and lost output (Herzlinger and Calkins 1986).

These direct costs are probably only a minor fraction of the true *preventable* costs of high-stress jobs. Exhausted or depressed employees are not energetic, accurate, or innovative at work. The indirect, *preventable* losses related to impaired job performance are estimated to be larger than the direct health costs.

Matteson and Ivancevich (1987) studied job stress in relation to four types of costs: absenteeism; the cost of additional employees hired to make up for the lost time or reduced productivity of stress-impaired workers; increased employee turnover; and sabotage by disgruntled workers. Absenteeism and extra employees accounted for the largest costs. Overall, the researchers estimated the total preventable cost of job-related stress to be

Table 7.1 Principal factors of the work environment that increase stress and are associated with stress-related illness.

Work Demand	High work demands relative to an individual's abilities and resources
Control	Low decision latitude in choosing how and when to meet job demands
Social Support	Little social support from coworkers and supervisors

7% of sales — not including the direct costs of additional health care to treat stress-related disorders. About 50% of absenteeism and 40% of employee turnover were considered to be the result of preventable stress-related factors.

STRESS AND THE WORK ENVIRONMENT

Human stress and the work environment have been intensively studied for over 50 years. Diverse theories have been proposed to explain the health effects of stress. However, they all recognize the individual's perception of his or her environment to be a major factor in stress-related illness.

Large-scale studies have shown that it is the interaction of job demands, control (the decision latitude the individual can exercise in meeting job demands), and the level of social support from coworkers that determine how stressful a job will be (Table 7.1). Jobs with high demands, low decision latitude, and low social support produce the highest levels of psychological stress and the highest incidence of stress-related illness (see, for example, Cox 1985; Frankenhaeuser 1992; Karacek and Theorell 1990).

The absolute level of demand placed on an individual is not as important a factor as the discrepancy between the demand and the person's ability to cope. Task performance and work satisfaction are optimized when job demands are high enough for the work to be challenging and interesting but not so high as to seem overwhelming.

The demands of a job, how hard a person works, depend not only on the amount of work done but also on the psychosocial conditions of the work setting. Imposition of a fast work pace, rigid scheduling, the need for a high degree of coordination and vigilance all add to the psychological demands of a job. Tight deadlines, personal conflicts arising from job pressures, fears of skill obsolescence and job loss also increase stress levels.

Social support and a measure of control over work scheduling and methods help individuals to cope by giving them some latitude to modify their situation and the opportunity to obtain moral if not substantive support from coworkers. A perceived lack of personal control, especially over work pace and work methods, and the lack of social support from coworkers and supervisors are strongly associated with an increased incidence of stress-related illness, whereas factors that promote a feeling of being in control and having the ability to influence activities can reduce or eliminate the negative side effects of a high-stress situation (Johansson and Aronsson 1991; Frankenhaeuser 1991).

Moderate stress tends to stimulate innovation; it provides an incentive to work smarter. But when a situation becomes too stressful, people's ability to be creative and work smart is impaired. Under high-stress conditions, people favor familiar, routine procedures over actions that require more creativity and intellectual strategy. Learning becomes more difficult, so it's harder to replace inefficient practices with new, innovative methods (Karacek and Theorell 1990).

In the office environment, some of the harmful effects of stress are quite tangible and readily appreciated. The psychological stresses of the office workplace, as discussed above, are widely known. Backaches caused by improper chairs or visual discomfort resulting from inadequate lighting are familiar examples of physical strain that are easily recognized and accepted as legitimate ailments (see Chapter 6). Physical aspects of the office environment such as uncomfortable temperature and humidity, high background noise levels, and poor indoor air quality can be potent sources of stress as well, but environmental stressors tend to be less direct and are not as readily accepted as legitimate ailments.

Efforts to reduce stress-related illness in the workplace commonly focus on changing the individual's behavior. Stress management techniques can improve the individual's ability to cope. However, coping with stress consumes energy that could otherwise be invested in productive work activities. Thus, it is in the interests of an organization to reduce employees' health risk and improve their performance by supplementing their coping efforts with organizational, technical, and environmental changes that will reduce their stress load.

High-stress jobs can be redesigned to distribute stressful work tasks among several people, or a task may be rotated so that it is only done for a short time. Annoyances, such as disruptive phone calls, can be reduced or eliminated through appropriate telephone-answering technology. Uncomfortable work settings can be adjusted to better suit individual needs by providing local control over lighting, air movement, and temperature.

The automation of the office has made electronic performance monitoring so easy to implement that it has become widely used. Computer technology enables virtually any work that can be quantified to be continuously monitored. But electronic performance monitoring can itself become a troublesome source of stress and actually reduce productivity if it is not properly implemented (Hart et al. 1987; Smith, Carayon and Miezio 1987). The principal factors associated with stress-related illness in the workplace — high job demand, low job control, and low social support — can all be accentuated by performance monitoring (Carayon 1993).

Intense effort does not necessarily cause strain. High job demands can raise productivity if those demands are accompanied by high decision latitude. But when job demands are high, decision latitude is low, and social isolation all but eliminates social support, the individual has no means to modify his or her situation, and the risk of stress-related illness is greatest. Then, higher levels of demand reduce productivity and are associated with depression, exhaustion, and job dissatisfaction.

Control and Work-Related Stress

The sources of stress in the office work environment are diverse. Some stress arises from the nature of the tasks, relationships with supervisors and coworkers, or the frustrations of wrestling with uncooperative technology (see, for example, Moser and Levy-Leboyer 1985). The physical office environment can also be a source of stress, adding to the overall stress load that workers must bear. Lack of control over conditions that make tasks more difficult to perform or make the environment less comfortable to work in is stressful. The less acoustic and visual privacy individuals are given, the less they are able to control noise disruptions and visual distractions. The more difficult it is for them to adjust the lighting (e.g., to minimize glare on their computer screens), temperature, and air movement (e.g., so as not to feel chilled) to suit their personal and work needs, the more the physical setting will add to the overall level of stress in a workplace.

The effects of predictability and control on stress response have been extensively studied and reported in the psychology literature. For example, the now classic noise experiments of Glass and Singer (1972) demonstrated that providing control over a noise source reduced stress even though that control was never exercised to turn off the sound. Similarly, providing a warning signal shortly before a disturbing sound was made also reduced the degree of stress that subjects experienced (see the "Acoustics" section in Chapter 5).

Considerable effort has been made to reduce stress factors in the work environment by adopting less autocratic supervisory styles or by making company policies more responsive to individual needs (such as offering flexible work hours, work-at-home options, or seminars on personal financial planning to ease the burden of family or communal demands). Similarly, stress can be reduced by improving the predictability of office occupants' physical work environment and their control over that environment.

Individual Control of the Work Environment

Office automation has tended to increase workers' stress load as well as their sensitivity to their lack of control over their work environment (Hockey et al. 1989). In the electronic office, a dependence on sophisticated equipment makes workers less self-sufficient and less able to control their work situation. New technology requires workers to become increasingly specialized and often leaves them feeling helpless when it suddenly refuses to function as needed. Myriad frustrating and mysterious glitches occur when people who are not experts in computers must use equipment that is too complex for them to operate proficiently.

With a typewriter, a page number can be placed on a sheet wherever it is wanted. But with a computer, when a page number doesn't print where it is supposed to appear and the source of the problem is not known, there is nothing the user can do until someone arrives to explain or fix it. Learning many feature-rich office systems such as telephone systems, copiers, fax machines, and electronic mail quickly overtaxes even the most dedicated technology addict.

The ability to shape the work environment to one's choosing is a highly valued benefit. Individual environmental control lies at the heart of most work setting preferences. People want to be able to control conditions in their physical work environment — to choose a comfortable temperature or suitable lighting, to shut out noise and visual distractions. But individual environmental control is not only about personal comfort. People need to adjust and use their work settings in ways that best support their activities (Figure 7.9). A project team may elect to be seated together as a group, making it easier to collaborate. Yet at other times, the individual members may require a quieter work space for focused concentration.

Given a choice, people invariably select a work setting that offers the greatest control over their personal work environment. An adjustable chair is favored over a fixed seat; an openable window is preferred over one that is permanently closed; controllable lighting, temperature, and air movement are perceived as significant benefits. Numerous studies have found that the major sources of occupant dissatisfaction with open plan layouts involve an inability to control the local environment. There is little the user can do to reduce the impact of noise distractions, a lack of privacy, uncomfortable temperatures, and inadequate ventilation. The desirability of environmental controls has made them a perk. Work settings that offer a greater degree of environmental control are invariably perceived to signify higher status.

Today's mechanically ventilated office buildings with their increasingly elaborate control systems are better able to maintain a desired indoor environment than ever before. Paradoxically, to achieve this, environmental controls have been progressively automated and made inaccessible to occupants. In part, this has been done to optimize the indoor office environment. For example, it is more difficult to optimize a ventilation system if windows are openable. The development of increasingly

Figure 7.9 With sufficient motivation and control over how and where their work is done, people can find a way to make do. However, makeshift solutions are not necessarily efficient. Here, large sheets were moved onto the floor when the work surface was too small.

sophisticated systems has enabled the climate of ever-smaller office areas to be individually monitored and regulated. Currently, in an open plan layout, the smallest individually controlled zones contain about six adjacent workstations. The more similar the heating and cooling loads of the individual workstations and the more similar the activity levels of their users, the better an environment comfortable to all can be achieved. Even so, having to satisfy a smaller number of people itself makes the job of setting environmental conditions easier. This approach is being extended to provide controls that service individual work spaces.

It was long believed that people would not use individual environmental controls "responsibly." It was feared that they might overuse the controls, changing the temperature settings so frequently that the heating and air-conditioning units would be overworked. They might leave controls at extreme settings or forget to turn them off when they were absent, such as leaving heating units on over the weekend.

The few tests done on the effect of individual environmental controls on energy consumption indicated that any change would be negligible (Seem and Braun 1992). What's more, a minor increase in energy consumption would be quickly recouped by virtually any increase in worker productivity. Experts expressed strong beliefs about the way people would use environmental controls if they had them, but there were virtually no rigorous studies to support their assertions.

THE FUNDI: STUDYING HOW INDIVIDUALS USE ENVIRONMENTAL CONTROLS

In 1983, Kaplan (1985, 1987a, 1987b) performed a comprehensive field trial to examine how occupants in a working office would use environmental controls. Part of this project involved the development of an innovative workstation named the FUNDI — to reflect its FUNctional and

Diagnostic features (discussed in the next subsection). The units offered individual environmental control of the immediate surroundings. Designed to be flexible and responsive to individual and group needs, the units could be rolled to different locations or reconfigured as the work required.

The FUNDI study sought to determine whether providing local environmental controls improved users' satisfaction with open plan work settings. Sixteen units were installed in an operating office for a period of 15 months, during which time objective and subjective data were collected. By extending the field trial well over a year, seasonal variations in the performance of the building systems could be taken into account. The study participants were support staff and knowledge workers who used computer-based office equipment. The support staff had previously worked in a conventional open plan office setting, whereas the knowledge workers had been in enclosed offices.

The FUNDI provided controls for heat, light, air circulation, visual privacy, acoustic privacy, and spatial layout. The settings chosen by the occupants were continuously recorded by instrumentation in the units and were periodically verified by direct observation. In addition, measurements of ambient office conditions — including sound levels, indoor and outside air quality, lighting, temperature, relative humidity, and spatial layout — were periodically taken. The occupants' assessments of their workstations and the office environment were collected through interviews and written surveys.

The study found that the environmental controls were used responsibly and were perceived to significantly enhance the quality of the work setting. Participants reported a strong preference for the FUNDI over traditional open plan office settings. They found it provided greater privacy and comfort. However, an enclosed office was still preferred. Not unexpectedly, those who were moved from enclosed offices to FUNDIs reported a reduction in privacy, whereas those who had always worked in open plan offices reported an increase.

Monitoring instruments built into the units provided valuable information on people's environmental preferences and behavior that is not readily collected in other ways. The data showed that users tended to find a spatial layout and a setting for air circulation that suited their work needs and rarely changed them. However, the lighting, radiant heat panels, and chair were adjusted more frequently to suit different tasks. One stormy day, a user was found comfortably working with his bare feet being warmed by the radiant heat panel while his shoes and socks dried.

An important conclusion from the FUNDI study was that there was a minimum set of environmental controls that had to be provided before occupants reported increased satisfaction with their work space — even though many of these controls were infrequently used. This finding is consistent with psychological research that has shown that people's perceived ability to control their environment decreases stress and improves satisfaction, even if the control is never exercised.

The FUNDI Design

The FUNDI progressed through three designs, each incorporating modifications suggested by users and experts in lighting, acoustics, and other office-related fields. In 1983, 20 FUNDIs were custom-built using wood-frame construction at a unit cost (material and labor) of CDN$5,000 (US$4,500 at that time).

The institutional obstacles encountered in having the FUNDI units constructed and installed illustrated the difficulties of integrating trades and areas of expertise that had traditionally remained separate. Electrical wiring, telephone cabling, and lighting had to be installed in an ergonomically appropriate and flexible furniture unit. Carpenters, electricians, and other tradespeople were required to work together on a single piece of furniture.

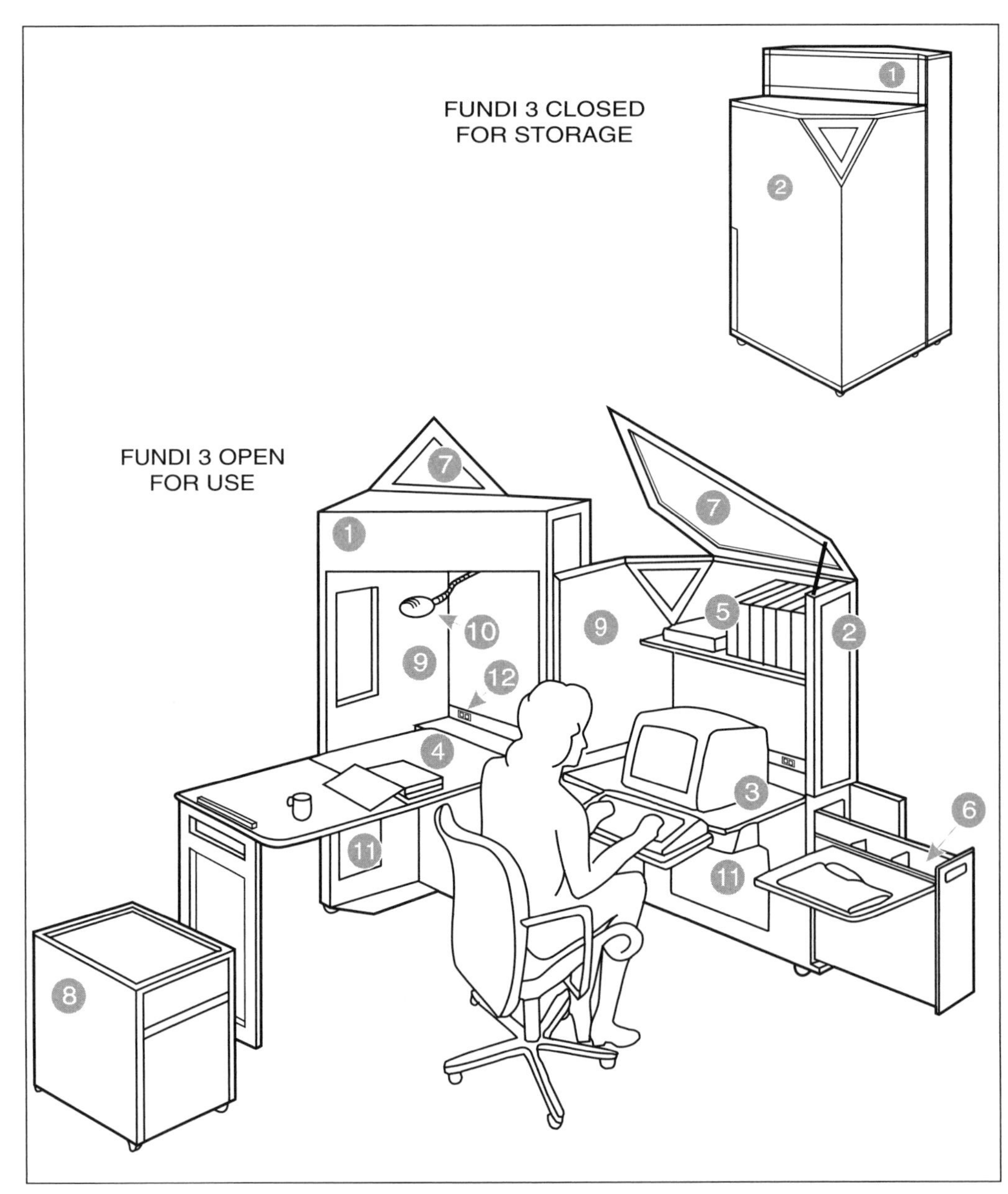

Figure 7.10 The FUNDI workstation and table of its dimensions, shown on the facing page. (*Source:* Adapted from Kaplan 1987b.)

Working to install the different systems in the restricted space of the FUNDI unit's components, they had to do their own work while ensuring that they left enough space for the other trades to complete their installations as well. It was a collaboration with which they were unfamiliar and not always comfortable.

The unit provided a horizontal work surface that could also be tilted to form a slanted surface for working in a standing position (Figure 7.10 and Table 7.2). Adjacent to this work surface was a height-adjustable surface intended for a computer monitor. An under-the-table sliding tray housed the keyboard. There was space for a document holder or for materials to be laid out flat next to the computer screen. A foldout surface to the right of the computer table could serve as a printer stand or an additional work area.

Storage was provided by an overhead bookcase and a movable filing cabinet unit

Table 7.2 FUNDI table of dimensions.

FUNDI III Component	Dimensions	
Complete unit	Floor area when closed	1.00 m² (10.75 ft²)
1. Tall section	Height	1.75 m (69″)
2. Short section	Height	1.45 m (57″)
3. Computer work surface with retractable keyboard tray	Area Height range, from floor Keyboard area Angle of tilt	.46 m x .88 m (19″ x 35″) .61 m – .81 m (24″ – 32″) .28 m x .66 m (11″ x 27″) Up to 45°
4. Other work surface, adjustable as a flat desk or a sloped stand-up table	Area of flat desk Height from floor Area of stand-up work surface Height from floor Angle of tilt	.76 m x 1.26 m (30″ x 51″) .72 m (29″) .76 m x .61 m (30″ x 25″) 1.04 m (42″) 30° – 60°
5. Storage shelves	Area—single shelf	.28 m x .88 m (11″ x 35″)
6. Storage in pull-out drawer	Area—flip-up table Interior of drawer	.41 m x .41 m (17″ x 17″) .44 m x .6 m x .44 m high (18″ x 6″ x 18″ high)
7. Top plates, which can be lifted open	Area—top plates	1.00 m x 1.00 m (39″ x 39″)
8. Movable file unit	Area—top surface Pencil drawer File drawer	.45 m x .61 m (18″ x 25″) .41 m x .57 m x .15 m high (17″ x 23″ x 5″ high) .41 m x .57 m x .32 m high (17″ x 23″ x 13″ high)
9. Tack boards—material around FUNDI	Total area	1.10 m² (11.80 ft²)
10. Task lamp	—	—
11. Radiant heat panels	—	—
12. Electric power and telephone jacks	—	—

with one drawer for office supplies and a standard-size file drawer. Making the filing cabinet separate from the main unit and the same finish as the desktop allowed it to serve as an additional work surface that could be positioned wherever needed. Since the unit was lockable, it was possible for a FUNDI to conveniently serve as a shared work setting. The individual using it simply had to roll his or her filing cabinet over to the FUNDI and it was personalized for that person's use.

The walls and the top of the FUNDI were covered with sound-absorbent material to reduce noise transmission. Testing showed that external sound levels were reduced by about 50% (4 decibels). The top was hinged and could be tilted at different angles to control the amount of light and airflow entering the unit. To complement the background room lighting, the FUNDI had an indirect light fixture and an adjustable task lamp mounted on a flexible "gooseneck."

A desk fan was provided to increase air

movement within the FUNDI. Testing showed that despite its small size, the fan ensured adequate air circulation around the seating area. Thus, the FUNDIs could be placed wherever they were needed in an open plan office area with reasonable assurance of sufficient air movement.

Sedentary work can make people feel cool, especially at their legs and feet. Radiant heat panels installed beneath the work surfaces allowed users to warm their legs and feet to a comfortable level.

All cabling was built into the walls of the unit. An electrical raceway and telephone jacks at the height of the work surface provided convenient access to power and communications. A single service panel connected the unit to the building's services. The space beneath the work surfaces was kept clear, leaving ample leg room. An adjustable, ergonomic chair completed the workstation.

The user could adjust the chair, the height of the computer table and keyboard, and the position of the rolling file cabinet. Work space configuration or layout could be altered by repositioning the file cabinet, employing the foldout work surface, and choosing the slanted or horizontal position for the worktable. The environmental controls provided continuous adjustment of temperature (radiant heat panel), lighting (both the task and indirect lighting), and air movement (desk fan). A window on the side of the unit was equipped with a roll-down blind so users could choose to see outside the unit or to have visual privacy.

The FUNDI was designed to be movable and collapsible. The two halves of the unit were hinged, and the work surfaces could be folded so the workstation collapsed into a 1 meter by 1 meter by 1.75 meter high box (39 inches by 39 inches by 69 inches) that could be locked with the rolling file cabinet and computer terminal inside. Mounted on casters, the FUNDI could then be rolled away for storage.

The design of the FUNDI made initial setup and subsequent adjustments or relocation sufficiently easy that it was practical to rearrange the workstations for short-term activities. For example, members of a work group could be moved together for the duration of a project. The FUNDI could be collapsed, moved, opened, and adjusted by the average office worker without using any tools. During the field trial, some participants did in fact adjust the units to suit their needs.

The approach to flexibility and portability demonstrated in the FUNDI design is also well suited to accommodate part-time office occupants. The office workforce has become increasingly mobile with the availability of more portable technology such as cellular phones and laptop computers. Traditionally, every employee had a permanently assigned work space, regardless of whether he or she used it every day or worked outside the office most of the time.

The FUNDI offered two ways to optimize the use of office space by part-time workers. The units could serve as shared workstations, assigned to individuals on an as-needed basis. Each user would be assigned his or her own lockable rolling file cabinet for personal files and office materials. Moving the file cabinet over to a FUNDI, equipped with hookups for telephone and computer, would, in effect, set it up for that person's use.

Another option was to collapse workstations that were not in use and roll them aside to reclaim the floor space for other activities. Alternative approaches to accommodate mobile office workers are now being widely implemented (see the "Flexibility of Location" and "Telecommuting" subsections in Chapter 2).

Applying the Concepts of Individual Control

The FUNDI project sought to define environmental features that would improve open plan offices for occupants and organizations alike. Not only were the accommodation needs of the open plan office examined in a novel way; the workstation that was built to test these ideas incorporated many features that anticipated and addressed several of the changes we now see in the way offices are used.

An underlying concept of the FUNDI design was that people experience the work setting as an integrated whole, not as the sum of its separate parts. If people's eyes tire from glare on their computer screen, they perceive their work setting to be poor. They do not judge the relative merits of the good seating, adequate desk space, and other positive features against the negative ones to arrive at a balanced weighting. Rather, they complain about their office accommodation in general as well as the glare in particular.

It is the way work settings perform as a whole that determines how well they support office occupants and their activities. Even though separate features may be adequate, in combination they may not provide occupants with a satisfactory environment. Office workstations must be cost-effective, space-efficient, and offer advantages that make them well suited for open plan layouts. Whatever environmental controls are provided must complement standard building services, not conflict with them.

The FUNDI was a research tool built to demonstrate innovative workstation features and rigorously test whether they were useful. It was not designed to be mass-produced nor to be rugged enough for the type of rough handling that commercial products are built to withstand. Commercially available modular furniture systems now incorporate many of the control features used in the FUNDI design. Controls for work surface height, lighting, air movement, radiant heat, and visual privacy are now readily available. In addition to these controls, more recently introduced workstations also provide control of acoustics, sliding doors, and other movable components.

Portability is one feature of the FUNDI that has not been incorporated into commercial office furniture. Although the flexibility of modular furniture is widely promoted, in practice it is rather difficult and time-consuming to change the layout of modular furniture or to move a workstation. However, other means have been used to achieve the same objectives.

It is increasingly common for office workers to regularly spend half-days, full days, or longer away from their workstations. They may be in the facility but working at different locations such as in meeting areas, libraries, and resource centers. Sales staff, consultants, and auditors are but a few categories of employees who may spend a substantial portion of their time outside the building yet require a fully equipped work setting when they return.

Rather than assigning furniture and floor space to each individual, work settings can be shared by a group. Each person has a lockable, portable file cabinet that is rolled to a work setting when she or he needs to be in the office. Each workstation has the same furnishings and services — a concept sometimes called the "universal footprint." This greatly reduces the disruption and expense of company reorganizations because only the people are moved, not the furniture. Personal belongings and some work-related materials are also transported, but this is a small portion of the load normally associated with a move.

Some organizations use technology to provide portability without physically moving workstations. Capitalizing on networked computer systems, a workstation can be electronically personalized by entering a password or inserting a computer-readable card. The individuals' computer files, software, and other utilities are then provided at that workstation. Even their telephone calls can be automatically routed to their new location. These "free-address" workstations or "nonterritorial" office arrangements are forms of shared accommodation well suited to organizations with mobile workforces (see the "Flexibility of Location" and "Telecommuting" subsections in Chapter 2). The concept has been success-

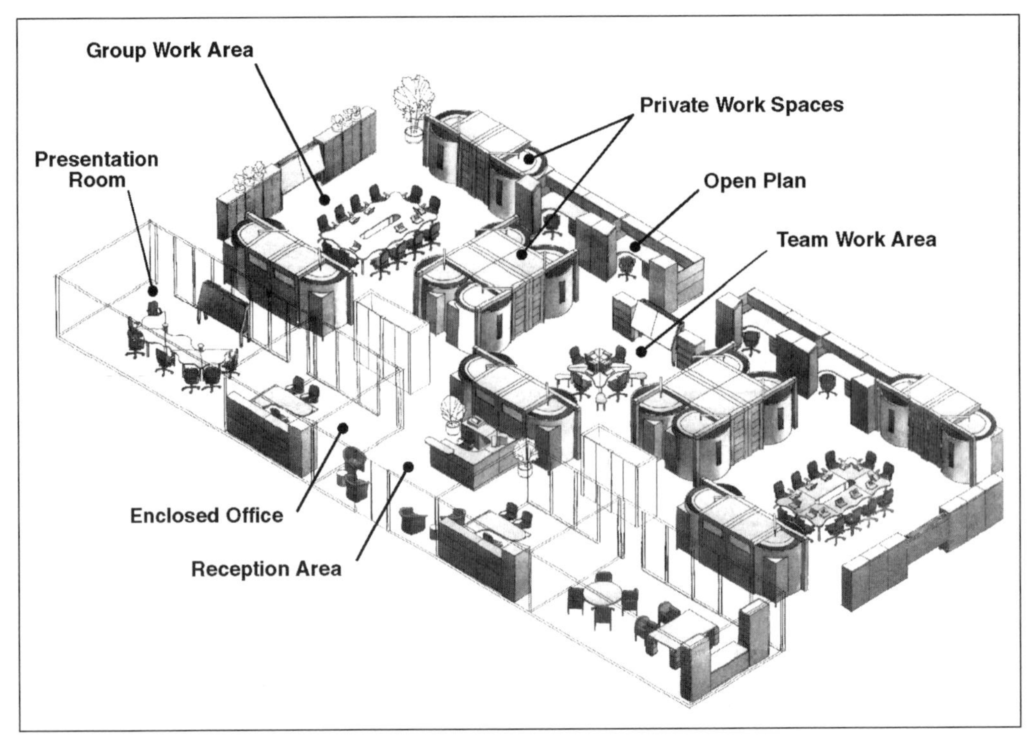

Figure 7.11 Sketch showing a range of work settings that can exist together in an office layout. Various sizes of meeting areas are available for collaborative work. Enclosed spaces can be used as private offices or for group activities when acoustic and visual privacy are desired. Individuals can use the circular work cubicles when they need a a quiet, private work space for concentrated effort. (*Source:* Steelcase, Grand Rapids, Mich.)

Figure 7.12 This office layout illustrates some of the design ideas shown in Figure 7.11. Group work spaces are shown in the foreground and private work cubicles are along the back wall. (*Source:* Steelcase, Grand Rapids, Mich.)

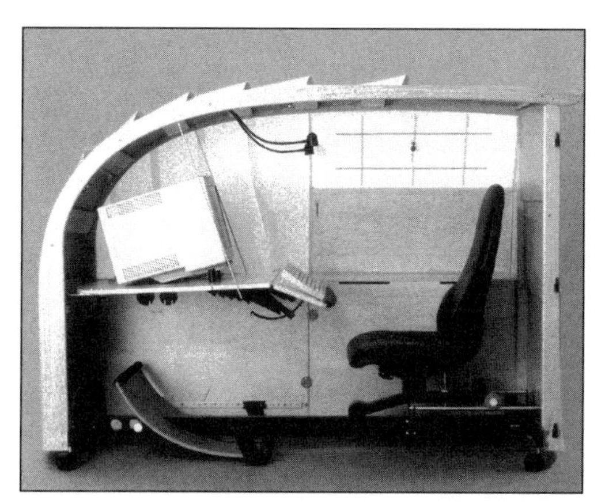

Figure 7.13 This "work capsule" is an unconventional approach to accommodating intensive computer-based knowledge work. (A side wall has been removed to show the interior.) The capsule offers seating and visual conditions suited to computer work in a self-contained unit designed to shield the occupant from office distractions. Lighting and airflow can be adjusted. The side walls can be partially or completely closed to control the degree of enclosure. (*Source:* New Space, Fort Worth, Texas. Design by Douglas Ball.)

fully implemented in offices in the United States, Japan, and elsewhere (Becker 1990).

In organizations where a significant portion of the workforce is mobile, free-address workstations can be a cost-effective means of reducing office space and the number of work settings without compromising work space quality. Although fewer work settings are needed if they are shared, they must be more flexible and durable to accommodate multiple users, so a higher-quality workstation can be justified.

The free-address concept is also valuable when special-purpose workstations are used for only a few hours or a few days at a time. The features that make special-purpose workstations quick to move into and that offer instant access to the same communications and computer networks as permanent work settings, can allow special-purpose settings to be used more efficiently.

No one setting can be optimal for the range of activities needed for creative and productive work, or for both independent and collaborative effort. Sometimes people need to work privately without distractions and at other times a group needs to have an animated meeting. Acknowledging the limitation of assigning individuals a single work area, some organizations offer a range of work settings and let people choose the environment in which they can best get the job done (Figures 7.11, 7.12 and 7.13).

Although people feel a greater sense of belonging and stability when they have their own personal work space, these types of shared arrangements offer practical compromise alternatives. In providing a considerable degree of work space personalization (e.g., automatic routing of phone calls to the person, ready access to personal files) and accommodation designed specifically for mobile workers, individuals are made to feel they have a place in their organization. Office facilities are provided to suit their needs, just as the needs of other office workers are met. Their facilities are just somewhat different because the nature of their work is different.

CONCLUSION

A person's behavior and perceptions are the result of multiple external and internal factors. Their reactions to stress, uncertainties about health risks, and challenges to their feelings of belonging and self-worth are all influenced by the social setting, the physical attributes of their workplace, and the way its operations are organized.

The physical similarities among office workplaces belie their uniqueness. Much of what distinguishes a workplace is the psychosocial environment produced by the interaction of the organization's management style, the personalities of the employees, and the characteristics of the physical office setting.

Ignoring the psychosocial processes at work in the office setting makes them baffling and unexpected sources of disruption to what would seem to be entirely reasonable and workable plans. By understanding the psychosocial dimensions of the office workplace their influence can be anticipated and capitalized upon to improve office design and facility management decisions.

LITERATURE CITED

Baker, G. W., and D. W. Chapman. 1962. *Man and society in disaster.* New York: Basic Books.

Becker, F. 1981. *Work space: Creating environments in organizations.* New York: Praeger Publishers.

Becker, F. 1990. *The total workplace: Facilities management and the elastic organization.* New York: Van Nostrand Reinhold.

Binder, S. 1988. *Corporate facility planning: An inside view for designers and managers.* New York: McGraw-Hill.

Block, L., and G. Stokes. 1989. Performance and satisfaction in private versus nonprivate work settings. *Environment and Behavior* 21(3):277–297.

Brookes M. J. 1972. Office landscape: Does it work? *Applied Ergonomics* 34:224–236.

Brookes, M. J., and A. Kaplan. 1972. The office environment: Space planning and affective behavior. *Human Factors* 14(5):373–391.

Carayon, P. 1993. Effect of electronic performance monitoring on job design and worker stress: Review of the literature and conceptual model. *Human Factors* 35(3):385–395.

Cohen, S., G. W. Evans, D. Stokols, and D. S. Krantz. 1986. *Behavior, health, and environmental stress.* New York: Plenum Press.

Cox, T. 1985. The nature and measurement of stress. *Ergonomics* 28(8):1155–1163.

Erikson, K. 1991. A new species of trouble. In *Communities at risk: Collective responses to technological hazards,* Edited by S. R. Couch and J. S. Kroll-Smith. New York: Peter Lang Publishing.

Frankenhaeuser, M. 1991. The psychophysiology of workload, stress, and health: Comparison between the sexes. *Annals of Behavioral Medicine* 4:197–204.

Frankenhaeuser, M. 1992. The human factor and technology. In *The technological future.* Copenhagen: The Council of the Academies of Engineering and Technological Sciences. 42–43.

Frankenhaeuser, M., and G. Johansson. 1986. Stress at work: Psychobiological and psychosocial aspects. *International Review of Applied Psychology* 35:287–299.

Gaillard, A. W. K. 1993. Comparing the concepts of mental load and stress. *Ergonomics* 36(9):991–1005.

Glass, D. C., and J. E. Singer. 1972. *Urban stress: Experiments on noise and social stressors.* New York: Academic Press.

Hart, S., V. Battiste, M. Chesney, M. Ward, and M. McElroy. 1987. Responses of type A and B individuals performing a supervisory control simulation. In *Social, Ergonomic and Stress Aspects of Work with Computers,* proceedings of the *Second International Conference on Human-Computer Interaction,* edited by G. Salvendy, S. Sauter, and J. Hurrell Jr. Amsterdam: Elsevier Science Publications.

Hedge, A. 1982. The open-plan office: A systematic investigation of employee reactions to their work environment. *Environment and Behavior* 14(5):519–542.

Herzlinger, R., and D. Calkins. 1986. How companies tackle health care costs. Part III. *Harvard Business Review,* January–February, 70–80.

Hockey, G. R. J., R. B. Briner, A. J. Tattersall, and M. Wiethoff. 1989. Assessing the impact of computer workload on operator stress: The role of system controllability. *Ergonomics* 32(11):1401–1418.

IFMA. 1994. *Benchmarks II.* Report #13. Houston: International Facility Management Association.

Johansson, G., and G. Aronsson. 1991. Psychosocial factors in the workplace. In *Work, health, and productivity,* edited by G. Green and F. Baker, 179–197. Oxford, United Kingdom: Oxford University Press.

Kaplan, A. 1985. A functional and diagnostic work enclosure. Master's thesis. Carnegie-Mellon University, Pittsburgh.

Kaplan, A. 1987a. The FUNDI project: A new approach to environmental design for office buildings. Architectural and Engineering Services Report AES 1-4:87-5. Ottawa: Public Works Canada.

Kaplan, A. 1987b. The FUNDI project: A research methodology for investigation of office environments. Architectural and Engineering Services Report AES 1-4:87-6. Ottawa: Public Works Canada.

Kaplan, A. 1989. Hamilton District Office: A total building performance assessment. Ottawa: Public Works Canada, Building Performance Division.

Karacek, R., and T. Theorell. 1990. *Healthy work: Stress, productivity, and the reconstruction of working life.* New York: Basic Books.

Klitzman, S., and J. M. Stellman. 1989. The impact of the physical environment on the psychological well-being of office workers. *Social Science Medicine* 29(6):733–742.

Kroll-Smith, J. S. 1993. Personal communication. Department of Sociology, University of New Orleans.

Kroll-Smith, J. S., and S. R. Couch. 1991. As if exposure to toxins were not enough: The social and cultural system as a secondary stressor. *Environmental Health Perspectives* 95:61–66.

Kroll-Smith, J. S., and S. R. Couch. 1993. Technological hazards: Social responses as traumatic stressors. In *International handbook of traumatic stress syndromes,* edited by J. P. Wilson and B. Raphael, 79–91. New York: Plenum Press.

Leaman, A. 1992. *Open plan offices: Kill or cure?* London: Building Use Studies.

Levine, A. G. 1982. *Love Canal: Science, politics, and people.* Lexington, Mass.: Lexington Books.

Lundberg, U., B. Melin, G. W. Evans, and L. Holmberg. 1993. Physiological deactivation after two contrasting tasks at a video display terminal: Learning vs. repetitive data entry. *Ergonomics* 36(6):601–611.

Matteson, M. T., and J. M. Ivancevich, eds. 1987. *Controlling work stress: Effective human resource and management strategies.* San Francisco: Jossey-Bass.

Miller, P. 1991. A comeback for nuclear power? *National Geographic* 180(2):74.

Moser, G., and C. Levy-Leboyer. 1985. Inadequate environment and situation control: Is a malfunctioning phone always an occasion for aggression? *Environment and Behavior* 17(4):520–533.

OTA. 1985. *Automation of America's offices 1985–2000.* Office of Technology Assessment. Washington, D.C.: U.S. Government Printing Office.

Perrow, C. 1984. *Normal accidents.* New York: Basic Books.

Peters, T. J., and R. H. Waterman Jr. 1984. *In search of excellence: Lessons from America's best-run companies.* New York: Warner Books.

Rissler, A. 1977. Stress reactions at work and after work during a period of quantitative overload. *Ergonomics* 20(5):577–580.

Schwartz, S. P. 1985. Environmental threats, communities and hysteria. *Journal of Public Health* 1:58–77

Seem, J. E., and J. E. Braun. 1992. The impact of personal environmental control on building energy use. *ASHRAE Transactions: Symposia,* part 1: 903–909. Atlanta: American Society of Heating, Refrigerating, and Air-Conditioning Engineers.

Selye, H. 1976. *Stress in health and disease.* Boston: Butterworth Publishers.

Smith, M., P. Carayon, and K. Miezio. 1987. Electronic monitoring and job stress. In *Social, Ergonomic and Stress Aspects of Work with Computers,* proceedings of the *Second International Conference on Human-Computer Interaction,* edited by G. Salvendy, S. Sauter, and J. Hurrell Jr. Amsterdam: Elsevier Science Publications.

Sundstrom E., R. K. Herbert, and D. W. Brown. 1982. Privacy and communication in an open-plan office. *Environment and Behavior* 14:379–392.

Sundstrom E., J. P. Town, D. W. Brown, A. Forman, and C. McGee. 1982. Physical enclosure, type of job and privacy in the office. *Environment and Behavior* 14:543–559.

Zalesny, M. D., R. V. Farace, and R. Kurchner-Hawkins. 1985. Determinants of employee work perceptions and attitudes: Perceived work environment and organizational level. *Environment and Behavior* 17(5):567–592.

1.000 1.000 4.000
5.000 5.000 3.000
4.000 4.000 1.898
3.204 3.146 0.918
1.118 1.010 0.131
0.160 0.146
MINIMUM
MAXIMUM
RANGE
MEAN
forward
upright
recline
Type
sit upright
recline
46%
Activity Level
active sitter
quiet sitter
neither
65%
24%
11%
65%
20%
15%
N=274
ILLUMINANCE RATIO (N/H)

Chapter 8

WORKPLACE DIAGNOSTICS

Buildings have always been evaluated by those who used them. When people built their own houses, they improved design and construction methods by trial and error; and the process of design evaluation and the introduction of improvements were straightforward. To improve the utility and comfort of their structures, people added new features they developed themselves or learned from others. Incrementally, traditional building designs evolved as a natural component of a region's resources and culture.

In cold climates, tight construction and good insulation kept out drafts and made dwellings warmer. In hot climates, increasing natural ventilation and using heavy walls could keep a building interior cool. Other innovations offered greater design flexibility, improvements in durability, ease of construction, and cost economies. The way buildings are designed and constructed continues to change in response to the evolving needs of the people and organizations that use them and as advances in building technology present new possibilities.

Today's office buildings are far more complex than the simpler structures of the past. Systems for lighting, electrical power, HVAC (heating, ventilating, and air-conditioning), and the structure are designed by specialists. The characteristics of the indoor environment are determined not only by the features of these systems but also by the myriad ways they interact. Although individual building systems are designed to meet specific performance criteria, the way people will perceive and react to the total office environment is only really known after it is in use.

As with any design profession, office building design has seen many styles and approaches come and go. Each has sought to change the established design ideas of its day. In promoting different design objectives and priorities, they altered the way in which trade-offs were made during the design process.

In the 1960s, there was pointed criticism of how poorly the buildings of the time met the needs of those who used them. Books such as *Personal Space* and *Tight Spaces* by Robert Sommer (1969, 1974) highlighted the deficiencies of the architecture and design professions' building practice. They portrayed architecture as a profession so enthralled with its own images of proper housing, schools, and offices that it had lost touch with or dismissed the way people actually lived, played, and worked in them.

Social scientists as well as members of the design professions participated in exposing these dysfunctions in the built environment and in calling for reform. In order for occupants to be better satisfied, their perceptions and opinions had to be heard and incorporated into evaluations of building performance. Social scientists were instrumental in developing a form of building evaluation known as **post-occupancy evaluation** (**POE**), which focused on the assessment of occupant satisfaction.

POST-OCCUPANCY EVALUATION

In the 1970s, there was tremendous interest in relating the behavioral sciences to the design disciplines (see, for example, Canter 1970; Gutman 1972; Newman 1972; Rubin and Elder 1980). It was assumed at that time that the study of user requirements in buildings would become a major research activity and that the training of architects would emphasize behavioral issues. However, the energy crisis of the mid-1970s shifted research efforts away from the broader issues of building performance to the narrower objective of conserving energy. That change in focus was soon followed by a wave of occupant complaints about the environmental quality of offices.

POEs were designed to evaluate building performance from the occupants' perspective. Over time, POE has developed into a wide range of evaluation procedures involving time frames of a couple of days to several months and commanding study teams of a few experts to large multidisciplinary teams. POE activity in the United States and Canada peaked in the 1980s, with most projects being sponsored by governments or large institutions.

POE activity fell off sharply during the economic recession of the early 1990s. Interest in occupant satisfaction became progressively more focused on such tangible and quantifiable issues as energy costs, occupancy cost per employee, absenteeism and turnover, the cost of reconfiguring work spaces, and white-collar productivity.

Initially, POEs emphasized the measurement of occupant satisfaction (see, for example, Becker 1989). An understanding of the way the built environment affects human behavior is valuable in recognizing and addressing many building problems. But the cause of most workplace performance deficiencies lies in the way buildings are designed, operated, and used (see the section "Why Buildings Fail" later in this chapter). Without an architectural and engineering understanding of how buildings function, management cannot successfully translate workplace evaluations into specific retrofits or design directives. An expert understanding of both how buildings function as well as a knowledge of the way they affect behavior are needed to resolve facility problems and optimize workplace performance.

What's more, the complex and diverse issues of today's offices demand that any diagnostic evaluation assess the combined effects of a building's systems on the activities of the organization and the individuals who use it.

A **building diagnosis** is a directed investigation of the performance an organization receives from the facility it occupies. A building diagnosis that is focused on the performance of office space we term a

workplace diagnosis. It limits consideration of general building system performance to those aspects that directly affect the areas where the work of the organization is carried out (i.e., the occupied space). However, the evaluation necessarily includes those aspects of the site, building enclosure, structure, and building services that have important effects on the interior space. For example, to assess thermal comfort in perimeter locations, it is necessary to consider the exterior walls' design and construction.

A building diagnosis, or the more focused workplace diagnosis described here, is an expert evaluation conducted under the direction of a qualified diagnostic specialist. Although the discussion in this chapter concentrates on the diagnosis of office space — the theme of this book — the principles can also be usefully applied to other types of facilities.

WORKPLACE DIAGNOSTICS

Workplace diagnostics is similar to the form of diagnosis used in medical practice. It is a directed inquiry performed by an experienced expert. The assistance of other specialists may be sought if more detailed testing and evaluation are needed.

The workplace diagnostics practitioner should possess a good theoretical background and considerable experience in how buildings are designed and constructed, the way building services operate and interact, and the way buildings affect people.

Workplace diagnostics draws upon such diverse fields as engineering, architecture, management, psychology, sociology, and medicine. The use of the extensive knowledge and techniques from these interrelated disciplines greatly improves the diagnostic effort.

The strength of a diagnosis rests on the use of a systematic but flexible investigative approach wherein progressively more detailed information is collected and analyzed. A more or less standard procedure may be used in the initial inquiry, but then subsequent tests and analyses are selected as the particular situation warrants. Such an approach improves the likelihood that the information needed to address an issue will be obtained and utilized in a cost-effective manner, and that unexpected but important issues that arise will be recognized and considered.

The course of an investigation, its time frame, and ultimately its success are as much dependent on the skills and experience of the diagnostician as they are on the complexity of the problem. Therein lies the art and science of a diagnosis. Every office is unique, yet with experience, the relevant similarities can be recognized and used to guide the development of realistic solutions to facility performance issues.

Why Diagnose a Workplace?

The principal concern of a workplace diagnosis is to evaluate how well a facility meets an organization's needs. Making changes to the facility, the way it is managed, or the way it is used can improve a building's performance and thus its usefulness to an organization and its occupants.

Every building design involves performance trade-offs. Once a building is in operation, undesirable and unexpected characteristics are invariably found. Mismatches between occupant needs and a facility's performance can be costly to an organization. In some cases, they can be resolved by modifying the building or the way it is operated. In other cases, they may simply be too expensive to fix, and either they must be tolerated or alternative accommodations must be found.

The most common reason that organizations commission a diagnosis of their workplace is to resolve specific occupant complaints such as poor indoor air quality, excessive noise, or troublesome lighting. But a diagnosis can also be valuable when there aren't specific problems to be solved. A diagnosis can be a proactive measure to improve the quality of a workplace environment, reduce costs, or enhance the value received from accommodation expenditures.

Baseline data collected when building operations were satisfactory are valuable in resolving building problems when they arise. A diagnosis may be used to establish baseline measures against which future changes to the workplace, such as a renovation, can be compared.

The regular collection and documentation of office quality measurements can be used to improve building operations and to demonstrate the measures the building owner has taken to identify and resolve potential health problems. With the increase in litigation related to the quality of the office environment, diagnostic investigations are also being seen as a way to document workplace conditions and to demonstrate that reasonable diligence has been exercised to ensure a healthy workplace.

The better an office facility is matched to the work activities housed within, the more effectively it can support the organization. Commercial office buildings are commonly designed and built before the tenant is known. The overall performance obtained from such facilities can often be improved by adjusting building operations and patterns of use so that the location and characteristics of the occupants' activities are better matched to the characteristics and capabilities of the building.

Findings from a workplace diagnosis identify what needs to be done, the order of priority, and the likely benefits — be they economic or directed at the workforce. Occupants generally view workplace improvements as a concrete demonstration of management commitment to and interest in their health and well-being. As such, improvements to the office environment can boost worker morale and enhance productivity.

What Should a Diagnosis Deliver?

A diagnostic workplace evaluation should define the objectives of the study and any specific issues that were to be addressed. The evaluation methods used, data collected, and analysis results should be documented. In order for the diagnostic process to initiate effective change, a prioritized set of recommendations must be developed that details specific actions to be taken and a way to monitor their effects. It is difficult to justify expenditures to enhance facility performance unless there is a reliable means to identify whether the desired results were indeed obtained.

The diagnostic process usually requires that the occupants and management of the client organization be kept informed of the evaluation activities. For example, some studies include questionnaires that the occupants complete. So it would be impossible to conduct the study without notifying them. In fact, to obtain good results (i.e., a high response rate and conscientious completion of the questionnaires), it is essential that the participants support the effort. This is often achieved by informing occupants of the study objectives and then later of the eventual outcome. What's more, by demonstrating a commitment to address and resolve building issues important to the occupants, the communication process can itself generate goodwill and raise employee morale.

For this reason, the way in which information about the objectives and results of a study are communicated is critical to the success of a diagnosis. Typically, the occupants as well as management must be kept informed of the progress of the evaluation activities. The information presented to different groups is usually tailored to their needs and interests. For example, occupants' interests are generally focused on the quality of the office areas in which they work, whereas facility managers have a broader range of concerns such as the operation and maintenance of building service equipment.

Key to a successful diagnosis is the development of objectives that will suit the client's needs and a project scope consistent with the available time and budget. The criteria by which the project's success will be judged can then be defined before work begins. In doing so, most misunderstandings between the client and diagnostician about the purpose of the work and the way it will be done can be resolved early in the process, and the diagnostic evaluation will be more likely to develop cost-effective workplace enhancements.

The Need for Periodic Workplace Evaluations

A diagnostic evaluation is not a onetime effort. The office workplace is dynamic. It is estimated that American organizations move about a third of their office employees each year (IFMA 1994; Brill 1987). As an organization's range of work activities and equipment change, the demands placed on an office facility are altered, and its operations and patterns of use should be adjusted accordingly. For example, computers and other electronic equipment are more sensitive to voltage fluctuations than mechanical and electrical equipment such as fans and lights. The widespread use of computers in offices has required that there be less variation in the voltage level of the electrical power supply. As well, the heat generated by computers, laser printers, and other office technology has greatly increased the cooling capacity required in office areas.

Occupants often try to modify the operation of building services that annoy them, and offices are rife with signs of the battles that people wage against their building systems. They block air grilles (also termed diffusers) to stop drafts, and cover windows to reduce glare. In doing so, they often affect conditions in areas other than their own. For example, blocking one air diffuser increases the air velocity at other vents along the same supply duct, so troublesome drafts may be created at another location. The frustration of wrestling with the work environment is wasted effort that might otherwise be used more productively (see the section "Stress and the Work Environment" in Chapter 7).

Some facility performance problems are created inadvertently, such as when furniture is rearranged, obstructing air vents, or the air circulation around a thermostat is blocked, compromising temperature regulation.

Changes that occur outside an office building can also affect the indoor conditions (see the section "Site" in Chapter 4). Renovations to nearby buildings, new transportation facilities, local amenities, and the installation of new municipal services may cause unexpected power disruptions, noise, increased particle load from airborne dust, and unpleasant odors.

The monitoring of building performance and mitigation of deficiencies should be a routine component of the facility management process (see the section "The Facility Management Domain" in Chapter 9). In most cases, problems can be handled as part of normal facility management services. However, when situations arise that are not adequately resolved with the available resources, the more specialized expertise and detailed analysis of a diagnostic evaluation may be required.

WHY BUILDINGS FAIL

No building is perfect. A building is the practical manifestation of its designer's ideal solution. The design process seeks to define a practical physical structure that will satisfy the client's objectives and aesthetic preferences.

Decisions made early on in the design process reduce the options available as the project develops. For example, the choice of structural system defines the number and size of supporting columns, which, in turn, constrain the possible floor layouts.

Figure 8.1 Conflicts between environmental control devices can interfere with their operation. This dimmer switch generated heat that warmed the thermostat mounted above it on the wall. As a result, the thermostat, sensing a warmer temperature than its setting, correctly signaled the mechanical system to cool the room. Since no amount of cooling could counter the heat from the dimmer switch, the room was continually cooled whenever the dimmer was on, making it uncomfortably cold for the occupants.

The range of options is progressively reduced as more and more design decisions are finalized.

Contemporary office buildings are complex structures. The separate building system components interact with each other in myriad ways, and the preferred solution for one system may compromise another. As a result, trade-offs must be made throughout the design process.

The complexity of office facilities also makes it virtually impossible to predict the way each building system will interact with every other. Oversights invariably occur. For instance, it is not unusual for components of different building service systems to conflict with each other. One example, from a recently renovated high-class hotel, involved interference between two control systems. A conference room remained cool even after the thermostat setting was repeatedly raised. Both the lighting and the air-handling systems were in good working order. The problem lay in the positioning of environmental controls on the wall. The ceiling lights were adjusted by a dimmer switch mounted on the wall just below the thermostat (Figure 8.1). This type of dimmer switch generated heat. The air heated by the dimmer switch rose, bathing the thermostat immediately above it in warm air. So the thermostat detected a high temperature and activated the air-conditioning. Though the occupants were cold, as long as the dimmer switch was in operation, the thermostat continually indicated a need for cooling.

When the interference was stopped, by switching the lights off or by taping a cardboard divider to the wall between the dimmer switch and the thermostat, the room heated up to a normal temperature. This facility performance problem had been "designed" into the building simply because the interaction of two apparently independent systems — heat and light — had not been foreseen. Correcting the problem simply required moving one of the controls.

Some design details are difficult or impossible to construct as specified. The weather, the weight and characteristics of the materials, the space needed for the assembler to work, and numerous other factors determine the degree to which a conscientious and skilled worker can build what has been drawn by the designer.

Figure 8.2 shows an example of a "watchmaker" detail, so named because a high degree of precision and skill are needed to construct it. The tradesperson is required to cut a concrete block to fit tightly around a steel I beam. Concrete block is an aggregate material with a hollow core. So the material tends to crumble and break at the edges when it is cut. It would therefore be virtually impossible to shape the block to achieve a tight fit with the beam. The space created by the irregular cut edge provided a path for air to pass into the wall cavity. In winter, humid interior air seeping through this opening condensed inside the wall, wetting the insulation and other materials. Not only was this area of the building uncomfortably cool and drafty from the high heat loss near this opening; the wetting accelerated deterioration of the wall, making the heat loss progressively worse over time and eventually requiring an expensive repair.

Figure 8.2 Example of a "watchmaker" construction detail, so named because it requires that components be assembled with high precision in order to fit correctly. Here, the design called for concrete block to be cut and tightly fitted against a steel I beam. But this material cannot be finely worked, so large gaps were left through which air could move freely, increasing heat loss.

Conflicting Service Specialties

Building performance deficiencies are often the result of poor coordination among the different building design specialties. No single individual has the knowledge and skill to design all the various systems required in today's complex office structures. So office buildings are in fact designed by teams of experts, united by the same goal but with somewhat different priorities and emphasis. Office building design teams typically include architects, interior designers, lighting engineers, acousticians, structural engineers, and HVAC system design specialists.

Architects are responsible for the building's aesthetic design and for ensuring that the different component systems are properly integrated and function together correctly. However, in practice, the experts who design each component system set specifications in accordance with the design standards of their specialties.

Specialists tend to operate separately, developing their own type of drawings, notation, standards, and language (jargon).

When the work of the different specialists is coordinated, their designs must be interpreted by experts in other disciplines, architects, and others less expert in a specific system than the designer. Problems can easily occur if this information is misinterpreted during the design and construction stages.

Much discussion and sincere effort have been directed toward integrating the work and responsibilities of the different building design specialties. But the increasing specialization of these professions runs counter to the need for them to understand each other's technical areas so that their designs will function better together. Coordinating the different building service specialties has always been a major challenge (see, for example, Leaman and Bordass 1993; Barton 1983; Butler 1977). To some extent, the problems of coordination result from human error. There are so many details that it simply isn't possible to get every one of them right.

Coordination problems most commonly occur where different services come together in a limited space. For example, lighting, air handling, and cabling may all be placed in the **ceiling plenum** (the area above a suspended ceiling). During construction or renovation, the installation of these services may conflict with each other and with the structure itself. For example, the opening in a concrete wall through which a ventilation duct is to pass may be missing, or an opening may be too small for all the services it must accommodate.

Service corridors are generally specified at an early stage in the design process to allow the architect to finalize the building shape and develop the overall design. So service corridor space requirements commonly must be derived from estimates of the expected service loadings rather than from the final specifications of the building's system designs. The building's owner may also pressure the designers to minimize service spaces so as to maximize the building's occupied or rentable areas. As a result, the size and shape of service corridors are often underestimated, especially for newer technologies such as computer networks. It is common when renovating or modernizing office buildings to find that there isn't enough space in cable service corridors for the amount of cabling to be installed.

Figure 8.3 This ductwork for a new air-handling system has to bend over structural floor supports, twist around columns, and fit in between ceiling lights. The circuitous routing reduces the systems' performance and also makes the work space look cluttered.

Poor coordination between the services compromises building performance in several ways. Unexpected changes made in the design or installation can easily impact the quality of the service or the cost to operate it. For example, unnecessarily large openings through a wall dramatically increase the sound transmission across it.

A design change that requires ducts to be routed around obstructions can significantly alter the performance of the ventilation system, especially if it affects multiple locations on every floor of an office tower (Figure 8.3). Each bend in a system of ductwork increases its internal resistance to airflow. More power is then needed to force air through the system, raising the energy consumption as well as the noise generated in the ductwork. Similarly, in constructing multistory office buildings, an error on one floor may be repeated on others, so problems can quickly multiply unless they are recognized early.

Figure 8.4 Designers, consultants, project managers, building foremen, contractors, and subcontractors meet regularly during construction to report on progress and resolve problems that occur. Good communication between the parties involved is a large part of a successful construction process and satisfactory completion of a building. (*Source:* Bell-Northern Research (BNR).)

Although rigorous project management can avert these types of problems, many services are only installed after the structure is well advanced, at which time there are fewer opportunities and fewer options for making corrections.

The inadequate coordination of service specialties causes inconsistencies in virtually every office building. Most problems are resolved on-site during construction (Figure 8.4). These ad hoc solutions may or may not impact the overall performance of the office facility. But the building that is delivered always deviates to some extent from the one shown in the plans. Sometimes it is only when problems arise in the office environment that these differences are discovered.

For example, air quality problems have been caused by **soil stacks** (pipes that vent exhaust fumes from the sewage plumbing) that were blocked by lunch bags and other debris left during construction. In another case, the soil stacks had not been extended to the roof and instead ended in the ceiling plenum. It was only after occupants complained of sewage odors in their office space that the problem was found and corrected.

Better coordination between the different system specialists at the design stage would be helpful but isn't always possible. Many buildings are designed and constructed before a purchaser or tenants have been identified. So the customization of the interior to meet the tenant's requirements (also called the **fit-up**) is done after the building is sold or rented, at which time it may be partially or completely finished.

Although a coordinated approach to the design and management of new construction is a worthwhile objective, it will be slow to achieve because it requires shifting the training and attitudes of several professional groups. A more immediate and feasible task is to evaluate the performance of completed buildings in actual use. Not only can the performance of the individual buildings be improved; the experience gained can be used to improve the design and construction of office workplaces.

It is simpler to design individual building systems in relative isolation (a building system can never be designed in complete isolation) than to adopt a more integrated approach. However, simplicity has

Figure 8.5 This hot-water heating system had to be installed early on in the construction process because its pipes were embedded in the concrete. Left unprotected, the delicate fins of this heater were easily damaged by construction activity and debris. Radiators damaged in this way work less effectively.

its costs in unexpected facility performance problems. The greater effort and initial expense that may be needed to improve design decisions should not serve as an excuse for providing inefficient or unsatisfactory buildings.

Construction Practices

There is a well-established sequence to the construction of office buildings. Unfortunately, the order in which tradespeople are scheduled often results in their inadvertently undoing the good work already completed. Through diligent on-site project management and field inspections, most of these problems are routinely found and resolved during construction, without incident. However, not all problems are found. Some are built in and become permanent features of the building.

Components that remain exposed for some time after they are installed may subsequently be damaged. In Figure 8.5, the fins of this radiator were bent and covered with debris during construction, impairing its performance. Because the pipes were embedded in the concrete floor, it had to be installed early on in the construction. As a result, the heater's relatively delicate fins were exposed to the traffic and debris of heavy construction work.

Electrical wiring is installed after most of the building's structure has been completed and after many systems, such as plumbing and ventilation, have been installed. Electricians often have to move batts of snugly fitted insulation to run electrical wiring through walls to install power outlets and overhead light fixtures. Unfortunately, the insulation may not be carefully replaced afterward, as shown in Figure 8.6. In this case, the insulation no longer filled the space tightly, so air moved freely through the gaps and much of the insulation's benefit was lost. Minor oversights such as this can have significant effects if they occur frequently. The insulating efficiency of a building can be

Figure 8.6 Good work can be undone when it must be disturbed for the installation or maintenance of other building services. The arrow indicates where well-fitted insulation was displaced during the installation of electrical wiring for an overhead light.

Figure 8.7 This hot-water radiator was incorrectly installed through a partition dividing two rooms. Not only would the radiator have performed poorly; sound would have been readily transmitted between the rooms. This error was found and corrected during construction.

substantially reduced and operating costs increased — for the life of the building — if the insulation is poorly fitted at many electrical outlets and light fixtures.

In Figure 8.7, a hot-water radiator along an exterior wall was installed through the partition dividing two rooms. Some 10 centimeters (4 inches) of the fin was enclosed within the wall, and the remainder was in the corner of the room rather than centered along the wall. Not only would the effectiveness of this radiator have been severely reduced; the hole in the wall for the radiator would have readily transmitted sound between the offices. The poor acoustic separation between the offices would have been problematic to the occupants. This error was identified and corrected before construction was completed. The single radiator was replaced with separate ones for each room, and the hole through the partition was sealed.

Accessing one building system during construction or maintenance activities frequently requires that others be temporarily disconnected. There is always the risk that a component will not be correctly reconnected. During one diagnostic investigation, it was found that some air vents in the ceiling plenum had been disconnected from their supply lines. The hoses interfered with access to other equipment being serviced, and it appeared that they had been disconnected and forgotten. As a result, several offices were not properly ventilated. Though the occupants had complained about the stuffiness of their work spaces, their complaints had been ignored — largely because it had been assumed that in a large modern office building designed to deliver consistent thermal conditions throughout, a *real* problem would have affected a larger area. But in practice, buildings often operate in unintended ways.

The process of converting a design into a built form requires that the tradespeople doing the work constantly choose the way each element will be constructed. For example, they frequently need to resolve mismatches between prefabricated components that don't quite fit. The innumerable difficulties they consider to be minor they resolve themselves. What they perceive to be serious problems they bring to the attention of the managing architect or engineer on the site.

The performance of the completed building, in the end, depends heavily on these myriad choices made during construction and the care with which the work is done. Competent workers are not infallible, nor is their work identical. There will be inconsistencies because individuals differ in the way they choose to do a job. So there will be some aspects of the building design that do not perform as intended because they were not built as well as they could be or because the tradespeople could not construct them as designed.

Operation and Maintenance Practices

The way a facility is managed directly affects the cost to operate and maintain it, the quality of the work environment, and as a consequence, occupant satisfaction and the facility's overall value to the organization. Facility management practices have a major influence on the level of performance that an organization receives from its office facilities. Traditionally, an organization's performance criteria have focused on monetary costs and financial returns. The capital cost of the building, the opportunity cost of investing those funds in real estate, the cost of rented space, the amount of floor area per employee, the annual accommodation cost per employee, and annual servicing expenses are hard costs that are readily calculated from standard accounting records.

More difficult to evaluate are the future costs of current maintenance procedures. For example, lax equipment maintenance will increase repair costs and the failure rate of building systems. Delayed recognition and repair of problems with the building exterior will increase long-term maintenance costs because, as the building's exterior protection is lost, deterioration caused by rain, snow, and temperature extremes will accelerate. As the performance of the building enclosure declines, the interior environment will be affected. Increased heat loss, uncontrolled airflow across the exterior wall, and the infiltration of water can damage the interior and make climate control more costly and less consistent.

Quantifying the cost of poor building services to an organization is difficult and controversial. In addition to such costs as increased energy consumption and maintenance expenses, there are costs resulting from lower worker productivity. People do not work as effectively and fatigue more quickly when they are stressed — be it from psychological or physical discomfort. The noise from a faulty light fixture or poorly installed ductwork, or a chilling blast of cool air received whenever the ventilation system starts up can be constant sources of annoyance. Though their productivity cost cannot readily be measured, as discussed throughout this book, people's physical comfort affects their behavior and performance. Thus, satisfactory facility management services are important not only to maintain the value of the building; but more importantly, by optimizing the performance of its office facility, an organization can ensure that the workplace environment is not compromising the performance of its workforce.

STANDARDS AND GUIDELINES

There is little that is standard about offices or people. Standards and guidelines provide a valuable starting point for the design of office environments. They should not, however, be used blindly. Strict adherence to accepted standards will not guarantee a suitable or desirable workplace solution.

As discussed in previous chapters, human response to the office environment varies considerably. Some people are more sensitive to environmental stressors than others. There are people who are larger or smaller than the range of body sizes that office furnishings are designed to accommodate. They tend to be less comfortable with and more inconvenienced by conventional furniture solutions. People with disabilities face additional challenges. To those in wheelchairs, a standard water fountain is virtually inaccessible.

Given the range of individual response, it can be expected that some portion of occupants will find certain aspects of the workplace to be poorly suited to their needs. What level of occupant satisfaction should be considered adequate? What level of occupant complaints is acceptable?

Most environmental irritants in the office, particularly toxic substances, exhibit a **dose-response** effect over at least a portion of their range of conditions. That is, as the level or dosage of the factor increases, the response — the number of people affected and the severity of their symptoms — increases as well. Air contaminants commonly behave in this manner. Some conditions exhibit a **threshold effect** — at levels below the individual's threshold, there are no symptoms. Odors below a person's threshold of detection have no effect. Other factors, such as illumination, have an optimal range. A room can be too dark as well as too bright.

In developing standards and guidelines for the office workplace, the severity of the human response as well as the type of response should be taken into account. Some environmental factors have such serious consequences that standards seek to ensure no one will be adversely affected. The level of asbestos fibers considered acceptable in office air is set low enough that no office worker would be expected to develop an asbestos-related illness (which is often fatal). Where the consequences resulting from a negative response are less serious, standards are generally set at a level expected to satisfy most people. The criterion commonly used is an occupant satisfaction of 80% (i.e., the level at which 80% of the workforce would be expected to be satisfied).

The 80% satisfaction guideline for a given environmental factor is usually determined by exposing a group of people, believed to be representative of the office workforce, to different levels of the factor and evaluating their responses. To ensure that the observed responses are a result of the environmental factor being evaluated, tests are conducted under controlled laboratory conditions to eliminate influences other than the one being tested. Although this procedure is necessary for the tests to be scientifically rigorous, these conditions also limit the relevance of the data. The environment of an operating office is quite different from that of a laboratory setting — even if it is designed to look like a standard office. In a real office, people work under the pressures of their jobs and are simultaneously exposed to multiple stressors, not to one suboptimal environmental factor at a time.

As well, the makeup of a particular group of office occupants may be quite different from the test group used to develop a particular standard or guideline. As a result, the proportion of occupants satisfied will be somewhat different from that predicted. For example, the average age of the occupants might be significantly higher. People tend to become less tolerant of physical stressors with age. Older eyes adapt less quickly to illumination differences, so bright areas in the field of view can be more distracting. Bacterial infections, such as Legionnaires' disease, are more likely to occur in older people and those already weakened by illness.

Office quality guidelines are almost always based on people's response to a single factor. But in the office, people are exposed to multiple environmental factors simultaneously. Many environmental stressors exhibit **synergistic effects** — two factors acting together have a greater effect than the sum of their individual effects. When an environmental factor is at a level close to but below an individual's tolerance, it can impose a stress on the body that increases sensitivity to other environmental factors. Thus, even when there are no apparent symptoms, an environmental stressor may have hidden effects.

Since standards are developed by testing one factor at a time, they tend to overestimate the proportion of occupants who will be satisfied. Even if synergistic effects are ignored and environmental factors are

Table 8.1 Expected effect of multiple environmental sensitivity on occupant satisfaction with the work environment.

Number of factors	% Satisfied with all factors	% Dissatisfied with at least one factor
1	80	20
2	64	36
3	51	49
4	41	59
5	33	67
6	26	74

assumed to act independently, the 80% guideline, blindly followed, still produces some unsettling results.

Assuming that the subjects used to develop the guidelines accurately represented the office worker population, then 80% of the occupants should be satisfied with any given factor. However, it is unlikely that the same 20% who are dissatisfied with the temperature would also be dissatisfied with the lighting. Due to natural variations among people, it can be expected that different people will be sensitive to different factors.

Thus, if it is expected that 20% of a group will be dissatisfied with the light level and 20% will be dissatisfied with the temperature, the proportion of people dissatisfied with the light level and/or the temperature would be somewhat greater than 20%. How much greater than 20% depends on how likely it is for someone sensitive to temperature to be sensitive to lighting as well.

If people sensitive to temperature have the same likelihood as anyone else of being sensitive to light level, then the proportion sensitive to temperature and/or light would theoretically be 36%. Sixty-four percent would be satisfied with both temperature and lighting. Only if *all* the people sensitive to temperature were also sensitive to light (a very unlikely event) would the proportion of people dissatisfied with light and/or temperature be 20% and the proportion of people satisfied with those factors be 80%.

So for two environmental factors, each set at levels designed to satisfy 80% of the office workers, between 64% and 80% would probably be satisfied. The more highly correlated the individual sensitivities of people, the closer would the proportion of occupants satisfied with all environmental factors be to the 80% level.

In practice, sensitivity to multiple factors is not perfectly correlated, and so as more factors of the office environment are considered, there will be fewer people satisfied with all of them (Table 8.1). The table assumes that a person sensitive to one factor is no more or less likely to be sensitive to the others. Note that for three environmental factors, the proportion of satisfied people is expected to be only 51%, even though the environmental conditions for each factor are expected to satisfy 80% of the group! As a result, even when it is assumed that guidelines correctly predict satisfaction, if environmental factors are maintained at the levels expected to satisfy 80% of the occupants, substantially less than 80% would find the office environment acceptable.

Results from occupant surveys suggest that the actual level of occupant satisfaction for multiple environmental factors is much *less* than these predicted values. Table 8.2 presents occupant satisfaction data from an office building that was known *not* to be a sick building. As expected, when the effects of more factors are considered together, the proportion of occupants dissatisfied with at least one of

Table 8.2 Survey data from a relatively good building showing the combined effect of multiple factors on occupant satisfaction (Leaman 1994). Key to factors: *L*, lighting; *N*, noise; *WAQ*, winter air quality; *SAQ*, summer air quality; *WT*, winter temperature; *ST*, summer temperature.

Groups of factors	% Satisfied with all factors in group	% Dissatisfied with at least one factor
L	40	60
L + N	14	86
L + N + WAQ	9	91
L + N + WAQ + SAQ	7	93
L + N + WAQ + SAQ + WT	5	95
L + N + WAQ + SAQ + WT + ST	3	97

them increases. For example, 60% of occupants were dissatisfied with factor 1 (lighting), but 86% were dissatisfied with factors 1 or 2 (lighting or noise). When all six factors are considered together, 97% of the occupants were dissatisfied with at least one of them.

This is a considerably higher rate of dissatisfaction than predicted in Table 8.1, suggesting that the assumptions on which the predicted values were based are optimistic — at least in the case of this building. For example, satisfaction with lighting in this building was only 40%, whereas in Table 8.1 it was assumed that 80% of the occupants would be satisfied with the conditions for a single factor.

Simply exceeding performance guidelines by two or three times to counteract this degradation of satisfaction levels by multiple factors is no guarantee of improved office quality. For example, increasing the proportion of outside air brought into a building can improve indoor air quality by diluting chemical contaminants — but not in all cases. It depends on the rate of outside air already being supplied to the space and the rate at which air contaminants are being released (see the subsection "Increase Dilution by Increasing the Outside Air Fraction" in Chapter 5). At low rates of outside air intake, increasing the outside air fraction can produce dramatic improvements. But the dilution effect is diminished as the outside air fraction is increased. So if it is already high, increasing it further will yield little improvement.

Little is currently known about synergistic air quality effects (Lippy and Turner 1991; Mølhave 1990). As a result, measuring the level of a selected group of air contaminants will not necessarily rule out the presence of an air quality problem. It can only determine whether the factors measured fall within current guidelines. Guidelines change as new information becomes available. During the energy crisis of the 1970s and 1980s, ASHRAE lowered its recommended outside air guideline from 10 liters/second/person (20 cubic feet/minute/person) to 2.5 liters/second/person (5 cubic feet/minute/person). In 1989, the society raised the rate back to the higher level. Before this fourfold change, the lower level was thought to be adequate, but opinions later changed and it was considered insufficient.

It is a mistake to assume there is no problem, despite occupant complaints to the contrary, solely because instrument measurements do not indicate that one exists. It is more likely that the wrong things are being measured or, as in the case of synergistic effects, that the significance of the environmental factors and their interactions are not fully understood. Instrument measures of the physical office environment can only suggest factors that may be causing particular human responses. When instrument measures indicate that factors are within generally accepted norms but occupants experience illness symptoms, it is the measures that are suspect because they have not correctly predicted the observed human response.

Measurements and guidelines can be useful indicators, but ultimately, it is occupant response and management choices that determine whether indoor environmental factors are considered acceptable. Even if adherence to performance guidelines resulted in 80% of the occupants' being satisfied, would that be adequate? Would it be reasonable for 20% of office occupants to have headaches every afternoon? Some organizations might find this level acceptable; others might not. The level of satisfaction that an organization considers acceptable is a matter of judgment, not a value that can be determined by calculation or testing.

Performance guidelines are just that — *guidelines*. They need to be used appropriately by someone who understands their technical basis. Each facility is unique and will have characteristics that differ from the norm. Good judgment is needed in the application of guidelines to take into account the level of office quality the organization wishes to achieve.

Similarly, in comparing facility costs to those of similar organizations, how should values different from the norm be interpreted? If an organization's facility costs are lower than average, is this good or bad? Is the facility operated more efficiently, or is it providing a lower level of quality? An organization might want to provide a level of office quality that meets the norm, or it might seek to provide a higher level of quality in an effort to boost productivity (see the subsection "Benchmarking" in Chapter 9). The relevance of performance guidelines to a particular organization has a great deal to do with its corporate objectives and culture — which guidelines cannot define.

A satisfactory office environment cannot be defined by physical parameters alone. The complexity of human response to environmental factors requires the use of an adaptive approach. By monitoring the response of the occupants and adjusting facility operation, maintenance practices, and work scheduling, or by making physical modifications to the facility itself, a level of environmental quality can progressively be achieved that suits the organization's specific needs and objectives. The key to successfully applying an adaptive approach to facility management is a sound diagnostic process.

THE DIAGNOSTIC CYCLE

The process of diagnosing an office involves a repeating cycle of activities to monitor, evaluate, and improve the performance of the workplace as a whole (Figure 8.8). Fundamentally, every diagnostic activity is concerned with adjusting conditions to better suit the activities and needs of the occupants.

Based on the information produced by a diagnostic evaluation, a course of action can be chosen and implemented. It may be found that the office conditions are satisfactory and there is no need to make changes to a facility or the way it is operated. However, if it is known at the outset that no significant changes will be considered and the data will not be used for comparative analyses, then there is no purpose in undertaking the diagnosis.

1. Awareness of Workplace Conditions

Before a workplace diagnosis will be considered necessary, there must be an awareness that some aspect of the physical environment may be unsatisfactory. Typically, it is the occupants of an office or those responsible for its operation who first become aware of performance deficiencies. A diagnosis may also be undertaken as a proactive measure to collect baseline data for comparison with previous or later assessments of workplace performance, such as conditions after a renovation, or to

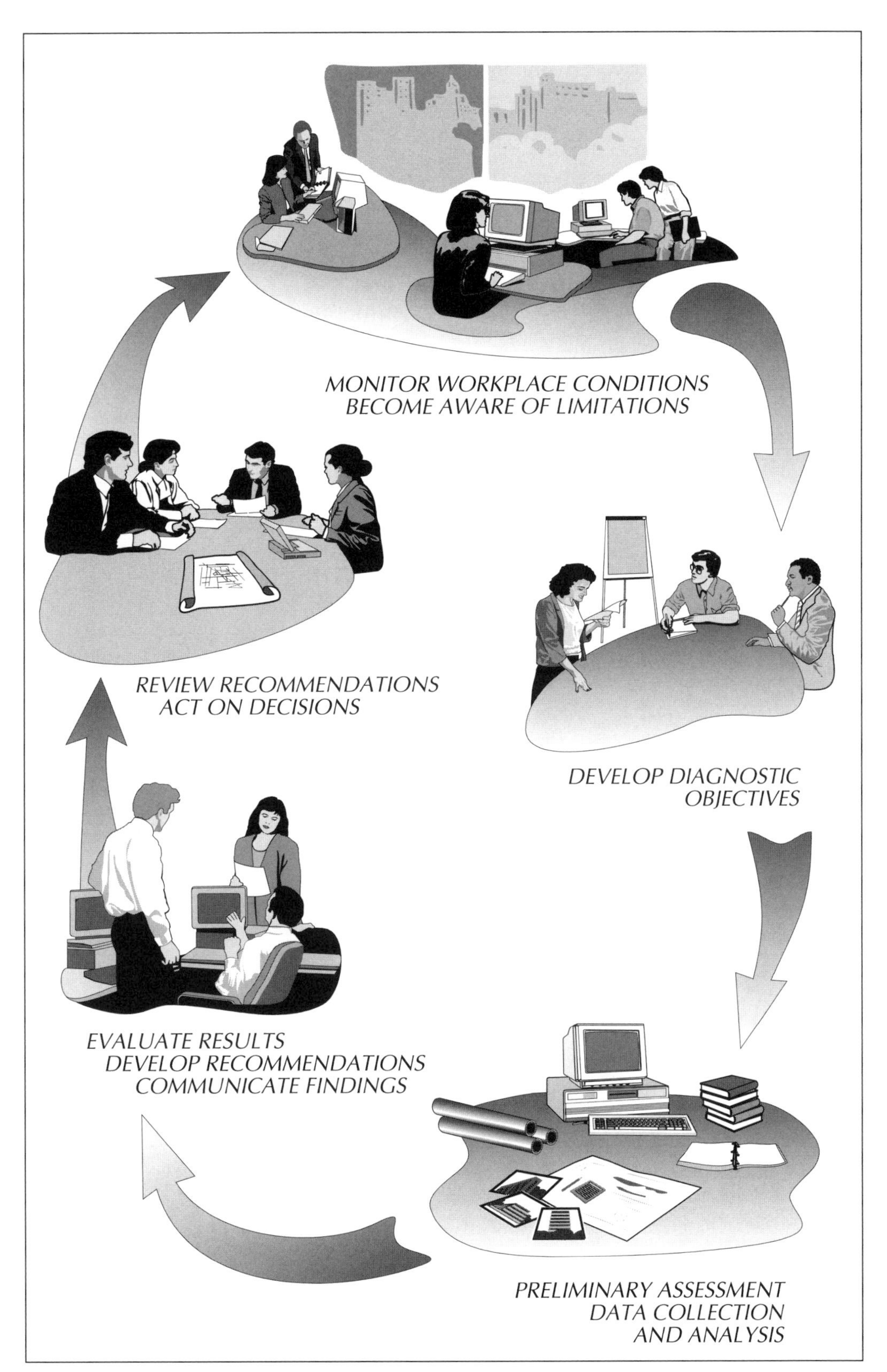

Figure 8.8 The diagnostic cycle of workplace evaluation.

monitor the office environment over time. Diagnoses for these purposes commonly originate from the facility management group.

As discussed throughout this book, organizations have become increasingly concerned about the liability risk of deficiencies in the office environment. They have used environmental evaluations as a means to identify and address deficiencies as well as to document that reasonable efforts have been made to ensure a safe work environment.

Once the need for a diagnostic investigation is recognized, there are generally consultations among various groups within the organization, including facility management, senior managers, and concerned occupants. The issues raised may be resolved easily by changing facility operating practices, adjusting management policies (e.g., flexible work schedules, designated smoking areas), or changing the way occupants use a facility. In this way, most workplace performance issues are addressed in the normal course of the facility management process. Where more detailed information is required or specific problems cannot be resolved, a more sophisticated diagnostic evaluation may then be needed. It is this kind of diagnosis to which the remainder of the chapter is devoted.

2. Develop Diagnostic Objectives

The objectives of a formal workplace diagnosis should be defined in the form of a written document agreed to by representatives of those who will pay for and use the results. One individual should be given the final authority and responsibility to commission and manage the project.

Critical to the success of a diagnostic evaluation is the visible support of senior management. Its level of interest will largely determine how seriously the organization will approach the diagnostic process, the level of cooperation people will offer, and the attention that will be paid to the results.

The diagnostic service provider should then be selected. Some large organizations can call upon a wide range of in-house experts — in which case, the work may be performed internally. Most organizations do not have the necessary experts on staff and will have to contract the work out.

A provisional budget for the work should be established, recognizing that it is often only after discussions with diagnostic service providers that realistic estimates can be made regarding the scope of the work and its cost. It should be expected that each service provider will examine the issues to be addressed and suggest changes in the project scope or timing so as to match the project objectives to the available budget and to establish realistic expectations.

The quality of a diagnostic evaluation depends on expert assessment, good communications skills, and the appropriate use of measurement tools. The more comprehensive the study and the more complex the issues, the greater the range of expertise required.

It is rare that a single individual can perform a major diagnostic study without the support of other specialists. For this reason, a workplace diagnosis commonly involves a team of specialists reporting to a diagnostic expert.

The success of a diagnosis depends more on astute observation and incisive, systematic analysis than it does on wholesale efforts to assess every potentially relevant factor. Brute force approaches that involve very large data collection and processing efforts are generally less successful than more focused studies that employ highly selective measurements of judiciously chosen factors.

At the conclusion of this second stage, the following decisions should have been made and formalized in writing:

There should be a clear and measurable set of objectives, scope of work, time frame, and budget for the project. If there are a large number of objectives, they should be prioritized so that effort is focused on the higher-priority issues. It is important that the objectives be measurable; otherwise, there will be no way to judge whether the project was successful. For example, an objective might be to reduce by half or eliminate occupant complaints of headaches and drowsiness in the afternoon.

An individual should be selected to represent the organization commissioning the study and act as the client for the project. This individual should have final authority to decide the scope of work, to accept reports and other deliverables, and to authorize payment. From a managerial standpoint, the diagnostic work is, in effect, done for this individual.

The diagnostic service provider should be selected, and a statement of work, schedule of deliverables, and payments should be agreed on.

3. Preliminary Assessment, Data Collection and Analysis

In the third stage of the process, diagnostic field work is begun. The diagnostician usually makes an initial assessment, which includes an inspection of the facility (termed an **expert walk-through**); interviews with selected individuals; examination of existing facility documentation such as architectural drawings, floor plans, and mechanical layout; and a review of occupant information such as complaint records and absenteeism.

A typical study examines a basic set of environmental factors broadly grouped into the six categories listed alphabetically below. Each category is significant. It is the interaction of all these factors that together creates the workplace environment people experience.

1. Aesthetics
2. Air quality and odors
3. Layout and ergonomics
4. Light
5. Sound and vibration
6. Thermal comfort (temperature, relative humidity, and air movement)

Additional factors may be examined to address specific issues. For example:

- Amenities (e.g., child-care and sports facilities, parking, food outlets)
- Conservation measures (e.g., energy conservation and recycling)
- Elevator service
- Security
- Signage and wayfinding
- Water quality

The data selected for a given workplace diagnosis depend on the unique circumstances of the project. No two diagnoses are done the same way. In general, the following three categories of data are used:

Existing data. Organizations have relevant data in formats such as architectural and engineering drawings and specifications, records pertaining to the way a facility is used, and reports related to occupant health and satisfaction such as absenteeism, turnover, and complaint records.

Occupant perceptions. These are typically collected through written questionnaires, meetings, and interviews.

Instrument measurements. These data would be collected, as needed, for factsors such as, for air quality, lighting, sound levels, temperature, and relative humidity.

Organizations commonly have a great deal of information that would be valuable for assessing workplace performance even though it was collected for other purposes. For example, the number of sick leave days taken by each employee is recorded by the payroll office. These data can be used to evaluate the time of year, type of task, and locations within a building with which illness absenteeism may be associated. The data might also be useful for comparison with similar organizations or job categories.

Departments responsible for an organization's information systems track the number and location of computer terminals as well as the individuals who use them and can often provide data on the length of time the equipment is used. This information may be valuable in identifying those workers at greatest risk for computer-related health problems.

Human resources departments have data on the length of time that employees stay with an organization. The rate of staff turnover, or **churn rate,** is influenced by workplace conditions and can be a useful indicator of environmental problems.

Data collection is costly. Before any new data collection is planned, all existing data should be reviewed to determine whether they are of suitable quality. By incorporating existing data into a diagnostic evaluation, costs can be considerably reduced.

Except for small jobs, it is generally difficult to estimate the cost of an entire diagnostic investigation in advance because the level of testing and analysis needed is better understood after the project is under way and the preliminary assessment has been done. A diagnostic evaluation can be more tightly specified and more closely managed if it is divided into a number of phases, each of which has a separate statement of work, schedule of deliverables, and cost. In the original project proposal, the particulars of all the phases can be outlined; however, as each phase is completed, the work plan and costing of the subsequent phase can be adjusted as required to reflect what has already been learned.

A phased approach benefits both the client and the diagnostic service provider in a number of ways. Work plans and costs generally can be more accurately defined for the next phase than for an entire project. When it is recognized in advance that adjustments may be made as the project progresses, the process can be made more predictable and therefore less costly to both client and service provider by incorporating change into the process. One of the deliverables for each phase can be proposed modifications to the subsequent phases.

For example, an preliminary assessment is relatively inexpensive, and if it is structured as a fixed-price contract, the cost is known in advance. Then, if a more detailed investigation is warranted, its costs and benefits can be better estimated based on the findings from the first phase. Upon completion of the first phase, the client can then judge whether it is worthwhile to proceed further.

The results of the preliminary assessment are normally delivered in the form of a written report and a presentation at which the findings can be discussed. In some cases, an issue can be resolved at this point. If additional diagnostic work is required (the usual case), the report should recommend the types of data collection and analysis needed and, depending on the nature of the work, may suggest alternative approaches that differ in cost, timing, level of disruption, and expected results.

Diagnoses intended to provide baseline data require that the client agree on the factors to monitor. For example, in collecting baseline air quality data, a choice must be made about which chemicals will be measured and at which locations. Over 300 volatile organic compounds may occur in the indoor air. Measuring all of them would be prohibitively expensive. But knowing the type of work activities and the locations in the workplace where they are done, a diagnostician can suggest which contaminants would be more likely to cause problems or be more useful indicators.

If the decision is made to proceed with the more detailed phase of the diagnosis, a data collection plan is prepared based on the information needs identified in the preliminary assessment. Sometimes, data can be collected progressively. For example, the cost of air quality testing depends on the number and type of chemicals assessed. Measuring carbon dioxide concentrations is less expensive than assessing volatile organic compounds. Instead of addressing a broad range of chemical compounds, a few contaminants most likely to be problematic can be measured first, and subsequent tests can be done as indicated by the initial results.

Instruments are used to measure a variety of physical environmental factors such as temperature, illumination, acoustics, and air circulation. For the test results to be valid, measurements must be made at appropriate locations within the facility and often at specific times of the day or seasons of the year.

Taking samples of the air supplied to a room does not constitute a complete measurement of the air quality to which each occupant is exposed. Occupants experience the air that is at their head level when they are seated at their work setting. How the air quality they experience is represented by the measurements depends on the pattern of circulation in the work space, and the locations where the measurements were taken.

To interpret measurements of the office environment the diagnostician must understand the phenomenon being studied, the capabilities of the instrument, the data collection method being used, and the significance of the instrument readings in assessing human response to the environment. However, measurements alone will not necessarily clarify an environmental quality problem. A plethora of data may only hide relevant clues rather than advance an investigation.

Questionnaires and interviews are valuable means to systematically collect data on the perceptions, observations, and attitudes of the people who use the office. However, the value of survey results is greatly dependent on the management climate that prevails at the time the survey is administered, the occupants' belief in the sincerity and commitment of management to act upon the diagnostic results, the assurance of confidentiality of individual responses, and the reliability of the survey process that is used. The more that occupants see the benefits they will receive from the diagnosis, the more willing they will be to support it. The cooperation of all parties involved improves the quality of the data that are collected and ultimately improves the value of the results.

Before any data collection is begun in the office area, occupants should be informed of the diagnostic study. They should be told the purpose of the project, who is involved, the types of activities that will take place (e.g., occupant surveys, instrument measurements), when results can be expected, and what results they will be given.

Survey design and analysis is a specialty in its own right. A poor survey process can easily produce misleading and incorrect results. The design of a survey, the way it is carried out, and the methods chosen to analyze it determine the quality of the information it can provide. Key considerations related to designing and administering occupant surveys are discussed in the section "Occupant Surveys" later in this chapter.

At this point of the diagnostic cycle, all occupants affected by the diagnostic study should be aware of the project, the preliminary assessment and subsequent more detailed investigations should have been done, and occupant perceptions should have been surveyed, thereby completing this phase of data collection. Data analysis is begun and, depending on the findings, additional field testing or site visits may be required.

DATA ANALYSIS

Data analysis involves a series of procedures tailored to the specific diagnosis. In general, the data analysis will include the following five procedure.

Encoding. All diagnostic analyses are now done using computers, so if the data are not already in computer-readable form, they must be encoded.

Quality Assurance. Before any data are used in an analysis, they should be appropriately inspected and tested to find and correct errors. For example, values can be checked to ensure that they fall within the allowable range for each item. The reliability of questionnaire responses can be evaluated to eliminate respondents who either did not appear to understand the questionnaire or did not give reasonable answers. For example, measures of the randomness and internal consistency of questionnaire responses can be used to search for erroneously coded or otherwise unreliable data.

Stratification. Data need to be grouped or stratified for many analysis procedures. For example, commonly used groupings for questionnaire data are age, sex, and job category. Instrument measurements are commonly stratified by time of day (e.g., morning, afternoon, outside standard business hours), time of week (e.g., workdays or nonworkdays), and other characteristics specific to the factor.

Some conditions such as air quality are affected by the season, so measurements taken during the winter and summer should not be combined but treated separately. Otherwise, significant differences may be obscured. For example, an air quality problem that only developed under very cold weather conditions could easily be missed unless weather conditions were taken into account in the analysis.

Similarly, survey data from areas of a building that may have substantially different physical environments should not be grouped together. Conditions can vary widely within a building; such as from the perimeter to the interior zones, or the southern to the northern exposures. Combining the data from potentially dissimilar areas makes it more difficult to identify conditions related to those differences.

Design of the Statistical Analysis. How data will be analyzed is usually determined before any data are collected. The analysis design should specify the information that is to be generated and the types of data and analytical procedures necessary to produce it. As a general rule, the more accurate and reliable the information needs to be, the more expensive it will be to obtain. So the analysis design should take into account the way the information will be used. The greater the cost of an incorrect decision, the higher the level of accuracy and the greater the level of detail that can be justified.

Even in the execution of well-established procedures, numerous choices are made that can affect whether an association that exists in the data will be found. Data analysis is a somewhat heuristic process — that is, the findings from one step may influence which procedure should be done next. In some cases, as the data are evaluated, questions may arise that are of sufficient importance to justify verification by additional site visits or tests.

Compilation and Validation of Results. After the various analysis procedures have been completed, the results are inspected for values that may be invalid because there were errors in processing or in the original data or because the data have unexpected characteristics. Any problems found are addressed and the results adjusted accordingly. The results are then assembled and output in the format needed for their evaluation. They may be presented in the form of tables, graphs, maps, explanatory notes, and data files for subsequent computer processing.

The analysis work generally does not involve the client or the occupants. However, clients will benefit from an understanding of the analysis procedures used and the reasons they were chosen. Selected aspects of data analysis that clients and occupants would find useful are presented in the section "Some Technical Issues of Workplace Diagnosis" later in this chapter.

4. Evaluate Results, Develop Recommendations, and Communicate Findings

In the fourth stage, the diagnostic information is evaluated with reference to the organization's performance objectives for the facility and the workplace as a whole. If the diagnosis is focused on resolving specific deficiencies in the office setting, then prescriptions for change are developed. Where multiple recommendations are proposed or alternative approaches are outlined, they should be prioritized by their expected benefits and costs.

Recommendations should also indicate how the effects of proposed changes would be monitored and the time frame within which results should be observed. Occupant complaints, instrument measures, facility maintenance costs, and other indicators may be used to monitor implementation results. It is essential that there be some form of follow-up activity to determine whether the recommendations that were implemented actually delivered the intended results. Otherwise, it will not be known whether the workplace deficiency was successfully addressed.

Diagnostic results and recommendations are normally delivered to the client in the form of a written report and an oral presentation. A summary of results should also be communicated to the occupants to inform them of the findings, demonstrate that their concerns were heard and understood, and indicate what steps will be taken to address their concerns. All participants should be formally thanked for their contribution to the diagnostic effort.

The communication process is an important component of any diagnostic evaluation. It includes both communication between management and employees, and communication between experts and their clients. Communication with employees demonstrates the organization's commitment to them — which itself can be a positive benefit of the diagnosis.

The communication between experts and their clients should demystify as well as resolve the workplace issues to be addressed. It's easy to be mystified by experts. Magicians, for example, are experts at illusion. We are mystified by a magic trick not because it is beyond our comprehension; if the illusion is explained to us, we are surprised by its clever simplicity. The magician's art is founded on well-practiced skills in misdirection. A magician focuses our attention away from the hand that conceals the coin or the device that hides the rabbit until it is to miraculously appear.

When an expert seems to be a magician, it is because we are mystified. We do not know which details are important or on which we should focus our attention. Experts cannot be managed by trying to understand their speciality, any more than magicians can be managed by trying to know their craft. However, good management skills and a fundamental technical understanding of the disciplines involved go a long way to ensure that the work delivered is useful; that it clarifies rather than mystifies; and that it directly addresses the issues that were to be resolved. At the outset of a diagnosis, preparing a clear statement of objectives and how "success" will be measured increases the likelihood that the appropriate expertise will be contracted and directed to solve the right problem.

Ideally, there would be a set of performance standards or objectives against which every measurement could be compared. Then, by correcting the ones that deviated from the standards, a high-quality workplace environment would be assured. Unfortunately, such is not the case. The single and synergistic effects of the many environmental workplace factors are too complex, and individual variations are too great. Office workplaces that conform to all existing standards may still have serious environmental deficiencies. The reasons for this are threefold, involving (1) the relevance of occupational health and safety standards that were not designed to address issues specific to an office setting, (2) the limitations of those guidelines that have been developed specifically for offices, and (3) the objectives of the particular organization with respect to the environmental quality it wants to maintain in its office facility.

There is a legal obligation for the office workplace to conform to occupational health and safety regulations. Individual workers or their unions can seek redress for substandard working conditions. In recent years, **OSHA** (Occupational Safety and Health Administration) has cited a number of major companies for workplace deficiencies that were associated with a high incidence of cumulative trauma disorders, particularly among computer operators. Fines and mandatory workplace improvements were imposed (see the section "VDT-Related Legislation and Liability" in Chapter 6).

However, occupational health and safety standards were originally designed to address dangerous working conditions in industrial or manufacturing settings. They sought to minimize life-threatening injuries such as those that occurred in using heavy equipment, working in hazardous settings such as mines or construction sites, and from acute exposures to toxic chemicals. These standards were not intended to regulate conditions in the office setting. It is not surprising, then, that environmental conditions in most offices, including those known to cause sick building symptoms, are generally well within occupational health and safety standards (see, for example, Lippy and Turner 1991). This situation is changing as new standards are being developed specifically for the office workplace. Though our understanding of the causes of deficiencies in the office workplace has increased considerably in recent years, it is still quite limited. For example, the synergistic effects of multiple environmental stressors are very poorly understood. Yet most occupant complaints related to the physical office setting involve multiple stressors.

As a result, adherence to existing standards does not ensure that the office workplace will not cause illness or otherwise impede people's work activities. An office can meet all the minimum standards for ventilation yet still have poor air quality that causes an unacceptably high incidence of illness absenteeism.

But the most important reason there is not a comprehensive set of performance standards that will guarantee a suitable workplace is probably the most obvious one: organizations don't all strive to maintain the same environmental quality in their office facilities any more than they seek to have the same corporate culture. Each organization sets its own standards — whether by design or by default.

An above-average workplace setting may be an important expression of a corporate culture devoted to leadership and quality. A more conservative culture might consider that providing a safe and comfortable office in conformance with industry norms is a more prudent but fair objective. For other organizations, cost containment is the overriding consideration, so minimizing facility expenditures might be the determining factor in office quality.

In some cases, looks are deceiving. The furnishings of an executive suite may look more expensive than those of an open plan work setting, but they are not necessarily more costly or of better quality. The closed-loop, static-resistant, heavy-duty carpeting commonly used in open plan areas is less glamorous but more expensive than many rich-looking shag carpets. Similarly, high-quality ergonomic chairs for computer workstations can cost more than an impressive-looking executive model. A fair and equal distribution of accommodation resources does not mean giving everyone the same work setting. An individual's workplace needs to be matched to the range of work activities she or he performs. What's more, not everyone in an organization is given the same quality of office environment.

5. Review Recommendations and Act on Decisions

Once the diagnostic information has been provided, the final stage of the cycle is to decide on a course of action. A decision to make no changes may also be appropriate. For example, a baseline study may have found no deficiencies that need to be addressed. Studies of specific performance deficiencies sometimes conclude that there is no practical way to resolve a problem and that a more suitable office facility should be found, or the workplace's limitations can be tolerated with management changes that give workers more control over where they do their work. In most cases, specific actions are recommended to resolve or at least improve shortcomings in workplace performance.

Whatever decisions are made, occupants should be informed of the actions, if any, that will be taken, who will be affected, when they will occur, and the results to be expected. In this way, people's expectations will be reasonably set, and they will be more likely to recognize and appreciate the changes made to their workplace.

The completion of this phase of the diagnostic cycle leads back to the occupied workplace where the conditions should, once again, be monitored for factors needing improvement. In this way, the diagnosis is integrated with the process of managing a facility by repeating the cycle of monitoring, evaluating, and improving the performance of the total workplace.

SOME TECHNICAL ISSUES OF WORKPLACE DIAGNOSIS

A full discussion of workplace diagnostic methods would be a book in itself, well beyond the scope of this chapter. However, there are some important data collection and analysis issues that would be useful to the recipients of diagnostic information, be they the client commissioning a study or office occupants.

The information presented here concerns fundamental principles upon which the success of any diagnostic evaluation ultimately depends.

The Strategy of Measurement

The data collected in diagnostic investigations are selected measurements of a very complex system — the workplace environment. They are always an abstraction, a more or less crude representation of what really exists.

You can't use data you don't have.

Choosing the data to collect and the existing information to use places inherent limitations on the results that will be obtained. In selecting data sources, there is always the risk that something critical to the study might be left out, and as a result, the cause of a deficiency might not be recognized or some baseline measurement needed for future comparisons might not be collected. It is a necessary constraint that all investigations face.

Then why not measure everything? It would be impossible to collect *all* the data — there is no way to record every minute aspect of an environment. Every measurement is in itself an abstraction. The temperature is not measured everywhere in a room, only at a few locations and at certain times during the day. It is assumed that these measurements adequately represent (for the purposes of the study) all the other possible measurements that could have been made.

But perhaps more important, one would not want *all* the data even if they were available. To be inundated with data would not be cost-effective and would more likely detract from the analysis than improve it.

The most cost-effective data collection is to gather only the data you need.

Data collection should be designed so that the information produced from it will be appropriate for the decisions the data will influence.

Data collection is expensive. Instrument measurements, occupant surveys, and interviews all consume costly resources. Although instrument measurements and associated laboratory analyses may carry what seem to be high price tags, the greatest expense is time. The time of the diagnostics providers is covered in the project budget. But there are hidden costs to the client, such as the loss of productive work time from any disruptions caused by the diagnostic process. Occupant surveys, for example, consume some work time from every respondent. In addition, there are information meetings, interviews, and management briefings. These activities are all important to the success of a diagnostic evaluation; however, they must be judiciously managed to avoid unnecessary expenses.

Data collection should be planned to minimize the length and frequency of disruptions. Some measurements can be taken when the building is unoccupied, but most must be collected under normal workday conditions. To maintain consistency between measurements, many need to be collected together on the same day or even at specific times. The organization should be informed of the data collection plan well in advance. Frequent unscheduled visits to the office facility for data collection may indicate that the process is not well planned and that the analysis procedures probably are not well thought out either.

It is tempting to use data that are readily available or to take measurements because the necessary instrument is on hand. Although it may seem economical to include such data in a diagnosis, there are hidden costs that may compromise the overall project. Collecting, storing, and analyzing data that are not needed represent expenditures of time and money that could otherwise be applied to improving the analysis or implementing recommendations. What's more, unnecessary data may simply divert attention and obscure important information. The purpose of every item of collected data should be known before it is collected. However "interesting" a data set might be, if the information it provides will not change any decision, it will not make a difference and hence should not be collected. The same holds true for data quality.

The optimal level of data quality is the minimum level that will do the job.

The quality of the data should be matched to the analysis in which it will be used. In evaluating thermal comfort, there is little point to collecting temperature data with a precision of 1/100th of a degree. People don't perceive such small temperature differences, nor can the building systems regulate the temperature that precisely.

Data quality specifications should also take into account current standards of practice. For the data collected to be comparable to those from other studies, they should be of the same or higher quality. This is especially important in planning baseline data collection.

It is important that the information about the quality of the data and the way they were produced be documented and kept with the data set. The type of analyses that will be conducted months or years after the data were collected is largely unknown. Those who prepared the data may no longer be available or may not be involved. At that future date, the only way to judge the suitability of the data will be to assess the method used to collect it.

It costs more and more to gain less and less data quality.

There is always a trade-off between higher data quality and higher data cost. Gains in data quality tend to be progressively more costly to obtain (Figure 8.9). For example, data on indoor air contaminant levels that are of poor quality because they are not collected at the same time each day can be improved by specifying the time when samples must be collected, a relatively inexpensive change that would correct the problem. However, once a high level of data quality has been obtained from indoor air testing, further improvements to data quality typically require the use of more sophisticated and significantly more expensive equipment.

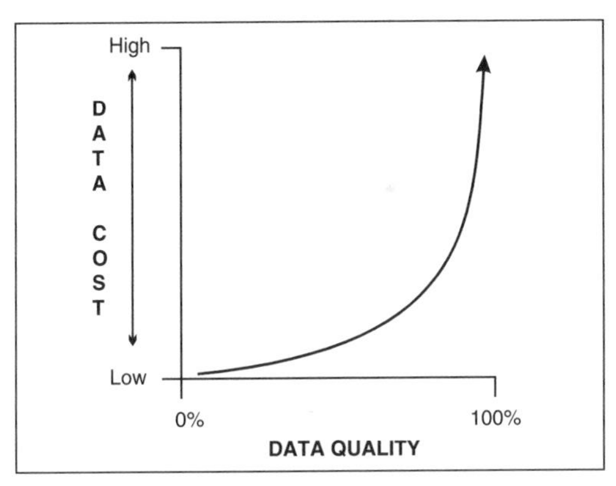

Figure 8.9 The relationship of data quality to data cost.

Target data collection to reduce uncertainty — the triage approach.

In the preliminary phase of a diagnostic investigation, expert judgment is used to assess the status of the workplace environment and to decide the type and quality of data to be collected. A triage approach (from the French word *trier,* meaning "to sort") is particularly useful in focusing data collection efforts.

Triage was a system originally developed to produce the greatest benefits when there were limited resources to treat battlefield casualties. Full treatment was given first to those likely to survive only with prompt treatment. Those who had little chance of survival and those who would survive without treatment did not receive immediate attention. Fundamentally, triage is a system of rationing scarce resources to maximize their benefit by allocating them to those capable of deriving the greatest utility from them.

The triage approach is applied to workplace diagnostics by rating each of the six basic environmental factors (aesthetics, air quality and odors, layout and ergonomics, light, sound and vibration, and thermal comfort), as well as additional factors that may be added to meet the needs of a given evaluation. Each factor is assigned to one of three categories:

1. Performance judged to be good, unlikely to be a source of problems.
2. Performance judged to be poor, clearly a source of problems.
3. Performance unable to be judged because the evidence is insufficient or unclear.

Factors in category 1 rarely need to be tested. Factors in category 2 are clearly deficient and need to be addressed. There is little point in spending money to test the amount of airborne particles if the air filters are clogged with dirt and unable to function effectively. The filters obviously need to be cleaned or replaced.

Testing and data collection are likely to produce the greatest benefits for category 3 factors because they are the ones that might be resolved by the additional information. They are issues that could be a source of workplace deficiencies but for which there is considerable uncertainty. For the factors in the other two categories, uncertainty is considered to be low. The issues in this category will differ for each diagnostic investigation, depending on the objectives of the study and the characteristics of the facility being assessed.

Where a diagnosis is to document existing conditions and establish baseline measurements for comparison, data collection must necessarily be broader. Still, the triage principle can be applied to choose environmental measurements that will be most useful in detecting those problems that would not otherwise be readily apparent.

The Nature of Workplace Data

The data used in workplace diagnostics are fundamentally observations that have three important components:

1. the attribute of interest, usually expressed as a **magnitude** (e.g., a sound level of 45 decibels) or **class** (e.g., an occupant is male or female)
2. the **location** at which the observation was made.
3. the **time** at which the observation was made.

Attention is usually focused on the first component (i.e., the magnitude or class), perhaps because it is the most obvious characteristic to record. But time and location are also essential and, if ignored, can seriously compromise the value of the data collected or render them unusable.

The location, the time, and the method of collection will determine the types of analytical procedures for which the data can be used. For example, for instrument measures to be correlated with occupant perceptions, they must have been collected at times and locations that represented the environment the occupants experienced. It is particularly important that this information be recorded if the data are to be used in future comparative studies. Moreover, time and location are essential data for spatial analysis procedures (discussed below).

TIME

The office workplace is dynamic. People are moved to different workstations; there is staff turnover; departments expand, and others are downsized or eliminated. So the relevance and validity of any measurement of the office setting depend on the time and location of the observation. (The importance of location is discussed in the following subsection.) A floor layout that is a few weeks old may be quite suitable for developing a new seating plan, but one that is a year old may be too outdated for that purpose.

Many aspects of the workplace seem to change rapidly because the human body is itself a dynamic system. An individual's metabolism changes over the course of the workday. The same conditions perceived as comfortable at the beginning of the day may be uncomfortably cool just before lunch when people are hungry or after they have been sedentary for a length of time. People dress somewhat differently with the changing seasons, wearing slightly heavier clothing in winter than in summer. Data collection must therefore be timed to capture the conditions that represent what is being evaluated.

Building systems are adjusted over the course of the day and with the seasons to accommodate the changing needs and activities of the occupants as well as to match facility operations to changing climatic conditions. For example, when a building is unoccupied, system operations are commonly scaled back to conserve energy. Ventilation rates are decreased, and temperature regulation is relaxed. Before occupants arrive for work, these systems are then ramped up.

Some aspects of environmental quality change more slowly than others. If the rate of outside air intake has been reduced overnight, there will have been a lower rate of dilution of the chemical contaminants in the indoor air. Some contaminants are introduced by the occupants, and so less dilution is needed when the building is unoccupied. But others are not occupant-related, such as those emitted by building materials, furnishings, and cleaning supplies.

The higher outside air exchange rates used during the day may be sufficient to dilute chemical contaminants, but they would not do so instantly. Depending on the characteristics of the building and the way it was operated, the concentrations of contaminants would tend to be higher in the morning and fall over the course of the day.

As well, the outside air exchange rate is changed over the year according to outside climatic conditions. As a result, the level of contaminants from indoor sources will tend to be lower at the times of year when a higher air exchange rate is used. For this reason, regions with harsh winters tend to have more frequent indoor air quality problems during periods of very cold weather. The rate of outside air intake may be reduced to save on heating costs or because the HVAC system does not have the heating capacity to deliver higher rates of outside air.

The time when occupant surveys are administered and instrument measurements are taken must be carefully chosen so that the observations are indeed representative of the environmental conditions and occupant perceptions being investigated. For example, if the objective is to assess the worst-case air quality conditions, then measurements should be taken when the outdoor climate severely taxes the HVAC system (such as very cold or very hot weather conditions) and the building is at peak occupancy. However, if the objective is to assess usual daytime conditions, data should be collected under the less stringent conditions typical of an average day.

LOCATION

For observations to be representative of the conditions being assessed, they must be collected at appropriate locations. Temperature measurements of the supply air at the outlet into a room are not representative of the temperature that a person experiences when seated at his or her workstation. Depending on the pattern of airflow, there can be significant differences between the temperatures at floor level, at work surface height, and at the ceiling. Office environment measurements used for diagnostic evaluations must be taken using controlled methods, at specified locations, and at times that suit the analysis objectives.

It is important that the location of every workplace measurement be recorded and stored together with the observation. If location information is collected with all diagnostic measurements, then powerful spatial analyses can be performed.

The spatial pattern of environmental measurements as well as data on occupant perceptions (such as questionnaire responses) can provide important clues to the cause of facility performance problems. Although an isolated complaint may simply indicate that an individual is unusually sensitive to one or more environmental factors, it could also be a valuable clue to an elusive but potentially serious building failure. The following case illustrates the importance of the isolated complaint.

One secretary in an open plan office complained of severe afternoon headaches, yet those at nearby workstations did not report similar illness symptoms. The situation had so seriously impaired the secretary's job performance that reassignment or dismissal was being considered. A diagnosis was done to determine whether the building contributed to this problem.

The diagnostic investigation to resolve the problem was neither expensive nor lengthy. It involved a review of the building drawings to examine the structural design and routing of services within the building. Brief, focused interviews were conducted with the secretary and the occupants of several nearby workstations. A few relatively inexpensive tests were performed to verify the paths by which air entered the work area.

From the building drawings, it was noted that the secretary's workstation was adjacent to a structural column along the line of an expansion joint. Then, while inspecting the workstation and surrounding area, it was seen that the caulking material used to seal the joint had not adhered properly, leaving a gap. It was found that fumes from the underground parking garage were traveling along the expansion joint and entering the office through this opening near the secretary's work space. The highest concentration of car exhaust in the garage occurred during the morning and evening as people arrived and left work. But it took several hours for the fumes to infiltrate along the expansion joint into the office and accumulate to problematic levels.

This air quality problem was easily corrected with some caulking compound to close the gap, and the secretary's afternoon headaches ceased. As a precaution, the seals on the expansion joint on other floors in the building were checked as well. The secretary was exposed to a higher concentration of air contaminants than her coworkers and exhibited more severe symptoms. But the vehicle exhaust, which contained carbon monoxide, posed a health risk to everyone in the office, even though they did not report symptoms. Some serious contaminants, such as carbon monoxide, are colorless, tasteless, and odorless even at toxic concentrations.

The secretary's location was key to solving this problem. It was by assessing the servicing and structural design of the building, particularly in the vicinity of the secretary's work space, that the problem's cause was postulated. As well, the diagnostician had to understand how the building systems functioned and were integrated and how people used the building. Only then were air quality tests ordered, and these were tightly specified to investigate a specific suspected cause.

The diagnostic evaluation proceeded from the general to the specific, beginning with a review of the building systems and interviews with the occupants and then progressively narrowing the focus of attention to the most likely causes. Similarly, data collection proceeded from the more general and less expensive (i.e., assessment of building drawings, expert inspection of the space, and interviews with occupants) to the more specific and more expensive testing (i.e., analysis of air samples for carbon monoxide). By this process, the convergence of information enabled the air quality testing to focus on a few key chemicals instead of assessing a broader range of contaminants at considerably higher cost.

Spatial Analysis of Workplace Data

Measurements of the workplace environment are inherently spatial data: they represent conditions that existed at a specific location and at a specific time. The location component permits the data to be analyzed spatially — an analysis procedure that often uncovers important relationships that would otherwise be missed.

Consider, for example, a set of temperature measurements taken at different locations throughout a room where the values ranged from 18°C to 25°C (65°F to 77°F) with an average of 22°C (72°F). This would generally be considered an acceptable temperature range for an office area. But if there was a heat loss problem in one corner of the room, the clustering of low temperatures in that area might easily be missed if only the data values or the average was reviewed. However, if the temperature data were displayed in the form of a map overlaid on the floor plan, the lower temperature readings concentrated in one corner area would be readily apparent.

In recent years, computer-aided design (CAD) software has increasingly been used for facility management. This technology enables floor plans to be drawn, edited, displayed, and plotted. The floor plans can also serve as a base for handling furniture tracking, charging space costs to departments, and designing space plans and renovations. The graphic information can thus serve as an effective means to access and manipulate a wealth of building data. Computer-based systems designed for facility management are known as computer-aided facility management (CAFM) or computer-integrated facility management (CIFM) systems. They are generally comprised of a database capable of storing, analyzing, and reporting building information together with some level of CAD capability to display information graphically and produce drawings on paper, film, or other media.

The capability to generate graphic displays and plots, termed **spatial mapping,** is distinct from spatial analysis capabilities. Graphic display and plotting features provide control over the way in which items are represented and labeled, such as control of line weights and color, text placement and fonts, copying of line work within a drawing or between drawings.

A software package can have sophisticated spatial mapping capabilities and rudimentary analysis functions. The converse is also found — a full-featured spatial analysis package may have limited drawing capabilities. It is the spatial analysis capabilities that are critical for diagnostic analyses.

Spatial analysis is a sophisticated and well-developed analytical discipline that is widely used in science and engineering. It involves evaluation of the spatial characteristics of a set of data, such as the degree of aggregation within a set of observations. For example, the set of temperature measurements discussed previously would have a higher level of aggregation (because the lower temperature values all occur in one corner) than if the low temperature readings were scattered throughout the room. Other commonly used spatial analysis functions assess such characteristics as proximity and adjacency.

These spatial attributes may themselves provide important information, or they may be incorporated into more complex functions such as the generation of a two-dimensional surface, a three-dimensional volume, or the classification of regions from multiple environmental factors and spatial queries (i.e., identifying regions that satisfy a specific set of spatial characteristics). Integrated spatial analysis tools are a valuable means to identify deficient areas within a facility through the simultaneous evaluation of multiple environmental factors. They can also be used to model the behavior of environmental factors over an entire area from a set of measurements collected at individual points, a form of **spatial modeling.**

Spatial modeling is used in a wide variety of geographic analyses, from mapping mineral bodies and oil reservoirs to estimating population densities and modeling surface topography. It is also central to machine vision applications such as automated product inspection systems and robotics.

A great deal more diagnostic information can be gleaned from office environment data by using spatial analysis methods than by using conventional nonspatial methods alone. The results of spatial analyses are commonly presented in the form of graphic outputs such as images, maps, or drawings together with statistical data summaries. Not only can the measurements for individual environmental factors be better evaluated using a graphic format to visualize the results; the relationship of the environmental measurements to the building services and structure is much more easily assessed. Instrument measurements, occupant surveys, and other observations can all be analyzed spatially if the locations to which these data pertain are recorded.

It is essential that spatial data be consistent and accurate. In advance of collecting data, a suitable reference grid should be established for the areas being evaluated. Then, the spatial coordinates of all measurements should be referenced to this grid to ensure that locations will be accurately represented. Otherwise, significant errors can be introduced into the analysis.

The following examples illustrate the application of spatial modeling in workplace diagnostics.

The simplest use of spatial data is for the display of environmental measurements. Figure 8.10 is a computer-generated display of illumination measurements for an open plan office area. To describe the background illumination, several measurements were taken at each workstation. This display shows the data for one of those measurements — the amount of light falling at the location where operators placed the reference materials they used while working at their computers.

The range of observed illumination values was divided into five classes representing equal intervals of illumination values and displayed as shaded dots over the office floor plan. The lighter the dot the higher the level of illumination at that location. To produce such a display, the spatial data were used only to position the dots on the floor plan. No spatial analysis was required.

Unusual conditions are easily identified from this type of graphic display of the data. The two highest illumination categories include light levels that are too high for comfortable viewing of a reference document while using a computer monitor. It

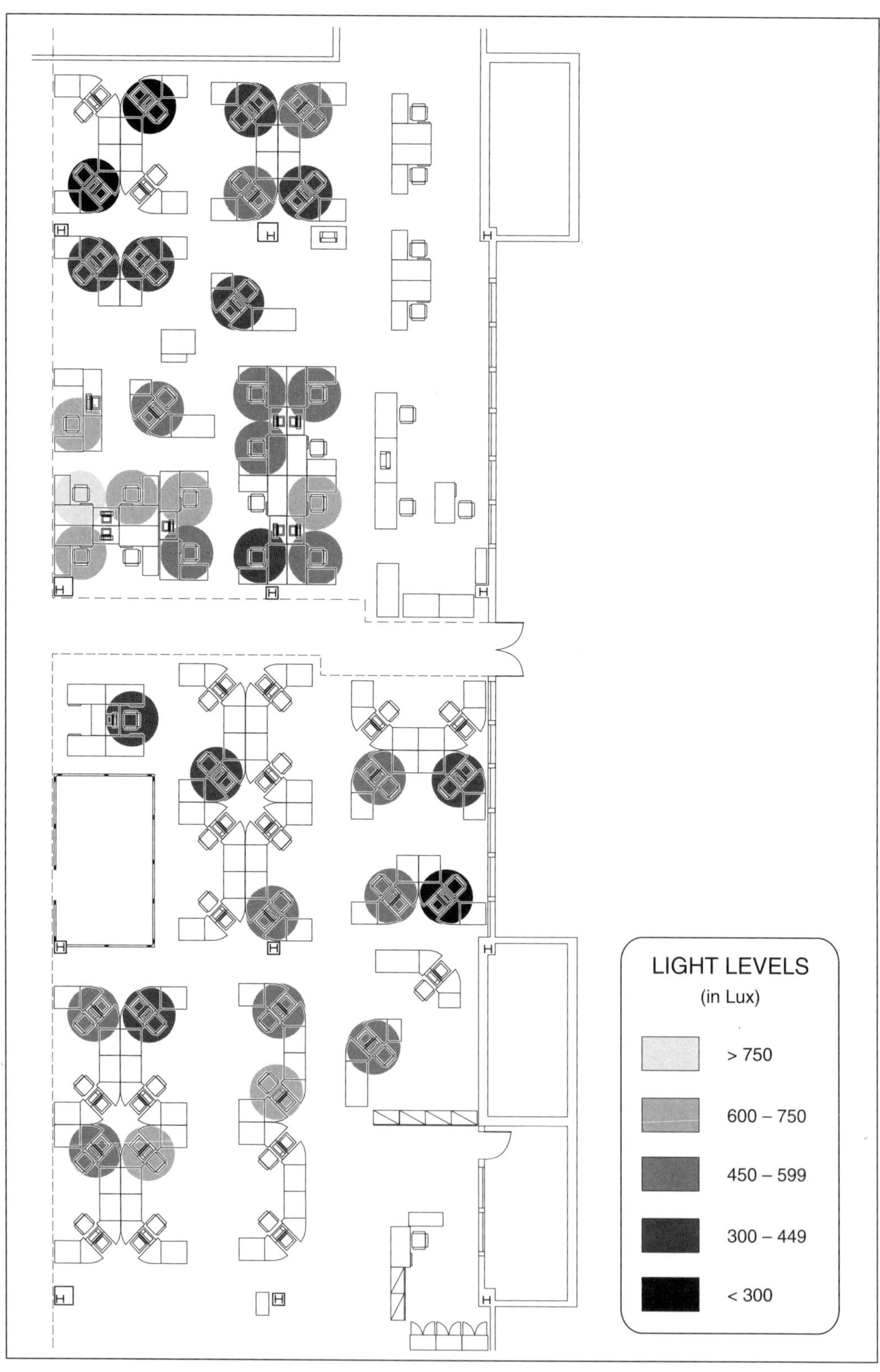

Figure 8.10 The reflected light level at each computer workstation was measured where the user's placement of reference documents could be determined. Shaded dots show the spatial distribution of these light — the lighter the shade the higher the illumination.

is not surprising then that the high light levels at the two workstations in the upper right corner of the illustration were reported to be problematic by their occupants.

Spatial display and analysis methods can be applied to occupant survey data as well. The spatial coordinates of each occupant's work location are assigned to his or her questionnaire responses. Figure 8.11 shows the results of a spatial analysis of occupant satisfaction ratings of their own work areas. The patterns represent ratings from "very dissatisfied" to "very satisfied." Instead of simply displaying the ratings as patterned dots, as in the previous example, spatial modeling software was used to estimate satisfaction values for the entire office area from the individual data points. The results were then displayed as a pattern-coded map overlaid on a line drawing of the floor plan.

The algorithm used in this analysis generates a mathematical surface. A value for satisfaction is calculated for each location based on the pattern of measurements and assuming a smooth transition between measurement points. Conceptually, it is as if a land surface were being modeled based on the height measurements taken at points scattered throughout the area. In this case, an algorithm was selected that forces the values at the location of the data points to be the actual values. Only the intervening points, for which there are no data, have been estimated.

From this illustration, it is apparent that the most dissatisfied occupants are aggregated in a few areas. In a diagnostic evaluation, this plot would be used in combination with plots derived from the analysis of other questions or from instrument measurements to identify areas that may have facility deficiencies and to investigate their likely causes. The spatial patterns in the data and their location relative to building features such as service runs and structural elements would be used in interpreting the plots and developing recommendations.

From the floor plan, the number of workstations associated with each area of dissatisfaction is apparent. The largest area of dissatisfaction in this example is in the upper right and includes six workstations. Though there are fewer occupants in other regions with low satisfaction ratings, they all should be considered. Anomalous responses could indicate a facility deficiency that needs to be addressed but to which only a few individuals are currently sensitive.

The presentation formats illustrated in Figures 8.10 and 8.11 explicitly show the values obtained at each workstation. Because presentations of this type allow confidential information, such as occupant responses, to be readily traced back to the individuals, they should be restricted to those directly involved in the analysis. However, to resolve facility-related problems that individuals experience, those individuals must at some point be identified in order for their complaints to be investigated. If occupants are concerned about reprisals for negative comments, it may be necessary to make these plots available only to third-party investigators.

Data that describe the workplace environment are fundamentally spatial data, whether the spatial component is defined explicitly or only implied. The information that can be derived from these data pertains to the locations where they were collected. The validity of any analysis for which they are used depends as much on the suitability of the locations at which the data were collected as on the measurement method chosen.

It is the co-occurrence of evidence pertaining to a certain location that leads to a specific diagnosis. Spatial analysis methods take full advantage of the spatial component inherent in these data. As such, workplace data are more effectively integrated and interpreted when analyzed in their spatial context.

Occupant Surveys

A workplace diagnosis usually includes an assessment of occupant perceptions about their office setting. Written ques-

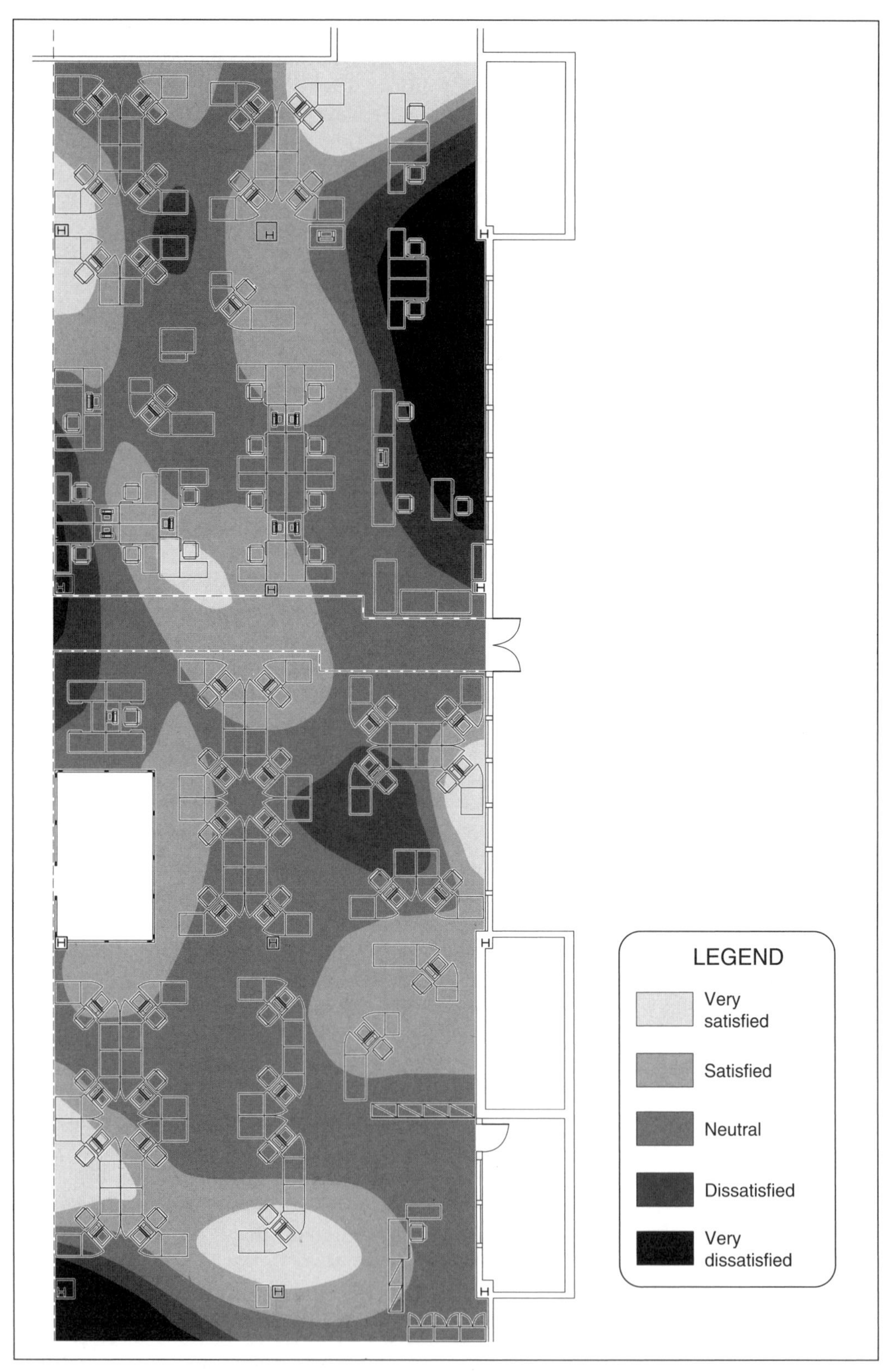

Figure 8.11 Spatial modeling of occupant satisfaction data. Ratings of "satisfaction with own work area" from an occupant survey were used to generate a continuous map of satisfaction for the entire work area using a spatial modeling program.

tionnaires and face-to-face interviews are the survey methods most commonly employed. More recently, interactive computer and telephone-based surveys have been developed in which responses are entered on a keyboard or telephone keypad. In this way, the data are immediately converted into computer-readable form ready for analysis.

During the preliminary stages of a diagnostic investigation, most of the information about occupant attitudes is collected by interviews. Interview sessions usually follow an unstructured or semistructured discussion format. An unstructured interview is essentially a free-form discussion. In a semistructured interview, there is a prescribed set of questions to be answered, but the discussion is allowed to pursue related topics of interest that may arise.

Designing and administering questionnaires requires somewhat more advance planning than interviews. The written questionnaires are predominantly multiple-choice with some provision for writing in comments. The multiple-choice format is favored because it simplifies coding and analysis and can be completed more quickly.

The following discussion focuses on the written questionnaire because it is more structured and is normally administered to a much larger number of occupants than are interviewed. However, both interviews and questionnaires are important methods of obtaining information on occupant perceptions.

Many office facilities have well-defined procedures for collecting and recording occupant comments on the quality of the work environment. People can phone the facilities group directly or place written notes in a suggestion box. These can be valuable sources of information about occupant attitudes, but the method by which they are collected biases the information they provide. They represent the views of those who, for one reason or another, chose to speak out — a self-selected group generally motivated by the need to cope with some annoying aspect of their work environment. As such, they are not representative of the office workforce as a whole.

Surveys are a more systematic and comprehensive method to collect occupant perceptions. Every occupant can be given the same opportunity to comment on the same set of issues at the same time (Figure 8.12). As a result, the range and prevalence of attitudes among office occupants can be more accurately assessed.

Occupant surveys can be used as part of a regular facility management monitoring program to identify deficiencies and also to recognize those settings that perform well. It's the type of information that promotes proactive management. It is also a visible activity that builds trust and opens communication between facility managers and office occupants. Organizations where this trust exists are better able to resolve any workplace health issues that may arise (see the subsection "Addressing Uncertain Health Risks in the Office Setting" in Chapter 7).

Questionnaires and interviews are well-developed survey instruments. They are widely used in social science research and find extensive application in the assessment of consumer preference, marketing, and political polling. When correctly designed and administered, surveys provide reliable qualitative and quantitative information.

A considerable investment of resources is needed to conduct an occupant survey. In addition to the direct costs of designing, administering, and analyzing the survey, there are many significant indirect costs. The time that occupants spend in interviews and information sessions or completing questionnaires is itself a considerable investment.

It is important that occupants be formally given the necessary time to participate. It generally takes 20–60 minutes to complete a questionnaire or be interviewed. In addition, participants must be given some preparatory information about the study before they can participate effective-

Figure 8.12 To ensure that everyone had the opportunity to participate in this occupant survey, the questionnaires were attached to and distributed with the paychecks.

ly. Being expected to simply fit these additional activities into an already filled work schedule can generate resentment and a tendency to give them less than full attention — compromising the quality of the data collected as well as the study results. For this reason, it is important that management ensure that work time is allocated for occupant participation.

Given the significant investments in carrying out occupant surveys, it is shortsighted to "economize" by using a survey poorly suited to the organization, administered in a way that does not appropriately prepare the respondents, or analyzed without sufficient knowledge of how the facility functions.

The application of occupant surveys to the assessment of the workplace environment continues to develop. Many different approaches can produce useful and reliable information. Although there is no *one* right way to survey office occupants, there are many wrong ways. It would seem to be a simple task to select and administer a survey and then to tally up the results and calculate some summary statistics; however, the value of the information is largely dependent on the quality of the survey methods. Unfortunately, the quality of a survey process is not readily apparent from the results alone. To ensure that an occupant survey is of value it should be designed, administered, and analyzed by those well-qualified and experienced in the task.

Results from so-called quick or short-form surveys may be worse than having no information at all because their reliability is poor. Although *wrong* methods sometimes produce *right* results, their inconsistency may misinform or suggest actions that are counterproductive. What's more, poor data are a liability. Data sets have an uncanny habit of being applied in unintended ways. They may continue to mislead and misinform long after the original users have abandoned them.

A comprehensive discussion of occupant surveys could itself fill a volume. In the following subsections, some important issues that can invalidate the information derived from a survey are explained. An appreciation of these fundamental principles of survey design and analysis can be useful in interpreting and applying the information provided by surveys. A technical discussion of the statistical methods applied to workplace surveys can be found in Scharf and Margulis (1992).

SURVEY DESIGN

Survey design is both an art and a science. For occupant surveys to deliver reliable information, they should be designed, administered, and analyzed by qualified personnel experienced in occupant surveys and building performance. The way questions are phrased, the order in which they are asked, the format used to present them, and the response scales that are chosen can all bias the data that are collected. Some examples follow.

Questions can be asked in a way that has implied bias. In the following example, respondents are asked to report on a negative aspect of their lighting.

How often do lighting problems interfere with your work?

1	2	3
Often	Sometimes	Never

Responses from this type of question are more likely to be negative. Questions should be phrased in a neutral form to avoid such bias. For example:

How does the lighting at your workstation suit the requirements of your tasks?

1	2	3
Poorly	About right	Well

Multiple-choice questions often offer a selection of categorical responses rather than a numerical rating scale (see the subsection "Response Scales on Occupant Surveys" later in this chapter). A set of categorical responses must be carefully designed to ensure that there is a suitable response for every possible case. Otherwise, the data will be biased by respondents who selected the answer that was "closest" but that did not represent their opinion well or by respondents who simply did not answer. The following example illustrates the difficulty of correctly framing this type of question when several interrelated environmental factors are included.

Which of the following describes the acoustic conditions at your work setting?

1. Conditions are satisfactory at all times.
2. There are predictable periods of loud and disturbing sounds from equipment such as impact printers.
3. There are occasional background conversations that disrupt my work.
4. I can never count on being able to work without noise disruption.

Here, many commonly encountered workplace conditions are not represented. For example, there is no appropriate response to indicate "a continuous background noise level of low intensity that is very disturbing." Another limitation of this descriptive type of question is that there tends to be a lot of text to read, so it takes longer to complete the survey and respondents fatigue and lose interest more quickly. For this reason, short, direct questions with numerical response scales are preferred.

The order in which questions are asked can also bias the responses. The phrasing in the following example is overly blunt but is used here to illustrate a point.

Comment on the following aspects of your work environment.

1. What aspect of the lighting in your office bothers you?
2. When do you feel uncomfortably cool or uncomfortably warm in your office?
3. When are noise disruptions most frequent in your office?
4. What is your overall impression of your office environment?

The one question that is neutral and general has been asked last. Before answering it, respondents are asked to focus their attention on three questions dealing with negative aspects of the work environment. Despite the respondent's efforts to address each question independently, a response to one question is readily influenced by those that precede it. In this case, there will be a tendency for responses to the general question (number 4) to be negatively biased because some people would rate the overall environment lower after being asked to think about three negative aspects.

If the questions were instead ordered from the general to the specific, with number 4 asked first, the response to that overview question would likely be more representative of the respondents' overall impression. Since it is the first question, the response would not be influenced by the other responses. For this reason, questionnaires are commonly organized so as to poll general attitudes first, before asking more detailed questions.

Occupant surveys may be customized for the specific facility and organization being polled, or a general-purpose survey may be used. Information from customized surveys is usually more useful, detailed, and reliable than that from general-purpose ones. In part, this is because the survey is focused on the identification and resolution of problems specific to a facility. Equally important, presenting respondents with a survey tailored to their building and their specific concerns highlights the fact that the issue is considered important enough to warrant a specially designed questionnaire.

When no specific concerns are being addressed and broad-based monitoring information is wanted, a general-purpose questionnaire may be found to suit the purpose. However, only questionnaires that have been well tested and shown to deliver reliable results should be considered.

CENSUS OR SAMPLE

In diagnosing a workplace, identifying the exceptional event is essential. Unusual conditions commonly indicate the presence of a subtle deficiency or the beginnings of a major problem. We have found occupant surveys to be of greatest benefit when they are administered to everyone (i.e., a **census**), not just to a portion of the occupants (i.e., a **sample**).

Workplace deficiencies do not generally occur randomly throughout an office space. They tend to be clumped where one or more building services are performing poorly. Since a sample involves only a portion of the occupants, those seated where a building problem occurs might not be polled, and the facility deficiency would go unrecognized even though the information could have been obtained. Environmental conditions are not uniform throughout an office space. People next to a window may find that the daylight makes their work space too bright, whereas those a short distance away find that the lighting conditions perfectly suit their needs. Polling occupants is an effective and inexpensive way to find those facility problems that are readily identified by occupant discomfort reports. A census ensures that any locations where occupants can perceive deficiencies will be noted.

Polling every occupant also increases the statistical validity of the results. In a sample, the responses from a portion of the occupants are treated as representative of the perceptions of the entire group. The statistical reliability, or confidence, that the sample data truly represent the group's attitudes depends on the pattern of responses actually obtained. If the sample responses vary widely, there is less confidence that they are good predictors of the attitudes of those who weren't polled. A census eliminates this problem entirely. Since everyone is polled, there is 100% confidence that the responses represent the attitudes of the entire group.

Benefits accrue from the process of administering an occupant survey as well as from the information obtained. A highly visible, professionally conducted survey reaffirms management's interest in and commitment to the well-being of the workforce. This, in turn, can improve morale, especially when it is followed by visible changes that occupants perceive as enhancements to their workplace.

A census maximizes these communication benefits of the survey process. Everyone is given an opportunity to have his or her say, and everyone is informed about the survey and its role in the workplace diagnosis. Subsequent briefings should update all occupants on the evaluation's progress, the findings, and any changes that are to be implemented. Renovation work may be implemented in stages, done outside of standard business hours, or performed in areas of the building that the occupants rarely see. Unless they are informed that something is being done, occupants will assume that the issues they identified have, in the end, been ignored. People are more willing to tolerate a problem if they are confident that their concerns have been heard and will be addressed fairly. Skillfully handled, the communication process can build occupants' trust and foster cooperation with the facility management services and corporate management in general. By polling every occupant, a census design extends this communication to everyone, not just the select few in the chosen sample.

In evaluating buildings, we have found that administering surveys to every occupant is more cost-effective than polling a sample. In comparison with the total cost and effort to carry out a workplace diagnosis, the risk of missing critical information and the reduced data quality of a sample survey are, in the end, more costly than the additional expense of surveying everyone.

RESPONSE SCALES ON OCCUPANT SURVEYS

When surveys are analyzed, occupants' answers are generally given a numerical value. Even open-ended questions can be categorized and assigned a number. But not all numerical data are the same. The four categories of numerical data — **equal interval, ratio, nominal,** and **ordinal** variables — are described briefly below. Statistical tests that are valid for one category of data are frequently invalid for others. Most occupant survey data consist of nominal and ordinal values.

Equal-Interval Scales

The centigrade and Fahrenheit scales used to measure temperature are examples of equal-interval scales. As the name implies, the divisions of such scales represent quantities that are inherently equal. An increase in temperature from 3° to 4° represents the same amount of heat gain as an increase from 4° to 5°, whereas on a rating scale (see "Ordinal Values" below), an increase from a rating of "*3. Indifferent*" to "*4. Satisfied*" does not necessarily represent the same increase in satisfaction as from "*4. Satisfied*" to "*5. Very satisfied*".

Averages are the appropriate measure of central tendency for equal-interval scales. But the zero point on an equal-interval scale is arbitrary. Zero degrees Fahrenheit or centigrade does not represent zero heat, but an arbitrary point selected on a continuous temperature scale. Colder values are simply given negative numbers. For this reason, ratios are not meaningful. For example, 20° is not half as hot as 40°. The value may be half the magnitude, but the quantity of heat is not half as great.

Ratio Scales

Ratio scales are equal-interval scales that have a true zero point. Weight, for example, is measured on a ratio scale. The value zero represents no weight, and so ratios of these values are meaningful. A weight of 40 kilograms is twice as heavy as 20 kilograms (i.e., 40/20 = 2). As well, the average is the appropriate measure of central tendency for a group of ratio scale values.

Nominal Values

A nominal value represents a **category.** For example, a value of 1 could be

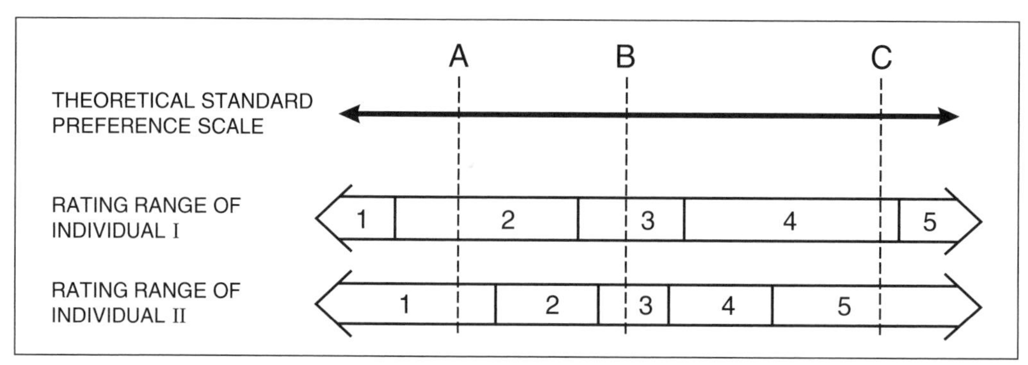

Figure 8.13 No two individuals consistently assign their subjective preference levels to a rating scale in the same way, nor do they space their ratings evenly across a scale. This is illustrated conceptually by showing the rating scales for two individuals with reference to a hypothetical standard preference scale.

assigned for blue eye color and a value of 2 for brown eye color. Although the value 2 is greater than 1, it is meaningless in this context. Brown eyes are neither greater or less than blue eyes; they are just different. Similarly, the number of brown-eyed and blue-eyed people can be reported and proportions calculated, but an average of the eye color values is not meaningful. An average eye color of 1.5 is undefined. The measure of central tendency most appropriate for nominal values is the **mode** — which is the category having the greatest number of occurrences.

Ordinal Values

Ordinal values are **ratings.** Most of the data collected in occupant surveys are ratings. When people appraise their workplace by selecting a value from *"1. Poor"* to *"5. Excellent,"* they are expressing their opinion by means of a numerical rating.

For ordinal data, the order of magnitude is significant. The value 2 represents an opinion that is in some sense greater than 1. However, the intervals are not necessarily equal. The interval between 1 and 2 does not necessarily represent the same difference as between 2 and 3. That is, when people choose among these ratings, the additional quantity of a characteristic that causes them to raise their rating of 1 to 2 is not necessarily the same amount that would cause them to raise their rating of 2 to 3.

It is difficult to ascertain the mental scales individuals use when they express opinions as ratings. Some people tend to assign extreme values only rarely, whereas others assign them frequently. What's more, it is difficult to establish consistency between people. One person's 2 might be another's 3.

To illustrate this concept suppose that people's ratings could be measured against a standard scale of preference (Figure 8.13). As already noted, ratings cannot be assumed to be equal-interval values. In this example, many more preference levels would be rated as 2 by individual I than by individual II. The preference level at A on the hypothetical standard scale would be rated 2 by individual I and 1 by individual II. Similarly, to express the preference level at C, individual I would assign a rating of 4, whereas individual II would assign a rating of 5. They would both choose a rating of 3 for the preference level at B.

This example illustrates two of the difficulties inherent in ratings: an individual's rating scale cannot be assumed to be an equal-interval scale, each unit of their mental rating scale is not necessarily equal (**internal consistency**); and different people may use the same value to represent different levels of preference (**external consistency**). While there are a number of statistical procedures to minimize such inconsistencies, peoples' preferences cannot be accurately determined and calibrated to a standard preference scale. However, there are a number of ways to make ratings more consistent so that comparisons between individuals are more reliable.

CONSISTENCY AND RELIABILITY

The way rating scales are labelled and the number of values in the scale greatly affect both the internal and external consistency of the data. The numeric rating on a scale of 1 to 5 given in response to the following question would be a fairly reliable indicator of the respondent's opinion.

Rate your opinion of the building in which you work.

1. Like very much
2. Like
3. Indifferent — neither like nor dislike
4. Dislike
5. Dislike very much

At first glance, the values would be expected to mean the same thing to different people, so the ratings of different people could be compared with some confidence. But upon further reflection, we would be more confident of some comparisons than others. Comparing a rating of 2 to a rating of 3 is more certain that comparing a rating of 1 to a rating of 2.

This is because it is unlikely that two people will assign the same amount of "liking" to the point where a 2 becomes a 1. It is a more or less arbitrary point on a continuum of progressively more positive perceptions (the issue previously illustrated by preference level A in Figure 8.13). The difference between a 3 and a 2 is much more certain because it is a qualitative difference between indifference and a positive opinion. So, we would be quite confident that someone rating the building a 2 really likes it better than someone rating it a 3.

Since some ratings are more reliable than others, our confidence in these data can be improved by eliminating the less reliable ones, specifically the ratings of 1 and 5. This reduces the scale to only three choices. (They would normally be assigned values of 1, 2, and 3, but are shown here as 2, 3, and 4 to be consistent with the ratings in the previous five-point scale.)

Rate your opinion of the building in which you work.

2. Like
3. Indifferent — neither like nor dislike
4. Dislike

By eliminating intermediate values of liking and disliking, the less consistent decision points have been removed (i.e., where a 2 becomes a 1 and where a 4 becomes a 5). Individuals will clearly understand the meaning of each option, and different people will understand them the same way. With this three-point scale, the options match the understanding that *people have in common* more closely than with the five-point scale.

But there is a trade-off. We are more confident that the ratings represent the underlying preferences of the people surveyed, and so the **accuracy** has been increased. However, the **precision** of the measure has been decreased by giving only one degree of liking or disliking instead of two. Sometimes, increasing the precision does more to reduce the reliability of a rating (i.e., its accuracy) than to reveal additional information. To make this trade-off, the designer of the questionnaire should consider how the data are to be used and the way the people to be surveyed will understand the scale. The more closely the labeling and size of the scale match the way people think about their preference, the better will be the trade-off between accuracy and precision.

Occupant surveys typically use scales with ranges of three to eleven items. We have found that a five-point scale generally works best for the type of questionnaires we use in diagnostic evaluations. It offers a good compromise between accuracy and precision.

Scales can be stretched so that all questions have the same number of response choices, simplifying the analysis. However, the subtle shades of meaning offered by the larger scales are interpreted inconsistently by respondents, increasing the level of random error in the data. At

How satisfied are you with the overall comfort of your work setting?

1	2	3	4	5
Very satisfied	Satisfied	Neutral	Dissatisfied	Very dissatisfied

1	2	3	4	5	6	7
Extremely satisfied			Neutral			Extremely dissatisfied

Figure 8.14 Comparison of questionnaire response scales

some point, finer divisions are not meaningful to the respondents, and the additional variations in the data arise more from people's uncertainty about the rating to choose than from any difference in the level of preference they perceive. For this reason, rating scales should be matched to the way people think of the distinctions they are being asked to make. During the data analysis, adjustments can readily be made for any differences in scaling among the survey questions. The reliability of the data should not be compromised in an effort to make the analysis more convenient.

The following example further illustrates this point. Here the data obtained using the five-point response scale would likely be more accurate than those from the seven-point scale for two reasons (Figure 8.14).

The first scale would likely have better external consistency because there are fewer ratings from which to choose and they are better defined — each value has a label that clearly indicates a different level of the attribute. In the second scale, there would likely be considerable variation among individuals in how dissatisfied they would have to be to rate something a 6. One person's 6 could easily be someone else's 5 or 7.

Also, in the second scale, there are labels only for the end points and the midpoints. Respondents are given less guidance to help calibrate their ratings. If the questionnaires were administered a second time, the same people might choose a different value because the distinction between adjacent values is not clear in their own minds. The two additional values in the seven-point scale creates uncertainty about how best to choose an answer; it does not represent true distinctions in people's opinion. That is, the internal consistency of the second scale would probably be poorer than the first. In this case, the additional levels in the seven-point scale would be more likely to add random error to the data than to contribute any additional information.

The same can be said of scales that force people to choose options that do not represent their opinion. Some questionnaires are designed with rating scales that force respondents to choose a negative or positive position. For example, there may be an even number of choices, half positive and half negative. The restricted choice adds uncertainty because respondents who want to express a neutral opinion are unsure of which option to choose, thereby introducing a degree of randomness into the selections they make.

For many environmental features, a neutral rating is actually a good indicator and a desirable score. People generally perceive their physical work setting as a backdrop to their activities. It tends to be noticed only when it is negative or objectionable. People who are bothered by background noise are painfully aware of this annoyance in their environment. But if noise is not a problem, they are unlikely to rate the lack of noise as a boon to their productivity.

Positive ratings may indicate features that are performing particularly well. They might also be indicative of systems that are providing service levels much greater than is needed or simply those features most important to the occupants. For these reasons, we recommend the use of scales with an odd number of choices that offer a neutral response option.

BEWARE OF AVERAGES

Most people are familiar with using averages to summarize the value of a group of numbers. In statistics, this type of summary value is termed a **measure of central tendency.** Temperature values and other measurements of physical environmental variables are usually equal-interval or ratio values that are normally distributed. The average and standard deviation are appropriate measures of central tendency and variability for these data. (However this may not be useful for pinpointing problem locations in an office facility.)

The data in occupant surveys are predominantly ratings, which are ordinal values. The central tendency for a group of ratings is more reliably measured by the median than by the average.

The **median** is the value below which half the data in a group fall. Confidence intervals are calculated differently for medians than for averages. For a given set of values, the confidence interval is wider for the median than for the average. This is to be expected since there is greater uncertainty inherent in the ordinal scale of a rating than for equal-interval and ratio scales.

Statisticians prefer to treat ratings as if they were equal-interval variables because more powerful parametric statistical analyses can be applied. **Parametric statistics** assume that the data being analyzed are normally distributed. Where the distribution of sample data does not reasonably approximate a normal distribution, **nonparametric statistics** should be used. They are less powerful than parametric statistics (i.e., for a given sample, there will be a lower level of confidence in the statistical assertions that can be made), but they do not assume that the data conform to a particular distribution.

In some cases, the characteristics of a particular data set may allow it to be treated as normally distributed. Transformation functions can sometimes be used to convert ratings to values that approximate a normal distribution. The abundance of user-friendly statistical software makes it easy to perform a host of sophisticated analyses without having the expertise to assess whether the analytical procedures chosen are valid for the data set being analyzed.

Considering the highly subjective nature of the ratings in an occupant survey, it is not surprising that they generally do not satisfy the data quality requirements needed for these sophisticated statistical analyses. For this reason, these types of analyses should be scrutinized by those with the expertise to assess both the information that an occupant survey is trying to obtain and the statistical methods being employed.

Averages *alone* are generally a poor way to convey diagnostic information about the office environment. For the purposes of a workplace diagnosis, averages tend to obscure more than they clarify. Detailed information about the distribution of responses for each question is more important. For a question about which all respondents are in agreement, the average can represent the answer most of them gave. But for a highly polarized issue, where half the respondents adopted one extreme and half the other, the average of their answers would be the response no one actually gave. The average would effectively hide what may be an important divisive issue.

Even when survey questions are skillfully framed so that summary statistics such as averages and medians are not misleading, how can the results be used to improve the occupants' workplace environment? There is no average occupant. People's work habits, sensitivity to environmental conditions, and attitudes make them unique. If the objective is to identify and mitigate facility-related factors that impair people's performance, then it is important to know who is satisfied and

How satisfied are you with the overall comfort of your work setting?

	1 Very satisfied	2 Satisfied	3 Neutral	4 Dissatisfied	5 Very dissatisfied
$N = 47$	(18) 38%	(6) 13%	(8) 17%	(13) 28%	(2) 4%

Figure 8.15 Reporting of questionnaire results.

who is not. Averages tend to hide this detailed information.

What is perhaps more germane is to consider the original objectives of the occupant survey. If someone complains that he or she feels unwell in the afternoon, but on average, the occupants rate the office environment to be satisfactory, what action will be taken? Though the average suggests that there is no problem, one person claims that a problem exists. Does the average value suggest that this individual is lying, lazy, or simply more sensitive to certain conditions than his or her coworkers? One workstation might happen to be in a particularly unlucky location, as in the case of vehicle exhaust fumes infiltrating into an office space through an expansion joint (see the subsection "Location" earlier in this chapter).

If the survey is being used to compare a group of buildings to each other, what does it mean if the occupants of one building rate it better than average? Should occupant complaints in the "better" building be ignored because the overall quality is high enough?

Ratings and categorical responses (i.e., ordinal and nominal values) are more clearly reported by showing each question and the number of responses to each selection (Figure 8.15).

Here, the total sample size, "*N*," is reported to be 47. Beneath each rating is shown the number of responses in parentheses. The percentages of respondents who chose each rating are shown on the second line. When interpreting percentages, it is important to know the sample size. Five percent could represent a single individual or hundreds. The number of people affected will influence the way an issue is addressed. If only a few people are involved, problems can be addressed on an individual basis. Where large numbers of people experience similar difficulties with their work setting, comprehensive investigations and more global solutions are generally more cost-effective.

As noted earlier in this subsection, for ratings, the median is generally considered a more representative measure of central tendency than the average. This is because the intervals between ratings cannot be assumed to be equal.

The median of a group of numbers is the value below which half, or 50%, of the values in the group fall. It is the same as the fiftieth percentile, which is why it is sometimes called the "middle value." More generally, the *N*th percentile is the value below which *N*% of the values in a sample fall.

Extreme values (also known as **outliers**) have less effect on the median than on the average. For data that are highly skewed (i.e., with a few values much higher or much lower than the bulk of the data), the median value will fall closer to the majority of the values (Figure 8.16). Out of 100 responses to a questionnaire item, 70 were ratings of 5 and 30 were ratings of 1. The average of these ratings would be 3.8, but the median would be 5.

Neither the average nor the median value indicates that some 30% of the respondents expressed an opinion opposite to that of the majority. To understand the distribution of responses, the frequencies of each rating should be examined. But in the case of the median, the value 5 better represents the rating given by the majority

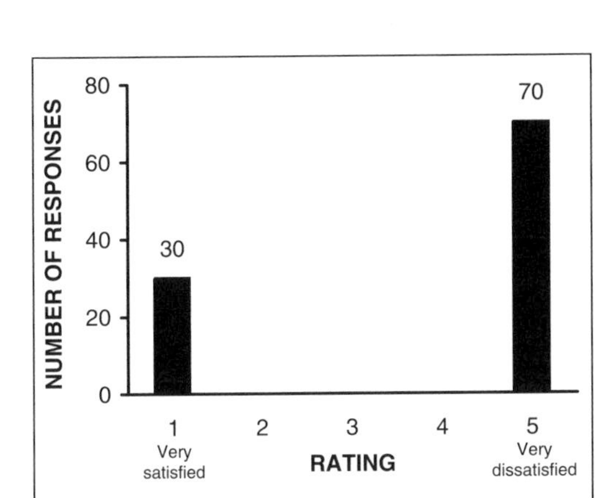

Figure 8.16 Comparison of the average and median for highly skewed data. Out of 100 respondents, 70% gave a rating of 5 and 30% a rating of 1. The average of the ratings is 3.8, and the median is 5.

of respondents. The average is more strongly influenced by the 30 low ratings.

Box plots are particularly valuable for evaluating rating data. They graphically depict the median as well as information about the distribution of the responses and the significance of differences in medians without assuming that the data are normally distributed. A brief illustration of the use of box plots in the analysis of diagnostic data is presented here because this valuable method of evaluating and graphically presenting rating data has been largely overlooked in workplace evaluation practice. (For detailed discussions of box plots, see McGill, Tukey, and Larsen 1978; and Velleman 1981.)

Box plots graphically display several nonparametric statistics for one or more groups of data values. The statistics commonly shown are the range and the twenty-fifth, fiftieth (the median), and seventy-fifth percentiles (Figure 8.17). The upper and lower bounds of the box are defined by the twenty-fifth and seventy-fifth percentiles. Thus, the length of the box indicates the range within which the middle half of the data values fall. The median is indicated by the "+" sign within the box. Whisker lines to either side of the box extend to the upper and lower extremes of the range. Thus a box plot clearly presents information about both the distribution and central tendency of a group of values as one simple icon.

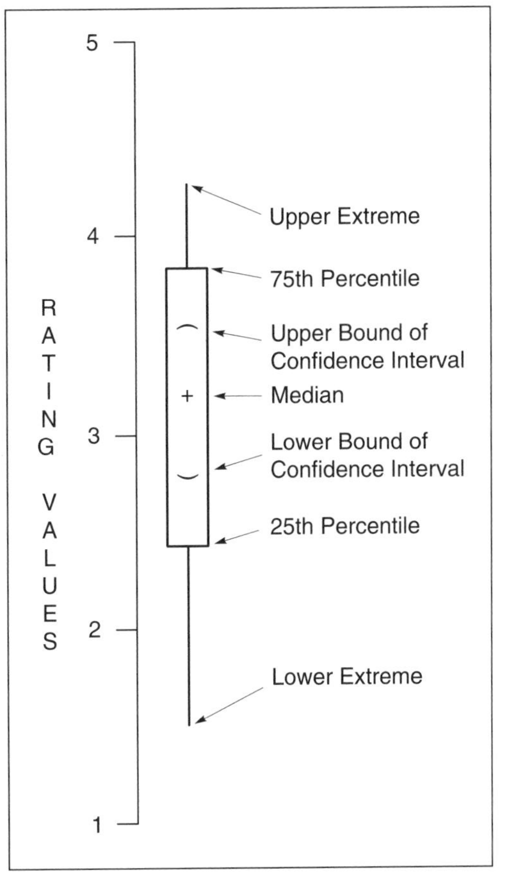

Figure 8.17 Components of a box plot symbol.

Box plots are particularly valuable for comparing the ratings given by different groups of respondents. Figure 8.18 displays occupant ratings of overall satisfaction with their workplace setting. In this case, the respondents have been grouped by job category. Respondents might also be grouped by their location within a building, by the length of time they spend in the office, or by other factors specific to a diagnostic evaluation.

In this example, the ratings of satisfaction were highest for the "manager" group, lowest for the "knowledge worker" group, and intermediate for the "support staff." The parentheses to either side of the median for each group give a 95% confidence interval for paired comparisons of sample data. Groups that have nonoverlapping confidence intervals have

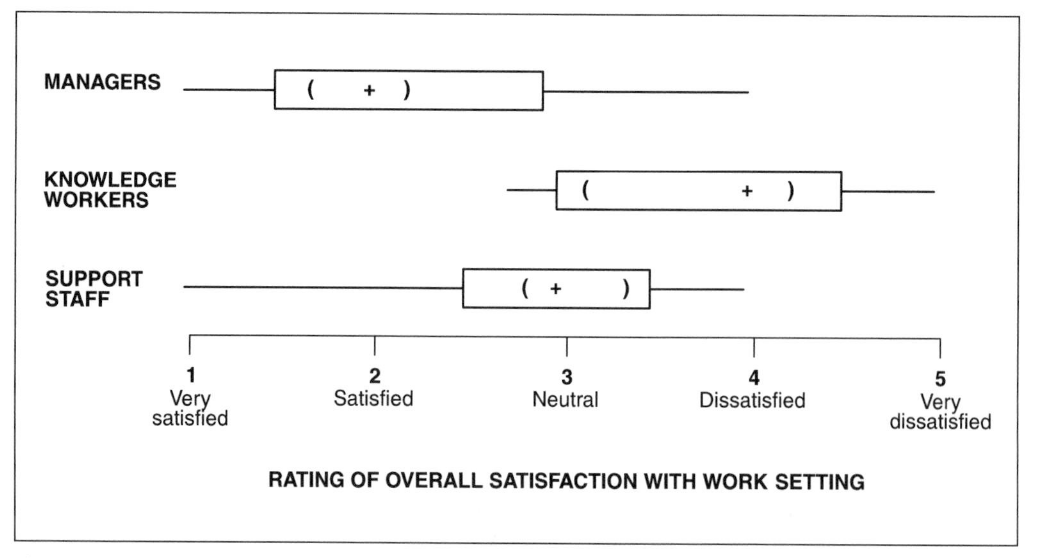

Figure 8.18 Multiple box plots for comparison of grouped rating data. Parentheses indicate the 95% confidence interval for paired comparisons of medians. Groups are considered to have significantly different medians if the confidence intervals of their box plots do not overlap.

medians that are significantly different at the 95% level of confidence. In this example, the confidence interval for the manager ratings does not overlap those given by knowledge workers and support staff, indicating that the managers' ratings of satisfaction were significantly higher than of the other two groups — *according to this test of significance.* The confidence intervals for the ratings of the knowledge workers and support staff have overlapping ranges. This indicates that although the median rating of the support staff was higher than that of the knowledge workers, the difference is not considered to be significant — *according to this test of significance.*

The test of significance used for these data is not the commonly used test which is based on the normal distribution of the mean. As discussed previously, ratings should not be assumed to be normally distributed. For ratings, the median is a more reliable measure of central tendency than the mean. For this reason the confidence interval for the median is used. It is calculated as:

$$\text{median} \pm 1.58\, H \div \sqrt{N}$$

where H is the range from the twenty-fifth to seventy-fifth percentiles, and N is the sample size.

This calculation of the confidence interval is sufficiently robust to provide a good estimate for a wide range of distributions other than normally distributed data (McGill, Tukey, and Larsen 1978; Tukey 1977; Velleman 1981).

If all occupants were surveyed (i.e., a census), then the confidence interval is not needed in the interpretation of the data. With a census, the median and other statistics *are* the population values, because they are calculated from the responses of the entire population being assessed. A sample seeks to estimate the population value by measuring or polling only a portion of the population. For a sample, the confidence interval is needed to express the uncertainty of that estimate. With a census this uncertainty about how the entire population would have responded has been eliminated.

The median and box plots are particularly well suited for analysis of environmental survey data, which, after they are divided into subgroups such as by job categories, often have a small number of values that are not normally distributed.

If the objective of a diagnostic evaluation is to optimize the office environment so that every occupant can do his or her best work, then diagnostic data, particularly occupant survey data, must be analyzed and presented in a way that highlights the unusual event. Fundamentally, optimizing the office workplace involves matching the work settings to the individuals who use them. An orientation toward average solutions produces only average results. Diagnostic analyses, whether they involve tens or thousands of occupants, are more successful if they focus on assessing the workplace experienced by each individual rather than looking at average conditions suited to average people — who don't exist.

THE CENTRAL LIMIT THEOREM AND LARGE SAMPLE SIZES

The **normal distribution** is a mathematical function widely used in statistics to calculate the probability of events. It produces the familiar bell-shaped curve known to everyone exposed to introductory statistics (Figure 8.19).

Political pollsters survey a sample of voters to assess their attitudes and estimate the outcome of an election. Their results are usually presented as a predicted value and a probability that the predicted value is within some specified range of the true value. For example, it might be predicted that a political party will receive 26% of the vote, and the estimated accuracy of the prediction is that the true value will be within plus or minus 3% of this predicted value 19 times out of 20. In this case, the "plus or minus 3%" specifies a range termed the **confidence interval.** The probability "19 times out of 20" specifies the **confidence level.** The normal distribution is used to calculate this prediction of accuracy. In predicting accuracy this way, an assumption is being made that the data are normally distributed. If the data do not behave in that way, then the predicted accuracy will not be valid.

Whenever the accuracy of a sample statistic is estimated, an assumption must be made about the distribution of the data.

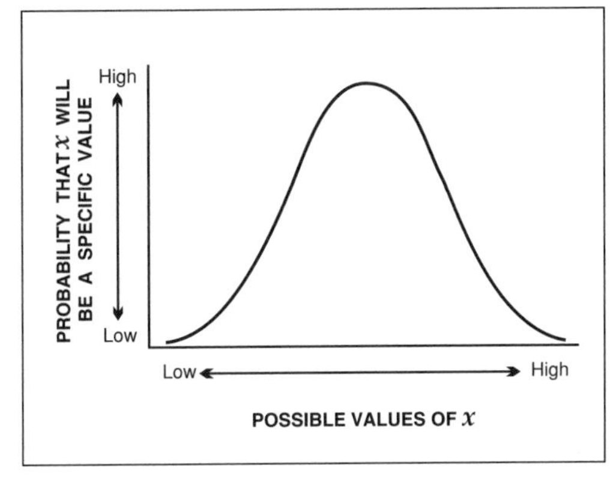

Figure 8.19 The normal probability distribution.

Many common statistical analyses require that the distribution of the data reasonably approximate a normal distribution. The accuracy of opinion polls is usually estimated using the normal distribution. Analyses of variance, factor analyses, and regression analyses also generally assume that the data are normally distributed.

Most of the data from occupant surveys are ratings. Ratings generally are *not* normally distributed. So before statistical analyses that assume normally distributed data (parametric statistics) are used, the actual distribution of a set of ratings should be evaluated to determine whether the statistic will be valid.

If data are not normally distributed, other statistical tests (nonparametric statistics) can be used that do not require this property. As noted previously, parametric statistics are preferred because they are more powerful (i.e., from a given set of data, assertions can be made with greater confidence). This is to be expected because parametric statistics assume that the data behave in a more predictable fashion — they are approximately normally distributed.

Even when the individual values of a data set are not normally distributed, there may be some useful properties that do behave in this way. One such property is the average or **mean.** For fairly large samples, the distribution of sample means has been shown to reasonably approximate a normal distribution even if the individual values are distributed very differently. This statistical principle is known as the **central limit theorem.** The number of observations needed for a sample to be considered "large" depends on the conventions of the discipline. In attitude surveys, a sample size of at least 50 is generally used.

The central limit theorem is a valuable statistical property. It justifies using an easily calculated method based on the normal distribution to estimate the accuracy of sample means. It is sometimes erroneously thought that for a large enough sample size, it can be assumed that the individual values are also normally distributed. This is not the case. It can only be assumed that the means calculated from the samples will be normally distributed.

A simple though admittedly contrived example will clarify this point. Suppose the lighting in an office was too bright to comfortably view computer screens and too dark for paper-based reading. Each occupant was asked to rate the lighting on a scale of 1 to 5 in which 1 was "too dark," 5 was "too bright," and 3 was "satisfactory." If half the people worked at VDTs and rated the lighting a 5 and the other half did paper-based work and rated it a 1, the average rating would be 3. In a randomly selected sample of people from this group, it would be expected that about half would give the lighting a rating of 1 and half a rating of 5, for an average value of about 3.

If many different random samples of the occupant's responses were taken, the mean of those values would vary slightly from the group's mean of 3 because, by the luck of the draw, there might not be exactly the same proportion of VDT users in the sample as in the entire group. The values of the means might vary from 2.8 to 3.2 or so, depending on the sample size. The larger the sample, the more closely the mean would be to 3. The central limit theorem says that these different *sample means* would have a distribution that is approximately normal. But the fact still remains that the individual values in the sample are all either 1s or 5s. There are no values of 2, 3, or 4, as would be expected if the data were normally distributed.

For this reason, in diagnostic evaluations, it is important to look at the distribution of questionnaire responses. As in this simple example, no matter how large the sample, there is no way to tell from an average value whether the individual values are tightly clustered around the average or whether there are distinct polarized groupings.

As previously noted, in diagnostic evaluations, the exceptional observations are important. To find them, the actual pattern of data values must be examined. Summary statistics can be useful but are not sufficient, regardless of how large the sample size may be.

INFLUENCE OF THE MANAGEMENT ENVIRONMENT ON OCCUPANT SURVEY DATA

Office occupants' perceptions of their physical work environment are influenced by their total experience at work. The responses given in occupant surveys reflect the influence of factors other than those examined in the questions. Relations with coworkers and supervisors, interest in their jobs, and attitudes toward their organization affect occupants' perceptions. As well, a work setting is a very public statement of the occupants' status and recognition within the organization. Dissatisfaction with this aspect of the work environment can cause deep resentment.

For this reason, occupant survey data cannot simply be taken at face value. Mistrust and partisan interests can make survey results grossly misleading. Survey data must therefore be analyzed in the context of a workplace's prevailing management environment. To extract the useful facility performance information, the influence of confounding factors must be minimized or controlled.

When people are dissatisfied but are unable to address or resolve a problem directly, they express their feelings in other ways. An occupant survey provides an ideal vehicle for people to vent their frustration. This was well illustrated by an occupant survey of several floors of an office building. In the course of the analysis, the response data were grouped by location and by job category. The environmental ratings from one group of managers were much lower than the ratings from other managers or from other people working in the same area but doing different jobs. This group of dissatisfied managers was located in the same wing of the building and worked for the same department. They were accommodated in an open plan layout, interspersed with other workers who did not report workplace problems.

Though these managers rated their physical office setting to be poor, the workplace was not really the source of their dissatisfaction. They resented being the only group of managers who did not have enclosed offices. The occupant survey was a means for them to vent their dissatisfaction with what they regarded as a lower-status accommodation than their peers. But their low ratings were more a comment on the management environment than on the physical workplace.

For this reason, it is important to gauge the attitude of respondents before an occupant survey is administered. Health concerns about the physical workplace setting can easily become emotionally charged and highly contentious issues (see the section "Psychosocial Response to Health Risks in the Office Setting" in Chapter 7). The interests of building owners, the management of a tenant organization, and employees are frequently in direct opposition. Mistrust among the different stakeholders can raise concerns that occupant data will not be kept confidential and that partisan interests will influence evaluation results.

For example, it generally is not in the interests of building owners for data to be collected that may show deficiencies in the facility. If problems are identified, there will be pressure for the owners to pay for their correction. However, it is in the occupants' interest to have as much information about the quality of their workplace as possible. The more informed they are, the better they can safeguard their health and well-being and the more persuasive a case they can make for improvements.

Where the management environment in a workplace is very negative and highly polarized, it is difficult to obtain any reliable data from an occupant survey. Steps must first be taken to deescalate the confrontational atmosphere. It may not be acceptable for facility issues to be evaluated by in-house personnel. Instead, an outside consultant who is viewed as an independent third party may be better able to collect sensitive information, and the study results will more likely be judged on their own merits rather than dismissed as a biased and self-serving exercise.

Polling occupants need not be onerous, expensive, or time-consuming. A well-designed occupant survey can meet the objectives of the client organization within a reasonable time frame and budget. Key to a successful process is to explicitly recognize the purpose of the work at the outset, include and communicate regularly with the parties involved, and ensure that the participants see tangible benefits to their involvement.

CONCLUSION

Diagnostic evaluations are a valuable means to address specific facility problems and to periodically review a facility's performance. The communication process that forms an integral part of the diagnostic process can build trust between those responsible for managing an office facility and those using it. That trust can make facility management more responsive and proactive to the needs of the organization as well as individual occupants. Moreover, it can make occupants more likely to cooperate with management in resolving facility problems and to forgive minor shortcomings.

As with any diagnostic endeavor, success depends on the use of comprehensive and systematic procedures by skilled and experienced practitioners. Checklists and surveys administered by those unfamiliar with building design and operation are of limited use in assessing the performance of office facilities or determining effective corrective measures. Tools cannot replace experienced judgment and in-depth knowledge of building performance.

Many workplace diagnostic methods can be readily incorporated into the facility management process. As the pervasive influence of the office environment on human health and performance has been recognized, facility managers have been expected to address an ever-wider range of issues. The following chapter examines the role that the facility management process plays in optimizing the office workplace for an organization.

LITERATURE CITED

Barton, P. K. 1983. *Building services integration.* London: E. & F. N. Spon.

Becker, F. 1989. Post occupancy evaluation: Research paradigm or diagnostic tool. In *Building evaluation,* edited by W. F. E. Preiser. New York: Plenum Press.

Brill, M. 1987. When politics is the name of the FM game. *Facilities Design & Management* (July–August):58–61.

Butler, H. 1977. *Co-ordination of building services.* Bracknell, United Kingdom: Building Services Research and Information Association.

Canter, D. V., ed. 1970. *Architectural psychology.* London: Royal Institute of British Architects.

Gutman, R., eds. 1972. *People and buildings.* New York: Basic Books.

IFMA. 1994. *Benchmarks II.* Houston: International Facility Management Association.

Kaplan, A., and Workplace Diagnostics. 1989. *Occupant survey on the work setting.* Report prepared for Revenue Canada Taxation. Ottawa: Workplace Diagnostics Ltd.

Leaman, A. 1994. Personal communications. Building Use Studies, London, England.

Leaman, A., and B. Bordass. 1993. Building design, complexity and manageability. *Facilities* (September).

Lippy, B., and R. Turner. 1991. Complex mixtures in industrial workspaces: Lessons for indoor air quality evaluations. *Environmental Health Perspectives* 95:81–83.

McGill, R., J. W. Tukey, and W. A. Larsen. 1978. Variations of box plots. *The American Statistician* 32(1):12–16.

Mølhave, L. 1990. Volatile organic compounds, indoor air quality, and human health. In *Indoor Air '90, Proceedings of the 5th International Conference on Indoor Air Quality and Climate* 5:15–33. Ottawa: Canada Mortgage and Housing Corporation.

Newman, O. 1972. *Defensible space: Crime prevention through urban design.* New York: Macmillan.

Preiser, W. F. E., H. Z. Rabinowitz, and E. T. White. 1988. *Post-occupancy evaluation.* New York: Van Nostrand Reinhold.

Rubin, A., and J. Elder. 1980. *Building for people.* Washington, D.C.: U.S. National Bureau of Standards.

Scharf, T., and S. Margulis. 1992. Book review. *The Journal of Architectural and Planning Research* 9(1):83–90.

Sommer, R. 1969. *Personal space: The behavioral basis of design.* Engelwood Cliffs, N.J.: Prentice-Hall.

Sommer, R. 1974. *Tight spaces: Hard architecture and how to humanize it.* Engelwood Cliffs, N.J.: Prentice-Hall.

Tukey, J. W. 1977. *Exploratory data analysis.* Reading, Mass.: Addison-Wesley.

Velleman, P. 1981. *Applications, basics, and computing of exploratory data analysis.* Boston: PWS Publishers.

Chapter 9

MANAGING THE FACILITY FOR THE ORGANIZATION

The facility management process coordinates the way people, equipment, space, and information are brought together to support work activities. It strives to provide a work environment that is safe, cost-effective, and productive.

The physical attributes of office space and the manner in which it is operated have a more pervasive influence on the organization than is commonly recognized. Fundamental business decisions such as the scheduling of work, the work-force's size and distribution, changes in activities, the acquisition and disposition of equipment, downsizing, expanding, or restructuring the organization are constrained by characteristics of the facility and the way it is maintained. For example, the introduction of flexible working hours extends the period of time that a building must be fully serviced. The additional operating cost of such a policy change is, in turn, affected by a number of organizational decisions such as whether off-peak usage is concentrated in one area of the building or widely distributed. Work schedules might then become a consideration in the allocation of space within the building, with those who work extended hours being clustered so that services can be reduced in unoccupied areas. Indeed, the choice of building location might also be reconsidered if the current locale is unsafe at night.

Traditionally, in assessing its real estate or accommodation portfolio, corporate management focuses on monetary costs and financial returns. It makes extensive use of hard costs readily derived from conventional accounting information, such as the building's capital cost and rate of return on the real estate investment, the cost of rented space, the amount of floor area per employee, and annual accommodation cost per employee. Scrutinizing these numbers is vital, as some 25% to 50%

of an organization's assets and 10% to 18% of its annual expenses are facility-related (Ritchin 1992).

Facility costs are generally the second largest expense of office-based organizations — salaries and benefits being the first. Yet senior managers are commonly unfamiliar with the key issues addressed by facilities personnel. They are consequently unaware of how their decisions affect facility resources, operation and maintenance costs, the quality of the indoor environment, occupants' satisfaction, or the organization's return on its real estate investment. Facility issues tend to be treated as a background activity — attracting the attention of top decision makers only when an issue of direct interest arises, such as the selection of a new office location, construction of a new facility, or renovation of existing space.

Broad misunderstandings regarding the role of facility managers lead to their exclusion from key planning groups in the organization. For example, the responsibility for office automation is commonly divided among several groups. Specification of computer systems is most often assigned to the information management group. Defining new job functions and integrating them into the organizational structure falls primarily to the human resources group. It is expected that the facility management group will anticipate these changes and provide office space suited to the new equipment and positions even though it may not be directly involved in the planning process (Figure 9.1).

Figure 9.1 This outdated computer equipment cluttered hallways for weeks until its fate could be decided. Though the information management group had planned the upgrade well in advance, facility management had not been informed so neither storage nor disposal of the equipment had been arranged.

The quality of the work environment affects the health and morale of the workforce, the ability to attract and retain new talent, the flexibility to redeploy people and equipment in response to changing work demands, the quality of work, and ultimately the organization's productivity. Although, during economic down-turns, many people are pleased just to have a job, those who work in offices have come to expect more than simply a "safe" work environment. Office workers need a setting that provides the resources to accomplish their mind's best work — the equipment, information, control, and physical comfort to do their jobs well. Because their productivity ultimately determines an organization's success or failure, effective management of the accommodations provided to office workers merits the considered attention of the highest-level decision makers.

THE CHANGING OFFICE

The nature of workplaces has undergone a rapid transformation over the past decade. The widespread adoption of information technology has not only changed the tools of the office workforce; it has fundamentally altered the content of jobs, the way work is done, and the num-

Figure N9.2 Office facilities must support the more frequent use of collaborative work methods. Since project teams vary greatly in their size, duration of collaboration, and their pace and intensity of work a variety of workspaces are needed to accommodate them. (*Source:* Bell-Northern Research (BNR).)

ber of people needed to complete a project. With suitable equipment to support the work effort, it is often more productive to have one person handle an entire task than to have a number of people each do a portion, passing it along in assembly-line fashion. Routine tasks have increasingly been relegated to computers, and the tasks that are left have become more demanding, requiring specialized knowledge and decision-making skills.

The quality and content of work produced have become more dependent on the unique combination of skills and experience of the individual who performs it. This has directly affected the number and kinds of business activities as well as the facilities and services needed to support office workers.

Though automation may be the most visible change in the office, it is not the only one. External forces have fostered a number of important changes in the effect of the physical office on an organization's performance. They were discussed in Chapters 1 and 2 and are highlighted here.

Global competition and a painful recession have forced organizations to reexamine the allocation of all their resources and reevaluate their contribution to corporate objectives. Downsizing of the workforce required that the remaining individuals handle a greater diversity of tasks and become more productive. Organizations have adopted more varied work methods, such as ad hoc groups, quality circles, and task forces. It has become commonplace for critical projects to be completed by short-term work groups composed of individuals drawn from throughout the organization (Figure 9.2).

Contrary to common opinion, the office workforce is no longer dominated by clerical workers, as it was earlier this century. By some estimates, as much as three-quarters of office personnel are knowledge workers. They spend about seventy percent of their time on communication activities. As a result, it has become increasingly important to support collaborative work groups with the technology, administrative backup, and physical setting they

Figure N9.3 Though isolated from the noise and activity of the mainstream office, this software development lab is centrally located and surrounded by glass so people can view into or out from the area. Located just outside the labs are fun, nontraditional office furniture where workers can meet to discuss their ideas or simply relax. (*Source*: Bell-Northern Research (BNR).)

need to work effectively (Panko 1992).

Managers must rethink how both information and people flow in an office. Work groups vary in size, the pace of their work, and the duration of their collaboration. Their resource needs vary accordingly. They may require large open work spaces where shared documents, equipment, and other materials can be left. They also commonly require meeting areas for face-to-face discussions, work areas with specialized computer support, or quiet areas for individuals to think things through.

To support such diverse work activities, office facilities need to offer a wider range of settings and greater flexibility in their assignment. An alternative to limiting office accommodations to "one person, one place" is to provide a variety of shared activity settings. Unlike an assigned work setting that is used for all of an individual's work activities, activity settings are designed for a narrower range of uses and are assigned on an "as-needed" basis. These settings may house expensive equipment such as a graphics workstation, serve as informal areas conducive to the exchange of ideas, or they may simply be quiet places to work that are protected from the noise and bustle of the general office (Figure N9.3). (For a discussion of activity settings, see, for example, Stone and Luchetti 1985.)

With advanced telecommunications, many tasks can be done more effectively by staff at remote or mobile locations. Sales personnel or consultants can spend most of their time with clients yet be in regular contact with their office by telephone, fax, voice mail, and computer modem (Figure N9.4). Their work can be tightly coupled to an office — booking orders, submitting reports, and participating in collaborative projects on a daily basis — yet they may be physically absent most of the time. Instead of providing full-time office space for part-time occupants, innovative facilities can give these users work space that can be personalized for their needs when they are present and reassigned when they are absent.

To reap the greatest return from an office facility, not only must its form be optimized for the functions it provides; the way the facility is managed must keep pace with the rate at which office resource demands change over time. In many organizations, project teams are assembled for projects that are started and completed within a six-month period, after which the team members are reassigned. The more varied and rapidly changing the organization's activities, the more intensive are its facility management needs.

The hard costs of the office facility, its management, and operation have come under closer examination than ever before. With leasing costs at US$15 to US$60 per square foot, US$100 million buildings, US$10,000 workstations, and millions of dollars in information technology, communications equipment, and automated building management systems — office facilities are expensive. Mistakes

Figure N9.4 This video conference room allows participants to "meet" with collaborators at other locations. The necessary equipment (e.g., cameras, projectors, microphones) has been built into the furniture and walls. People are more comfortable conducting their business in a spacious room uncluttered by the sophisticated technology that makes their meeting possible. (*Source:* Bell-Northern Research (BNR).)

in their management have costly repercussions. Simple cost-cutting measures often waste a great deal of money on unnecessary equipment and inappropriate renovations as well as compromise individual productivity and severely degrade the environmental quality of the office facility. The greater recognition and understanding of sick building syndrome has not only drawn public attention to the health risks of simplistic cost-cutting measures involving building maintenance, office furniture, energy costs, and space; it has frequently precipitated vigorous legal action by workers and their unions to compensate injured employees.

Organizations need office environments that will minimize staff turnover, reduce absenteeism, mitigate health-related complaints, facilitate innovation, and encourage productive work. They need to maximize the work produced in each unit of space instead of merely trying to minimize the cost of the space. The purpose of having office space in the first place is to accomplish work activities, not to save money. A strategy of simply minimizing space cost assumes that spending less on accommodations or decreasing the space allocated per person does not affect work output. As discussed in Chapter 3, although the relationship between work space quality and office worker productivity may be difficult to quantify, it is nonetheless a significant hidden cost.

The resources and management of the office facility directly impact the overall success of the organization. Senior decision makers often regard facility management as too technical, too detailed, or too constrained for them to carefully scrutinize any aspects other than its costs. Yet failure to wring every last benefit out of accommodation resources would not be tolerated in any other aspect of corporate life. Senior managers need to provide informed input and regular support to the facility management process, not simply examine its costs.

THE FACILITY MANAGEMENT DOMAIN

The domain of facility management practice has expanded dramatically over the past decade in response to growing corporate needs and an ever wider range of responsibilities. From its origins in property management and building maintenance, facility management has come to include activities ranging from space planning to lease negotiation. In many ways, it has been a journey from the boiler room to the boardroom. Finance, budgeting, and asset management are an increasingly large part of facility management practice. The facility management domain has come to include facility operations and maintenance, planning and project management, human and environmental factors, finance, and real estate.

In-house facility managers have found themselves ever more closely scrutinized. They face shrinking budgets and escalating demands as organizations search for expenses that can be cut or activities that can be eliminated. The services they provide are compared with those offered outside. Individuals who do not measure up may face budget cuts, staff reductions, or loss of their jobs.

As organizations have been forced to respond to the health concerns of their employees, it has fallen to facility managers to identify the building problems to be addressed and the specialized services required. They have been charged with taking corrective action, measuring progress, and communicating with employees and management. It is a range of activities for which many were unprepared.

Facility Operations and Maintenance. The primary task of facility management is to manage an operating facility. To do so requires a working knowledge of building services, structures, exterior wall/roof systems, and furnishings. The acquisition, installation, operation, maintenance, and disposition of office accommodations are central functions of facility management. In recent years these traditional responsibilities have expanded to include the management of all fixed assets, from furniture to electronic equipment. Sophisticated computer-based inventory and tracking systems have been developed and are being widely adopted to perform this function (see the subsection "Automation in Facility Management" later in this chapter).

Planning and Project Management. Managing the allocation of office space, moving people and equipment, projecting future space requirements, and planning and overseeing renovation and construction activities are established facility management activities. In addition, there are specialized design activities such as **programming** (i.e., defining user needs and specifying space and other facility resource requirements by activity, department, or other organizational grouping), **space planning** (i.e., designing work settings and their arrangement on the floor plan), and specification of fixtures, furniture, and equipment. Often, these activities are performed by outside specialists.

Human and Environmental Factors. Safety and security have long been a part of facility management. Assuring compliance with health and safety regulations, developing emergency response plans, and ensuring the internal security of a building and its surroundings are well-defined and accepted responsibilities. More recently, facility management has been required to address health-related issues outside the bounds of current health and safety standards. Indoor air quality, ergonomic factors of office furnishings, lighting deficiencies, accessibility to the physically or mentally impaired, and other issues that commonly require the expertise of outside specialists have necessarily entered the domain of facility management because the problems that occur result from the particular conditions of an office facility. They are directly affected by the building's design, the way it is operated, the furnishings selected, the layout of work settings, and other aspects under the direct control of the facility management function.

Finance. Reporting accommodation costs, developing budgets, and projecting future building-related expenditures are standard facility management functions. Currently, faced with shrinking budgets and increasing demands, facility managers have had to become more skilled in analyzing and presenting the broader financial implications of facility decisions on performance and profitability. For example, the facilities group may implement charge-back systems so that the true cost of space and services is reflected in the profit and loss statements of separate business units. Sophisticated economic models may be used to project facility costs to support alternate corporate business plans and assess the financial performance of the facility and services. At a time of ever more rigorously scrutinized budgets, more comprehensive financial analyses have been a winning strategy to justify facility expenditures.

Real Estate. Office facilities have traditionally been thought of as places to produce goods and services. Today, however, some facilities are more valued for their income-generating potential as property to be sold, rented, or traded. In order to maximize the return on property without compromising business activities, real estate investment activities need to be integrated with facility planning and management as well as corporate strategic planning.

Such decisions as leasing versus owning, the sale and acquisition of office properties, and lease terms affect the facility resources available to the organization. Impacts on the organization's current and projected business activities must be taken into account as well as the investment return. Facility operations and maintenance procedures, building renovations, the upgrading or replacement of equipment, and other facility management activities affect the market value of the real estate and hence the return on investment. As a result, facility management personnel have become involved in comparing alternative real estate proposals in terms of their impact on the activities of the organization and its personnel. Their expertise in building systems, maintenance, and operations has also proved to be a useful contribution in assessing the condition and inherent value of a building.

Clarifying the Role of Facility Management

Facility management is a dynamic process. Few things are settled once and for all. Situations change — business objectives, financial constraints, new mandates and opportunities can alter facility needs and justify periodically reviewing decisions. In such a dynamic environment, effective management demands that authority and responsibility for facility-related decisions be clearly defined. In this way, the facility manager can be better informed of occupant needs and can better anticipate and address the consequences of new policies and programs on facility cost and occupant satisfaction (Figure 9.5).

Whether an organization uses outside contractors or in-house staff to manage its facility, the role and activities of the facility management function must be made clear. Otherwise, diverse participants with vested personal interests or simply the enthusiasm to become involved can undermine accommodation decisions.

For example, organizations with facilities in several cities often assign a specialist from the head office to select rented space and negotiate leases. The impact of location and the details of a tenant contract can be complex and have a major

Figure 9.5 Changes in facility policies can have unexpected and unwanted consequences. When smoking was no longer permitted in the office areas of this building, occupants smoked in the lobby and entrance ways. As a result, to enter this building, people had to pass through smoke-laden areas strewn with overflowing ashtrays. Not only were these areas unpleasant and unhealthy, they detracted from the organization's corporate image.

impact on occupancy costs and future business decisions. One such specialist arrived to find that members of the local sales staff had already done a location search, selected the "best" alternative, and were prepared to sign a lease! Although the location was convenient for them, the space was unsuitable in most other respects, and the terms of the lease were less attractive than would be secured by someone experienced in such negotiations. In the end, a more suitable space was found at lower cost and more attractive terms, and the sales staff gained new respect for the work done by the head office facility group.

Part of the facility management role is to keep occupants as well as managers informed about and involved in changes that affect their workplace. People's offices are their "homes" when they are at work. A seemingly trivial change may provoke an unexpectedly vehement response. Moving a coffee machine or a photocopier, replacing light fixtures, or adding a door can become sources of avoidable occupant dissatisfaction. A willingness to consult occupants about when and why changes are proposed and to consider alternative suggestions can prevent most complaints from ever developing. Facility changes may alter how some things are done but should not create obstacles to work activities.

In one head office, some directors attending semiannual board meetings disliked seeing the coffee machine and photocopier in an open alcove as they walked towards the conference room. Though the office floor was used only by in-house staff, the directors considered the open alcove to detract from the corporate image and insisted that a door be installed and kept closed. That door then became a constant irritant to the office occupants, who had to fumble with their coffee cups and papers every day to open it. To the occupants, the closed door became a lasting gripe and a daily symbol of management disdain. This backlash could have been avoided if the users' perspective had been addressed. The open alcove might have been tolerable after all, or perhaps an automatic or push-button door opener might have been an acceptable compromise.

Subtle changes that are early indicators of facility problems are often noticed first by the people who use a space every day. This "army of observers" can provide an early warning of facility problems before they escalate or become expensive to resolve. A drafty work space may indicate a fault in the ventilation system or deterioration in the building enclosure. Objectionable odors, an increase in headaches, drowsiness, and other illness symptoms may signify that air supply vents are blocked or that maintenance is required. All too often, occupant complaints are treated as a nuisance to be disposed of rather than as potentially valuable information.

At one time, the comfort of occupants was at the discretion of the organization. However, as the health effects of indoor air quality, lighting, and other environmental factors have been documented, the consequences of ignoring occupant complaints have become potentially more serious. Occupants have launched successful liability suits and exacted substantial compensation awards when facility managers and building owners were unresponsive to their complaints. Lack of action has in some cases become evidence of criminal negligence. In a recent court case, a judge held the building owner, the employer, and the facility manager to be personally responsible for the illness of employees exposed to poor air quality during office renovations (Levin 1990) (see the subsection "Accountability" in Chapter 1). Responding to occupant complaints should be a recognized and important responsibility embraced by facility management (see the subsection "Monitoring Facility Performance" below).

Education should be part of the ongoing interaction of facility managers and occupants. Occupants who are better informed about facility issues are more willing to take action to help themselves and less likely to make modifications that disrupt building system operation. For example, moving furniture next to thermostats can block air circulation and compromise temperature regulation. Blocking ventilation diffusers to prevent uncomfortable drafts can create problems elsewhere in the building. An uncomfortable work setting may be the result of single or multiple factors such as poor lighting or incorrectly adjusted seating, table height, and equipment layout. Facility management's role is to determine whether the problems identified by occupants can be resolved directly or are symptoms of a facility deficiency that merits a more thorough investigation.

Key Issues the Facility Management Process Should Address

To ensure that the office facility and the way it is managed are optimized for the organization's specific needs and style of work, the ten key issues summarized in Table 9.1 and examined in the following subsections, should be periodically reviewed. Then appropriate changes should be made to facility operation and maintenance.

SUITABILITY

As an organization's activities change, its resource needs shift and its priorities are altered. The facility management process must monitor how well a facility's resources and operating characteristics suit the needs of the organization it is to serve. Emerging requirements for new resources should be anticipated and planned, and those no longer needed should be eliminated.

Equipment once deemed nice to have can suddenly become essential, while other equipment becomes obsolete. Similarly, a level of service quality that was at one time acceptable may suddenly become inadequate. For example, voltage fluctuations in the electrical power supply (termed brownouts) were hardly noticed when the only consequence was a brief dimming of the lights. But with the introduction of computers to the general office setting, the quality of electrical power had to be improved because voltage fluctuations caused the computers to fail. It also raised the priority of resolving power quality problems.

The critical issue in suitability is not "What could be improved?" but "What will make a difference?" There are innumerable changes that might be made to improve a facility. There are differences in the benefits they could deliver, who will benefit, who will be disadvantaged, and the reliability with which those possible

Table 9.1 Summary of key facility management issues.

Facility Management Issues	Sample Questions
Suitability	Do people have the work settings and office resources they need when they need them? Are there facility changes that would significantly benefit the organization?
Quality of office space	Are office health and safety acceptable? Is there a high or increasing rate of illness absenteeism, work-related injuries, fatigue, headaches, or other illness symptoms that could indicate deficient work settings or facility operation? Is the facility managed proactively, with conditions being monitored to identify and resolve problems before they become serious?
Space utilization	How much space is actually unoccupied at any given time? Is a lot of full-time space being devoted to employees who must regularly work outside the office? Would alternative arrangements such as shared, reservable office space be more suitable?
Service delivery	To whom does the facility management process respond? Is the response time and the way complaints are addressed acceptable? Are the services provided adequate? Are others services needed? Are the maintenance and operation of the building system well suited to the specific needs of the organization? Are fixed assets such as furniture managed in a way that maximizes their service life and utility?
Layout flexibility and usable space	Can people be placed in arrangements optimal for their work activities? Are the cost and time to rearrange people or furniture and to reconnect telephones, computer networks, and other services acceptable? Does the layout prevent the effective use of space?
Location	Is the current location cost-effective? For whom is it convenient — employees, clients, suppliers, no one? For whom should it be convenient? Are there more suitable alternatives? If alternative work arrangements are being considered, would they affect the suitability of the current location?
Cost	Is the level of spending on facilities commensurate with the desired level of office quality and service?
Real estate management and leasing	If office space is leased, is the lease agreement appropriate and reasonable? Is there a way to test, monitor, or verify that the conditions contracted for were delivered? If the office is owned, is the real estate investment providing an adequate return to justify this use of funds?
Image	Are facility management procedures and results consistent with corporate policies? Do they present an appropriate image of the organization to the outside?
Monitoring facility performance	Are the facility management functions important to the organization adequately addressed, measured, and reported? Are the occupants satisfied and productive?

benefits can be predicted. Prioritizing facility management activities (e.g., operation, maintenance, enhancements, and space optimization), justifying those recommendations, then measuring and documenting results are key responsibilities of the facility management process. In this way, facility management can be more accountable and its contribution more visible to senior management so that it is supported at a level commensurate with its contribution to corporate objectives.

QUALITY OF OFFICE SPACE

Choosing how and to whom resources for office quality should be allocated is a difficult but important decision. It has a fundamental impact on the organization and so should be examined and guided by senior management. Few organizations have the financial resources to offer the ultimate in office quality to every occupant. Explicitly or implicitly, decisions are made that ration equipment, space, and funds differently among employees.

Apportioning facility resources — always a politically charged endeavor — impacts productivity. Ideally, space standards would assign quality according to overall benefits, providing the best-quality work environment to those who most need it to sustain their peak level of effort without injury or illness. In practice, facility resource allocation is determined by a mixture of need, power, and influence.

Anyone will benefit to some degree from a better-quality work environment, but this provides little guidance for prioritizing expenditures. In the past, quality was generally prioritized by status. The higher the rank, the larger and more private the space, the more expensive the furnishings, the more preferred the parking space. A high degree of environmental control is indicative of status. The large private office with individual control of lighting and temperature, a door that can be closed, good acoustic separation to ensure privacy, and a window with a pleasant view outside are the hallmarks of a high-status work setting.

Traditionally, this investment was justified as part of the compensation for high-ranking employees. Today, however, lower-echelon employees may use sophisticated equipment that requires a great deal of space and specialized, ergonomic furniture to prevent such illnesses as cumulative trauma disorders. Although everyone might be more comfortable in high-quality furnishings, those who rarely use a computer are at low risk for such occupational injuries. The organization would derive greater benefit if it prioritized ergonomic quality based on job-related need.

Visible indicators of status are important. They are a way for the individual's contribution to be publicly acknowledged and rewarded. However, the organization can use symbols other than scarce facility resources that may compromise the productivity of others. Additional privileges, holidays, perks, or access to equipment (such as laptop computers, cellular phones, or company cars) can serve as substitute status symbols recognized by the corporate culture.

Though office size may be the most visible aspect of status, it is only one of many indicators of quality. Indoor air, workstation ergonomics, lighting, noise distraction, odors, cleanliness, aesthetics, and other physical and psychosocial attributes of a work setting affect its quality as well (Figure 9.6). Their diverse effects are discussed in Chapters 5, 6, and 7.

Health and safety issues have, to some extent, forced the hand of facility managers. As the causes of occupational illnesses and injuries in offices have been more clearly defined, employees, unions, and government regulatory bodies have become involved. Legal action to redress injuries resulting from work settings of inadequate design or quality have become more common and more successful. As well, recent legislation requires that workplaces be designed to reduce or eliminate barriers that prevent disabled people from participating fully as workers and con-

Figure 9.6 The appropriate use of adjustable and moveable furnishings — such as the chair, keyboard tray, filing cabinet, and task lamp shown here — can provide a comfortable, efficient, and ergonomically appropriate work setting in a small space. (*Source:* Herman Miller Inc., Zeeland, Mich.)

sumers. The quality of office settings is no longer as discretionary as it once was. Consequently, organizations are rapidly preparing office environment standards to protect themselves from the emerging liability risks of inadequate office quality and facility managers are directly involved.

SPACE UTILIZATION

Space utilization may be assessed by the amount of time the accommodations are in active use, by the number of people who use the area, or by a combined measure that reflects the organization's priorities. All too often, so-called fully occupied office areas are not in active use most of the time. It is increasingly common for office personnel to spend days, weeks, or months away from the office working at remote locations. With innovative arrangements, such as a group of offices that are assigned for private use as needed, everyone can be accommodated in less area by using it more efficiently. (See the subsections "Telecommuting" and "The Virtual Office" in Chapter 2.)

Alternative officing arrangements — such as hoteling, telecommuting, and mobile offices — can substantially reduce the cost of accommodating part-time workers. Whether or not the use of shared office space is currently favored, the expense of providing underutilized areas should be reported and alternatives considered. Obstacles to alternative work arrangements arise less from the physical workplace than from managers who feel they need to "see" their staff in order to be sure they are working. Training them in the use of alternative management methods may be as important in implementing new work arrangements as modifying facility resources and operations to accommodate employees who frequently work off-site.

SERVICE DELIVERY

The way in which service is provided can be as important as the results that are finally achieved. Responsiveness, effectiveness, completeness, and occupant satisfaction reflect the facility manager's understanding of the organization's priorities and activities.

Responsiveness is the elapsed time between a request for service and completion of the task. **Effectiveness** is the degree to which the request has been satisfied. **Completeness** refers to the breadth of the action taken. Was it resolved at one time, or were there repeated incidents until the problem was finally identified and rectified? Looking beyond the immediate issue to view the broader implications provides an opportunity to turn a reactive activity into a proactive action.

For example, a request to lower illumination levels in order to reduce glare problems on computer screens can be addressed by simply removing some of the fluorescent tubes in the ceiling light fixtures (termed **delamping**). However, it is likely that other people working in the same area would also have the same difficulty. A more complete resolution of the issue would be to determine how widespread are glare complaints. Delamping may or may not be a satisfactory solution. Light levels might then become too low for other tasks. Delamping might be an acceptable stopgap measure until another solution is found, such as changing the light fixtures or reorienting users' workstations and their computer screens. Future facility plans can take these illumination requirements into account. In new layouts, workstations with similar illumination needs can be clustered. The limitations of the illumination system may also be considered when the lease comes up for renewal. If the illumination is seen as a major deficiency, this office space may become a prime candidate to be vacated.

The facility management process is heavily dependent on the cooperation of office occupants — from the managers trying to organize their workforce to the individuals trying to meet their work objectives. If people have built up a history of positive interactions, small issues are kept in perspective and differences are amicably resolved. If the relations between facility management staff and the office occupants they are serving become strained or antagonistic, then every issue is an opportunity to redress a previous wrong. Any issue is a big issue when people are spoiling for a fight.

Office occupants are the customers of the facility management process. Whatever the cause, when workers are dissatisfied, uncomfortable, or poorly accommodated for their jobs, productivity suffers. As with other aspects of organizational effectiveness, satisfied internal customers indicate a cost-effective in-house service. Dissatisfaction with in-house services suggests that corporate resources and effort are being wasted. If personality conflicts or other organizational issues prevent the delivery of acceptable facility management services, an outside source may be better able to do the job.

LAYOUT FLEXIBILITY AND USABLE SPACE

On average, about a third of American office employees are moved each year (Brill 1987), and their departments are reorganized about every 18 months (Bellas 1992). The time it takes to physically move, reestablish, and get employees back to work may cost an organization several days of lost productivity per person. So office space designed to be flexible and facilitate changes in layout or location of people can offer significant cost savings, especially for organizations that frequently need to redeploy staff and equipment.

Much of the space on a floor plan cannot be used to accommodate people or office resources. The **usable floor space** is the area left after deducting the building core and service areas such as washrooms, corridors, atria, and service closets (e.g., for telephone equipment and electric cables). It is not uncommon for 30% of rented office accommodations to be core space (Apgar 1993). In addition, the space within a room contains unusable areas such as those occupied by fittings and equipment along the wall such as radiators or struc-

Figure 9.7 This furniture grouping, located in a public area, was designed to foster informal discussions among the staff of this research organization. (*Source:* Bell-Northern Research (BNR).)

tural elements such as columns.

Space may be unusable because of the shape of the room. Office equipment and furnishings can fit into rectangular spaces more efficiently than along the curved walls or trapezoidal rooms of innovative building designs. Although the unique styling of curvilinear structures makes them distinctive, it usually results in more nooks and crannies of unusable space. To assess the amount of **assignable area** (i.e., the space that can accommodate people, furniture, and office equipment) the shape of the space must be considered. A critical assessment of usable space more clearly identifies true rental value than the average cost per unit of area.

An efficient layout should optimize the usable space. However, this is not simply a matter of cramming more people into a small area. People interfere with each other's work activities and become generally less effective if they are tightly packed into office space. More constructive gains in layout efficiency can be realized by judiciously designing corridors and other circulation spaces and by carefully scrutinizing and measuring the usable and assignable space when comparing rental accommodations (Figure 9.7).

Adjacencies — which people, departments, and activities need to be placed next to each other — should take into account who must work together and which activities should be separated because they are incompatible. Work that involves frequent telephone or face-to-face discussions or tasks with a lot of bustling around to get files, copy documents, or retrieve printouts should be kept away from quiet areas intended for concentrated effort. By monitoring the quantity of usable space and by planning adjacencies, the utility of the available office area can be optimized.

LOCATION

The characteristics of the office location should be periodically reviewed to ensure that it continues to be well suited to the organization, its clients, and employees.

Office space in downtown cores or central business districts can be substantially more expensive than comparable suburban accommodations in the same metropolitan area. A site may have been chosen for reasons that are no longer relevant. What was once a convenient location for clients may have become difficult to reach or run-down and unsafe.

The style of work may have changed. Face-to-face meetings may have shifted to the client's place of business or be infrequent. Of greater concern may be a location that reduces employee commute time or that is safer outside normal business hours. Telecommunications and the use of networked computers for information storage, retrieval, and communication can now free the work process from many physical constraints. If a downtown location is important, it can be a small "front office" operation, with "back office" functions housed in less expensive accommodations closer to where employees live.

Although the fact that more suitable locations are available will not in itself justify the expense of moving, it is worthwhile to periodically review the location issue. There may be opportunities to upgrade accommodations when there is a glut of office space and landlords offer attractive terms. If the organization's long-term direction could benefit from one or more alternate locations, then the facility management group should monitor the real estate market for appropriate space and be prepared to act when suitable opportunities are found.

COST

Facility costs are, to some extent, unique to the activities and characteristics of the organization. It is more costly to move people and/or furniture than to keep them static. But if the nature of the business involves changing activities and arrangements frequently, then the additional facility expense may be unavoidable. In certain types of business and at higher levels of management, client expectations may require sumptuous executive offices. However, offsetting higher expenditures in one area by underspending in others can inadvertently compromise critical activities.

Comparing facility costs to those of similar organizations, an aspect of benchmarking, can be helpful in evaluating whether facility expenditures are reasonable (see the "Benchmarking" subsection later in this chapter). In addition to comparing facility operating costs and procedures, benchmarking studies also document such factors as building age, location, staffing levels, salary ranges, and how often key operations are performed. Because these factors can differ widely between organizations, a simple comparison of facility costs with the average can be quite misleading. The low facility costs of one organization may represent operating standards unacceptable to another. So rigid conformity to industry norms for facility costs may be counterproductive and can actually place an organization at a disadvantage.

However, more detailed comparisons of facility costs with those of similar organizations can be valuable in flagging expenses that appear out of line and merit investigation. There may be alternative operating procedures, equipment, or service providers that can reduce or eliminate some costs. It may also be that not enough is being spent in some areas and the organization is placing itself at a competitive disadvantage. By treating facilities as an investment rather than as an expense, it is easier to justify buying what is needed to support current requirements and allow for future changes. Better equipment, higher facility operating standards, or shorter response times could improve workforce productivity.

REAL ESTATE MANAGEMENT AND LEASING

Office facilities are a substantial real estate investment to organizations that own their accommodations. For large organizations with multiple facilities and changing space requirements, balancing the return on real estate investments, buy versus lease decisions, lease terms and conditions, and retaining suitable space for business activities are important and complex aspects of facility management. To maintain a consistent level of accommodation quality, the facility management group needs to be involved in these decisions.

Lease negotiations can become exceedingly complex. Not only must the quantity, quality, and cost of the space be considered; detailed technical requirements to support current and future needs should also be specified. This is especially true for computer and telecommunications equipment. The quantity and quality of electrical power, access to cable conduits, and the amount of available space for cabling can make the difference between a functional office and a costly mistake. Inadequate cabling provisions can make the maintenance and upgrading of telecommunication and computer services significantly more expensive or altogether impractical.

It is not only in providing for sophisticated technology that facility-planning blunders occur. The specification of office facilities involves so many details that basic, mundane issues can easily be missed as well. For example, employees of one organization that had round-the-clock work shifts noticed that the air was stale on the first night in their new location. Unwittingly, management had signed a lease stipulating that the building's air handling system would only operate from 7 A.M. to 7 P.M. To obtain ventilation throughout the night, the tenant had to pay for the installation, operation, and maintenance of additional ventilation equipment and also commit to paying for its removal when the space was vacated. In the end, the lease obligation proved to be a very costly mistake.

IMAGE

Intentionally or not, the office is a reflection of the enterprise it accommodates. Employees, customers, suppliers, and investors make judgments about an organization based on the look and feel of the office space in which it is housed. The built form is, in effect, a physical expression of policies and objectives.

When the message of the built form is consistent with the direct expressions of corporate attitudes and direction, the two avenues of communication reinforce the message. When they are inconsistent, the perceived sincerity and commitment of the message is weakened. It's difficult to believe an organization that proclaims its people to be its most valuable asset if it can offer nothing better than a shabby workplace.

Similarly, facility management activities should reflect the broader objectives and priorities of the organization. The commitment of a recycling company would appear hollow if it had no in-house recycling program. A company specializing in office lighting systems would be expected to have excellent illumination in its own offices to showcase its corporate expertise for visitors and employees alike.

MONITORING FACILITY PERFORMANCE

Performance monitoring is part of every facility management program. Operation and maintenance costs are tracked to predict future expenditures for repairs or replacement and to warn of deterioration before an equipment failure occurs. The condition of furnishings, floor coverings, safety equipment, and general cleanliness is periodically assessed and maintained as required.

Occupant perceptions of the office setting should also be monitored. Obtaining systematic and reliable feedback from the users of an office facility need not be expensive and can generate positive support for the facility management function, offer cost savings, and improve morale. Actively seeking feedback enables management to address potential problems in a timely manner before they become so serious or politicized that there is insufficient time to develop a cost-effective solution.

The systematic collection of occupant comments provides a broader perspective of facility conditions than simply tracking complaints. Complaint reports are not representative of the office population as a whole. They are the views of a self-selected group of individuals — those sufficiently bothered by some facility issue to take the time to express their dissatisfaction. Complaint reports also tend to focus on a specific problem, usually related to an individual's work space. A systematic polling of occupants seeks both positive and negative reports about conditions throughout the facility as perceived by everyone or by a representative sample of every group it is to serve.

Systematic polling enables facility managers to more readily identify the frequency, pattern, and severity of deficiencies, which, in turn, allows problems to be diagnosed earlier and resolved more quickly and less disruptively. Systematic feedback can also be a means to collect quantitative information on how facility design and operation decisions affect occupant performance and satisfaction. For example, the effects of altering the operation of a ventilation system can be monitored by measuring the number of absence days due to illness and the frequency of occupant complaints.

By regularly soliciting the input of office occupants and in turn keeping them informed of facility actions, a positive rapport is developed. Not only is morale improved; users are more tolerant of facility limitations when they see that everything is being done to provide them with an efficient and comfortable workplace.

Both direct and indirect feedback measures should be used. There should be a well-defined and well-publicized system for accepting, logging, and addressing occupant comments. Anonymous notes should be accepted to alleviate concerns of retribution for unfavorable remarks. Comments should be evaluated for content as well as for the frequency and periodicity of complaint categories. Similarly, indirect measures of facility performance — such as the rate of illness absenteeism, occupational illnesses and injuries, worker turnover, and interdepartmental moves — should be periodically assessed. These indicators are affected by many factors other than physical workplace conditions. Alone they do not necessarily indicate deficiencies in the physical office setting, but when analyzed together with occupant comments and data on facility equipment and operations, they provide valuable diagnostic information.

DELIGHTED CUSTOMER CARD

1. How do you evaluate our response time?
   ❒ Excellent ❒ Good ❒ Fair ❒ Poor
2. How do you evaluate the quality of work?
   ❒ Excellent ❒ Good ❒ Fair ❒ Poor

Figure 9.8 Occupant response card. To highlight their efforts to have occupants delighted with the quality of the office environment and facility services, this facility management organization titled their occupant response card accordingly. (*Source:* Celestica, North York, Ontario.)

There should also be a mechanism for occupants to report facility-related complaints directly to senior management, circumventing facility management personnel. There are occasions when the facility management process is so unresponsive or antagonistic that occupant complaints are ignored or actively discouraged. These situations are extremely destructive of morale as well as productivity and demand prompt and vigorous attention.

Performance measurement need not be cumbersome or expensive to produce practical results. For example, one facilities group instituted a performance-monitoring program for a 31,000-square-meter (330,000-square-foot) facility accommodating 830 software developers (Meri 1993). Each time a facility service request was completed, a "customer" reply card was left on the desk of the requester. The card asked the occupant to rate the quality of work done and the acceptability of the response time on a scale from "Excellent" to "Poor" (Figure 9.8). A tally was kept of the number of "Excellent"

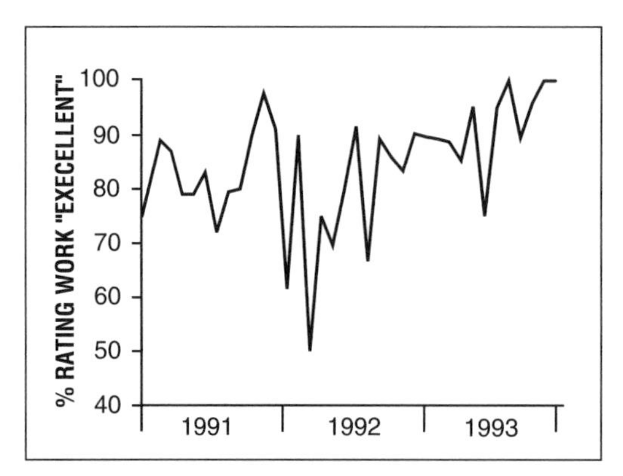

Figure 9.9 Percentage of occupants rating facility management services to be "excellent" each month. (Source: Celestica, North York, Ontario.)

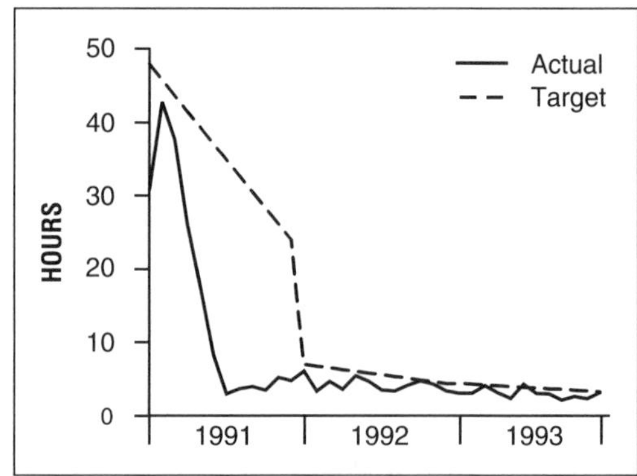

Figure 9.11 Unscheduled maintenance cycle time per month. (*Source:* Celestica, North York, Ontario.)

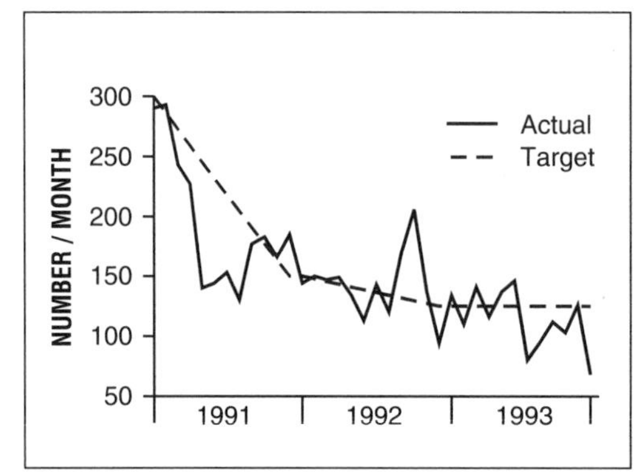

Figure 9.10 Number of unscheduled maintenance activities per month. (*Source:* Celestica, North York, Ontario.)

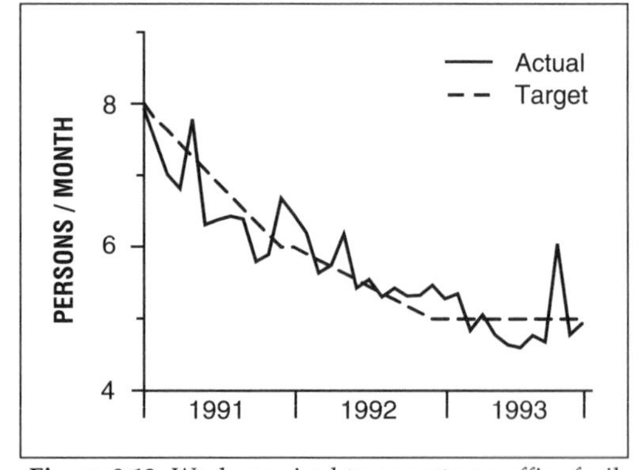

Figure 9.12 Work required to operate an office facility each month. (*Source:* Celestica, North York, Ontario.)

responses to each question. These were plotted by month to show how the facilities group was progressing toward its goal of having every occupant delighted with the facility management services (Figure 9.9).

Unscheduled maintenance activities (i.e., work on anything that is broken or in disrepair) was used as a defect measure of the facility management service. Such interruptions in a building's service impact occupant productivity. By analyzing the cause of each unscheduled maintenance event, preventive maintenance procedures were augmented and the incidence of unscheduled maintenance was halved within a year (Figure 9.10).

The time to complete unscheduled maintenance was seen as a valuable measure of both responsiveness and the efficiency of facility management resource use. If repairs could be completed in a more timely manner, occupants would be less disrupted and facility staff would be available for other activities.

In this organization, facility services are requested via electronic mail. The time and date the message was sent are automatically recorded. The time it takes from the request for service to completion of the work is termed the cycle time for unscheduled maintenance. The average monthly cycle time was graphed and then used to track improvements in this performance measure (Figure 9.11). In a similar way, a measure of facility reliability was obtained by tallying the number of power interruptions per month.

Overall effectiveness was measured by calculating the equivalent number of person-months that were used to operate the building each month (Figure 9.12). This measurement included people who were permanently stationed at the building and those who were called in on a demand basis (e.g., technicians doing equipment repairs).

Not all aspects of facility performance and management are amenable to measurement, and quantitative measures commonly assess only a portion of what is important. Despite these limitations, measurements of facility performance are a useful means to evaluate service quality over time as well as a source of valuable feedback to guide improvements.

Benchmarking

Benchmarking is a process of comparing the characteristics of one or more systems to a set of standard measurements, known as benchmarks. Fundamentally, the objective of benchmarking is to evaluate the performance of a system by comparing selected measurements of its status or operating characteristics to a suitable set of benchmark values. The benchmark measurements are thus *indicators* of performance. The benchmarking process implies that the more closely the benchmarks are satisfied, the better the performance. If the wrong benchmark measures are chosen, then changes that improve the benchmark rating may actually degrade system performance. As such, the value of a benchmarking exercise depends on how well the chosen indicators represent the system characteristics to be optimized. The factors chosen necessarily reflect the values of those designing the benchmark procedure — essentially judgments of what are "good" and "bad" conditions. For example, occupant satisfaction ratings and accommodation cost per employee are not in themselves value-laden characteristics. But choosing to give first priority to minimizing accommodation costs represents an entirely different value judgment than choosing to maximize occupant satisfaction.

Benchmarking can be a valuable facility management tool to reduce costs and improve effectiveness. However, the process is both time-intensive and expensive. In a survey of over 80 companies that do benchmarking projects, the average benchmarking process took 15 person-weeks, including the time spent planning the project, visiting other companies, analyzing results, and follow-up monitoring of recommendations. The average benchmarking team consisted of 5.6 people. The cost of an entire benchmarking project — including training, site visits, and salaried employees' time — averaged US$70,000 (American Productivity & Quality Center 1992). Although the survey could not quantify benefits, the participating companies found that significant gains were realized, with some reported payoffs greater than five times the cost of the benchmarking project.

It is always interesting to know how one's facility compares to others. However, unless there is a commitment to act on the benchmark findings, the investment of time and resources will likely be wasted. The underlying purpose of benchmarking is to rate performance in order to identify opportunities for improvement. If there is no possibility of implementing changes, there is little point in the exercise.

Once a benchmarking process is established, it should be repeated on a regular basis because an organization's activities continue to change, as does the competitive environment in which it operates. Technological advances and new systems become available. Without periodic review, an organization may fall behind and miss out on competitive developments.

The process of preparing to benchmark can itself offer valuable insights. Selecting what to measure, deciding how to establish benchmark standards, and determining what units to use require that objectives and priorities be explicitly stated. Competing objectives, which are easily glossed over in less formal evaluations, are immediately highlighted when it is necessary to define measures of performance.

Making comparisons of facility performance is rarely as straightforward as it would at first seem. For example, measuring a building's operating costs tells little about how well it is managed without knowing the context. The building's age, design, maintenance history, the activities it supports, its location, and local climate are all important factors in judging whether or not it is performing well. On the other hand, benchmarks defined too narrowly can exclude important information about innovative facility management methods. The chosen benchmarks might simply miss important but unexpected benefits. This also highlights the importance of choosing appropriate indicators to benchmark.

To prepare for benchmarking, an organization must first identify the factors that most significantly affect its performance. This requires rigorously reviewing the organization's mission and objectives and recognizing its strengths and weaknesses. Then the organization measures the selected factors for itself to assess the difficulty and cost of collecting the information. Vague or unclear definitions of the conditions to be measured can easily lead to inaccuracies that produce misleading or incorrect results. For example, despite efforts to standardize the way floor area is measured, there is considerable variation in the methods used to calculate the size of office facilities. Usable space, rentable space, and gross area measures will give very different estimates of facility costs per unit area.

Giving feedback on performance is an excellent way to identify wasteful procedures, motivate individuals, and boost productivity. Traditionally, companies give feedback to their staff by looking internally to make comparisons and set goals. External comparisons can be valuable but require greater care to ensure that the comparisons are appropriate. Comparing two facilities that support very different activities may be quite useful in identifying alternative facility management techniques. However, applying the methods successful in one setting to a very different set of conditions may not be appropriate. Although benchmarking can be a valuable guide in suggesting areas for improvement and identifying alternative facility management approaches, a good deal of judgment is needed to find suitable benchmark partners and then to develop appropriate recommendations from the benchmarking results.

Automation in Facility Management

Specialized facility management software has developed rapidly in recent years and there is now a wide range of products to support this function. Ideally, all the facility management programs for an enterprise would be integrated into one seamless information system. In practice, more than one software package is generally needed to provide the range of functions required for a particular installation. Some packages can easily share data, whereas others have limited capabilities to exchange information. In general, these systems can be technically complex, so the assistance of personnel experienced in the design and implementation of facility management information systems is strongly advised.

The principal functional areas of facility management software are briefly discussed below. A particular software product generally offers some capability in several if not all of these areas.

Space Planning and Management. Computer-aided facility management (CAFM) systems provide a wide range of data storage, analysis, reporting, and presentation functions, from the inventory and tracking of furniture to the management of real estate. More than simply a quick way to generate drawings, CAFM systems can also produce a variety of reports related to space use and management, such as the floor area occupied by each department, group, individual or activity, and the location of unassigned spaces. Analytical functions can calculate the ratio of space per person for a given department or

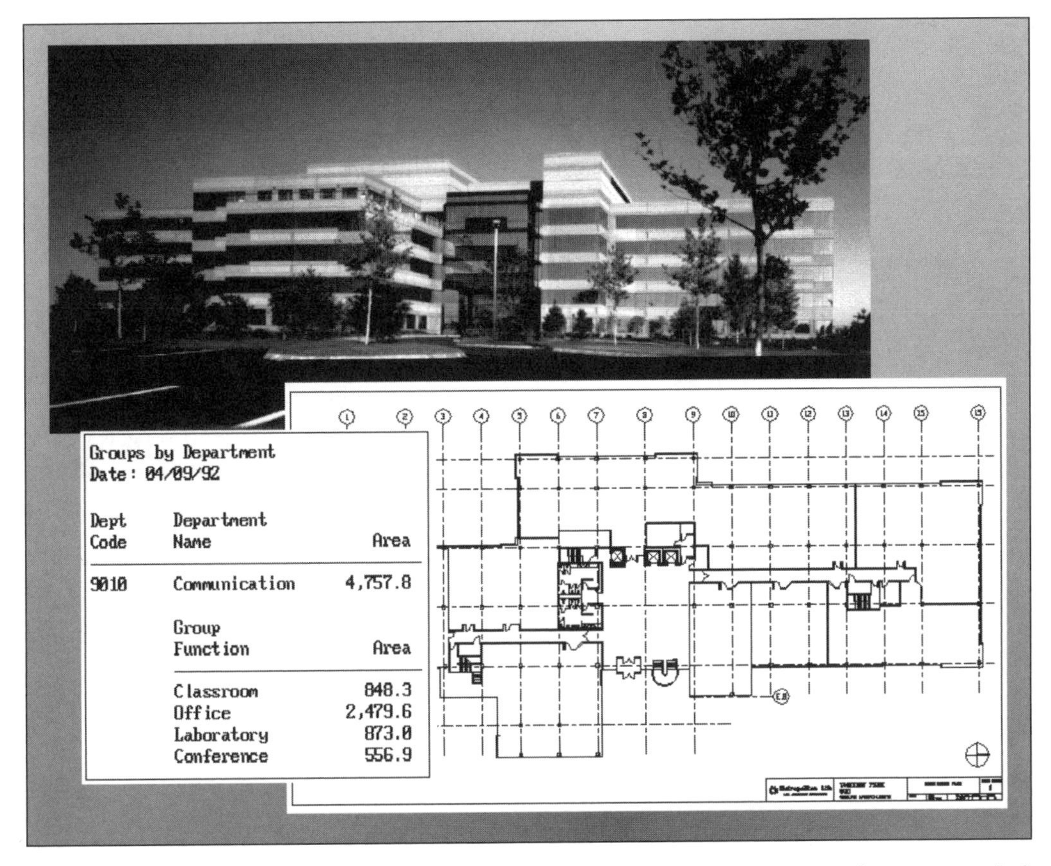

Figure 9.13 Digital facility information may be in the form of images, CAD drawings, and text or numerical data. This figure illustrates the way these different types of information can be presented — a photograph stored as a digital image, a floor plan, and tabular summary of occupancy and floor space data. (*Source:* ARCHIBUS, Boston.)

work group, the ratio of workstation space to support space, the accommodation expense of each department, or other quantities useful in comparative evaluations of space usage. Depending on the capabilities of the software, statistical summary tables, graphs, and charts may also be produced. These software tools are valuable not only to plan and manage existing facilities but also to project future space requirements (Figures 9.13 and 9.14).

The initial facility space planning done at the building design stage involves the assignment of organizational units to different floors of a building (termed stack planning) and the placement of work groups within a floor area (termed block planning). Stack and block planning are normally done together so that space and adjacency requirements (i.e., which facilities or groups should be near each other) can both be taken into account. It is necessarily an iterative process. The initial specifications and design are evaluated and progressively refined until an optimal spatial arrangement is achieved. Without computers, this procedure is time-consuming and expensive. For this reason, virtually all stack and block planning is computer-based.

For purposes of space management, spatial information, such as floor plans and engineering drawings of the building systems, can be stored electronically and used in stand-alone computer-aided design (CAD) systems or a CAD system that has been incorporated into a CAFM system. In addition to the spatial characteristics of a room or work space, such as its shape, size, and position, non-spatial attributes such as the power rating of an electrical

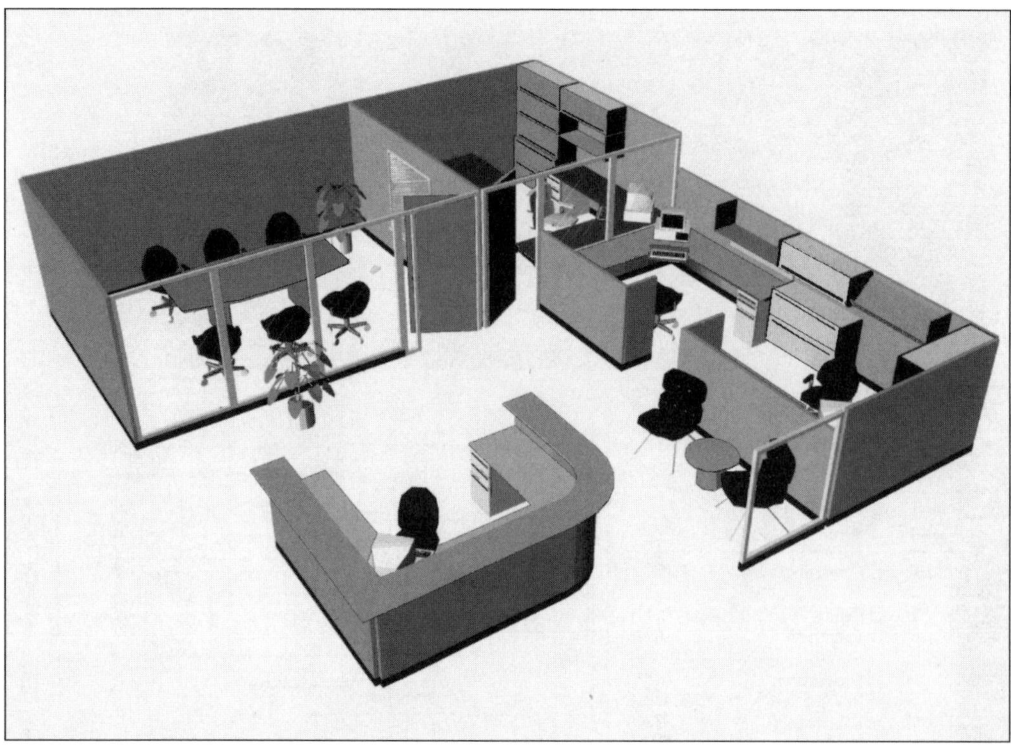

Figure 9.14 Computer-generated three dimensional presentation of interior spaces and furnishings. Such images can help people to visualize existing or proposed office layouts and provide an effective way to experiment with different design ideas. (*Source:* ARCHIBUS, Boston.)

cable, the group to which a space is assigned, and the activities for which it is used are also encoded and maintained in the computer database (Figure 9.15).

Many furniture manufacturers now supply their catalogs in computer-readable form. The dimensions, color, material, manufacturer, cost, and other attributes are included. CAD and CAFM software can access these data directly and use them for space management, to develop floor plan layouts, and even to generate furniture and equipment purchase orders.

Facility space planning software enables the operator to select and arrange furniture elements to form the desired work setting layouts and then to move and duplicate those work settings as needed to create a complete floor plan layout. A graphic user interface displays each element as a color-coded outline drawing making it easy to see department groupings. Plans are then readily created and edited on the computer monitor. The operator can rapidly experiment with different arrangements and evaluate the attributes of alternate space plans.

Asset Management. Asset management systems track the location and attributes of individual items. This information is stored in a computer database and regularly updated. Bar-code systems are increasingly being used to make tracking the location, condition, and other relevant aspects of furnishings and equipment more efficient. The location and attributes of each item are coded to a unique identification number and entered into the asset management database. A bar-code label with the identification number is also affixed to every item. In addition to the location and status information, the attribute data typically entered include specifications from supplier catalogs (if available) and financial information such as the date of purchase, cost, order number, and cost center, in addition to depreciation, insurance, and warranty provisions. Information can be updated using handheld equipment to scan the bar-code labels

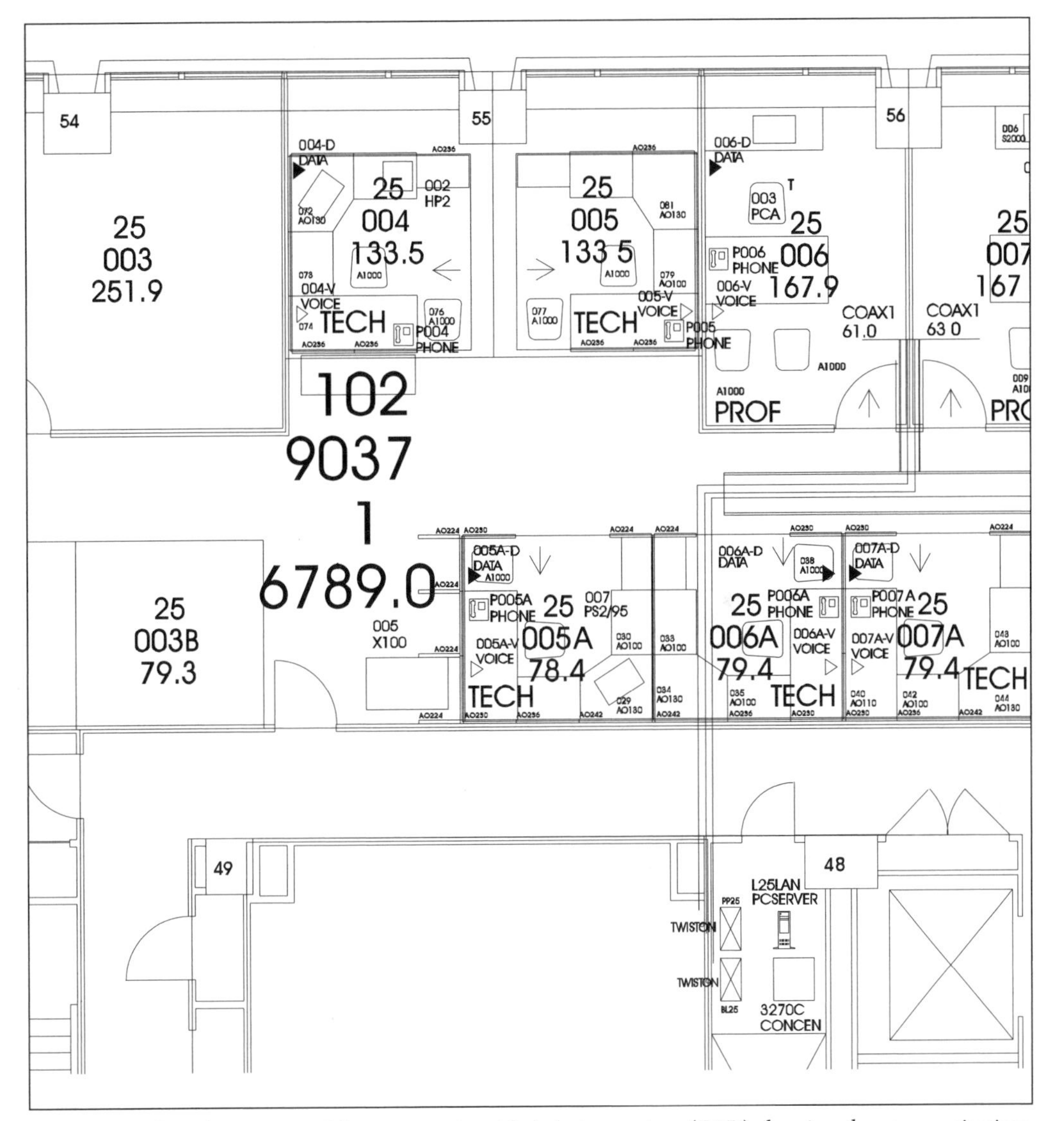

Figure 9.15 Drawing generated by a computer-aided design system (CAD) showing the communications cabling in a block of offices. (*Source:* Fifth Dimension, Ottawa.)

and enter the changes. The data from the portable scanning equipment are then downloaded to the asset management database to perform updates (Figure 9.16).

Implementing an asset management system is a significant investment. However, it can yield substantial savings by reducing purchases of new furnishings. For a large organization with multiple office locations, it can be so difficult to locate office equipment and furniture that is somewhere in storage that it often is easier and less expensive (in terms of person-hours) to purchase whatever is needed. Asset management systems provide an efficient way to find items that are available for reuse or to schedule and track the refurbishing or reassignment of office components. Organizations most likely to benefit from asset management systems are those that have a high churn rate, experience rapid changes in workforce size, have excess furniture and equipment, or are users of systems furniture. Enterprises that have implemented a system to charge accommodation expenses back to their respective cost centers can use information from an asset management database to calculate the respective fixed asset values.

Figure 9.16 A penlike scanner is shown being used to read bar-codes for office furnishings. Either one of the handheld computers and scanners shown would be taken to an office where it would be used to read bar-codes affixed to furniture, equipment, and the building proper (e.g., doors, window units, lighting fixtures). Then information pertaining to a piece of inventory would be displayed and updates could be entered and stored. (*Source:* Sage Data Solutions, Nepean, Ont.)

Cable Management. The management of telephone and computer cables in office facilities has become a complex task. Cable management functions track the location, specification, and function of each cable.

Operation and Maintenance. Operation and maintenance functions track preventive, corrective, and predictive repair activities for the overall facility — the building enclosure, structure, services, and furnishings. Work orders and routine maintenance schedules can be automatically generated while the time and cost of staff, contractors, parts, and supplies are tracked. With this information, the system can be used to analyze maintenance and operating costs, develop more accurate budgets, and identify opportunities to reduce operating expenses.

Property Management. Property management systems can assist organizations with multiple leased facilities. Data about land, buildings, leases, upcoming lease options and expiration dates, and tenant spaces can be recorded. These systems can be used to report the amount and location of space already secured and project when shortfalls or oversupply might occur. They are also used to alert property managers to upcoming critical dates such as lease expirations so that negotiations can be conducted well in advance (Kimmel 1993; Snyder 1992).

TRENDS IN FACILITY INFORMATION MANAGEMENT

Ideally, all of an organization's facility-related information, whether physically residing in one database or in many, would be structured so it is available as one integrated information system that is easily accessible to everyone who pro-

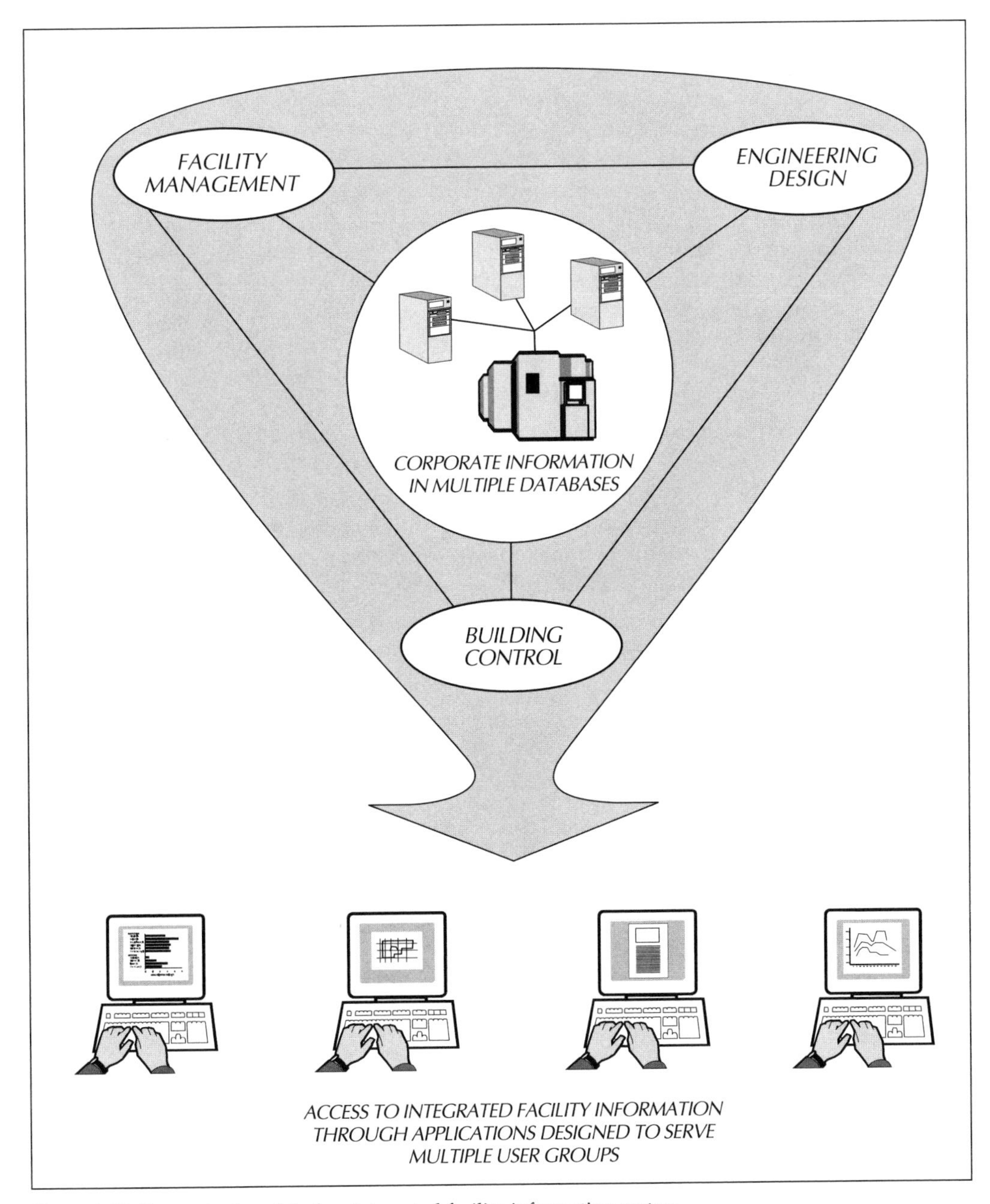

Figure 9.17 Conceptual model of an integrated facility information system.

duces or uses the information. Such a system would enable data that are traditionally managed by separate departments in an organization to be available to all who could make use of them (Figure 9.17). For example, information about changing occupancy levels that are held by the human resources department could be used together with engineering details of the lighting and air distribution systems and environmental performance objectives to make adjustments to the program of the automated building control system.

The drive to deliver more integrated facility management information systems is drawing together three domains of building information that have generally remained distinct and have been supported by their own specialized software. They can be broadly categorized as facility management, engineering design, and building control.

CAFM systems are designed to support building management activities. They provide occupancy planning and evaluation tools for apportioning existing space among individuals, departments, or activities, and planning future space allocation and servicing. Provisions for the tracking and scheduling of building maintenance activities are usually included as well. Real property and lease management, furniture and equipment management, and cable management are additional functions that may be provided in a CAFM system or as separate software modules.

Specialized CAD systems are used by engineers and other professionals to design the building structure and its services such as electrical power, mechanical systems, plumbing, and telecommunications cabling. They commonly include design tools specific to the engineering specialties for which they are used. Project management software is used to plan and manage major construction and renovation activities.

Building control systems monitor and regulate the interior environment. They control services such as airflow and lighting, and provide systems for emergency response, surveillance, and control of access within a building. These building control functions may be provided by multiple systems or a single automated building control system.

Automated building control systems use a network of sensors to detect conditions within a building and control the operation of service equipment to maintain the desired indoor climate and operating state. These computer-based systems offer sophisticated scheduling options to alter building operations for the entire facility or parts of the facility according to work schedules, the number of people using a space, the type of activity, the outdoor climate, a disaster event, or other factors. They can improve operating efficiency by providing building services when and where they are needed and adapting the service delivery to the conditions. They can also offer appropriate and quick actions in response to emergencies such as fire, flood, or explosion. (See the subsection "Automated Control of Building Services" in Chapter 4.)

Automated building control systems, although computer-based, have been developed by building system manufacturers and the makers of building control equipment. This industry is entirely different from the one developing CAFM systems and, as yet, there has been little integration of these two domains of facility management automation. The software for these systems is custom-designed to operate a particular manufacturer's equipment.

The information stored in CAFM, CAD, and building control systems can all be usefully applied to the ongoing management and operation of an office facility. As well, other corporate information such as human resources data, strategic plans, and business management strategies can enable valuable and insightful analyses to be efficiently done. For example, major changes in business activities will affect the quantity and types of space that will be needed. This in turn can be used in deciding whether or not individual leases should be renewed, the lease period that would be appropriate, and improvements to the space that may be needed. For large organizations operating multiple facilities the ability to integrate facility information with other corporate data is essential in order to rationalize facility operations across an enterprise.

Until recently, sharing information among multiple databases and diverse applications was severely limited. The development of technology to provide efficient computer networks and distributed databases has enabled the development of information systems that offer access to diverse applications by using data held in multiple databases residing on different systems that may even be located in different cities.

Systems are now being developed that offer increasingly sophisticated building management functions. The term computer-integrated facility management

(CIFM) has been introduced to refer to a more integrated level of facility information management system that, through a single user interface, enables a wide range of facility-related business analyses to be done (Forbes 1976). A CIFM system accesses multiple databases and may use multiple software applications to perform a particular analysis. CIFM provides access to CAFM functions as well as to common business data analysis tools such as spreadsheets and may also use a geographic information system (GIS).

Geographic information systems are used extensively for such diverse applications as city planning, municipal information management, land records management, market analysis, and a wide range of natural resource fields (see the subsection "Spatial Analysis of Workplace Data" in Chapter 8). Organizations with large facility holdings may use a GIS to perform spatial analyses outside an individual building, such as displaying the location of an organization's city-wide or nationwide lease holdings. Many CAFM systems are essentially geographic information systems and some vendors produce both CAFM and GIS software products based on a common set of modules that are tailored to address these different markets.

A comprehensive facility information system can facilitate a more integrated level of facility management and use. However, new software and hardware cannot itself change the way people make decisions that affect the office facility. To take full advantage of such technology will require a fundamental rethinking of the way that all of an organization's building-related information is collected, maintained, and utilized.

Much valuable building information that is already in digital form is lost or unused simply because it was not requested or was not known to be available. Today, computers are used extensively in the design of office buildings. Every facet of a building project from its inception to completion are now commonly recorded in some form of computer file. Architectural plans, engineering drawings, material specifications, contracting records, and correspondence are most often generated by computer.

At the completion of construction, the client usually receives a set of as-built drawings, specifications, and equipment operation manuals that document the design and maintenance of the building that was delivered. But digital files are generally not provided. They tend to be retained by the prime contractor (e.g., the architectural or engineering firm with overall responsibility for the project) or by the individual subcontractors who worked on the building systems. Because computer records accumulate rapidly during the course of a project and paper records become voluminous, many files — be they minutes of key decisions or routine progress reports — are simply destroyed when they are no longer needed by those who produced them. To avoid this unfortunate loss of information, all contractors should be informed at the outset of a project that they will be required to provide a complete set of as-built facility data in digital format.

Although much of this building history information would be of use in managing and operating an office facility, it is only of value if the data are suitably documented, organized in an appropriate format, and assembled in a manner relevant to facility management. For this reason, a detailed specification of how the facility data are to be submitted must be provided to all contractors. In order to produce such a specification, a comprehensive building information plan must be developed as part of the overall contracting process.

Fundamentally, it is the data that are of critical importance. The software used to generate the output is secondary. Software products come and go. A building's service life is much longer than even the most successful software product. It can be expected that data to support ongoing facility management will have to be used with many different types of computer software and hardware. For this reason an organization should avoid tieing itself to a particular software product or vendor by storing data in formats that are difficult for other software to use. By choosing appropriate formats, an organization ensures that it will have the flexibility to use software products it does not currently have and to upgrade to newer products that become available.

How facility information will be used is the fundamental issue in deciding what building information should be collected, how it should be managed, and what software and hardware will be needed to access it. Facility information will be of greatest benefit if it is treated as a corporate resource — part of an organization's enterprise-wide information system. Individual departments may be given the responsibility to collect and manage specific data sets, and they may have a say in how data are best used, but data should not be considered to be "owned" by any one group. The data belong to the organization and should be made available to anyone the organization sees fit to give access to it. Adopting such an approach will require a major shift in attitude for most organizations.

Today it is common for individual departments to maintain their "own" data. In some cases the data reside on computer systems separate from the corporate computer system. For example, CAFM software is commonly run on dedicated standalone systems. Accounting records, customer profiles, marketing information, and many other data sets may effectively be managed as "private" databases available only to the department that generates the data it contains. This approach to corporate information is rapidly changing as organizations have seen the value of interconnecting or networking these databases. At the same time, the technology to do so has emerged. The inclusion of facility data within an organization's corporate information network is a consistent extension of this trend in corporate computer system design. It also reflects a trend to provide wider access to corporate information.

In restructuring and reengineering themselves, organizations have sought to streamline their operation and find ways to make decisions more rapidly and more effectively. Not only has this required changes in the way work is done, it has also required major changes in the way information must flow within an organization so that people can meet the demands of their new and expanded roles. This has invariably meant giving employees wider access to corporate information and demanding that they consider a broader range of factors so as to make better decisions.

The operation of an office facility and the activities it accommodates are tightly interconnected and benefit substantially from the integrated planning that broader access to corporate information can offer. The assignment of personnel to new projects, corporate downsizing or expansion, the acquisition of new equipment, changes to business procedures and hours of operation can all be implemented more effectively and at lower cost if they are coordinated with facility operations. By making people more aware of the ways that facility management can support their endeavors, by providing the technology to make such coordination practical, and by requiring that departments keep facility management informed of changes in their activities, the facility management function can substantially increase the value an organization receives from its office facilities.

OBTAINING FACILITY MANAGEMENT SERVICES

Every organization obtains facility management services from both in-house and outside personnel. At a minimum, outside contractors are used to service equipment that is technically too complex and requires service too infrequently to justify having that expertise permanently on staff. Virtually any facility management service can be provided by outside personnel. Indeed, some organizations have

Figure 9.18 Facility management services can be provided by an in-house department or outside contractors can be hired to do some or all of the work. (*Source:* Herman Miller Inc., Zealand, Mich.)

chosen to contract out the entire facility management function. Using in-house versus outside facility management services is not an either-or choice. It is a matter of finding the most cost-effective combination that provides the required level of service.

In-house facility management services have traditionally been protected from outside competition. An increasing number of organizations are questioning whether those services could be provided at lower cost by an outside supplier. Conversely, facility managers operating with less money and asked to compete with the service levels of outside providers are demanding that they receive increased funding commensurate with what an outside contractor would charge.

Outsourcing — hiring a vendor to provide some or all facility management services — is a controversial issue. There are important trade-offs to be weighed in choosing which services, if any, should be outsourced. Control of the facility management process, its cost, quality, and response time may be very different when the provider is an outside contractor instead of in-house personnel. However, each can offer the better solution under certain circumstances (Figure 9.18).

An organization's facility management needs are unique, and the best way to satisfy them will depend on the alternatives available for a particular situation at a given time. Service costs change over time, as does the availability and quality of in-house staff and outside service personnel. For these reasons, facility management requirements should be individually assessed and periodically reviewed. There is an inherent conflict of interest in having in-house facility management staff review their own performance and compare outsourcing alternatives. Outside consultants can provide more objective assessments as long as they do not have a vested interest in the outcome. However, outsiders may not be able to appreciate an organization's needs as well as the in-house staff.

Facility management is a complex field. A large and diverse staff may be needed to accomplish all the required tasks internally. Outsourcing facility management services establishes a contractual obligation that can give the client more control over the work that is done and offer access to greater expertise without increasing staff.

In-house staff requirements can then be leveled out, with sufficient full-time personnel retained to satisfy minimum workload requirements. When additional personnel are needed — such as for emergencies, renovations, or construction projects — contract experts can fill the gaps. Contracting provides access to individuals who have specialized knowledge, certification, or equipment that is needed only occasionally. Those individuals have gained experience from their work on other projects and can bring innovative ideas and perspectives. Since they are usually independent of the corporate political system, they can approach sensitive issues with greater neutrality. Perceived as unbiased third parties, they can exercise a freer hand in developing solutions. At the same time, some facility management issues benefit from an insider view of the organization and culture of the enterprise — information that, at least initially, an outsider may not readily obtain.

In-house facility management staff can offer an organization greater and more immediate control of its facility. Being involved in day-to-day activities, they can more closely tailor facility operations to an organization's needs. Facility operations and projects can be handled in a more consistent manner because corporate staffers know the organization.

Some contracted facility management services are more easily monitored and controlled than others. For example, janitorial, grounds maintenance, and food services are well-defined activities for which a definitive scope of work can be developed and performance readily monitored. These activities are usually outside the company's core business, and managing them requires work that rarely contributes significantly to profitability, such as selecting which type of detergent or coffee cup to use. Indeed, these services are the ones most likely to be completely outsourced, sometimes called **outtasked** since one task is contracted rather than the complete facility services (IFMA 1993).

It is more difficult to successfully outsource facility management activities that are more abstract or are critical to an organization's success. For example, the success of a floor plan layout of circulation and work spaces depends on the skill and perceptiveness of the designer. Being heavily influenced by corporate politics, the layout's acceptability depends on the degree to which these undercurrents of organization dynamics have been understood and addressed. An outsider can be at a considerable disadvantage in deciphering an organization's political nuances. For long-range planning, forecasting, and design tasks, there can be no clear definition of the outcome before the project begins. However, some organizations have found ways to specify suitable performance criteria to successfully outsource such activities.

Contracting out certain projects means that fewer full-time employees are needed. This is attractive to companies because it reduces their financial responsibility — such as salary, benefits, and overhead — for in-house staff not involved in the organization's core business activities. Specialized personnel, such as those trained in facility management, are not easily able to work in any other areas of the business and so cannot be reassigned to departments that need additional staff. When facility management staff requirements fluctuate sharply, such as for infrequent but large renovation projects, the organization can achieve considerable cost savings and greater flexibility by using contract personnel. Moreover, if management is not satisfied with the service provided by outsiders, the contractors can readily be replaced. So outsourcing offers greater flexibility in the allocation of human resources because adding or subtracting staff does not involve negotiations, the payment of termination benefits, or a loss of morale.

The quality of work done in support functions is largely dependent on the career track open to people who provide them. Good performance in the mail-sorting room of a company is unlikely to win promotion to an executive position. But it can be a ticket to advancement in an outsourcing firm, especially if mail processing is its core business area. For the contractor who offers mail services, this activity is an income-generating product, not a support function.

Organizations have a hard time keeping pace with rapid technology advances in their core activities. To keep pace with developments for support activities is difficult, expensive in terms of both time and equipment, and focuses effort on non-core business areas. An outsourcing firm can spread the cost of keeping up to date over its entire client base. What's more, it has an incentive to remain current — its future business depends on it.

Outside contractors must be chosen judiciously. As with letting contracts for any major work, a formal request for proposal needs to be posted and a rating system or criteria for selection prepared in advance. References given by potential contractors should be contacted, the personnel who would actually perform the work should be identified, a suitable reporting structure should be set up, and the size and capability of the contractor should be matched to the scale of the project. Other more subtle and less objective criteria may be needed to assess whether a contractor's attitude toward facility management is suitable and acceptable to the prospective client.

It is tempting to choose one supplier to provide all outside facility services. But companies differ in the services they do well. Even a large company may not be able to provide a consistently high level of expertise for every service it offers. Large companies serve as training grounds for young talent, and there is always the chance that some of that training will be done on a client's key project. Although a larger firm may have the depth and staff to handle large projects, smaller firms are often comprised of mature professionals who can offer excellent service within their specialties.

Conflict-of-interest situations frequently arise in outsourcing facility services. Often, these services go hand in hand with large capital expenditures. Some organizations prohibit architectural and interior design firms from working on projects they defined in a strategic-planning contract. Others do not allow furniture manufacturers or suppliers to develop furniture standards or layouts (Drebelbis 1991).

As part of the ongoing search for cost-effective ways to conduct business, more organizations are defining the full-time facility services they require and hiring outside help to supply infrequently needed expertise. In-house facility management services can be cost-effective and responsive, and they can make a significant contribution to their organization's success. However, many organizations have realized substantial savings, improved service, and greater control by contracting out selected facility management functions. Contract and in-house personnel can together make a good team, offering both the continuity and intimate knowledge of the corporate culture that in-house staff provide while being able to draw on a diverse pool of outside expertise for the additional human resources and specialized skills that are needed only occasionally. When outsourcing is well managed, it can provide a cost-effective way to expand the quality and range of facility services.

PRESCRIPTION FOR CHANGE — THE NEW AGENDA

Organizations are reengineering themselves — reevaluating how they work and how performance can be improved. As the ways of doing business have become more diverse, so, too have the facilities that support these emerging styles of work, and managing them has become more complex.

Facility management is as important for small organizations as it is for large ones.

In small organizations, the senior manager who oversees facility issues usually handles other responsibilities as well. But in larger organizations, facility responsibilities are often assigned to a full-time manager, such as a vice president of facilities. The issues for small enterprises are generally less complex and can be handled more directly because the quantities of space, people, and equipment are much less. They are nonetheless important. The more closely that facility management is integrated into the corporate planning process, the more direct will be its contribution to an organization's success and the greater will be the value obtained from expenditures on office accommodations.

Facility management needs to be seen in a broader perspective than that of an overhead expense to be minimized. It should be viewed as an integral part of an organization's resources. How office facilities are managed either contributes to productivity or detracts from it. Well-managed facilities contribute to an organization's effectiveness and improve employee morale. Office characteristics that create obstacles occupants must overcome — such as noise disruption, sick building symptoms, insufficient work area, or poorly adjusted seating — sap energy that could otherwise be applied to productive work. If ignored, they can be an unrecognized but costly burden that drains productivity and compromises corporate objectives.

To capture the full potential of an office facility, it needs to be managed in concert with the organization's corporate objectives and strategic planning. Only at the corporate level can facility management become an integral part of an organization's decision-making process. Facility management should therefore be expected to participate in a corporate-level forum and given the commensurate visibility, influence, and accountability. Otherwise, facility decisions are made from too narrow a perspective, and the benefits captured in one domain are more likely to be lost by unforeseen costs in another. Measures that were designed to reduce facility operating costs but also resulted in occupant health problems are one of the more highly publicized examples.

Organizations should acquire the facility management resources and expertise commensurate with their specific needs. Service requirements should be established and performance criteria defined to evaluate the facility management process. Criteria must be periodically reviewed, because as facility needs change and the mix of facility services is altered, service priorities will shift as well. Organizations should develop realistic goals and objectives, which they can use as a basis for specifying which of the broad range and sophisticated levels of facility management services they need. As previously discussed, choosing between in-house and outside service providers is not an either-or decision. Full-time employees may satisfy normal operating requirements, with outside contractors providing the additional staff needed for emergencies and major or specialized projects. A large organization may require a dozen or more full-time staffers to handle daily tasks, headed by a facility manager who has the expertise to oversee all the services used and is capable of representing facility management in the boardroom. A small office may contract out all its facility services.

An ongoing monitoring program is essential to maintain satisfactory facility performance — to retain sufficient control and ensure acceptable service. Every office will have some unexpected deficiencies or operating anomalies. In addition, building performance changes as the spatial layout is altered, renovations are done, and the occupants vary their usage patterns.

To monitor facility management performance, there should be a well-defined procedure to solicit, document, and address occupant comments about office quality and the performance of the facility service providers. The documentation of facility management activities can provide important evidence of an organization's diligence should office quality be questioned in a liability claim. However, the reporting process represents a use of resources that could otherwise be devoted to other facility management or enhancement activities. Excessive reporting and documentation will compromise the quality of facility services that can be provided.

Facility management tends to absorb additional responsibilities as new issues arise. For example, with office automation, facility managers suddenly found that their jobs had expanded to include cable management and consideration of workstation ergonomics. Environmental issues like recycling, the proper handling of waste, or phasing out the use of chlorofluorocarbons (CFCs) have also added to facility managers' workload and liability. The enlargement of facility management responsibilities has affected the number of staff, training, and skills required to manage offices and should be reflected in the facility management budget.

Facility management expenses are not as predictable as they would at first seem. Although traditionally 75% or more of the annual operating costs may be reliably estimated because they are foreseeable expenses such as for electrical power or rent, there are a growing number of unexpected issues for which contingency funds should be set aside. For example, a change in business activities may require substantial changes to office layouts and furnishings. An increase in occupant illness symptoms, cumulative trauma disorders, or other health-related issues may arise that require contracting outside experts and making modifications to building system operation or maintenance procedures. It may be necessary to supply additional office furnishings or work accommodations to alleviate health problems such as allergic reactions or cumulative trauma disorders.

Whether the organization is large or small, there needs to be a clear understanding at the corporate level of the criteria by which the facility management process will be judged. In a sense, two masters are being served — the occupants who use the space and corporate management that allocates the funds to pay for facility services. Their objectives often conflict. Though clarifying objectives, responsibilities, and performance criteria will not eliminate these conflicts, it can at least provide an explicit and consistent framework within which they can be resolved.

Clear lines of authority and accountability need to be established so that it is recognized who may participate in facility-related decisions and what their role can be. Everyone has a personal stake in at least some facility decisions. Plans to change office layouts, rearrange parking assignments, or upgrade office equipment are very important to the people affected. The various stakeholders in facility choices have a legitimate role in the decision process. However, for the facility management function to be held accountable for its results, the participation and authority of facility management personnel must be well defined. Otherwise, the decision making process can become such a complex web of special-interest choices that it no longer serves the broader needs of the organization.

To be more fully utilized and closely scrutinized, the facility management process must be better understood. All too often, the inconsistent and unpredictable involvement of senior management can seriously undermine facility management service levels, increase waste, and inflate costs. Cavalier facility decisions imposed by senior managers are often inconsistent with the corporate objectives and priorities that they are charged with advancing.

Poorly timed and ill-considered directives from senior management can render facility cost control and strategic-planning efforts an expensive and futile exercise. One CEO overruled the findings of a comprehensive site selection process and chose a location near the airport. He and other senior executives were private pilots with their own aircraft and wanted convenient access to the airport. If airport access was to have been the dominant criterion for site selection, a great deal of time, effort, and expense could have been saved had that criterion been stated at the outset.

The role of senior managers in facility management decisions should be well defined and consistent with the authority and responsibilities of the facility management function. In this way, it becomes an expected contribution to the facility management process. Despite the rhetoric of reasoned decision making, the heavy influence of personal preference all too often prevails. The same managers who maintain that people are the organization's most important resource choose to become involved and influence the selection of a new office location for their own convenience. In itself, the contribution of individual choice is not an obstacle to effective decision making, as long as its weight is explicitly defined and the implications are accepted.

Facility costs are among the largest expense categories in a service organization, second only to salaries. The senior managers who are involved in scrutinizing the management of the office facility and ultimately decide on the level of facility funding should recognize the broad contribution that facilities make to an organization. They should also be familiar with how building systems operate and are maintained and appreciate the diverse and substantive effects that the office environment has on occupant health, safety, performance, productivity, and morale. Although they may be knowledgeable about the operation of their family home, office buildings are substantially more complex. Many factors critical to their operation are entirely different from anything a homeowner might encounter. To be constructive, then, the contribution of senior managers needs to arise from an awareness of the larger context — the overall impact of facility management on the organization.

Organizations only realize the full potential of their office facility when its management is integrated with corporate-level decision making. Facility management needs to be represented at the top level of management, for it is there that facility funding decisions are ultimately made. Consequently, the value of facility management must be recognized at the corporate level in order that it receive the share of resources justified by its contribution.

LITERATURE CITED

American Productivity & Quality Center. 1992. *The benchmarking management guide.* Cambridge, Mass.: Productivity Press.

Apgar, M. 1993. Uncovering your hidden occupancy costs. *Harvard Business Review* (May–June):124–136.

Bellas, J. 1992. President, Interior Space International, Chicago. Comments quoted by L. Monroe in "What do facility managers need?" *Buildings* (October):38–45.

Brill, M. 1987. When politics is the name of the FM game. *Facilities Design & Management* (July–August):58–61.

Drebelbis, J. 1991. Learn to delegate: Hire a consultant to work for you. *Today's Facility Manager* (November):1.

Forbes, B. K. 1976. *Guidelines for computer-aided architectural practices.* Washington, D.C.: American Institute of Architects.

IFMA. 1993. *Outsourcing.* Research report 10. Houston: International Facility Management Association.

Kimmel, P. 1993. The changing role of the strategic facilities plan. *Facility Management Journal* (May–June):24–29.

Levin, H. 1990. Multimillion-dollar SBS lawsuit settled. *Indoor Air Quality Update* (Cutter Information Corp). 3(11):1–5.

Meri, J. 1993. Quality: A facilities perspective. *Facility Management Journal* (July–August):16–22.

Panko, R. R. 1992. The office workforce: A structural analysis. *Office Systems Research Journal* (spring):3–20.

Ritchin, K. 1992. It ain't just space. *Facility Management Journal* (January–February):8–9.

Snyder, A. 1992. Are you sitting on a gold mine? Asset management can save your bottom line. *Facility Management Journal* (September–October):35–37.

Stone, P. J., and R. Luchetti. 1985. Your office is where you are. *Harvard Business Review* (March–April):102–115.

Chapter 10

CONCLUSION

The office as we know it today evolved from a need for organizations to handle a greater volume of increasingly complex information. Whether for the day-to-day running of an industrial enterprise or government department, or for the long-range planning of business strategy or national policy, the office workplace became the nerve center in which decision-making activities were concentrated. In industry, government, and more recently, service organizations, the office has provided a work setting well suited to accommodate a wide range of clerical and knowledge intensive tasks, as well as an organization's mission-critical information and information-processing equipment.

The office facility has developed from a simple heated, lighted structure offering basic shelter from the elements, to the climate-controlled, technology-intensive environments common today. Though building systems now provide sophisticated control of temperature, humidity, air quality, and other environmental factors, our ability to predict the effects of manipulating these controls is far less developed. The indoor environment has been made a more closed system in order that it may be more precisely controlled. For example, by making windows unopenable, uncontrolled air exchange between the indoor and outdoor environment can be minimized. However, in so doing, the settings chosen to operate the ventilation system have a much more dramatic effect on the quality of the indoor environment, because the ventilation system is the only source of outdoor air in sealed buildings.

Despite our having gained a high level of control over the indoor climate, it is difficult to predict all the complex effects that a particular choice of climate settings will produce. Each setting chosen can have multiple consequences. For example, the humidity level affects perceived thermal comfort, the growth of microorganisms, and the incidence of computer failures caused by static electricity.

As with other complex systems in which it is impractical to predict all relevant interactions, an adaptive approach is needed in the management of office facilities. Though perhaps not explicitly recognized as such, adaptive management has always been an integral component of facility management. What has changed is that interior office environments have become tightly controlled, closed systems where deficiencies can be more costly in terms of lost productivity and human health. In this context, to improve the performance of office facilities, adaptive management must be more broadly and systematically applied. In order for sophisticated building controls to be operated so as to optimize indoor environments, the consequences of any manipulation must be systematically monitored. Without knowing what effects an adjustment has produced, it is difficult to ensure that operating procedures actually optimize facility performance and suit the occupants' needs. For this reason, facility management increasingly involves monitoring ever more diverse factors in the office workplace.

Human performance is profoundly influenced by the physical and social setting in which it takes place. In this respect, office work is no different from other endeavors. What has been controversial is the effect of specific workplace characteristics on the productivity of those who use the office. Throughout this book, we have demonstrated that matching the physical work environment to occupants' needs and their job-related activities benefits both the organization and the individuals. Though productivity may be difficult to measure, fundamental indicators such as injury, illness absenteeism, and employee turnover clearly show some of the hidden costs that deficiencies in the office facility can impose.

Occupational health and safety standards, designed originally for industrial workplaces, have not guaranteed office environments of satisfactory quality. Many buildings that cause an unacceptably high incidence of occupant complaints or ailments have complied with these regulatory standards. No built environment is perfect, whether it be an office facility, a factory, or a residence. Building standards seek to ensure a reasonable minimum level of quality, consistent with the knowledge and technology of the day. As more information becomes available, as better technology is developed, and as societal values change, building standards must be modified accordingly.

The impact of the computer on office workers has been very complex. It has made office work physically more demanding and psychologically more intense. A variety of unexpected and serious health issues have arisen, such as cumulative trauma disorders, that have been difficult to address. As well, a general increase in public concern for environmental health risks — such as airborne chemical contaminants, toxic wastes, radiation from power lines and electrical equipment, radon gas, and other controversial, highly political and often emotionally charged issues — has been reflected in workers' concerns about their office environment. The perception that a technological hazard may exist can readily precipitate highly polarized and emotional group behavior. When health risks of the office environment are the issue, the facility management process usually becomes the focus of attention. Public relations has thus become an increasingly important skill for facility managers.

More often than not, greater leeway could be exercised in making facility decisions without compromising the quality or cost of services. Too often, rules exist because they were never changed, not because they are the best way to proceed. So past mistakes are repeated, blocking future innovations. This is evident in the highly emotional issue of work space allocation and furniture entitlement. Rather than specifying exactly the same area, work surface, chair, and storage space for each job category, these resources can be allocated more flexibly to better account for the different needs of the people using them. Then, as teams regroup for a new project, facility resources can be redistributed to support their activities. It may be more involved to administer such flexible facility policies, but the benefits of improved morale, lower incidence of occupational ailments, and reduced fatigue can more than compensate for the additional effort.

There are opportunities to provide greater individual control over selected aspects of the workplace. Within a framework set by their organization, people can be allowed some choice in where they work — selecting the setting that best suits their particular task. They can also be allowed to express their preferences in workplace furnishings, spatial arrangements, and local environmental control (e.g., temperature, light, and airflow). Flexible work hours are increasingly common, especially in companies that conduct business around the world and have to monitor global events. As a result, office facilities will increasingly be expected to deliver a setting suited to whatever work activities the occupants need to perform and whenever they need to do them.

At one time, ensuring that the office was cleaned, there was enough fuel for the heating system, that the roof didn't leak, and the windows could shut out the weather represented a more or less sufficient level of facility management. Now facility management responsibilities extend from selecting an outdoor air exchange rate that will ensure adequate indoor air quality to selecting ergonomically appropriate furnishings to minimize the risk of injuries. This expansion of responsibilities and the increased cost and complexity of accommodating office workers have led to greater scrutiny of the facility management process and budget, the development of a wider range of facility management services, and alternate sources for those services.

It is no longer taken for granted that facility management must be an in-house activity. Many organizations have found outsourcing some or all of their facility management services to be a cost-effective alternative.

Such changes in service delivery are but one reflection of the rapid and profound shifts in the office workplace that have occurred over the past decade and continue today. The revolution in computing and communication technology is restructuring not only the way work is done but also what work is done in our society. It is not surprising, then, that the place where work activities are performed — specifically the office workplace — must change as well. An office is as much a concept as it is a physical entity. Its physical makeup needs to be increasingly flexible to meet the changing forms of office activities and the changing organizational functions that the office serves.

The office can serve those who are physically within its walls as well as those in remote locations. It can have well-defined hours of operation or be used around the clock. It can be filled with thousands of people or operate virtually unattended, serving users electronically. It can be so amorphous as to become a concept without discrete physical form at all — a virtual office defined solely by the tightly integrated communication of its members, who may never even meet face-to-face. Regardless of the office's physical form, organizations need to wring ever greater levels of performance from it. They need to capture the greatest contribution possible from their investment in office accommodations.

Organizations have become increasingly dependent for their success on the quality of work their personnel deliver. Employee turnover, absenteeism, dissatisfaction, and office-related illness and injury lower the effectiveness of the office workforce, thereby, compromising the organization's core capabilities. Yet nonexperts routinely make decisions that affect, in a fundamental way, the quality of the work environment. For example, capital spending on facilities is typically decided by top-level executives who have little or no background in building performance and its effects on human behavior. Their decisions profoundly affect accommodation cost, office quality, and employee performance. As a consequence, they affect workforce productivity in subtle and unintended ways that can compromise an organization's overall success. By being aware of the possible ramifications of their choices, these nonexpert decision makers can better assess the trade-offs that must inevitably be made in choosing and sustaining the office setting for their organization.

The office facility and the way it is managed have a pervasive influence on the activities of the organization — how flexible and responsive it can be to changing needs, how supportive it can be of the individuals who use it. Where facility management is integrated with corporate planning, its services can be aligned with the organization's goals and strategies as well as its commitments to its people. Greater management awareness, direction, and support; more focused facility management services; and direct occupant involvement promote this objective. The optimization of the office facility needs to be seen as a continuous process — constantly monitoring, assessing, and responding to changing demands. In so doing, the management of the office facility becomes a tool in the management of work effectiveness and an active contributor to corporate success.

INDEX